NUTRIX

STUDIES
IN LATE ANTIQUE
MEDIEVAL AND
RENAISSANCE
THOUGHT

STUDI
SUL PENSIERO
TARDOANTICO
MEDIEVALE
E UMANISTICO

Directed by
Giulio d'Onofrio

4

Ubi in eam deduxi oculos
intuitumque defixi
respicio nutricem meam
cuius ab adulescentia
laribus obversatus fueram
Philosophiam

BOETHIUS
Consolatio Philosophiae, I, 3

The publication of this volume has been assisted
by a grant from MIUR (Italy) within the following
«Progetto di Ricerca di Rilevante Interesse Nazionale»
directed by Giulio d'Onofrio: PRIN 2003
(Research Units of the Università degli Studi di Salerno,
of the Libera Università «Maria SS. Assunta» [LUMSA] Roma
and of the Università degli Studi di Roma «Tor Vergata»);
PRIN 2007 (Research Unit of the Università degli Studi di Salerno);
and by a grant from the Università degli Studi di Salerno

Nutrix is a peer-reviewed Series.
The content of each volume
is assessed by specialists chosen
by the Direction of the Series.

The logo of the series Nutrix
– a miniature from Ms. New York,
Pierpont Morgan Library, M. 302
(*Ramsey Psalter*), f. 2[v] – portrays the Christ Child
among the Doctors in the Temple.

Photographic credit:
The Pierpont Morgan Library, New York.

D/2012/0095/175

ISBN 978-2-503-52549-5

Printed in the E.U. on acid-free paper

The Medieval Paradigm

Religious Thought and Philosophy

Papers of the International Congress
(Rome, 29 october - 1 november 2005)

ed. by Giulio d'Onofrio

BREPOLS

Paul's conversion on the road to Damascus (*Ac* 9, 3-4)
Livre d'Heures d'Étienne Chevalier (c. 1450-1460) by Jean Fouquet
Musée Condé, Bibliothèque du Château de Chantilly, ms. 71 Horae, f. 31^{r}.

TABLE OF CONTENTS

VOLUME ONE

VOLUME TWO

THE MEDIEVAL PARADIGM

RELIGIOUS THOUGHT AND PHILOSOPHY

VOLUME ONE

GIULIO D'ONOFRIO

BETWEEN LARISSA AND DAMASCUS

PHILOSOPHICAL PARADIGM AND MEDIEVAL THOUGHT: A HISTORIOGRAPHICAL THEORY

Since there is only one God, our God and your God are not two gods, but one and the same God. We Christians believe, confess and defend with every possible formulation of the truth that God is one. But you also share with us this same wisdom, because reason itself shows you with evidence that there cannot be many Gods. Pray therefore that the paltriness of my intellect may correctly comply with your intention. And I pray that you may yield, at least for a moment, to the faith. In fact, in yielding to the faith, you will arrive at the better understanding (*cognitio*) of this highest reality. Indeed, even in the mastering of the liberal arts, those who begin the studies yield to authority. They are not allowed to formulate immediately critiques, contradictions, and doubts, at least until they have acquired sufficiently a clear and precise comprehension (*notitia*) of the things that are the object of the sciences; and thus they may know how, and may be better able, to ask and resolve questions (*quarere ac respondere*). And so I say to you that God is that than which there is nothing better (*Deus est quo nichil melius est*)[1].

[1] GILBERTUS CRISPINUS (GILBERTUS vel GISLEBERTUS WESTMONASTERII), *Disputatio Christiani cum Gentili*, 15-16, in *The Works of Gilbert Crispin*, ed. by A. Sapir Abulafia – G. R. Evans, Oxford 1986 (Auctores Britannici Medii Aevi, 8), [pp. 61-87], pp. 65,29 - 66,5: «CHRISTIANUS. Quia Deus est unus, noster ac vester Deus non sunt duo Dii sed unus Deus. Unum Deum esse credimus, confitemur, et omni veritatis assertione astruimus. Vos etiam idem nobiscum sapitis quia vobis *ratio* ipsa monstrat plures Deos esse non posse. Patere, rogo, ingenii mei tarditatem ut tuam exaequatur voluntatem. *Cede paulisper fidei*, nam cedendo fidei, venies ad *cognitionem* tantae rei. In studiis quoque artium liberalium cedunt auctoritati qui ad studium accedunt nec permittitur eis ut statim contendant, opponant et

10.1484/M.NUTRIX-EB.1.101231

Cede paulisper fidei, «yield, at least for a moment, to the faith!». These words come from a little known text by Gilbert Crispin, abbot of Westminster in the first decades of the twelfth century and a friend and student of Anselm of Aosta, that was composed in the climate of the enthusiastic acceptance of Anselm's theoretical proposal for demonstrating the rational coherence of Christian truth[2]. They are proclaimed by the character of the Christian sage in Gilbert's *Disputatio cum Gentili*, a dialogue between a believer and a philosopher that anticipates the formal situation of the better known, and more recent by some years, *Dialogus* (or *Collationes*) of Abelard. Though not a great speculative spirit, Gilbert does demonstrate with these concise words his solid grasp of the value ascribed to the profession of the philosopher and to philosophy itself according to the perspective of those who belong to an intellectual community permeated, through an indisputable foundational assumption, by the universal acceptance of a higher revealed truth.

The methodological attitude that the believer here suggests to the pagan, by asking him at least to accept the instrumental consideration of the affirmations of religion as true, is in no way a banal attempt at conciliation, nor is it a renunciation of the rights of rational science. With a rather original intuition for his time, he in fact invites the philosopher, who is used to proceeding in his investigations with only the instruments of rational critique, to recognize that even the coherence of natural knowledge cannot ground itself exclusively on the dry progress of argumentation within argumentation inching toward the acquisition and increase of scientifically demonstrated and irrefutable certainties.

obtendant, donec circa rerum ipsarum *notitiam* aliquantisper affecti *quaerere ac respondere* melius sciant et possint. *Deus*, inquam, *est quo nichil melius est*».

[2] Cfr. G. R. Evans, *«Omnibus Hiis Litteratior»: Gilbert Crispin, Noted Theologian*, in «Studi Medievali», Ser. 3ª, 22.2 (1981), pp. 695-716. On the rational speculative systematization of Anselm's theology and on its reception by contemporaries, cfr. my articles: *Anselmo d'Aosta*, in *Storia della Teologia nel Medioevo*, 3 voll., dir. di G. d'Onofrio, Casale Monferrato 1996, I, pp. 481-552; *Anselmo e i teologi «moderni»*, in *Cur Deus homo*, Atti del Congresso Anselmiano internazionale (Roma, 21-23 maggio 1998), a c. di P. Gilbert – H. Kohlenberger – E. Salmann (Studia Anselmiana, 128), Roma 1999, pp. 87-146: *«In cubiculum mentis». L'«intellectus» anselmiano e la gnoseologia platonica altomedievale*, in *Rationality from Saint Augustine to Saint Anselm*, Proceeding of the International Anselm Conference (Piliscsaba, 20-23 June 2002), ed. by C. Viola – J. Kormos, Piliscsaba 2005, pp. 61-88.

Even in the study of the seven liberal arts, according to his words, the young student, before understanding the theoretical roots of their rules, must accept in the first phase – either as a provisory or instrumental step – the passive belief, without formulating doubts or manifesting uncertainties, in the formally established teachings of the ancient masters, who first codified these arts. Only once he has sufficiently perceived the intimate connections that exist among the real forms of things, will he see these same teachings as true in so far as they are no longer grounded on the authority who had temporarily established their credibility, but on a correct intellectual comprehension of their contents: that is, a «cognitio» or «notitia» of the truth, which the student initially did not perceive with clarity, but then, after having experienced it as temporarily persuasive (or 'probable') information that was yet to be validated, he was finally and definitively able to clarify it in his own mind, enclosing it in his collection of irrefutably true (or 'necessary') competencies. Gilbert therefore invites the pagan philosopher to do the same with Christian revelation, that is, to accept from it, on the basis of the sole authority of the one who proclaimed it, at least certain affirmations, the veracity of which is not yet evident, with the goal of reaching, by developing and exploring from within the system of truth connected to it, the full recovery of the cognitive evidence for it. This is what it means to acquire the correct and definitive «cognitio» or «notitia» of this truth[3]. A mental concept of this kind is true in so far as it

[3] This terminology, drawn from the manuals that transmitted to the Early Middle Ages the rhetorical-dialectical competencies of Late Antiquity, appears hardly by chance. *Notitia*, or more generically *notio*, is the term introduced by Cicero into the Latin language as corresponding to the Greek ἔννοια, popularized in the philosophical lexicon above all through the Stoics (for them, the term is equivalent to πρόληψις, that is, to the representative anticipation in the knowing subject of the connotative aspects of the known objects); it is commonly used, in the late ancient and early medieval periods, to indicate the presence in the mind of a solid cognitive datum (in practice, a correct *definitio* of the object of discourse), which is coming either from an innate cognition, or as that which springs forth from a process of empirical acquisition. Cfr. MARCUS TULLIUS CICERO, *Lucullus (Academica priora)*, II, 10, 30, ed. C. F. W. Müller, *Scripta*, IV/1, Leipzig 1889, p. 35,30-31: «*Notitiae* rerum, quas Graeci tum ἐννοίας tum προλήψεις vocant»; therefore, in order to describe the common human sharing of the foundations of theological knowledge: ID., *De legibus*, I, 8, 24 ed. Müller, IV/2, Leipzig 1898, p. 389,28-29: «Itaque ex tot generibus nullum est animal praeter hominem, quod habeat *notitiam* aliquam Dei»; *De natura deorum*, I, 16, 43,

is endowed with intrinsic intelligibility, dependent not on the greater or lesser credibility of the source from which it arises, but on its concrete capacity of 'corresponding' to the effective conditions of the *res*: for, if something known is true, when it is grasped – that is, when it has been communicated by one intelligence to another through a comprehensible formulation that is coherent with the laws of logic –, it necessarily manifests itself as characterized by established evidence that leads the recipient to assent. If a truth is evident in itself, it is such whether it presents itself to the mind as the result of an original or innovative discovery (that is, an *inventio*), or it is acquired by way of mediated information, coming from someone who assumes the responsibility of that which he asserts. Independent from the process of acquisition, a notion endowed with the character of evidence maintains it

ibid., p. 18,35-37: «In omnium animis deorum *notionem* impressit natura»; ibid., II, 5, 13, p. 51,23-24: «In animis hominum informatas deorum esse notiones»; *De finibus bonorum et malorum*, V, 21, 59, ed. Müller, IV/1, p. 261,23-24: «[Natura] ingenuit sine doctrina *notitias* parvas rerum maximarum»; and with an evident platonizing structure: *Tusculanae disputationes*, I, 24, 57, ibid., pp. 300,35 - 301,2: «Nec vero fieri ullo modo posse, ut a pueris tot rerum atque tantarum insitas et quasi consignatas in animis *notiones*, quas ἐννοίας vocant, haberemus, nisi animus, antequam in corpus intravisset, in rerum cognitione viguisset»; and *ibid.*, V, 39, 114, p. 463,36-37: «Sine varietate colorum licebat vivere beate, sine *notione* rerum non licebat». In the *Topica,* therefore, Cicero himself, confirming the philosophical origins of the term *notio,* also consolidates its more strictly logical use according to which this term indicates the mental anticipations embracing the truth of things, which reason then develops through logical-deductive procedures. cfr. Id., *Topica*, 7, 31, ed. W. Friedrich, *Opera rhetorica*, in ed. Müller cit., I/2, Leipzig 1891, p. 431,26-31: «Genus et formam [= speciem] definiunt hoc modo: genus est *notio* ad plures differentias pertinens; forma est *notio* cuius differentia ad caput generis et quasi fontem referri potest. *Notionem* appello, quod Graeci tum ἔννοιαν, tum πρόληψιν dicunt, Ea insita et ante percepta cuiusque formae *cognitio*, enodationis indigens». Again, for the equivalence, in similar contexts, of *cognitio* and *notio,* or *notitia*, cfr. Id., *De natura deorum*, I, 14, 36. p. 16,29-30; 17, 44, p. 19,11-12; *De finibus bonorum et malorum*, I, 9, 31, p. 104,9-11; and *ibid.*, III, 6, 21, p. 179,8-9. The technical use of such terminology passes from Cicero to the Fathers and from there, through the tradition of the liberal arts, to the intellectuals of Late Antiquity, who highlighted the original theological shadings of the terms; cfr. Marius Victorinus, *De definitionibus*, PL 64, 902B, ed. in T. Stangl, *Tulliana et Mario Victoriniana*, München 1888, p. 17,18-19; Augustinus Hipponensis, *De Trinitate*, IX, 12, 18, PL 42, 970, ed. W. J. Mountain, 2 voll., Turnhout 1968 (CCSL, 50-50A), I, p. 309,28-31; VIII, 2, 3, 948, p. 270,14-16; cfr. also *ibid.*, V, 6, 7, 915, p. 211,21-22. – Cfr. G. d'Onofrio, *«Notio fidei». La concordia di filosofia e religione. Lettura di «Fides et ratio», IV, 36-48*, in «Aquinas», 44.1 (2001), pp. 47-78.

in any case, no matter the way through which it was rendered knowable.

The aim of the mental operation to which Gilbert Crispin invites the non-believer is now clear: if a notion is communicated to you that you cannot manage to acquire by way of natural *inventio* – it is the meaning of his words –, try at least to interiorize its significance on the basis of the representation alone that follows from the communication: if such a notion is true, and if therefore the authority of the one who communicates it is authentic, by embracing it in your knowledge you will be able to perceive and evaluate its veracity. It is also significant that Gilbert, a convinced follower of Anselm, concludes his peroration, as the first application of such a method, by exhorting the pagan to recognize, before every other concept, the evidence of the formula according to which it is affirmed that God is that than which there is nothing better (*melius*): it is a principle, according to the application which Gilbert proposes (as the later developments of the dialogue indicate), which is not so much a demonstration of the existence of God (as in the *Proslogion*), as of the necessity of the incarnation of Christ (as in the *Cur Deus homo*)[4]. The form of knowledge that Gilbert seeks to promote in the course of the discussion with the pagan sage is not a 'science of the faith', in the sense of a rational, scientifically consolidated comprehension of revealed dogmas (that is, an established *theologia* or *sacra doctrina*, according to the vocabulary perfected in the following centuries): this is implicitly confirmed when the same dialogical treatise moves on to present and discuss the theme of the Trinity, and the non-believing philosopher, incapable of confronting such a problem, abandons his post to another Christian interlocutor (who assumes the role of a Disciple, who asks questions to which the first Christian responds in the role of a Teacher)[5]. Therefore reason is only invited to become provisorily (for a de-

[4] Cfr. ANSELMUS CANTUARIENSIS, *Proslogion*, 4, PL 158, 229B, ed. F. S. Schmitt, *Opera Omnia*, 6 vol., Roma – Edinburgh 1946-1961, I, p. 104,2-4: «Deus enim est 'id quo maius cogitari non potest'. Quod qui bene intelligit, utique intelligit id ipsum sic esse, ut nec cogitatione queat non esse». And again, toward the conclusion of the work, cfr. *ibid.*, 26, 242B, p. 121, 16: «Proficiat hic in me *notitia tui*, et ibi fiat plena».

[5] Cfr. GILBERTUS CRISPINUS, *ibid.*, 86 seqq., ed. Sapir Abulafia – Evans cit., pp. 81 seqq.

termined time, «paulisper») an adherent to the affirmations of the faith, with the goal of verifying the concomitant results of such an adherence and of evaluating whether such a verification might produce an eventual advantage for its research[6].

It is interesting to note how such a procedure seems symmetrically the inverse of that which supports the intellectual construction of Christological knowledge in Anselm's *Cur Deus homo*, where, in order to confront the objections of the infidels who consider the hypostatic union of the two natures of Christ to be contrary to reason («rationi repugnare»), the believer strives to show the truth of the Incarnation with necessary arguments of the exclusively scientific-rational order («rationibus necessariis» and «aperta ratione et veritate»), as if putting in parenthesis, at least 'instrumentally', the truth of revelation («remoto Christo, quasi nunquam aliquid fuerit de illo» and «quasi nihil sciatur de Christo»). In Crispin's dialogue, on the contrary, it is natural reason itself that is 'provisorily' placed between parentheses. Such an inversion is, however, justified by the sharing of the same speculative foundation: that is, of the conviction that human rationality, when it is true, must be entirely coherent with the higher divine reason. Whether one maintains that human understanding should work in complete autonomy apart from dogma, or that the faith should ask the intellect first to accept its own initial affirmations as true before submitting them to logical judgment, both the statements of faith and the conclusions of reason should only be in the end superimposable.

In this minor episode in the history of medieval thought it is possible to see how Christian intellectuals began to comprehend effectively the 'philosophical' potential inserted into their very condition as believers and investigators of the truth: religion may manifest and submit to the examination of rational critique its own capacity for introducing philosophical knowledge into a more ample knowledge of the common object of investigation; but philosophy, in an agreement of mutual assistance with faith, maintains the right to verify in turn, with complete freedom of judgment, whether such a penetrating study was useful for the

[6] Cfr. Anselmus Cantuariensis, *Cur Deus homo*, praef., PL 158, 361D-362A, ed. Schmitt, II, pp. 42,8 - 43,3.

perfection of the *inquisitio veri*. Later, toward the end of the twelfth century, on the cusp which separates the early medieval period from the maturation of the new epistemological consciousness of the university *magistri*, Alan of Lille, in *De planctu naturae*, demonstrates the already acquired comprehension of such a reciprocity between philosophy and theology, which are not opposed, but remain distinct within a symmetrically inverse relation. According to Alan, the 'Nature' itself, which is the archetype of the *ratio philosophica*, claims its own autonomy and, at the same time, its own complementarity with the *ratio theologica*:

> And since in all these mysteries natural reason lies helpless, only with the solidity of the faith do we adore the mystery of such a lofty truth. And there is no surprise if, regarding such questions, theology does not assure for me accustomed assistance, because in the majority of the arguments *we do not have contradictory, but distinct, opinions*. I measure the prerogatives of the faith with the critique of reason; theology, however, measures reason with the faith. I have knowledge in order to believe; theology believes in order to have knowledge. I concede my assent to the things that I perceive; theology perceives the things to which she concedes her assent[7].

***

The hope for a complementarity between rational-scientific knowledge (which uses natural instruments to investigate the manifestations of the truth in order to progressively submit them to the critical appraisal of the intellect) and religious revelation (which investigates the same truth, hidden and ungraspable in itself, by opening itself to that which it accepts as a spontaneous and satisfying self-manifestation of its truth) is not a novelty of the Christian era.

[7] Cfr. ALANUS DE INSULIS, *De planctu naturae*, 6, 829-830, PL 210, 466A ed. in N. HÄRING, *Alain of Lille, «De planctu naturae»*, in «Studi Medievali», 3ª Ser., 19/2 (1978), [pp. 797-879], p. 829,150-155: «Et cum in hiis omnis naturalium ratio langueat, sola fidei firmitate tantae rei veneremur arcanum. Nec mirum si in hiis theologia suam michi familiaritatem non exhibet, quoniam in plerisque *non adversa, sed diversa sentimus*. Ego ratione fidem, illa fide comparat rationem. Ego scio ut credam, illa credit ut sciat. Ego consentio sentiens, illa sentit consentiens».

Philosophy has yearned, since its distant origins in presocratic Greece, for a cognitive approach to the more perfect and remote forms of reality, guided by revelation and poetry. In the first verses of the parmenidean poem *On Nature*, the philosopher is lead by the goddesses, who «show him the way» to the house of Justice. They welcome him by warning that the power guiding him «on this way», which is «outside of the path of men», is «a divine command and justice». Behind the veil of this allegory one already perceives in these words the hope for a self-disclosure on the part of truth itself: that is, the desire for that highest identity of trueness that the human mind on its own cannot investigate, but which the mind is nevertheless capable of recognizing and making its own when it encounters it, since it is revealed and rendered manifest by a worthy, and therefore entirely faithful, witness[8]. For the ancient philosopher, the possibility of receiving divine revelation does not have the defect of the intellect's banal submission to an external authority, because it involves, in a more generic manner, the intellect's recognition of its obligation to receive the evidence with which the truth reveals itself, no matter how the truth in fact does reveal itself.

One finds in the works of Plato the intensification of such a relationship between the intellect's investigation and the truth's self-manifestation. This occurs not only through the use that he makes of myth as a source of communication of the truth[9], but also because myth itself – like the dialogic form, the maieutics, and the hermeneutics of an authoritative witness – has the function of demonstrating how it is impossible for the mind to refuse its own assent in regard to any epiphany of the truth that is absolute and spontaneous, that is to say, not imposed. Plato openly considers such an assent to be the result of a free 'act of faith' on the part of the knowing subject when, at the conclusion of the *Republic*, after the account of the myth of Er, the character of Socrates af-

[8] PARMENIDES, in *Die Fragmente der Vorsokratiker*, edd. H. Diels – W. Kranz, 3 voll., Berlin 1951-1952 (Dublin – Zürich 1971[15]), I, 28B, 1, pp. 228-230, vv. 1-29 (tr. it. di P. Albertelli, in *I Presocratici. Testimonianze e frammenti*, 2 voll., Bari 1959, I, pp. 269-270).

[9] Cfr. L. ELDENSTEIN, *The function of the Myth in Plato's Philosophy*, in «The Journal of History of Ideas», 10 (1949), pp. 463-481; L. BRISSON, *Plato the Myth Maker*, Paris 1982 (Chicago – London 1998[2]).

firms that through the very act of 'believing', the mind may acquire as its own the 'self-expression' of the truth developed in the myth: «Thus, Glaucon, the myth was saved (ἐσώθη, it was preserved) and was not lost, and will be able to save us as well (καὶ ἡμᾶς ἂν σώσειεν) if we believe (ἂν πειθώμεθα, if we have faith) in it»[10]. If there are in fact, among the ample and not always governable variety of mythical accounts introduced by Plato into the plot of his dialogues, passages seeking to evoke mysterious features of reality not immediately perceived by human sight, one may then correctly recognize, at least in part, the Platonic myth's capacity to draw out, through non-discursive anamnesis, a wisdom higher than that which is introduced by the normal stages of reason[11]. In this sense, already for Plato and for his followers in Antiquity and the early medieval period, the mythological account reclaims its right to be received as a possible way for reconciling the limited intuitive capacity of the human mind with the traces of the divine which remain dispersed – above all for one who is a true philosopher – in the scattered evidence found in natural and accidental physical phenomena.

It would not be a mistake to see in this openness to mythical discourse a direct application of the polypartite psychology that was shared by Platonists throughout the centuries. In light of the division of the soul into multiple faculties, ordered according to a scalar succession of increasing perfections – from the senses to the imagination, from the imagination to abstract and discursive reason and, still higher, to the noetic intuition of the first and eternal principles – the recourse to myth seems to function as a poetic-intuitive anticipation of the contemplation of higher truths, which the intellect reaches in the fullest and definitive

[10] PLATO, *Respublica*, X, 621c.

[11] Cfr. F. FERRARI, *Filosofia e mitologia in Platone*, in *I miti di Platone*, a c. di F. Ferrari, Milano 2006, [pp. 11-71], pp. 21-22: «Esiste anche un mito rammemorativo e non produttivo, ossia un mito che non imita poieticamente il dato (sensibile e degradato) che ha di fronte, bensì si propone di ritornare alla fonte di un sapere lontano e inaccessibile ai sensi (...). In questa nuova prospettiva il mito 'buono' (...) dovrà venire garantito non direttamente dal protagonista del dialogo ma da figure misteriose e dotate di un prestigio eccezionale (come la sacerdotessa Diotima nel *Simposio*), o da una tradizione lontana e fondata su qualcosa di simile alla memoria collettiva. Tutto ciò – è quasi superfluo constatarlo – è perfettamente solidale all'idea platonica della conoscenza come reminiscenza».

sense only through the recovery of the original mystical connection with the Highest Good. Thus, as a myth that speaks also of myth, the account of the cave at the beginning of book VII of the *Republic* was anticipated, at the conclusion of the preceding book, by the metaphor (or analogy) of the line, which illustrates the division of knowledge into progressive forms for improving the mind's approach to the pre-discursive truth of the non-hypothetical principle of that which is real[12]. The possibility that mythical discourse is sometimes presented as more suitable than the language of logic and science for describing higher and ungraspable traits of such a principle is evidently grounded on a gnoselogical doctrine that allows a hierarchical succession of distinct capacities of access to the truth, without excluding aprioristically the introduction, among such capacities, of worthy and qualified forms of external communication: that is, of an authorized account that is both expressive and allusive, and yet, though not definitive, nevertheless informative and exhaustive, in so far as it is grounded on that which seems to be, from the perspective of the witness, a tenable perception of the most intimate essence of truth.

Human reason is therefore authorized, within such a perspective, to take advantage of the deciphering of signs deduced from that which presents itself as a discourse of divine origin, while also entirely maintaining its own autonomy of judgment. Revelation may function only as the principle of inspiration, the object of verification, and the acquaintance with unconfirmed information, rather than as an immediate, acritcal and indisputable adherence to a declared truth. It may be an instrument that is useful for helping and orienting the progress of philosophical investigation. In the *Phaedo*, recognizing the impossibility, or at least the great difficulty, of speaking philosophically about the soul and about purely intelligible entities, Plato admits that the most difficult philosophical navigation would be more accessible if it could proceed «with a means of more secure transport» (ἐπὶ βεβαιοτέρου ὀχήματος) in respect to the fragile raft of rational investigation, that is, with what could be «a certain divine word» (λόγος θεῖος)[13].

[12] Cfr. F. F. REPELLINI, *La linea e la caverna*, in *Platone, Repubblica*, a c. di M. Vegetti, 5 voll., Napoli 2003, V, pp. 355-403.

[13] PLATO, *Phaedo*, 85cd. Cfr. the commentary on this passage in G. REALE,

As if drawing inspiration and encouragement from similar statements in the *libri Platonicorum*, Augustine writes at the beginning of his *De vera religione* that, if Plato had lived in his own time and he had been able to question him and to make him once again acknowledge that the truth enjoys the characteristics of inalterability, wholeness, and absolute identity; and also, if he had been able to explain the foundation of the gospel message to him, Plato himself would have admitted, without a doubt, that the divine word (*verbum divinum*), which the sages longed for, made itself a creature by incarnating itself and in this way made itself known to all men in order to assure a definitive possession of the truth. This Augustinian text is intentionally characterized by a stylistic procedure that retraces the formal procedure of the philosophical dialogue:

> I would say, however, with absolute faith, and in agreement with all those who stubbornly love their philosophical texts, that in Christian times it is no longer possible to doubt which religion one ought to prefer absolutely over the others, and which is the way that leads to truth and happiness. If in fact Plato himself were alive, and were not to refrain from responding to my questions, or better, if someone from among his disciples, at the time in which he was alive, were to have asked such questions, certainly such a disciple would have allowed himself to be persuaded by him that *the truth cannot be seen with the eyes of the body, but only with the pure mind;* and that when any soul adheres to the truth, it reaches happiness and perfection, while nothing impedes it from seizing the truth more than a life dedicated to sensual pleasures and false images of sensible things, which come from the sensible world and are impressed in us through the body, and which generate in us various opinions and errors. For this reason it is necessary to heal the mind in order that it may directly perceive *the immutable form of things, which always maintains itself as unalterable*, and enjoys a beauty equal to itself, neither scattered into the diversity of space, nor altered in time, since *it is always and in its every part the One and the Same* (...). If, however, all these things had been confirmed by the

Agostino e il Contra Academicos, in *L'opera letteraria di Agostino tra Cassiciacum e Milano*, Atti del Colloquio Internazionale *Agostino nelle terre di Ambrogio* (1-4 ottobre 1986), Palermo 1987 (Augustiniana, Testi e studi, 2), [pp. 13-30], pp. 25-27; repeated by the same Reale in his *Introduzione*, in Agostino, *Amore assoluto e «terza navigazione»*, a c. di G. Reale, Milano 1994, [pp. 7-68], pp. 49-55.

> teacher for the disciple, and the disciple had then asked him whether there had ever existed such a great and divine man who was capable of persuading all peoples that it is at least justifiable to believe in such a truth, even if they are not capable of understanding it (...), I believe that Plato would have responded to him that this could not be the work of a man, unless one were dealing with the case of someone whom the very Virtue and Wisdom of God would have removed from the normal laws of nature and whom He would have enlightened from the moment of birth, not through human teachings, but with an interior illumination. Such a man would be ennobled with such a free gift and would be strengthened with such solidity of mind and would be raised up with such majesty, so as (...) to render him capable of converting the entire human race, with tremendous love and the highest authority, to a faith that may truly be called salvific. (...) Thus, if now it is true that all this has effectively taken place, and that it is celebrated with writings and monuments; and if from the sole region of the earth where a single God was worshipped and where it was therefore fitting for the birth of such a man, chosen men have been sent into the whole world, who have enkindled hearts with divine love through their virtues and preaching, (...) and if today among all the nations and all the peoples one hears that 'in the beginning there was the Word, the Word was with God, and God was the Word, and this Word was in the beginning with God, and everything was created through him and without him nothing was created' (...), why do we continue to be dazed with the drunkenness of the past, since we continue to see the words of God in the entrails of dead animals; and, when we enter into a philosophical discussion, why do we only show how to fill the mouth with the name of Plato, rather than display our heart full of truth[14]?

[14] Cfr. AUGUSTINUS HIPPONENSIS, *De vera religione*, 3-5, PL 34, 123-124, ed. K.-D. Daur, Turnhout 1962 (CCSL, 32), pp. 188,1 - 192,101: «Illud tamen fidentissime dixerim, pace horum omnium, qui eorum libros pervicaciter diligunt, Christianis temporibus quaenam religio potissimum tenenda sit, et quae ad veritatem ac beatitudinem via, non esse dubitandum. Si enim Plato ipse viveret et me interrogantem non aspernaretur, vel potius, si quis eius discipulus eo ipso tempore quo vivebat, cum sibi ab illo persuaderetur *non corporeis oculis, sed pura mente veritatem videri*, cui quaecumque anima inhaesisset, eam beatam fieri atque perfectam, ad quam percipiendam nihil magis impedire, quam vitam libidinibus deditam et falsas imagines rerum sensibilium quae nobis ab hoc sensibili mundo per corpus impressae varias opiniones erroresque generarent, quamobrem sanan-

Augustine highlights this recourse to a divine revelation, external to the investigations of human science, as an openness to the truth that the pagan intellectuals themselves not only had already considered possible, but also yearned for as something effective and indispensable for the weaknesses of philosophical reason: all this, despite the fact that none of them had at his disposal such a communication of the truth that was effectively tenable and not falsely drenched in the artificial and anthropomorphic inanities of the poetic fables. They had, however, vainly maintained their recourse to ancient myths – tales more suitable for the ridicule of the writers of comedy or for the superstition of slaves than for providing divinations worthy of coming to pass (as opposed to the evident result of all the scriptural prophecies) – in order to construct on this basis the doctrines which would sufficiently explain both the natural causes (*physiologiae*) and the supernatural causes (*theologiae*)[15].

dum esse animum ad intuendam *incommutabilem rerum formam*, et *eodem modo semper se habentem* atque undique sui similem pulchritudinem, nec distentam locis, nec tempore variatam, sed *unum atque idem* omni ex parte servantem (...), cum haec ergo sibi a magistro persuaderentur, si ex eo quaereret ille discipulus, utrum si quisquam exsisteret vir magnus atque divinus, qui talia populis persuaderet credenda saltem, si percipere non valerent (...), responderet credo ille non posse hoc ab homine fieri, nisi quem forte ipsa Dei Virtus atque Sapientia ab ipsa rerum natura exceptum, nec hominum magisterio, sed intima illuminatione ab incunabulis illustratum, tanta honestaret gratia, tanta firmitate roboraret tanta denique maiestate subveheret, ut (...) genus humanum ad tam salubrem fidem summo amore atque auctoritate converteret. (...) Quae si facta sunt, si litteris monumentisque celebrantur, si ab una regione terrarum, in qua sola unus colebatur Deus, et ubi talem nasci oportebat, per totum orbem terrarum missi electi viri, virtutibus atque sermonibus divini amoris incendia concitarunt, (...) si hodie per gentes populosque praedicatur 'In principio erat Verbum, et Verbum erat apud Deum, et Deus erat Verbum, hoc erat in principio apud Deum, omnia per ipsum facta sunt et sine ipso factum est nihil' (*Jo* 1, 1-3) (...), quid adhuc oscitamus crapulam hesternam, et in mortuis pecudibus divina eloquia perscrutamur, si quando autem ad disputationem venitur, Platonico nomine ora crepantia, quam pectus vero plenum, magis habere gestimus?».

[15] Cfr. Id., *Contra Faustum Manichaeum libri triginta tres*, XII, 40, PL 42, 275: «Nec Pagani nobis in hoc obstrepunt; neque enim audent contradicere, ne illa non solum dicta, sed etiam facta, figurate accepta interpretemur ad Christum intelligendum: praesertim quia ea quae praenuntiata intelligimus, etiam demonstramus impleta, cum fabulas suas ut aliquo modo commendent, ad nescio quas *physiologias* vel *theologias*, id est, rationes naturales vel divinas, interpretando referre conentur, ex parte plane satis indicantes qualia sint, ex parte autem dissimulantes, dum ea rident in theatris quae venerantur in templis, in turpitudine nimium liberi, in superstitione nimium servi».

Thus Augustine considers Plato to be the main witness to the possible opening of philosophical thought to the sapiential contribution coming from a higher authority. One sees this, for instance, in the *Meno*, which illustrates the advantage of such an openness by another well-known literary image, the road to Larissa – an image that is, yet again, more a metaphor than a myth, but particularly suitable for demonstrating the force which the hidden truth enjoys in the encounter with one who searches for it with frankness and labor[16]. In these passages from the last part of the dialogue, Socrates observes that it is not true that only under the guidance of the rigorous rules, which govern the discourse of science, can one properly fulfill human action and render minds virtuous: one may pursue such goals even by taking advantage, beyond the rules of reason, of the tenable testimonies coming from honest and correctly informed persons, suitable for directing the ignorant. He illustrates such an affirmation by imagining a group of pilgrims that, without sufficient knowledge of the way, must reach the city of Larissa (a rhetorical example, since one could speak of «the road to Larissa or wherever one wants»). Obviously, if they are guided by someone who knows the way well (εἰδὼς τὴν ὁδόν) – for instance, because he made the trip in the past – they will obtain from him the best information in order to reach the destination. Yet, they could also find an adequate guide in one who had never been to Larissa and did not know the way, but had nonetheless a correct opinion about it (ὀρθῶς δοξάζων). One may conclude, therefore, that one who «has a correct opinion» on that which in fact is true is no less a guide for the discovery of the truth than one who does have rational knowledge of it: thus «a correct opinion (ὀρθὴ δόξα) will be no less useful than science (ἐπιστήμη)»[17]. And Meno comments: «I'm amazed, Socrates, that, if things are this way, science may be considered more worthy than right opinion, and I ask why they are considered to be so different from one

[16] Cfr. V. VITIELLO, s. v. *Metaforologia*, in *Enciclopedia filosofica*, Fondazione Centro di Studi filosofici di Gallarate, 12 voll., Milano 2006, VIII, [pp. 7366-7372], p. 7368b: «La metafora, quindi, che nell'oratoria e nella poesia è d'uso comune, sembra essere 'fuori luogo' nei discorsi della scienza. Eppure questi son pieni di metafore».

[17] Cfr. PLATO, *Meno*, 97ac.

another»[18]. Socrates then clarifies that opinion is furtive and unstable, like a slave in flight or like the legendary living statues carved by Daedalus, and that to posses such a thing is not something of great value; yet science, on the contrary, is a stable recognition of the truth which manifests itself – that is, it is unveiled – in the soul through the process of anamnesis[19]. If, therefore, science is more solid than correct opinion, it is because scientific discourse, with its logical and defining rigor, guarantees a *stable* possession of the truth, grounded in a synthesis of direct experience and the formal ordering of the connotations which allow one to grasp it; opinion established through the authority of the witness, however, inserts between the subject and object of knowledge the uncertain mediation of a third external element ('having heard something', custom or tradition, the conjecture), which is itself the only guaranteed insurance of the tenability of the information that it provides: this fact condemns opinion, in so far as it may be true, to the coils of an inevitable hermeneutical circle.

Some of the most important Christian thinkers of the early centuries, confronted with the contemporary and discomforting results of pagan thought, intentionally took on a daunting task: once having confirmed the inherent lack of surety in scientific-rational knowledge, they strove to verify whether it might be possible to entrust to an impassioned and absolutely faithful adherence to the very inevitability of such a hermeneutical circle the possibility of assuring a new, inalienable stability for knowledge, characterizing it with that completeness of information that was always lacking in the results of philosophical investigation.

***

In the II-III centuries a.d., the Christian religion spread throughout the Mediteranean, inserting itself into a cultural context that was visibly characterized by a generalized mistrust – sometimes only thinly veiled – in philosophy and in its theoretical-cognitive

[18] *Ibid.*, 97cd.

[19] Cfr. *ibid.*, 97d-98a.

investigations, in favor of an accentuated pragmatic recovery of the ethical-practical judgment of reason. At the root of such a widespread simplification of the speculative vocation of philosophical knowledge one finds the Skeptical-Academic criticism of Stoic dogmatism, which had been promulgated in the Latin world by Cicero. In the speculative program of Academic thought, which provides the background of all the philosophical dialogues of the Arpinian, the probabilistic reduction of knowledge presents itself as the support and guardian of the unreachable and absolute perfection of the truth that Plato so insistently demanded. A dismaying acceptance of the incapacity on the part of human reason to attribute the quality of evidence to any knowable datum – something demanded as indispensable by the anti-Platonic polemic of the Stoics –, drove the Academic thinker to condemn irrevocably the failure of the theoretical claims of classical philosophers[20].

According to Cicero, the sages of antiquity were capable of establishing, within the complex codification imposed by the science of logic, the formal norms that a statement must respect in order to be true; yet they did not succeed – or at least they didn't *always* succeed – in determining an effective coherence between the requirements of logic, and the representations of reality introduced by experience and organized by physical or metaphysical knowledge: not all that which is logically true is always true in reality, and not all that which is true in reality corresponds absolutely to the rules that knowledge must respect in order to be scientific. Philosophy, accepting such limitations and renouncing the foundation of its own affirmations as based upon an adequate appreciation of the evidence of reality (that is – according to the late-ancient terminology – on the *inventio* of the truth), may only claim for itself the ability to recognize the truth when it manifests itself through any kind of cognitive mediation

[20] On this theme cfr. G. D'ONOFRIO, *Il parricidio di Cicerone. Le metamorfosi della verità tra gli* Academica *ciceroniani e il* Contra Academicos *di Agostino (lettura di testi)*, in ΕΝΩΣΙΣ ΚΑΙ ΦΙΛΙΑ. *Unione e amicizia. Omaggio a Francesco Romano*, a c. di M. Barbanti – G. R. Giardina – P. Manganaro, Catania 2002, pp. 207-236, now found in the first chapter of ID., Vera philosophia. *Studies in Late Antique, Early Medieval and Renaissance Christian Thought*, Turnhout 2008 (Nutrix, 1), pp. 11 seqq.

(*iudicium*, that is, the pure 'dialectical' capacity of the appreciation of the truth that makes itself known, without ever having the possibility of grounding it on the 'apodictic' form). Cicero himself distinguishes in the *Topica* these two functions of logic (or *ratio disserendi*): the application (or *iudicium*) of the rules of truth, prescinding from the content of the argument, which Cicero calls διαλεκτική, or, in Latin, *ars iudicandi* in the strict sense; and the discovery (or *inventio*) of the sources of the truth (the *loci* or τόποι), which allows for putting into concrete motion the mental structures that assure both the correspondence between the truth and reality, and the passage from one truth to another, which is called τοπική or *ars inveniendi*. In his opinion, only classical (Platonic-Aristotelian) philosophy has adequately cultivated this second discipline, while the Stoics contented themselves with exercising the first. But in his works in defense of Academicism, the Arpinian denounces the weakness and formal emptiness of the philosophical hope for the *inventio veri*, reducing the only constructive task of philosophical knowledge to the simple phase of the *potestas iudicandi*[21].

The intellectuals of the imperial Roman civilization therefore saw Cicero as the witness – a particularly trustworthy one, in so far as he attentively evaluated the speculative tendencies most in vogue in the late Hellenistic world – to an epochal elimination of the human hopes for the foundation of a fulfilled rational science; or at least of a science sufficiently capable of assuring the *stability* which must characterize not only the forms, but also the most important contents of human knowledge. Philosophy is inadequate for providing any sufficient response to the fundamen-

[21] Cfr. MARCUS TULLIUS CICERO, *Topica*, 2, 6, in ID., *Opera rhetorica*, ed. Friedrich cit. (above, note 3), p. 426,20-27: «Cum omnis ratio diligens disserendi duas habeat partes, unam inveniendi, alteram iudicandi, utriusque princeps, ut mihi quidem videtur, Aristoteles fuit. Stoici autem in altera elaboraverunt: iudicandi enim vias persecuti sunt, ea scientia quam διαλεκτικήν appellant. Inveniendi vero artem, quae τοπική dicitur, quae et ad usum potior erat et ordine naturae certe prior, totam reliquerunt. Nos autem (...) ab ea quae prior est, ordiemur». And cfr. also ID., *Lucullus* (*Academica priora*), II, 3,7-8, ed. Müller cit. (above, note 3), pp. 24,37 - 25,7: «Nec inter nos et eos qui se scire arbitrantur quidquam interest, nisi quod illi non dubitant, quin ea vera sint, quae defendunt, nos probabilia multa habemus, quae sequi facile, adfirmare vix possumus; hoc autem liberiores et solutiores sumus, quod integra nobis est *iudicandi potestas*, nec, ut omnia, quae praescripta et quasi imperata sint, defendamus, necessitate ulla cogimur».

tal questions that (according to the intentions explicitly listed by Cicero himself when he drew up a catalogue of his own philosophical writings) would be its main task to clarify, confront and resolve: the meaning of life and death; the explanation of pain and suffering, and of insatiable desires; the evaluation of the disturbances of the soul, of fears and of the empty cares of life; and above all, as the synthesis of all these questions, the final inquiry regarding the possibility of happiness or *beatitudo*[22].

Such questions are the same that would later challenge Christian reflection upon the revelation regarding the person and teachings of Jesus Christ. Once transferred from the dimension of logical-epistemological justification to that of religious hope, such problems assume, if possible, a still greater sense of urgency. If it is God who speaks of himself to man, one must inevitably expect that, in the theoretical field, the universe reveals its own order and its own dependence on the omnipresent guide of a divine principle and good governor of all things; and, in the practical field, that a final and exhaustive response may be given to the dramatic observation of the disorder and injustices that disturb the outcomes of human enterprises, both individual and universal, in history. Thus revelation offers itself as a sapiential alternative for every philosophically trained mind that has been shaken up by its incapacity for mapping out, through natural means, a satisfying response to the fundamental questions of existence: the same questions formulated, with an unquenchable thirst for an assuring meeting between the absoluteness of the divine and the evidence of the concrete, in the wisdom literature of the Old Testament (Job, Quoheleth), which would be reconsidered and presented with a philosophical radicalism in Boethius' *Consolatio*, and with a new theological rigor in Gregory the Great's dramatic fresco of existential theology, the *Moralia in Job.*

[22] Cfr. Id., *De divinatione*, II, 1, 2, ed. Müller cit. (above, note 3), IV/2, pp. 196,15 - 197,3: «Totidem subsecuti libri Tusculanarum disputationum res *ad beate vivendum* maxime necessarias aperuerunt. Primus enim est de contemnenda morte, secundus de tolerando dolore, de aegritudine lenienda tertius, quartus de reliquis animi perturbationibus, quintus eum locum conplexus est, qui totam philosophiam maxime inlustrat: docet enim ad beate vivendum virtutem se ipsa esse contentam».

Augustine's competent and inquisitive mind received its formation, under the guidance of Cicero himself, through the study of all the responses of past philosophers who vainly strove to provide answers to such questions. This led him to call for a radical choice between the defective natural demand for establishing the proper conditions for the truth, and the possibility of bringing about a new evaluative capacity for philosophers that follows from the free adherence to a religious revelation:

> Since the formal concatenations (*conexiones*) of both true and false propositions (*sententiae*) are true, it is easy to move on to study the truth of such concatenations (*conexionum veritas*) even in the schools that are outside of our Church. Yet, for the truth of the propositions (*sententiarum veritas*), it is indispensable to search in the Holy Scriptures of the Church. The truth of the logical concatenations, in effect, was not established by men: they discovered it (*animadversa*) in natural things and therefore formalized it with rigorous norms (*notata*), so as to make it the object of learning and teaching. Their validity lies in fact in the eternal order of things and was established by the very will of God[23].

In this famous passage from the second book of the *De doctrina Christiana*, Augustine, as a philosopher, takes up the limits of scientific knowledge in order to move on to the recognition, as a believer, of how and why the intellect illuminated by revelation may render itself scientific on the basis of the simple decision to accept something as true only because God communicates it. The natural truth is, in harmony with Cicero's language and with his critique of philosophy, a purely dialectical, that is formal, truth; it guarantees the correctness of the formal connections of the propositions (or *sententiae*, in Augustine's technical language), in so far as they are true or false. Such correctness, which allows at least for a par-

[23] Augustinus Hipponensis, *De doctrina christiana*, II, 31, 48 - 32, 50, PL 34, 58, ed. J. Martin, Turnhout 1962 (CCSL, 32), pp. 68,12-20: «Cum ergo sint verae *conexiones* non solum verarum, sed etiam falsarum *sententiarum*, facile est *veritatem conexionum* etiam in scholis illis discere, quae praeter ecclesiam sunt. *Sententiarum* autem *veritas* in sanctis libris ecclesiasticis investiganda est. Ipsa tamen veritas conexionum non instituta, sed animadversa est ab hominibus et *notata*, ut eam possint vel discere vel docere; nam est in rerum ratione perpetua et divinitus instituta».

tial description of the connections among natural causes – which are apprehended through experience and thus transformed into *notitia* («ab hominibus *notata*») –, is indeed a form of truth, and as such must be recognized also by the believers in Christ, who are therefore obliged to train themselves in the schools of the best philosophers: yet it is not sufficient for grasping the ultimate reasons for the world and its laws. In this regard the *dialectica* is capable of formulating correct (but not necessarily 'true') deductions even by departing from false premises: if it were true that 'all men have wings', since 'the Greeks are men', it would be true, according to the correct procedure of dialectic, that 'the Greeks have wings'. But it is evident that the formalism of the mental discipline does not explain if and why men do not have wings, just as it does not know how to explain the how and why of life itself, of death, of suffering, of injustice, and of the conflict between good and evil. The *sententiae* from which one may draw indispensable teachings on these fundamental topics will not be obliged to be merely correct, but also to be absolutely 'true'. Dialectic alone, the pure *ars iudicandi*, does not know how to recognize which *sententiae* related to higher and more decisive things are true, and which are false. On the other hand, the *ars inveniendi*, the *topica*, which should have supplied for dialectic the contents of true knowledge in order to formally organize it, could be carried out in the schools of ancient philosophers only to the point of identifying the most generic orderings of the truth, which are evident and accessible to all: for example, the first logical-epistemological principles or the axioms of the mathematical sciences, which are original certainties that nevertheless are still nothing more than formal instruments and not suitable explanations fit for justifying and validating the reality of things. The true *topica disciplina* therefore is not and cannot be the prerogative of man. This leads one to admit that the participant in this knowledge can only be the one who accepts and shares the divine communication of the *notitia veritatis*. Since we are not capable of assuring on our own the truth of the *sententiae* from which we develop our reasonings, we cannot refuse to recognize it if we encounter it in the sacred texts, the patrimony of the Church.

The intent of describing the historical passage from the classical to the Christian conception of philosophical thought now explicitly invites historians to pursue a precise delineation of the historical conditions of such a transformation. For this purpose, one has to move forward from a correct and complete reading of the sources and prescind from prejudiced interpretations tainted (in one sense or another) by an ideological radicalism that would be foreign to the medieval world. One must recognize the innovative and common characteristics of doing philosophy in the medieval environment as shaped by believing intellectuals' inevitable and programmatic renunciation of any hope for the natural *inventio* of the truth, which they considered illusory; and, in a complementary way, one must consider their inverse exaltation of the task of the philosophical *iudicium*, which now lies within their competence thanks to a 'new' and stable foundation for the truth that could only be acquired through the faith and assured through rational critique.

***

Regarding the platonic pilgrim going to Larissa, the philosopher inspired by revelation enjoys – according to the teachers who work within such a speculative frame – yet another means of orientation: the witnesses to whom he has decided to entrust himself are for him – that is, in his opinion –, *certainly* tenable, in so far as they are God himself, as well as the prophets and saints who receive inspiration from Him. His condition therefore is no longer that of one who seeks an unreachable truth, but that of one who puts faith in a witness who assures the knowledge of the truth and the possibility of communicating it. And, as Augustine confirms, it is not a disgraceful form of science to know how to recognize one who possesses the science. According to the words of the thirty-sixth Psalm:

> But God is the one who «truly sees», while you are not capable of seeing. He has indicated to you the ones who are truly capable of seeing. (...) It is no small gain to possess the science of knowing how to reach the one who has science. He has the eyes of knowledge; you have the openness to believe in him. That which God sees, you must believe[24].

[24] AUGUSTINUS HIPPONENSIS, *Enarrationes in Psalmos*, 36, s. 2, 2, PL 36, 365, ed.

In a surprising passage from *Homiliae in Ezechielem*, Gregory the Great openly directs Christians toward the possibility of perfecting the metaphor of the «urbs incognita» in respect to Plato:

> There are things that speak of celestial realities in such a way as to be perceptible only to the higher citizens who inhabit the country that lies beyond this world, while these things are not clear to us who are still on our way toward it. This is in fact what happens to a pilgrim who has as his destination a city that is unknown to him: on the one hand, during the journey he hears many things about it; on the other hand, he will conjecture some things about such a city by means of his own reason, but there will always remain some details that he could in no way know, since he is not yet capable of having a direct vision of them. The citizens who already live there, however, see all of it, even that which has not yet been told, and they understand all that which has been said of it. We therefore, who are still on the way, may hear some things about the celestial country that have been declared by one who knows; we may know other things by working them out with reason and by intuiting them with the spirit; and still other things, finally, we may venerate as holy since they remain unintelligible for us[25].

E. Dekkers – J. Fraipont, 3 voll., Turnhout 1966 (CCSL, 38-40), I, p. 348,11-16: «Sed Dominus 'prospicit' (*Ps* 36, 13), tu autem non prospicis; indicavit tibi qui prospicit. (...) Non parva pars scientiae est scienti coniungi. Ille habet oculos cognitionis, tu habeto credulitas. Quod videt Deus, crede tu». Cfr. also Id., *De trinitate*, IX, 1, 1, 961, ed. Mountain cit. (above, note 3), I, pp. 292,21 - 293,29: «Tutissima est enim quaerentis intentio donec apprehendatur illud quo tendimus et quo extendimur. Sed ea recta intentio est quae proficiscitur a fide. Certa enim fides utcumque inchoat cognitionem; cognitio vero certa non perficietur nisi post hanc vitam, cum videbimus 'facie ad faciem' (*1Cor* 13, 12). Hoc ergo sapiamus ut noverimus tutiorem esse affectum vera quaerendi quam incognita pro cognitis praesumendi. Sic ergo quaeramus tamquam inventuri, et sic inveniamus tamquam quaesituri».

[25] Gregorius I papa (Magnus), *Homiliae in Ezechielem*, II, 5, 4, PL 76, 986CD, ed. M. Adriaen, Turnhout 1971 (CCSL, 142), p. 277,87-97: «Sunt enim quaedam quae ita de caelestibus loquuntur ut solis illis supernis civibus in patria sua persistentibus pateant necdumque nobis peregrinantibus reserentur. Nam si quis ad urbem incognitam pergens multa de illa in via audiat, quaedam quidem ex ratione colligit, quaedam vero, quia necdum videt, nullo modo cognoscit, ipsi vero cives qui in ea sunt et quae de illa tacentur vident, et quae de illa dicuntur intellegunt. Nos igitur adhuc in via sumus, multa de illa caelesti patria audimus, alia iam per spiritum et rationem intellegimus, quaedam vero non intellecta veneramur».

As «pilgrims» on their earthly way, men must take into account how much their approach to the truth is condemned to an ever partial comprehension in respect to the fullness of knowledge that the faith promises to the blessed alone: this is a distinction in grades of true knowledge which anticipates that which later scholastic authors will establish between *theologia nostra* (or *in nobis*) and *theologia in se*. If the truth exists – a fact that our reason is capable of grasping on its own – and if it is knowable, but remains unavoidably unknown to every living creature, it will now be possible for men to know it only if someone who has authentic and full knowledge of the truth, and who is a worthy witness, may freely decide to communicate it.

As Plato pointed out, evaluation of the tenability of such a witness may only be entrusted to the intrinsic evidence of its words: that teaching is true which, once having been received through faith and acquired by the intellect, fully manifests an absolute and uncontradictable quality, to the point that the intellect cannot but recognize its necessity. Since Christian revelation is, for Gregory, effectively the truth, the automatic rehabilitation of the stoic criteria of *evidence* – which Cicero had opposed and substituted with *probability* – becomes possible. One finds a clear argument for this perspective in a work that may be called a true manifesto for the possible recovery of ancient philosophical speculation by the believers in Christ, the *Contra Academicos* of Augustine. When the believer, who entrusts himself to the testimony of Christian revelation, opens up this renewed cognitive perspective, the criteria of *evidence* may acquire new force: in respect to all the other sources of knowledge, direct or indirect, the reading of the Scriptures introduces to the mind a *notitia* that fully responds to the expectations of philosophical reason, and it is therefore complete and sufficient in respect to the human capacity for *iudicium*[26]. Then, inspired by an impassioned examination of the reasons that first lead him to conversion, and by an attentive and in depth consideration of theoretical problems that bet-

[26] For a fuller consideration of this problem, cfr. G. D'ONOFRIO, *Il pensiero «convertito»: il giovane Agostino*, in «Archivio di filosofia», 59 (1991), pp. 323-337, now found in the first chapter of ID., Vera philosophia cit. (above, note 20), pp. 44 seqq.

ter take into account the ontological distance between creator and creature, such as the cognitive value of memory and the incomprehensibility of the nature of time, the mature Augustine then entrusts to the literary and speculative portion of the *Confessions* his own assured celebration of *verum* as that which is stable and immutable, or that which is not subject to the variations of accidents and which, as such, is truly divine. For the philosopher who takes into account the reasons of his own knowledge, to know the truth can mean nothing else but knowing the true God, 'if' and 'when' he manifests himself:

> And first of all, wishing to make clear to me (...) that «the Word was made flesh and come to dwell» among men, you made certain books of the Platonists, which had been translated into Latin, come into my hands (...). In them I read how it had been fully demonstrated with many different rational arguments – arguments which certainly did not pronounce these same words, but were fully identical to them in meaning – that «in the beginning was the Word and the Word was with God and God was the Word». (...) *O eternal truth and true love and eternity full of love!* You are my God, to you I sigh «day and night». And when I had not yet known you, (...) suddenly I realized that I was far from you, in the region of dissimilarity, as if I had heard the very voice distinctly coming from on high. (...) And I investigated all the other things which are below you, and I realized that these are neither true being nor true non-being: they are something, since they are from you, but they are nothing, since they are not what you are. Only *that which endures* in fact *truly is*[27].

[27] Cfr. AUGUSTINUS HIPPONENSIS, *Confessiones*, VII, 9, 13 and 10,16 - 11,17, PL 32,740-742, ed. L. Verheijen, Turnhout 1981 (CCSL, 27), p. 101,1-9 and pp. 103,12 - 104,4: «Et primo volens ostendere mihi (...) quod 'Verbum' tuum 'caro factum est et habitavit' inter homines, procurasti mihi (...) quosdam Platonicorum libros ex Graeca lingua in Latinam versos, et ibi legi, non quidem his verbis sed hoc idem omnino multis et multiplicibus suaderi rationibus, quod 'in principio erat Verbum et Verbum erat apud Deum et Deus erat Verbum'. (...) O *aeterna veritas* et *vera caritas* et *cara aeternitas*. Tu es Deus meus, tibi suspiro 'die ac nocte' (*Ps* 1, 2). Et cum te primum cognovi (...) inveni longe me esse a te in regione dissimilitudinis, tamquam audirem vocem tuam de excelso. (...) Et inspexi cetera infra te et vidi nec omnino esse nec omnino non esse: esse quidem quoniam abs te sunt, non esse autem quoniam id quod es non sunt. Id enim *vere est*, quod *incommutabiliter manet*».

In an intuitive and immediate form, such *self-evidence* of the truth, which Augustine acquired with such fatigue in his reflections, is reformulated, within the intellectual chiaroscuro of the Iberian peninsula in the seventh century, in the Prologue of the *De virginitate perpetua Mariae adversus tres infidels* of Ildephonsus of Toledo. This text, which is certainly not among the most well known by historians of philosophy, invokes God in the form of a prayer in order to defend the truth of the virgin birth against the Jews and heretics, while resorting to the almost obsessive style of listing words and propositions that have the same meaning, as found in the *Synonima* of Isidore of Seville[28]. This prayer asks that the complete coherence of the truth, which concedes to authentic knowledge, be rendered manifest and indubitable. The highest possible form of such knowledge was in fact seen and directly experienced in its most profound intimacy, at the moment of the annunciation by the angel, by the pious intellect of the virgin Mary, the model whom all believing searchers for the truth must imitate:

> The truth in fact *remains in eternity*. That which is true lives. That which comes forth from the truth does not cease to exist. Trueness should not be tarnished by falsity. The truth is not conquered by deceptive fallacies. The things that are true never have relations with the false. And if, however, the truth should ever be obscured by the shadows of falsity, even the hidden truth will reveal things that are true. That which is false, in fact, will never be *stable*, that which is true will never be less; that which is outside of the truth will be emptied; and that which is far from the truth will be dissolved into nothing, since the truth is God, and the things which involve God are true, and the things which come from God subsist thanks to the truth alone. Thus, one who preaches the Lord, tells of the truth. Whoever says true things about God, distributes knowledge of the truth. One who asserts true things, defends the right of the truth. One who embraces the truth, loves the Lord. One who does the truth, fulfills the will of the Lord. God certainly understands hidden things, God knows the veiled things, God penetrates the things immersed in the abyss, God examines thoroughly the secret things. Thus he recognizes one

[28] Cfr. G. D'ONOFRIO, *Il rinascere della* Christianitas *(secoli VI-VIII)*, in *Storia della Teologia nel Medioevo*, dir. di G. d'Onofrio, 3 voll., Casale Monferrato 1996, I (*I princìpi*), [pp. 37-105], pp. 67-68 and 83-84.

> who tries to contaminate the truth, knows one who tries to change the truth, recognizes one who diminishes the truth, knows openly one who tries to quench the truth[29].

These words are striking in their simple and immediate profundity, which I would not hesitate to define as 'parmenidean'. The characteristics of the truth and the attributes of the divine coincide in a convincing unity, and are distinguished by absolute evidence: that which is true and is therefore stable (*manet*) and immutable (*in aeternum*) cannot surrender before the onslaught of falsity. If therefore such characteristics are declared and then understood, in whatever way they may occur, then they appear as necessarily true: all that which belongs to God and is preached about God and is derived from God, all that which proclaims God or communicates God, is true and evident. Whoever says something about God increases the knowledge of the truth, but, inversely, whoever says something about the truth, increases the knowledge that men have about God. This is the simplest, and at the same time strongest, motivation that could render philosophers open to the reception of revelation: if revelation speaks the truth, then, as soon as someone proclaims it, its trueness becomes immediately clear to the minds which perceive it.

It is not difficult to recognize the most mature and complete illustration of such a program in the work of Anselm of Aosta, who inspires Gilbert Crispin in his direct formulation of the

[29] HILDEPHONSUS TOLETANUS († 667), *De virginitate perpetua sanctae Mariae (adversus tres infideles)*, Praefatio (Oratio), PL 96, 53AC: «*Manet* enim veritas *in aeternum*. Vivit quod verum est. Non desinit quod a vero procedit. Falso non decidit verum. Fallaciis non vincitur veritas. Falsis non commutantur quae vera sunt. Et si fallaciarum umbris obtegatur veritas, revelabit quae vera sunt abdita veritas. Quod enim falsum est *non stabit*, quod verum est non deficiet, quod extra veritatem est cassum erit, quod a veritate procul est inanescet, quia veritas Deus est, et quae Dei sunt vera sunt, et quae ex Deo sunt sola veritate subsistunt. Inde qui Dominum annuntiat, veritatem enarrat. Qui de Deo vera dicit, veritatis cognitionem pandit. Qui ea quae vera sunt asserit, veritatis iura defendit. Qui veritatem amplectitur, Dominum diligit. Qui veritatem facit, Dei voluntatem adimplet. Deus certe occulta novit, Deus absconsa cognoscit, Deus abdita penetrat, Deus perscrutatur occulta. Proinde novit qui depravat verum, scit qui immutat veritatem, intelligit qui veritatem minuit, in aperto sapit qui veritatem exstinguit». I have also written on Idelfonso and on the speculative complexity of this passage in G. D'ONOFRIO, *Il* mysterium Mariae *nella teologia e nella pietà dell'alto medioevo latino (secoli V-XI)*, in *Storia della Mariologia*, a c. di E. dal Covolo – A. Serra, I, *Dal modello biblico al modello letterario*, Roma 2009, [pp. 505-566], pp. 517-520.

alethiological principle from which we have developed this essay, according to which the truth as such is self-evident, apart from the sources which allow one to know it. Such 'self-evidence' of the truth is clearly at the basis of the method of theological argumentation that Anselm applies in his speculative work. This is already evident in the *Monologion*, where the multiple steps applied by the mind in order to ascend *sola ratione* to the necessary admission of the existence of God are reducible to a single common formal procedure, which consists in the passage from the comprehension of the particular truth concerning some precise characteristics of created being (magnitude, quality and goodness, being and perfection) to that of the general truth of their fulfillment in the One through participation in a common and higher principle – a principle that evidently exists, or such a participation would not be possible. But the operative efficacy of such a speculative position becomes clear above all in the formulation of the *unum argumentum* of the *Proslogion*: the simple rational affirmation (necessarily true) of the manner of being that is (necessarily) proper to God if God exists, imposes (necessarily) the recognition of the distinguishing mark of reality in such a truth. It is essential to observe how the starting point of such a purely rational elaboration is rendered possible by the fact that the human mind comes to knowledge of such a *manner of being proper to God* not on the basis of an act of external experience (sensible or of any other possible kind), but thanks to the *communication* of such «notitia» from revelation:

> Therefore, O Lord, you who give understanding to the faith, allow me to understand that which you know as useful for understanding, that is, that *you are as we believe, and you are that which we believe*. Indeed, we believe that you are a being than which nothing greater can be conceived. (...) If therefore that, than which nothing greater can be conceived, were to exist only in the intellect, then that, than which nothing greater can be conceived, would be something than which a greater can be conceived. And this is certainly impossible. There exists therefore without a doubt something than which nothing greater can be conceived[30].

[30] ANSELMUS CANTUARIENSIS, *Proslogion*, 2, 227C-228A, ed. Schmitt cit. (above, note 4), pp. 101,3-5 and 101,17 - 102,3: «Ergo, Domine, qui das fidei in-

Only faith could introduce the *notitia* regarding God, which becomes evident as soon as it is pronounced, into the reflection. Thus faith, in this context, plays the role of an 'empirical source', that is, something outside of reason. Its function concludes by communicating to the intellect a comprehensible datum that is assumed apart from its effective veracity: only one who has faith can have experience of the comprehensible data present in revelation, and only one who has had such experience can have knowledge of such data[31]. But such a communication, once taken up by the intellect in its immediacy and simplicity as a comprehensible datum, imposes upon the intellect the evidence of the deduction which it derives from it: if the *id quo maius cogitari nequit* is equal to the *id quo maius cogitari nequit*, such an *id* cannot be something which does not exist and which, as such, could not be the *id quo maius cogitari nequit*. If *Deus* is equal to *Deus* – and it could not be otherwise – then *Deus* truly *est in re*. But only the faith is capable of communicating to the created intellect that which corresponds to the meaning of the expression «Deus est», that is, the «quo maius»[32]. Reread from such a perspective, the *unum argumentum* appears as a complete actualization of the model of thought that guides medieval knowledge: from the faith arises not the conclusion, which is strictly philosophical in its most genuine nature, but the premise (God is *quo maius cogitari nequit*), from which the development of the argument may arrive at its conclusion. The faith is not the result of the argumentation (one doesn't demonstrate to believe, but to know), but it is the source that proclaims an objective truth that would not be comprehensible otherwise.

tellectum, da mihi ut quantum scis expedire intelligam *quia es sicut credimus, et hoc es quod credimus*: et quidem credimus te esse aliquid quo nihil maius cogitari possit. (...) Si ergo id quo maius cogitari non potest est in solo intellectu, id ipsum quo maius cogitari non potest est quo maius cogitari potest. Sed certe hoc esse non potest. Existit ergo procul dubio aliquid quo maius cogitari non valet, et in intellectu et in re».

[31] Cfr. ID., *Epistola de incarnatione Verbi*, PL 158, 264C, ed. Schmitt, II, p. 9,5-8: «Nimirum hoc ipsum quod dico: qui non crediderit, non intelliget. Nam qui non crediderit, *non experietur*, et *qui expertus non fuerit non cognoscet*. Quantum enim rei auditum superat experientia, tantum vincit audientis cognitionem experientis scientia».

[32] Cfr. in D'ONOFRIO, Vera philosophia cit. (above, note 20), fourth chapter, pp. 209 ff.

The hermeneutical circularity between reason and revelation, which, as it has been said before, appears viable in such a model, is both unavoidable and solid; but it is also, at the same time, fecund. If the rationality of the philosophers may contribute to a systematic-organizational clarification of the contents of the discourse of faith (and this is the task of Christian *theology*), then, in a symmetrically inverse sense, it is the contents of the faith that become the causal occasion of a better philosophical comprehension of the world and of the truth of the reality. Theology learns from philosophy the appropriate instruments for the investigation of the truths of faith, while philosophy learns from the articulation of dogma the correct orientation for being more informed, more fertile, and more productive in the carrying out of its autonomous investigations. If, standing before the absolute truth of the faith, the human intellect is blinded, like Paul on the way to Damascus before the striking and incomprehensible appearance of Christ, and is incapable of understanding the mystery by applying its natural instruments and procedures, then «true» philosophy, that is, the philosophy instructed by the faith, is for the medieval intellectual like the hand of Ananias, which restores vision to the one who has chosen *to believe* and transforms him at the same time into a witness and investigator of the truth: a 'believing philosopher', capable of offering his own guidance to other travelers, who are less capable than he in the use of reason, in order to guide them toward the unknown city which is the goal of their common way.

The splendid illustration of such a 'new' condition of human thought has been given to us by the refined poetic wisdom of Dante Alighieri, in an explicit reference to the encounter between reason with truth on the way to Damascus:

> While I was doubting because of my quenched
> sight, I was made attentive by a breath that
> issued from the glowing flame which quenched it,
>
> saying: «Until you have again the sense of sight
> you have consumed on me, it is good you
> compensate for it by rational discourse.
>
> Begin then, and declare from where your mind is
> focused; and be assured that your sight within
> you is lost for a time, not destroyed;

> because the lady who is conducting you
> through this divine region has in her look the power
> that was in Ananias' hand»[33].

Blinded by the light of the apostle John, who is about to question him on charity, the celestial pilgrim is seized by *doubt* because he no longer manages to see Beatrice («while I was *doubting* because of my quenched sight»), who is the knowledge that guides him. John, symbol of the highest theological vision of all the ages, the one who grasped and proclaimed the mystery of the Word, invites him to compensate for this diminution of vision with the use of *reason*, reflecting on the final goal of human love («from where your mind is focused», that is the 'beatitude', which is the *eudaimonia* of the philosophers, the end of the human search for the good and the truth[34]). Thus, his vision, which was obscured for a while («lost for a time, not destroyed»), will revive, since Beatrice, the *vera philosophia* who guides him toward the truth, has the same miraculous power upon natural knowledge that the hand of Ananias had in restoring Paul's vision[35].

When, after having passed the exam, Dante retrieves his sight, the spirit of Adam appears before him, ready to offer him the response to the fundamental problems of humanity, which philosophy always pursued, and which are the same problems of

[33] DANTES ALAGHERII (DANTE ALIGHIERI), *Commedia, Paradiso*, XXVI, vv. 1-12, ed. G. Petrocchi, Milano 1966-1967 (Edizione Nazionale a c. della Società Dantesca Italiana), VII/4, pp. 425-426: «Mentr'io dubbiava per lo viso spento, / della fulgida fiamma che lo spense / uscì uno spiro che mi fece attento, / dicendo: 'Intanto che tu ti risense / della vista che haï in me consunta, / ben è che ragionando la compense. / Comincia dunque; e dì ove s'appunta / l'anima tua, e fa' ragion che sia / la vista in te smarrita e non defunta; / perché la donna che per questa dia / region ti conduce, ha nello sguardo / la virtù ch'ebbe la man d'Anania'».

[34] Cfr. also ID., *Convivio*, IV, 22, 18, ed. G. Vandelli, in *Opere di Dante*, V, Firenze 1934-1937 (Roma 1984²), p. 742a: «E così appare che nostra beatitudine (questa felicitade di cui si parla) prima trovare potemo quasi imperfetta ne la vita attiva, cioè ne le operazioni e le morali virtuti, e poi perfetta quasi ne le operazioni de le intellettuali. Le quali due operazioni sono vie espedite e direttissime a menare a la somma beatitudine, la quale qui non si puote avere (...)».

[35] See also Dante's answer to John: ID., *Paradiso*, *ibid.*, vv. 25-27, ed. Petrocchi, p. 428: «E io: 'Per filosofici argomenti / e per autorità che quinci scende / cotale amor convien che in me s'imprenti'». And John's conclusion, *ibid.*, vv. 46-48, p. 430: «E io udi': 'Per intelletto umano / e per autoritadi a lui concorde / d'i tuoi amori a Dio guarda il sovrano'».

Quoeleth, Job, and Gregory the Great: why there suffering in life? why did God punish man («the cause of so great an exile»)? and what did the forbidden fruit, which had determined the exile of man from paradise, signify? The solution is in the perception of the just limits that the original man chose not to observe:

> Now know, my son, that not the tasting of the tree
> was in itself the cause of so great an exile,
> but only the transgressing of the mark[36].

The true sin was not the taking of the forbidden fruit, but the failure to respect the boundaries that God had established for the human intellect; and the failure to exercise *discretion*, which alone allows the intellect to approach the created things that participate in the truth in an ever diminishing and imperfect way, in order to comprehend it[37]. Let philosophy accept its limits («be content, o humanity, with the *quia*», as Virgil exhorts in the third canto of the *Purgatorio*[38]). The result of the search that incessantly nourishes the questions of the human mind will not be a rational comprehension of the theological truth (which would be impossible), but a true philosophical knowledge: that is, knowledge of the natural order, but directed toward and submissive to the verification by the *fides*, which is established as the hypertext that encloses scientific knowledge between two parentheses, at its beginning

[36] *Ibid.*, vv. 115-117, p. 438: «Or, figliuol mio, non il gustar del legno / fu per sé la cagion di tanto essilio, / ma solamente il trapassar del segno».

[37] Cfr. Id., *Convivio*, I, 11, 3-4, ed. Vandelli, p. 686b: «Sì come la parte sensitiva de l'anima ha suoi occhi, con li quali apprende la differenza de le cose in quanto elle sono di fuori colorate, così la parte razionale ha suo occhio, con lo quale apprende la differenza de le cose in quanto sono ad alcuno fine ordinate: e questa è la discrezione. E sì come colui che è cieco de li occhi sensibili va sempre secondo che li altri il guidano, o male [o] bene, così colui che è cieco del lume della discrezione sempre va nel suo giudicio secondo il grido, o diritto o falso; onde qualunque ora lo guidatore è cieco, conviene che esso e quello, anche cieco, ch'a lui s'appoggia, vegnano a mal fine. Però è scritto che 'l cieco al cieco farà guida, e così cadranno ambedue ne la fossa (*Mt* 15, 14)». Regarding this theme, cfr. G. d'Onofrio, Consequentia rerum*: le* parole *e la* distinzione de le cose *nel pensiero di Dante,* in *Oggetto e spazio. Fenomenologia dell'oggetto, forma e cosa, dai secoli* XIII-XIV *ai post-cartesiani*, Atti del Convegno (Perugia, 8-10 settembre 2005), a c. di G. Federici Vescovini – O. Rignani, Firenze 2008 (Micrologus' Library, 24), pp. 37-57.

[38] Dantes Alagherii, *Commedia*, *Purgatorio*, III, v. 37, ed. Petrocchi, VII/3, p. 41: «State contenti, umana gente, al *quia*».

(from which it takes its start) and at the end (toward which it tends in order to be verified).

A new manner of thinking is therefore born on the way to Damascus: a manner of thought which renders the society of believers an authentic intellectual community, consolidated by the adhesion to a common mode or *model* (and therefore to a *paradigm*[39]) for the consideration of and search for the truth, and for conducting and developing scientific knowledge. The common aim is to make all procedures and results of reason enter into this model. He who, with such a way of thinking, sets out toward the «urbs incognita», still does not know it; but when he reaches it, he will know how to recognize it as if he had already known it. Such a conception of the relationships between reason and faith seems to have functioned for centuries as a solid system for supporting the search for *the truth* within the development of human science: that is, a system enclosed between the conditioning borders of scriptural wisdom (and of the dogmatic tradition founded upon it), but at the same time interiorly open to many possibilities of development governed by various articulations for the use of reason. Given that there was *a general paradigm* which was commonly shared, one may certainly also find various expressions of the adaptation of the instrumentalizations and speculative perspectives within the boundaries established by it. One may recognize, therefore, the emergence of several *particular paradigms*, corresponding to various conceptions of the origin, method and finalities of science, as well as to many different expressions of it[40].

[39] At least in the sense suggested by T. S. KUHN, *The structure of scientific revolutions*, Chicago 1962 (1996^3). Cfr. REALE, *Agostino e il* Contra Academicos cit. (above, note 13), pp. 13-20.

[40] In this sense, I would highlight the complex diagnosis of medieval thought delineated by Tullio Gregory in Helsinki in August of 1987, at the opening of the Eighth International Congress of the Société Internationale pour l'Étude de la Philosophie Mediévale, which was dedicated to the theme of knowledge and the sciences in the Middle Ages. Gregory offers a lucid synthesis in which one sees how, during the Middle Ages, the branches of many progressive deformations, specifications and articulations, to which the concepts of 'knowledge' and 'science' were submitted, emerged – all of which took place in a complex way from relating natural intelligence to a higher truth of supernatural origin. Cfr. T. GREGORY, *Forme di conoscenza e ideali di sapere nella cultura medievale*, in *Knowledge and the Sciences in Medieval Philosophy*, Proceedings of the Eighth international Congress of Medieval Philosophy (S.I.E.P.M.) (Helsinki, 24-29 August 1987), 3 voll.,

Research on the *medieval paradigm* does not at all pursue, in substance, the hope of reproducing the idea of the existence and eventual commendation, as such, of a medieval 'Christian philosophy'; nor is it reduced to the project of evaluating the possibilities that were established in the Middle Ages in order to form a dialogue between philosophy and faith. The problem is not to establish to what degree, and with what results (condemnable or appreciable) the faith conditioned philosophy in the medieval centuries during its objective search for the truth: rather it is to manage to appreciate the determining effect on philosophical thought that this period had through its continual recognition of itself as commensurable with the foundations of the faith (not only of the Christian faith in both the East and West, but also of the Islamic and Hebrew faiths). It also asks what meaning, what importance, what originality, what authenticity and capacity of being verified in other cultural contexts, could a philosophical project have when carried out in a world in which there was a dominant and unavoidable adherence to an overarching religious confession. The evaluation of the modalities that allow for and determine the existence of philosophical thought within a civilization entirely and universally distinguished by the formal adherence to affirmations of the revealed faith is the object of the research upon the *medieval paradigm*; the specification and verification of the models, diagrams or grids which direct, according to more or less shared modalities, the various formations of thought within this common ideological frame, are, however, the object of every form of research on the *paradigms* introduced and developed within the sphere of medieval thought.

The medieval philosopher (Christian, Islamic, or Hebraic) departs from the presupposition that his philosophy is a conversation with faith, composed of questions and responses; but within this dialogue, it is not philosophy, but faith, that is asking the questions. Augustine understood this well when he reflected on

Helsinki 1990, I, ed. by M. Asztalos – J. E. Murdoch – I. Niiniluoto, pp. 10-69; and in Id., Mundana Sapientia. *Forme di conoscenza nella cultura medievale*, Roma 1991 (Storia e letteratura, 181), pp. 1-59. In general regarding the relationships between philosophy and theology in the Middle Ages, cfr. the studies collected in *La servante et la consolatrice. La philosophie dans ses rapports avec la théologie au Moyen Âge* (Textes et Traditions, 3), éd. par J.-L. Solère – Z. Kaluza, Paris 2002.

the image of the child Jesus, who questioned the sages in the temple: Jesus remained not in order to learn from them, but, starting from his own perfect knowledge, in order to verify the degree of their competency. The faith investigates in order to ask philosophy to what degree it, as philosophy, is capable of grasping and justifying that of which the faith already has a full and complete knowledge[41].

For this reason, all thinkers, literati, spiritual figures, poets and scientists of the medieval millennium could have expressed agreement regarding the sole desired outcome for human intellectual research by making the following words their own:

> No other glory, in effect, has been promised us than the knowledge through direct experience, in the future life, of the things that, in this life, are believed through faith and are examined and, to the degree that it is possible, are made the object of conviction on the part of reason[42].

(English translation by John GAVIN S. J.)

[41] Cfr. AUGUSTINUS HIPPONENSIS, *Enarrationes in Psalmos*, 118, s. 22, 3 (explanation of *Ps* 118, 99: «Super omnes docentes me intellexi, quia testimonia tua meditatio mea est»), PL 37, 1563-1564, ed. Dekkers – Fraipont cit. (above, note 24), III, p. 1737,1 - 1738,37: «Sed quid est hoc quod sequitur, 'Super omnes docentes me intellexi'? Quis est iste qui super omnes docentes se intellexit? (...) Agnosco eum plane qui super omnes docentes se intellexit, quando cum esset annorum duodecim, remansit puer Iesus in Ierusalem, et a parentibus suis post triduum inventus est illic in templo sedens inter doctores, audiens illos et interrogans; ubi stupebant omnes qui eum audiebant, super prudentia et responsis eius (cfr. *Lc* 2, 42-47). (...) Ideo 'super omnes docentes' se intelligebat, quia 'testimonia' Dei meditabatur: *quae melius quam illi de seipso noverat*».

[42] IOHANNES SCOTUS ERIUGENA, *Periphyseon*, I, PL 122, 451C, ed. É. Jeauneau, 5 voll., Turnhout 1996-2003 (CCCM, 161-165), I, p. 16,393-396: «Praesertim cum nulla alia promittitur nobis gloria praeter eorum, quae hic per fidem creduntur et ratione quaeruntur et quantum licet suadentur, in futura vita per experimentum cognitionem».

ARMANDO BISOGNO

THE PHILOSOPHICAL MIDDLE AGES: HISTORY AND PERSPECTIVES OF A SPECULATIVE PARADIGM

In 1962, the physicist Thomas Kuhn published *The Structure of Scientific Revolutions,* entering powerfully into the debate in the middle of the twentieth century on the epistemological foundations of scientific progress. The idea, which had been that of Bacon, Descartes and John Stuart Mill, that science could predetermine a method «for discovering true theories» having been abandoned, modern epistemology, from the first appearance of the Kantian critique, had accepted the appearance, in the slow evolution of scientific progress, of reversals and radical changes of perspective such as to change acquired knowledge and equilibriums[1]. Along these lines, the reflections of Kant were evidently oriented towards that Newtonian system able to see a transcendental invisible force which structures the system of the universe and to revolutionize in this way the system of reference of modern science.

Even though it is possible to reason in terms of revolutions, a full observation of such epochal events, of their effects and the contexts which produce them and to which they, in their turn, give rise, shows to what extent the radical nature of such changes does not necessarily imply that all their effects are always and immediately evident. In particular, reflecting on the Copernican astronomical revolution, Kuhn hypothesized that the periodic disturbances apt for changing the epistemological frame of refer-

[1] Cfr. T. S. Kuhn, *The Structure of Scientific Revolutions*, Chicago 1962 (1996^{3}), pp. 111 seqq.

10.1484/M.NUTRIX-EB.1.101232

ence were, silently, effects and causes of a much larger structural and organic change in the cultural conditions of an age. Integrating in this way science, history of the sciences and history of ideas, Kuhn affirmed that a constellation of results, not exclusively experimental, produced a *paradigm* historically linked to a precise phase of the evolution of human knowledge. The contrast between the Ptolemaic system and the Copernican method illustrates well this notion of *paradigm*. Both of the complex astronomical frameworks, beyond their real functionality and efficacy, descriptive or predictive, did not simply offer a collection of rules, methods or calculations, but represented the – theoretical – mirror of a cultural practice which imbued the environments and the epochs in which they had been developed. The Copernican method is therefore different from the Ptolemaic not just in its ability to offer answers to certain mathematical incoherencies, but because it represents at the same time the source and the fruit of a different conception of life, man and the world.

Understood in this sense, the *theory of paradigms* of Kuhn already reveals itself as a historiographic tool; in fact the theory, far from merely trying to describe a factual situation, analyzes the entirety of the factors which are, at the same time, cause and effect of such situations. Such a speculative openness, which in investigating into methods takes into account the contexts in which these were born and of the cultural identities which produced them (or which are derived from them) makes the Kuhnian perspective a flexible tool, applicable, *mutatis mutandis*, also in fields distant from epistemological research. If, however, this method of investigation is in itself exportable, in as much as it is a macrotheory of the evolution of human knowledge, the different subjects to which it can be applied change its utility noticeably. In particular, in the attempt to reconstruct, with an *iter* parallel to that used to delineate the *Copernican paradigm*, the features and characteristics of a hypothetical *medieval paradigm*, that is, the characteristics which identify the Middle Ages and make them radically different from the preceding and following stages in the history of thought, the first obstacle is created by the profoundly unformed identity of the subject under consideration; for the very idea of a Middle Ages, understood as an approximately delineated portion of a equally arbitrary division of the periods of history, is a historiographic violence, certainly functional for historiographic ends, because «la recherché historique vit d'abstractions» but devoid of real foundations in the flow of events[2]. If it is easy, therefore, to identify a *Copernican paradigm*, restricting the field of research to the theories elaborated by Copernicus, to his sources of inspiration and to the effects produced by them, it is far more complex to hypothesize the existence of a *medieval paradigm* which, avoiding the abstractions of an uncertain division into periods, on the one hand identifies methods, doctrines, knowledge and visions of the universe whose homogeneity would justify the use of the expression 'paradigm' and, on the other, is able to demonstrate that the sum of these methodologies and contents were particular to an era and to that era alone, so that this *paradigm* could be called properly and univocally *medieval*.

The colorful variety of the approaches, the doctrines and the speculative and cultural results in the chronological arc included, in the most common meaning of the term 'Middle Ages', between the fifth and the fourteenth century, would lead one to think both of the different phases of a slow evolution and of 'paradigms' profoundly different from one another, when not actually in open contrast. Impoverishing, in this way, the very notion of *paradigm*, reducing it, from a complex and complete macrovision of an epoch and of a method, to a punctual and chronologically defined group of theories and figures, one might be led to isolate an Occidental paradigm opposed to a Byzantine paradigm; a Christian paradigm different from a Hebraic paradigm or an Islamic one; a Platonic paradigm as an alternative to an Aristotelian paradigm, producing *ex post* artificial and abstract divisions compared to the intricate and indiscernible tangle of ideas and speculations of the cultural conscience of an era, and certainly misunderstanding the very notion of a *paradigm*. The partiality of such classifications, which dissect into unnatural sub-unities a historical and speculative *continuum*, can on the contrary be useful for the identification of the grand lines of development of medieval thought, which effectively drew nourishment from different and contrasting sources, united in their development but distinct in

[2] É. GILSON, *L'esprit de la philosophie médiévale*, Paris 1932 (1948[2]), p. 1.

their individual cultural identity. Taking therefore as true the classificatory consequences of such partial distinctions and certainly understanding their intrinsic limitation, it is useful, in order to identify a unique, omnicomprehensive *medieval paradigm*, to eliminate from them those specific elements which are completely incompatible with other elements, to verify if, through a progressive effort of generalizing the common parameters, it is possible to identify a common pool of ideas and systems of reference among the different thinkers who lived together in the so-called 'Middle Ages', which can represent a first sketch of a more general paradigm of that era.

Trying to take as a point of departure the idea of occidental Christianity, that is to say the community of intellectuals united in the fidelity, more or less absolute, to the Roman *magisterium*, it is possible to identify a rich list of characteristic elements. For no Christian knowledge is accepted, in Occident, whether in the Patristic or Scholastic era, without consideration: of the contributions coming from the Scriptures and their exegesis; of the adhesion of faith to the *magisterium*, to the doctrine and the liturgical and sacramental practice of the Roman church; of the knowledge deriving from the literary-philosophical tradition, experienced either as a positive inheritance or as an object of polemic. It is by basing itself on these three foundations that the entire history of medieval Occidental philosophy makes its advances; for, independently of a preference for particular parts of the Scriptures, discussions concerning the meaning of the *magisterium* of the Church, and the adhesion or not to a cultural model of pagan origin, these three aspects unite all the medieval theologians. Operating, as mentioned, by subtraction, this tripartite identity can be useful for describing also the Byzantine area, provided that the referral to fidelity to the Church of Rome is eliminated and replaced with a broader link with an established ecclesiastical institution, as the metropolitan authorities could be. In a similar way, modifying the limits of the first of the three elements and renouncing the Christian particularity of the New Testament Biblical text, considering instead the common link to the Old Testament, it would be possible to bring in the Hebraic identity also. Finally, if the fidelity to a canonized institution is removed, and reference is made to the simple existence of a revealed text, even the Islamic tradition could be absorbed. In this way, a first group of characteristic elements, necessarily generic and generalist, could be delineated, which would identify as medieval that model of thought and work within which the element which cannot be eliminated is the existence of a revelation of the divine which takes written form, integrated with human knowledge coming from speculative traditions not necessarily of religious origin and experienced within communities linked to politico-religious authorities of different individual weights. This group of elements, although apparently vague, unites all the intellectuals of the medieval era who lived in the geographical and cultural basin of the Mediterranean, and characterizes them compared to the preceding traditions and to the successors in later centuries who, in a different way in each case, denied the importance of one of the elements listed here. For the authors who lived between the fifth and the fourteenth century, on every shore of the *mare nostrum*, no culture existed which was not permeated with religious elements, vivified by cultural tradition, even if pagan, incarnated in some kind of communication and direct revelation of the divine to man and lived in the social environment of a brotherhood of believers.

The medieval intellectuals certainly were aware of the existence of this foundational identity. Although divided in particular by the role given to the sacred text, to tradition and to the ecclesiastical institution, none of the various speculative identities of the Middle Ages, especially of the Latin Middle Ages, ever doubted of the essential value of a scriptural exegesis, of the utility, more or less mediated or declared, of profane knowledge, or of the necessity of political and spiritual guides. In the light of these considerations it is possible to look for a *medieval paradigm* understood as a synthetic vision of an entire framework and not as a description of a specific configuration including sources, texts, contexts, and key figures. For the medieval paradigm, to be such, had to represent, for the men of the Middle Ages, not an artificial construction, but an undeniable principle of identity; not an abstract cultural project but a natural and shared way of understanding forms and methods of knowledge. Along these lines, the medieval paradigm cannot appear otherwise than as a hermeneutical concept, born *a posteriori* in the contexts which received, in the course of the centuries, medieval knowledge and tried to classify it precisely on the basis of the different interpretations given to that identity, having become an interpretative model in their hands as exegetes. That which for each of the medieval theologians was therefore the natural affirmation of a personal identity became, in historiographic investigation, the attempt, performed ever since the Renaissance era, to identify a paradigm, that is, a connection, beyond the individual particularities, of the grand lines of a more general shared identity.

The Renaissance spirit identified in the typically medieval attempt to incorporate into itself the fruits of the pagan tradition as well the most interesting feature of this identity and, therefore, the most characteristic element of this paradigm. Thus, when Marsilio Ficino, in a letter to Martino Uranio, indicates the necessity of reconciling two paths to reach the truth, the *sacerdotalis* and the *philosophica*, he seems to be in full agreement with the medieval tradition, except for the necessity of clarifying the precise features of this *sacerdotium*, given that the pagan Plato is placed as an example of reconciliation between the two areas and indicated as an *auctoritas* under whose tutelage all wise men must place themselves[3]. Capable of reconciling Socrates and Moses, Plato is taken by Ficino as a model for all philosophers and, therefore, also as an interpretative *exemplum* to evaluate the philosophical dignity of the thought of the medievals; in this way a speculative model arises, at the dawn of the Renaissance era, which creates in an artificial way an archetypical historic-exegetic model and tries to insert it into the reality of the history of philosophy to verify which eras and authors adhere to it and therefore how many of them are really worthy to appear in a complete historiographic treatment. The medieval era and its identity are not therefore evaluated in relation with what they really produced, but for their congruity with this preordained model; thus, for Ficino, it is not the identification of a particular medieval paradigm which provokes interest, but the search for authors, such as Severinus Boethius or Henry of Ghent, who adhered with the most

[3] Cfr. MARSILIUS FICINUS, *Marsilius Ficinus florentinus Martino Uranio Praenygero*, ed. in ID., *Opera omnia*, Basileae 1576, ex Officina Henricpetrina [repr. Torino 1962], p. 899,2; on this theme cfr. A. BISOGNO, *Il metodo carolingio. Identità culturale e dibattito teologico nel secolo nono*, Turnhout 2008 (Nutrix, 3), pp. 13-39.

naturalness and perspicacity to the concordist model exemplified by Plato. From Ficino and, in the same years, from the pages of the *Oratio de hominis dignitate* of Pico della Mirandola emerges in this way a concordist historiographic ideal, inclined towards ignoring the real contribution of the individual medieval authors, and engaged in classifying them according to their greater or lesser usefulness in demonstrating the existence of a speculative *continuum*, born in the ancient sapiential and patriarchal culture, pursued in the construction of the Platonic system and having reached, by means of a part of the Middle Ages, the Renaissance of the fifteenth century[4].

Opposed to this vision in terms of content, but closely related to it in terms of method, was the anticoncordist interpretation of this historical-doctrinal development. For the ideas expressed by Gianfrancesco Pico della Mirandola in his *Examen vanitatis doctrinae gentium* only apparently contradict those manifested by the «patruus» in his *Oratio*. Although Gianfrancesco says he is convinced that no relationship should be identified between the antique – pagan – wisdom and the medieval wisdom illuminated by the faith, his historiographic approach is methodologically identical to that proposed by his adversaries. The medieval centuries are in no way evaluated with respect to its speculative particularities, in the effort to identify a paradigm which describes its ideas and intellectual technique; on the contrary it is delineated only as a Christian era, and therefore totally different compared to a tradition which, even if it is luminous, remained irremediably pagan and therefore to be rejected[5].

The *Examen* of Gianfrancesco Pico della Mirandola was printed in 1520, a few months before Luther was excommunicated. The rupture within the Catholic world which the Protestant Reformation produced obviously had repercussions also on historiographic investigation and on the perception and reception of the medieval paradigm. Despite pursuing opposed and

[4] Cfr. Iohannes Picus Mirandolensis, *Oratio de hominis dignitate*, XXXI, 189 seqq., ed. E. Garin, Pordenone 1994 (Studio/Tesi, 1), pp. 50-54.

[5] Cfr. Iohannes Franciscus Picus Mirandolensis, *Examen vanitatis doctrinae gentium et veritatis Christianae disciplinae*, Mirandolae 1520, Iohannes Maciochius Bundenius (and in Id., *Opera omnia*, 2 voll., Basileae 1573, ex Officina Henricpetrina [repr. Hildesheim 1969], II, pp. 710-1264).

contrary apologetic goals, the newborn Lutheran historiography perpetrated the errors of method and content of Catholic historiography, imposing on the medieval era an exegetical cage useful for demonstrating an already predetermined thesis. For, if the motivation and goal of Protestant historiography was, coherently with the moralizing battle of Luther, the condemnation of the political and religious practices of the Catholic Church, historiographic investigation could not do otherwise than concentrate on finding the moment in which corruption had rendered the Roman see impure. The study of the history of medieval philosophy, far from trying to identify elements which could be considered common so as to reach a definition of a unitary medieval paradigm, became, thus, the terrain within which to isolate the moments which signaled the beginning, development and final corruption in the decline of the Church. Thus, in the *Chronicon* written between 1568 and 1572 by Philip Melancthon and finished by the husband of one of his daughters, Kaspar Peucer, a history is described of the *res ecclesiasticae* and Greek, Roman and Germanic politics, from the beginning of the world until the reign of Charles V, not in order to identify the particularities of the various eras which had succeeded one another, but to retrace, in the irregular movement of this analysis, the initial moment of the perversion of the Church. In the central part of the text, the *Chronicon* does not hesitate to identify precise stages in the corruption of the Roman dignity. Scholasticism is divided there into three great periods, each identified by various figures, and divided into precise chronological arcs, which proceed from Lanfranc of Pavia to Alexander of Hales, from Albert the Great to Durandus of Saint-Pourçain and from the latter to the posting of the theses of Luther. The era on the contrary which precedes these three periods, included between the pontificate of Gregory the Great and 1020, appears in the *Chronicon* as the beginning of the decline of Christian identity, from which condemnation only the action of Charlemagne is preserved, able to expand the borders of his empire but at the same time attentive to promote the spiritual and cultural progress of his people[6].

[6] Cfr. KASPAR PEUCER, *Chronicon Carionis*, Vitebergae (Wittenberg) 1572, Iohannes Crato. Peucer himself, in the work *Triplex aetas doctorum scholasticorum*,

Despite showing obvious methodological limits, Lutheran historiography, starting from the *Chronicon*, establishes a first, clean division within medieval thought, isolating two chronological subcategories which, even if they were born for purely polemical ends, turn out to be useful in a shorthand way for a generic description of the medieval paradigm. Thus, compared to a high medieval and patristic tradition considered partially incorrupt and luminous, Scholasticism is described as the era of barbarism, extremely refined in methods and language, but precisely for this reason poor in doctrine at the same time, more concerned with sophisms than seeking the truth. The diffidence when faced with the Scholastic system is revealed in all its force in the *De doctoribus scholasticis et corrupta per eos divinarum humanarumque rerum scientia liber singularis* of Adam Tribbechow, whose history of medieval thought is, starting from the title, essentially the story of a progressive decadence[7]. Tribbechow anticipates, compared to other historians, the date of the initial moment of this decline. For Scholasticism, to his eyes, had been prepared by five centuries of mediocrity, starting from the pontificate and the doctrine of Gregory the Great who, first of all, had advanced the claim to a universal power within the Church. The beginning of the Scholastic era and therefore of the decadence is indicated by Tribbechow – at a very early date on the basis of an elementary equivalence – with the emanation of the *Dictatus papae*; the desire of the Church to give official political status, with this document, to its own supremacy supposedly produced a Scholasticism understood as an intellectual tool of domination. All the *magistri* of this period, and in particular Peter Lombard, are accused of having rationalized and secularized theology, stuffing it with abstruse terms and sophistical reasonings, the cause of intentional, continual and useless quarrelsomeness, as in the case, which Tribbechow

published at Bern in 1757, denounces the betrayal of the Scholastics, respecting only the authority of Aristotle; cfr. G. d'Onofrio, *Lanfranco teologo e la storia della filosofia*, in *Lanfranco di Pavia e l'Europa del secolo XI, nel IX centenario della morte (1089-1989)*, Atti del Convegno internazionale di studi (Pavia, Almo Collegio Borromeo, 21-24 settembre 1989), a c. di G. d'Onofrio, Roma 1993 (Italia Sacra, 51), pp. 189-228, esp. pp. 192-194.

[7] Cfr. Adam Tribbechow (Tribbechovius), *De doctoribus scholasticis et corrupta per eos divinarum humanarumque rerum scientia liber singularis*, Giessae (Gißen) 1665.

offers as an example, of the sterile dispute about the universals. All the Scholastic speculation is thus criticized, denounced for its secular enslavement to power and cultural enslavement to Aristotle and the Arabs, sick with that technicality and complexity of language through which «in hanc vero aetatem omnis corruptelarum et barbarei sentina effusa fuit»[8].

Even if it was in the context of a ferocious criticism of the methods and the aims of the theology of the thirteenth and fourteenth centuries, the Protestant historiography had given birth, as mentioned, to a division of the history of medieval philosophy into Patristic and Scholastic which, mobile and not definitive, was very soon widespread and useful for a clearer definition of medieval identity. In 1737, in the *Histoire critique de la philosophie* of André-François Boureau-Deslandes, this division encounters, as the title specifies, a critical questioning, that is to say, an awareness of the necessity, within the context of the history of ideas, of a preliminary reflection on methods and aims[9]. For the critical approach of the *Histoire* is born, by the admission of Deslandes himself, from the necessity of clarifying the meaning of very concepts of philosophy and history before embarking on the treatment of the discipline which is born from their synthesis. The history of philosophy is thus indicated as the narration of the development of the human spirit, and as such is entrusted to the philosophers[10]. The erudition, the literary taste for the biographical detail, the absence in his contemporaries of a philosophical *vis* (which he, in contrast, claims to possess himself) are the limits of the historiographers who surround him[11]. The historian, according to Deslandes, must rather make philosophical choices, judge the coherence, the reliability, the depth and the utility of that which he is analyzing and, based on these parameters, evaluate whether to mention or not authors and doctrines in his work. In the light of this definition, it is easy to understand what the judgment expressed by Deslandes on the medieval period could

[8] *Ibid.*, p. 333.

[9] Cfr. A-F. Boureau-Deslandes, *Histoire critique de la philosophie*, Amsterdam 1737.

[10] Cfr. *ibid.*, pp. xvii-xviii.

[11] Cfr. *ibid.*, p. viii and p. 211.

be. For, accused of being incapable of balancing philosophy and theology, the Scholastics appear to Deslandes as a vein too difficult to excavate in order to reach the few really worthwhile authors (Roger Bacon, Lullo, Peter of Abano) or, to use the more colorful language of the *Histoire*, to find the gold hidden under the dung[12].

In this way the methodological distinction between the Patristic and Scholastic periods theoretically takes the place of that between concordism and anticoncordism, and repeats its errors, with often imprecise and forced associations and evaluations. In Italy Giovanbattista Capasso, «philosophiae ac medicinae doctor neapolitanus» dedicated a *Historiae philosphiae synopsis* to John V, king of Portugal[13]. The work proceeds by describing the *sectae* which followed one another in the centuries up to the greek philosophy, which goes from Homer (representative of the *philosophia mythica*) to the eclectics and which flows into the *recentior* philosophy which from the Middles Ages stretches to the speculation of Descartes. The imprecisions of Capasso, who includes in his analysis both poets and writers, and who does not produce any rigorous historical classification, derive from the desire to associate the various authors more according to a criterion of content than on the basis of a precise analysis of their relationships of dependence. The first completed work of history of philosophy, the *Historia critica philosophiae* of Johann Jacob Brucker (1767), synthesizes these beginnings. Methodological inquiry, already postulated by Deslandes and by a few of his contemporaries, becomes with Brucker, a method of study[14]. For in his *Dissertatio praeliminaris* Brucker indicates to the reader his intention of reconstructing the historical *iter* of philosophy understood as a well-defined discipline, distinguishing it systematically from erudition. If the latter confronts the history of the world in all its complexity, that is to say, in all the aspects (artistic, religious, cultural, etc.) of an era, philosophy should be able to provide a gen-

[12] Cfr. *ibid.*, pp. 269-271.

[13] Cfr. Iohannes Baptista Capasso, *Historiae philosophiae synopsis, sive de origine, & progressu philosophiae: de vitis, sectis, & systematis omnium philosophorum libri IV Johanni V Lusitaniae regi & c. dicati*, IV, 6, Napoli 1735, p. 289.

[14] Cfr. J. J. Brucker, *Historia critica philosophiae a mundi incunabilis ad nostram usque aetatem deducta*, 5 voll., Leipzig 1742-1746 (1766-1767^2).

eral and coherent interpretation of these data[15]. Despite starting from this inquiry concerning method, Brucker too, in investigating the speculative identity of the period with which he deals, describes the entire Early Middle Ages, starting from Gregory the Great, as a «infelix nox», in which «litterae», although not «extinctae», certainly remained covered by the darkness of barbarism[16]. In the reconstruction of Brucker, the speculative void of the first centuries is followed by the far worse corruption of Scholasticism, whose subjection to the authority of Aristotle is the most tangible sign of the absence of a frankly philosophical perspective[17]. Beyond his given opinion, Brucker was the first to lament the near total absence of studies dedicated to just the medieval period. Deeper analyses would allow, in his opinion, the denunciation, with a greater abundance of details, of the weaknesses of this speculation. Born with Augustine, having developed in confusion between faith and reason with John the Scot, having become dialectical with Anselm, systematic with Lombard and mature with Albert, Thomas, and Bonaventure, the medieval period seems to be characterized by the use of an «ars rixosa», of an eristic dangerously capable of constructing an apologetic physics and metaphysics without any speculative foundation.

This critical process – begun almost casually by Lutheran historiography and having reached a first maturity with the work of Brucker, thanks to whose work a particular attention seemed to be arising to the individual data of the various eras in the history of philosophy, and therefore to the identification of different paradigms succeeding one another through the centuries – suffered a brusque halt because of Hegelian historiography. The doctrine both of the *Vorlesungen* on the history of philosophy and of the *Einleitung* which precedes them poses, in the *iter* which analyzes the production, in the modern and contemporary periods, of the medieval paradigm, two problems. On the one hand, Hegel is obviously the recipient of the inquiries concerning the method and content of preceding historiography; he receives them, he reelaborates them and furnishes extremely personal vision of the histo-

[15] Cfr. *ibid.*, I, pp. 38-45.

[16] Cfr. *ibidem*.

[17] Cfr. *ibid.*, III, pp. 806-807.

ry of medieval philosophy and of its paradigm, which would constitute, for all the nineteenth and a good part of the twentieth century, the historiographic ideal of reference, both for those who would accept its message and for those who would oppose it decisively. On the other hand, Hegel indicates, from his pages, a precise and pressing methodological inquiry, which poses with urgency the problem of the speculative talent of the historian of philosophy.

In the Hegelian reading, medieval philosophy presents very clear outlines, and it is narrated essentially as the period of the triumph of Christianity. Medieval man is described as desirous of contact with the divinity, and, since capable of reaching this goal, exalted. God therefore does not remain abstract, but becomes particular, fits the world, becoming for this reason an accessible goal for mankind. The true world is not therefore (only) a beyond, but the finite is an integral part of the whole, because willed by its creator and oriented to him. Having become history and individual and, by this, humanity, God consented to the man, alone among the creatures, to surpass the limit of his naturalness to reach for the infinite, so that consciousness projects itself towards the universal.

> Der Kultus, das christliche Leben, ist, daß das Individuum, das Subjekt selbst in Anspruch genommen wird, gewürdigt wird, für sich zu dieser Einheit zu gelangen, sich selbst zu würdigen, daß der Geist Gottes, die Gnade, wie es genannt wird, in ihm wohne (...). In den älteren Religionen ist das Göttliche auch vereint mit dem Natürlichen, dem Menschlichen, aber nicht versöhnt, sondern nur auf natürliche Weise. Die Einheit Gottes mit dem Natürlichen, mit dem Menschen ist da eine unmittelbare und so geistlose Einheit, eben weil sie nur natürlich ist. Der Geist ist nicht natürlich, er ist nur das, wozu er sich macht; die nicht hervorgebrachte, natürliche Einheit ist die geistlose; der Prozeß in sich, diese Einheit hervorzubringen, dagegen ist die geistige[18].

Christianity represents therefore an essential step in the history of the spirit. Within Christianity, in fact, «der Mensch ist eben

[18] G. W. F. Hegel, *Vorlesungen über die Geschichte der Philosophie*, 2, *Philosophie des Mittelalters. Einleitung*, ed. H. Glockner, in Id., *Sämtliche Werke*, 20 voll., XIX, Stuttgart 1965, pp. 99-121; here p. 100.

dessen fähig – als Bewußtsein, daß für ihn das Wahre ist und daß er darin die Bestimmung zur Freiheit hat –, das Anundfürsichseiende anzuschauen, zu wissen, sich in ein Verhältnis zu demselben zu setzen, das Wissen zum Zweck habend»[19]. Because of this special identity of Christianism, Hegel attributes to this religious doctrine and to its medieval defenders three objectives. First of all, «die Verbreitung der christlichen Religion»[20]; secondly, the perfection of life in accordance with reason; thirdly, the penetration of the Christian ideal into history[21].

The first task, Hegel concludes, is suitable for anyone who has evangelizing impulses; the third, proposing to make the costumes and rules of the concrete common life religiously rational, concerns the concretization of a moral tension, to the search, that is, for forms of common life shaped by Christian doctrine. The second objective is, on the contrary, the subject of study of the philosopher, who takes upon himself the awareness of the movement of the spirit:

> Das zweite ist, daß das Prinzip der christlichen Religion für den Gedanken ausgebildet werde, der denkenden Erkenntnis angeeignet werde, in dieser verwirklicht sei, so daß sie zur Versöhnung kommt, daß sie in sich habe die göttliche Idee, daß der Reichtum der Gedankenbildung der philosophischen Idee vereinigt werde mit dem christlichen Prinzip[22].

The Messiah, as God who must live in men's hearts, cannot help preannouncing his existence in spirit following on his life in the flesh, trusting to men, implicitly, the task of finding this spiritual existence beyond the sensible appearances. In spite of being the privileged moment for this task, medieval thought never appears to Hegel to be a true philosophy, condemned to speculative poverty despite the pious effort of Charlemagne who had decid-

[19] *Ibid.*, p. 102.

[20] *Ibid.*, p. 106.

[21] Cfr. *ibid.*, p. 107: «Das dritte ist dann, daß die Idee der Wirklichkeit eingeimpft, immanent sei, daß nicht nur sei eine Menge von glaubenden Herzen, sondern daß aus dem Herzen vielmehr, wie Naturgesetz, so konstituiert werde Leben der Welt, ein Reich, – die Versöhnung Gottes mit sich sich vollbringe in der Welt, nicht als ein Himmelreich, das jenseits ist; sondern die Idee muß sich realisieren in der Wirklichkeit».

[22] *Ibidem.*

ed that in the monasteries there should be at least one more learned monk to teach theology to the others, in order thus to be for them a *scholasticus*, and of John the Scot, with whom «man beginnt die scholastische Philosophie gewöhnlich im neunten Jahrhundert»[23].

If the Carolingian period installs therefore the fundamental conditions for the rebirth and for the diffusion of the Scholastic movement, Anselm appears to Hegel as the speculative founder of this stage of thought. Despite acknowledging an important historical role to the archbishop of Canterbury, Hegel does not spare criticisms of his speculative identity, dwelling in particular on the structure of the *unum argumentum*, given, in his formulation, in idealistic terminology:

> Wir denken etwas, wir haben einen Gedanken: der Gedanke ist subjektiv einerseits, aber der Inhalt des Gedankens ist das ganz Allgemeine; dies ist nun zunächst als Gedanke, unterschieden davon ist das Sein. Wenn wir so etwas denken, Gott denken (der Inhalt ist gleichgültig), so kann es der Fall sein, daß der Inhalt nicht ist; für das Vollkommenste halten wir das, was der Gedanke ist und zugleich ist. Gott ist das Vollkommenste: wäre er unvollkommen, so hätte er nicht auch die Bestimmung des Seins, und er wäre bloß Gedanke; also müssen wir ihm die Bestimmung des Seins zuschreiben[24].

In reproposing and in commenting the proof of the *Proslogion*, Hegel as historian of medieval philosophy isolates Anselm completely from the speculative context of his period, transforming him into a living interlocutor of Idealism and therefore criticizing his *argumentum* in a sense diametrically opposed to the criticisms raised first by Gaunilon and later by Kant. Rather than underline the risks of an unjustified identity between to be thought and to exist, with an improper qualitative leap from the level of thinkability to that of real existence, Hegel brings into light that affirming that 'that than which nothing greater can be thought' cannot not exist means ignoring that existing is already assumed, implied in the infinity of that which is thought. It is precisely the indulgence shown by Anselm with respect to the separation be-

[23] *Ibid.*, 3, *Scholastische Philosophie*, pp. 132-212; here p. 159.

[24] *Ibid.*, p. 167.

tween thought and being which opens, according to Hegel, that breach in his argumentation through which both the criticisms of Gaunilon and those of Kant penetrate.

In this, as in other situations, Hegel shows a very powerful speculative pre-comprehension in his perception of the history of philosophy; in this, his identity as a historian of thought does not seem to differ from that of his predecessors, they too occupied in applying prejudicial categories to the historical *continuum*. That which however characterizes the Hegelian *modus* with regards to the preceding historiographic tradition is the capacity to unite to a *habitus* of a scholar, anything but superficial and inattentive, of the history of ideas, not a speculative category, but the precipitate of a true and proper organic system of thought. Hegel, unlike the authors of the four preceding centuries, and probably thanks to the inquiries of critical historiography, did not try to simply bend medieval thought to a predetermined exegetical model, but interpreted different steps of the Middle Ages in the light of the philosophical principles of his system. Thus, although trying to elaborate a unitary concept, the lines of a model which would allow him to hold together all the medieval centuries, Hegel had to admit the internal articulation of the theological and philosophical Middle Ages which, in his opinion, had expanded in the interpretable spaces which dogma, in an only partial institutional rigidity, had conceded. In these spaces left free, Scholasticism had put in his opinion a doctrinal and metaphysical inquiry with Anselm and Abelard, discovered a dialectical method with Peter Lombard and Thomas, and finally formalized and applied this method with Duns Scotus. Starting from the construction of the doctrine of the faith on metaphysical foundations, aiming at a methodical exposition of the doctrinal concept of the Church, reaching an adequate knowledge of the writings of Aristotle, living in the speculative opposition between realism and nominalism and, finally, producing the principles of a formal dialectic, the Middle Ages, read in the forms of the Hegelian triadic schematic, had traversed the period of the Anselmian thesis, the antithetical Thomistic affirmation, and finally the Scotist synthetic development. Thus, if Anselm had placed philosophy in the doctrine of the Church becoming, as mentioned, the founder of Scholastic theology, it is the true and proper Scholasticism of Lombard, Thomas and Scotus which turned this initial intuition into a system, thanks to the marked dialecticization of the process of knowledge.

The tools and goals with which Hegel fleshed out his historico-critical analysis of the Middle Ages posed, for the scholars of that particular portion of the history of philosophy, a pressing question of method. For the history of post-Hegelian philosophy was forced to respond to the question that Hegel himself had posed explicitly and implicitly in his pages concerning the necessary competence and philosophical sensibility of the historian of philosophy. Despite all the limits imposed by the scarcity (and sometimes by the scarce reliability) of the materials at his disposition, Hegel did not prejudicially refuse the concept of history of philosophy as a capability of the historian to retrace with rigor reliable sources, but declared with force that only an evaluation of such documents in the optic of a more general speculative context could reveal their meaning. The task of the historian of philosophy is to make himself the voice of a part of the phenomenology of the Spirit in the world; with this declaration of intention Hegel performs a task he himself considers absolutely necessary in every didactic relationship: to indicate, for the beneficiaries of this narration, the parameters on the basis of which the historian chooses which thinkers or which doctrines should be included in his account and why.

> Der Gedanke, der uns bei einer Geschichte der Philosophie zunächst entgegen kommen kann, ist, daß sogleich dieser Gegenstand selbst einen inner Widerstreit enthalte. Denn die Philosophie beabsichtigt das zu erkennen, was unvergänglich, ewig, an und für sich ist; ihr Zeit ist die Wahrheit. Die Geschichte aber erzählt solches, was zu einer Zeit gewesen, zu einer andern aber verschwunden und durch Anderes verdrängt worden ist. Gehen wir davon aus, daß die Wahrheit ewig ist, so fällt sie nicht in die Sphäre des Vorübergehenden und hat keine Geschichte. Wenn sie aber eine Geschichte hat, und indem die Geschichte dies ist, uns nur eine Reihe vergangener Gestalten der Erkenntnis darzustellen, so ist in ihr die Wahrheit nicht zu finden; denn die Wahrheit ist nicht Vergangenes[25].

[25] Id., *Einleitung in die Geschichte der Philosophie*, *Heidelberger Niederschrift* (*Be-*

The Hegelian assumption, «die Wahrheit ist nicht Vergangenes», seems as much Augustinian as Ficinian, as much Platonic as Thomistic, and would have easily found a place in the pages of the *Historia* of Brucker. But, if in pre-Hegelian historiography, a generic devotion with regards to a *prisca sapientia* led historians to identify stages and moments of its evolution (or, in the case of the Lutherans, of its mortification), in Hegel it is the consciousness deriving from the existence of a self-manifesting Spirit which leads him to consider himself not as a simple historian of philosophy, but as a philosopher who knows and studies history (since philosophy tries to understand that which is immutable and eternal). Hegel thus rejects the possibility that a paradigm could be discussed while dividing historical competence from philosophical profundity. The philosopher without historical foundation would be unsteady; the historian without speculative identity would remain mute:

> Somit stoßen wir denn sogleich auf die sehr gewöhnliche Ansicht von der Geschichte der Philosophie, daß sie nämlich den Vorrat von philosophischen Meinungen herzuerzählen habe, wie sie sich in der Zeit ergeben und dargestellt haben. Wenn glimpflich gesprochen wird, so heißt man diesen Stoff Meinungen. (...) Diese Geschichte, so als eine Hererzählung von vielerlei Meinungen, wird auf diese Weise eine Sache einer müßigen Neugierde, oder wenn man will, ein Interesse der Gelehrsamkeit; denn die Gelehrsamkeit [besteht] vornehmlich darin, eine Menge unnützer Sachen zu wissen, d. i. solcher, die sonst keinen Gehalt und kein Interesse in ihnen selbst haben als dies, die Kenntnis derselben zu haben. (...) Was fürs Erste dies betriff, daß die Geschichte der Philosophie eine Gallerie von Meinungen – obzwar über Gott, über das Wesen der natüralichen und geistigen Dinge – aufstelle, so würde sie, wenn sie dies nur täte, eine sehr übeflüssige und langweilige Wissenschaft sein – man möge auch noch so vielen Nutzen, die man von solcher Gedankenbewegung und Gelehrsamkeit ziehen solle, herbeibringen. Was kan unnützer sein, als eine Reihe bloßer Meinungen kennenzulernen, was langweiliger? Schriftstellerische Werke, welche Geschichten der Philosophie in dem Sinne sind, daß sie die Ideen der Philosophie in

ginn der Vorlesungen am 28.X.1816), in Id., *Einleitung in die Geschichte der Philosophie*, ed. J. Hoffmeister, Hamburg 1940, pp. 1-19; here, pp. 14-15.

> der Weise von Meinungen aufführen und behandeln, braucht man nur leicht anzusehen, um zu finden, wie dürr, langweiling und ohne Interesse das Alles ist[26].

The prose of the *Einleitung* indicated (and indicates), in its hardness and efficacy, the presence of the question of the meaning of the study of the history of philosophy, which would soon become the background of the entire historiographic debate between the nineteenth and the twentieth centuries; Hegelianism places the history of philosophy before the necessity of either defending a clearly historiographic-speculative approach or denying the definition of erudition which Hegel, with pungent sarcasm, had opposed to his meta-historical reconstruction. Hegel represents, thus, the synthesis of the preceding historical-historiographic paths, but also a turning point. For in Hegel, not only is the anti-medieval and especially anti-Scholastic prejudice of the entire eighteenth-century tradition represented, but above all the critical inquiry of Brucker becomes a fundamental question of method. For, whereas in the middle of the 18th century this appears as the noble preoccupation of the erudite, sensitive to the distortions due to non-rigorous historiographic approaches, in Hegel it becomes a necessity, the need for a preliminary methodological clarification. No longer a passionate historian of philosophy, but a philosopher who investigates the history of his own doctrine, Hegel vivifies the Middle Ages by means of his speculative paradigm, verifying points of contact, and castigating the erudite practice of the simple scholars of the history of ideas. With the vision of the adult who regards the ingenuous errors of his adolescent years, Hegel turns to the imperfections of the medieval period declaring that the full idealist overcoming is the last step of a process which studies its own history to gather the elements which contributed to the development of its own identity and in that produces a Hegelian paradigm later applied to the medieval context, in which the two parts appear indivisible.

In the same years in which the *Einleitung* of Hegel was published, Victor Cousin printed his *Cours de philosophie*, the first step of

[26] Id., *Einleitung in die Geschichte der Philosophie, Berliner Niederschrift* (*Angefangen am 24.X.1820*), *ibid.*, pp. 19-77; here p. 27.

one of the most famous cultural conversions of the history of historiography. For the same Cousin who in the *Cours* indicated the Middle Ages as such an obscure period as to legitimize the criticism of those who maintained that between the ancient period and Descartes practically nothing intervened, revaluated so radically the weight of medieval thought as to become the first modern editor of the works of Abelard, deserving to be considered among the founders of French medieval studies[27].

The strongly partisan interpretation of the Middle Ages and, at the same time, the impulse furnished by the Hegelian *Einleitung* to rethink the role itself of the historian of philosophy led on the one hand to the birth of independent lines of research, aimed at recovering a positive complex image of a period and, on the other, to the appearance of new methodological inquiries in research. For Hegel had not only indicated in the anti-speculative Middle Ages a part of the more complex plan of the phenomenology of the Spirit but, above all, he had delineated a figure of the historian of philosophy for whom progress on his own personal and speculative path flowed together in research, that is, who did not divide the precision of the philologer from the exegetical-speculative capacity of the philosopher.

It is not, therefore, by chance when Ernst Renan, in the clarification of the methods and goals of his investigation, which a few years after the death of Hegel put for the first time the theme of Latin Averroism at the center of the historiographic debate, realized the necessity of indicating with clarity not only the object of his own research, but also what the duty and the role of a historian of philosophy were.

In his *Examen de conscience philosophique*, Renan writes:

> Le premier devoir de l'homme sincère est de ne pas influer sur ses propres opinions, de laisser la réalité se refléter en lui comme en la chambre noir du photographe, et d'assister en spectateur aux batailles intérieurs que se livrent les idées au fond de sa conscience. On ne doit pas intervenir dans ce travail spontané; devant les modifications internes de notre ré-

[27] Cfr. J. Jolivet, *Les études de philosophie médiévale en France de Victor Cousin à Étienne Gilson*, in *Gli studi di filosofia medievale fra otto e novecento. Contributo ad un bilancio storiografico*, Atti del Convegno Internazionale (Roma, 21-23 settembre 1989), ed. R. Imbach – A. Maierù, Roma 1991, pp. 1-20, esp. pp. 1-3.

> tine intellectuelle, nous devons rester passifs. Non que le résultat de l'évolution inconsciente nous soit indifférent et qu'il ne doive entraîner de graves conséquences; mais nous n'avons pas le droit d'avoir un désir, quand la raison parle; nous devons écouter, rien de plus; prêts à nous laisser traîner pieds et poings liés où les meilleurs arguments nous entraînent. La production de la vérité est un phénomène objectif, étranger au moi, qui se passe en nous sans nous, une sorte de précipité chimique que nous devons nous contenter de regarder avec curiosité[28].

This reflection expresses in a complete and lucid way, three years before his death, the convictions which Renan had only mentioned, forty years earlier, in the lines of the introduction to his famous *Averroès et l'averroïsme*:

> S'il ne fallait chercher dans l'histoire de la philosophie que des résultats positifs et immédiatement applicables aux besoins de notre temps, on devrait reprocher au sujet de ces recherches d'être à peu près stérile. Je suis le premier à reconnaître que nous n'avons rien ou presque rien à apprendre ni d'Averroès, ni des Arabes, ni du moyen âge. Bien que les problèmes qui préoccupent aujourd'hui l'esprit humain soient au fond identiques à ceux qui l'ont toujours sollicité, la forme sous laquelle ces problèmes se posent de nos jours est si particulière à notre siècle que très peu des anciennes solutions sont encore susceptibles d'y être appliquées. Il ne faut demander au passé que le passé lui-même (...). Il faut pourtant s'y résigner à l'avance: il ne sortira de cette étude presque aucun résultat que la philosophie contemporaine puisse s'assimiler avec avantage, si ce n'est le résultat historique lui-même. Ce n'est pas à la race sémitique que nous devons demander des leçons de philosophie (...). En supposant que la philosophie soit condamnée à n'etre jamais qu'un éternel et vain effort pour définir l'infini, on ne peut nier au moins qu'il n'y ait dans cet effort, pour les esprits curieux, un spectacle digne de la plus haute attention (...). Le système personnel de l'historien qui raconte les luttes des écoles et des partis ne sert le plus souvent qu'a fausser son jugement et à gâter l'effet de son tableau (...). Ce n'est là, remarquez-le

[28] E. RENAN, *Examen de conscience philosophique*, in «Revue des Deux mondes», 59 (1889), [pp. 721-738], p. 721.

> bien, ni l'indifférence ni le scepticisme, c'est la critique: on n'est historien qu'à condition de savoir reproduire à volonté en soi-même les différents types de la vie du passé[29].

The study of the history of philosophy, and thus the search for a paradigm, even medieval, does not have, in the eyes of Renan, any value beyond pure research. For if, as earlier for Hegel, history belongs to history, because it is not possible to bring back to life Averroism or other schools of thought of the past, Renan differs from Hegelianism because he does not identify the study of this history with the analysis of the stages across which the philosophical consciousness of modernity has come in creating itself, but with the entirety of the failures or the victories which have a meaning since they are part of human history; pieces, therefore, and not stages. Truth is objective, not in the Hegelian sense of an order which is not structured by men but which structures them in manifesting itself, but much more in the sense of a reality external to the investigating subject, who must therefore limit himself to photographing its characteristics and history.

In the light of these considerations, the task which Renan took on appears even today overwhelming. For to reconstruct the identity and fortune of Averroes and of Averroism with philologically based and rigorous criteria was an enterprise rendered difficult by the state itself of the tradition and the obvious difficulties linked to the language and to the location of texts; to this objective effort, Renan added also the personal conviction of the inutility of that which he was investigating, condemning himself thus to a work of simple cultural archaeology. The same motivations which moved Renan to begin the research seem to confirm this limited vision of the history of ideas.

Beyond the doubts raised by the premises mentioned up to now of his investigation, but certainly linked to them, the monumental work of Renan hides an enormous contradiction of method. Its author had specified, with force, in the preface, his desire to not link the writing of his essay to the contemporary world, refusing therefore to identify in the past speculative beginnings for the present and invoking, in this regard, the necessity of

29 Id., *Averroès et l'averroïsme*, Préface, ed. H. Psichari, in Id., *Oeuvres complètes*, 10 voll., III, Paris 1949, pp. 15-365, p. 15.

a scientifically rigorous method of analysis of the facts. The very definition of Latin Averroism as a movement having its own historical-speculative identity, however, betrays both the principles of Renan. In the second chapter of the second part of the work, in fact, *L'averroïsme dans la philosophie scolastique*, Renan tries to apply, to the medieval Latin West, the definition of Averroism understood as «l'ensemble des doctrines communes aux péripatéticiens arabes»[30]. In analyzing its Scholastic reception, Renan passes in review all those who, from Alexander of Hales to Thomas, had in any way speculative relationships with Arab thought in general, distinguishing a first period, of translation, and a second, of reception. The importance of Averroes and of his system seems to grow, in the analysis of Renan, with the passage of the decades, until reaching the clear judgment on the relationship between Thomas and the Commentator:

> Saint Thomas est à la fois le plus sérieux adversaire que la doctrine averroïste ait rencontré et, on peut le dire sans paradoxe, le premier disciplie du grand Commentateur. Albert doit tout à Avicenne; saint Thomas, comme philosophe, doit presque tout à Averroès[31].

Averroes shows thus for Renan precisely in the relationship with Thomas his most honest physiognomy: on the one hand, Aristotelian inspiration and source of Scholasticism; on the other, «le fondateur d'une damnable doctrine, le représentant du matérialisme et de l'impiété, un hérésiarque»[32]. Based on this definition, modeled on the relationship with Thomism, Renan identifies all the adversaries of the Averroistic theses, reaching the condemnation of Tempier in 1277. Dante, Gilles of Rome and Lullo are the last representatives of this «croisade contre l'averroïsme» fought in Occident by valiant soldiers. Renan, however, is incapable of giving a precise face to their enemy.

> Ainsi les docteurs les plus respectés du XIIIe siècle sont d'accord pour combattre l'averroïsme, et les formes de leur polémique ne permettent pas de supposer que ce fût là pour

[30] *Ibid.*, p. 83.
[31] *Ibid.*, p. 188.
[32] *Ibid.*, p. 189.

> eux une dispute oiseuse et sans adversaires. Il y avait évidemment, en présence de la scolastique orthodoxe, une école qui prétendait couvrir ses mauvaises doctrines de l'autorité du Commentateur. Mais où chercher cette école, dont aucun ècrit n'est parvenu jusqu'à nous? J'espère démontrer que, sans abuser de la conjecture, on peut designer comme les deux foyers de l'averroïsme, au XIIIe siècle, l'école franciscaine et surtout l'Université de Paris[33].

The critical method, the analysis of the bare facts seems to put Renan in great difficulty. For there did not exist, in the years in which his work saw the light, any manuscript proof of the existence of an Averroistic current in western Scholasticism, because Mandonnet or Van Steenberghen would only find the works of Siger or of Boethius of Dacia fifty years later, on the basis of which it would be possible to infer such a presence – for Renan only a hypothesis. That which the rationalist historian Renan can do is only therefore to propose a «conjecture» for the possible lack of foundation of which he excuses himself in advance. Thus, in the absence of textual references, the Averroistic paradigm is designated as heterodox because attacked by the Thomistic orthodoxy, and is linked to those figures which appear to Renan as the most extravagant compared to the DeWulfian cathedral of Thomism, according to the logic by which, if the «docteurs les plus respectés» attacked Averroism, Averroism must be looked for among the less respectable doctors. This game of definitions by negations, by means of which Latin Averroism is heretical not because of what it says, information which Renan largely does not know, but because attacked by holy theologians, finishes with an arbitrary identification of a Averroistic *pars* with the Franciscan school, which «nous apparait comme beaucoup moins orthodoxe que l'école dominicaine»[34] since popular in origin and not according very well with ideas of discipline and hierarchy:

> Tandis que les dominicains, fidèles à la direction qu'ils recevaient de Rome, couraient le monde en vrais limiers de l'Église pour dépister les hérétiques et faire à l'hétérodoxie la

[33] *Ibid.*, p. 204.
[34] *Ibidem.*

> rude guerre du syllogisme et du bûcher, la famillie de saint François ne cessait de produire d'ardents esprits[35].

From here, various «démocratiques et communistes» movements are included in the classification of Renan, such as Joachimism, the Cathars, the Lollards and the «hardis penseurs, presque tous fort hostiles à la cour de Rome» such as Duns Scotus, Ockham and Marsilius of Padua[36]. This proof by exclusion becomes the general, generic and generalist framework within which to locate, in order to justify the identification between Averroism and Franciscanism, the proximity of some doctrines of a not better identified «école franciscaine» of disciples of Alexander of Hales with those condemned by Tempier in 1277, the «respect» which Bacon nourishes with regards to Averroes, and, even the unconscious fault of Duns Scotus who, despite having fought Averroism and reproved Thomas for having given it space with his theory of individuation, was dragged towards the heretical thesis.

Despite, therefore, affirming with clearness, in the preface, the necessity of a historical investigation which does not allow itself to be conditioned either by the personal inclinations of the historian nor by those of the cultural context in which he operates, Renan does not keep faith, in practice, with the basic criterion of his investigation. No text existed, in the years in which he was attending to his work, which could justify the identification between Franciscanism and Averroism, and the method itself with which Renan reached such a conclusion is not dissimilar, in its approximativity, to that with which the learned of the sixteenth century distinguished the philosophers according to the *sectae* in which it was possible to locate them. The same idea of analyzing the history of thought from the outside, as a passive observer, delineated in the preface, fails in the writing of the text. The rationalism of Renan, despite starting from the conviction of the cultural inferiority of the Arab world, could not help but appreciate, in pages in which the postulated neutrality of the historian is completely absent, the spirit of this culture. Although destined to slide into materialist despotism, for the absence of a charismatic figure such as the Pope in the West, Renan can not help but feel

[35] *Ibid.*, p. 205.

[36] Cfr. *ibid.*, pp. 205-213.

admiration for the Arabs, «race ingénieuse»[37]. Promoter of a historiographic investigation which implicitly superceded Idealism and produced an objective historical knowledge, not influenced by the ideas of the historian and completely free of relationships with the contemporary culture, Renan composes therefore a capital work, falling however into the same errors which, in the preface of the work itself, he had indicated as fatal for historical research. The attempt of Renan to produce an objective analysis of the Averroist Middle Ages seemed to go in the direction of overcoming Hegelianism towards the production of a epistemologically founded historiographic knowledge. This process of freeing the investigation of the medieval paradigm from the ideological constraints of the historiography born between the sixteenth and eighteenth century, already begun within the critical history of the middle of the eighteenth century and braked, a first time, by the speculative inquiry of Hegel, took a second hard knock at the end of the nineteenth century following the publication of *Aeterni Patris*, the encyclical with which Leo XIII indicated in Thomism the official theological doctrine of the Church. *Aeterni Patris* gave strength and motivations to nascent Neo-Thomism, which moved in apparent contradiction with the Hegelian prospective, which although acknowledging for Scholasticism a cultural dynamicity more marked than the early medieval immobilism and inserting the speculation of the Middle Ages in the more general movement of self-revelation of the Spirit, did not save from censure any particular theological system, not even that of Thomas. The very idea of dialectical development of philosophy in history impeded Hegel from accepting that a philosophy of the past could become *perennis*, a system valid beyond its historical period, the period of the Spirit in which it came to life.

The Thomist identity was on the contrary exalted, in the words of Leo XIII, precisely in its being at the same time properly medieval and universally true, which is to say in the biunivocal identity between speculative system and historical period. Thomism became in this way the official 'medieval paradigm', the structure of thought to whose production the early medieval

[37] Cfr. *ibid.*, pp. 223-227.

centuries had contributed and from whose *magisterium* the succeeding centuries were nourished (or should have been). Thus, a Thomist Middle Ages substituted itself for the Hegelian Middle Ages, a speculatively poor moment of the manifestation of the Spirit; for a exegetical scheme which described the Middle Ages as a dialectical passage between antiquity and Renaissance was substituted the prospective of a long, slow Patristic incubation, which later came to light in the luminous synthesis of Thomas.

> Thomas a le sens de la parcimonie; son abbattage de ce qui est inutile ou illogique fait ressortir la ligne architectonique de sa philosophie. Il est de tous les scolastiques celui qui explique le *maximum* d'un problème avec un *minimum* de notions. La scolastique qu'il édifie est comparable aux cathédrales du début du XIIIe siècle qui, elles aussi, cherchent la puissance dans la logique et dans la sobriété[38].

Even if it in part refuted Hegelian doctrines, Neo-Scholastic Thomism was therefore very close, in its methodological orientation, to Hegel's perspective. For, even if with different specific goals, both systems pursued the same end, which went well beyond the scientific ends of historiographic research. For many of the thinkers and the centers of studies which gave life, for different reasons, to Thomist teachings and studies, the adhesion to such an theological-speculative model was not simply produced from the will to conform oneself to the teachings of the Church, but became a true and proper personal *habitus* which, as such, was defended and spread wherever possible. This existence *more thomistico* was perfectly coherent with the invitation, given by Hegel in the *Einleitung,* to the historians of philosophy, to live the object of one's own study and to receive the history of philosophy as the live narration of one of the periods of one's own speculative identity. That which divided Hegelianism and Neo-Thomism was rather the Neo-Scholastic choice to identify just one of these periods as its own spiritual fatherland, without grasping, in a Hegelian way, in the flux of all the phenomenology of the Spirit, the sense of the evolution of the history of ideas;

[38] M. De Wulf, *Histoire de la philosophie médiévale*, Paris – Louvain 1925^{5}, p. 370.

the choice of a precise period of the evolution of philosophical thought to elevate as a model for all human speculation as its apex was in fact in evident contrast with the very idea of history of philosophy defended by Hegel. The wish which was expressed in the *Einleitung* – that is, that the history of philosophy could be studied while feeling oneself part of it, being conscious of the past not as an anonymous ordered series of philosophers, but as the slow progress of a philosophical consciousness which finds, in the interpreter, a final step which accepts the preceding ones, being aware of them as moments in its own development – was partially accepted, although with dubious awareness of its source, by the Neo-Thomistic reflection. The system of Thomas was not, for its scholars, one of the images of an ideal gallery of ancestors of philosophy, but the only true theological system, experienced by its interpreters as a life prospective rather than as an object of study.

Along these lines, in his intellectual autobiography, *Le philosophe et la théologie*, Étienne Gilson illustrates, as he himself indicates, the complex «art d'être thomiste». In describing the problems linked to the adhesion to Thomism, Gilson lists both the hostilities born within the Thomist family and those introduced from the world external to Thomism. Among the first, writes Gilson, dominates the conviction that the adhesion to Thomism must take place unconditionally; the majority are uninterested in the thought of Thomas, who should rather, Gilson adds, first be studied and then chosen as one's own speculative model: «ce qu'ils veulent, c'est que vous vous disiez thomiste. Que vous fassiez inscrire officielment au parti thomiste»[39]. It is, therefore, paradoxically, precisely among the Thomists that Thomism itself would include the greatest number of those ignorant of the theories of Thomas, because «il semble que beaucoup acceptent d'abord de se laisser appeler thomistes par une répugnance profonde à dire qu'ils ne le sont pas»[40].

Even worse, Gilson continues, is the ostracism which the Thomist must suffer at the hands of the «philosophes d'obédience rationaliste, les 'vrais philosophes'»[41]. Whoever wants to ad-

[39] É. GILSON, *Le philosophe et la théologie*, Paris 1960, pp. 217-218.
[40] *Ibid.*, p. 218.
[41] *Ibidem*.

here to Thomism «ne doit pas être surpris de la solitude qui va se faire autour de lui»[42]:

> L'essentiel est que, chez un grand spirit qui est aussi un grand coeur, cet isolement n'engendre jamais aucune amertume (...). Nous pouvons bien être des isolés pour notre pays, et même dans nostre pays, pour notre temps et dans notre temps, mais il ne faut pas, il ne faut à aucun prix que notre pays et notre temps deviennent des isolés pour nous. Au contraire, et c'est peut-être la sele raison légitime qu'on ait de se dire thomiste, il faut se sentire heureux de l'être et vouloir partager ce bonheur avec ceux qui sont faits pour lui[43].

«Au fond, c'est cela même qui entretient chez le thomiste cet état de joie dont l'expérience seule puet donner idée: il se sent enfin libre»[44]. Hegelianism and Neo-Thomism shared the motive of the search for this liberty, not the means by which to reach it. Both tried to identify the lines of development of a philosophy which had a *perennis* identity; Thomism, in contrast with the Hegelian philosophy, did not experience the aspiration to find, in the entire history of philosophy, a common path, but traced, within a single system of thought, the archetypical elements of thought. In the light of this distance, delineating, on the morrow of the first World War, the new guidelines of the «Rivista di filosofia neoscolastica», Agostino Gemelli could speak of gentilian Hegelianism from the pulpit of a militant philosophy, accusing European Idealism of having refused the Thomist *philosophia perennis*, in order to not identify the phenomenological *iter* with one of its stages, but having dissolved in this way the spiritual edifice of the West from its foundations, opening the gates to militaristic and warlike logic[45].

No speculation more than the Hegelian, and therefore Gentilian, had lived the idea of a philosophy which traverses the centuries, gaining awareness of itself, maturing without ever chang-

[42] *Ibid.*, p. 220.

[43] *Ibidem.*

[44] *Ibid.*, p. 221.

[45] Cfr. A. GEMELLI, *Per il programma del nostro lavoro*, in «Rivista di filosofia neoscolastica», 11 (1919), pp. 1-26, esp. p. 20; C. VASOLI, *La neoscolastica in Italia*, in *Gli studi di filosofia medievale fra otto e novecento* cit., pp. 167-189, esp. pp. 170-172 and 180.

ing the essential vital points of its identity; to the eyes of the Neo-Thomists, Hegelianism had known how to correctly underline the existence of transcendental elements of philosophy which, in its evolution, had remained intact, in a perspective of a perennial knowledge, but had, at the same time, affirmed falsely that none of the stages of this evolution had recapitulated this model in itself completely, to become itself *perennis* in its historically determined form:

> L'equivoco della storiografia neoscolastica consisteva nel ritenere possibile che Tommaso d'Aquino rinascesse e disimparasse la sua scienza, e imparasse la nuova, la coordinasse con la sua filosofia, e vivesse e poi insegnasse ancora tra noi tardi nipoti[46].

Hegelianism and Neo-Thomism, structurally in agreement on the existential role which the study of the history of philosophy must have for the historian himself, disagreed on the other hand about the idea itself of history of philosophy, an absolute development for Hegel, expectation and then gloss of Thomism for the Neo-Scholastics. Two predefined methodological and medievalist paradigms, therefore, spiritually and methodologically close but distant in contents, which seem to impede the location of a properly medieval meta-paradigm. The vigor of the two founders, in the Hegelian system on the one hand and the papal encyclical on the other, gave an absolute value and weight to these exegetical perspectives, so much as to be able to affirm that there was no medievalistic historiography, between the end of nineteenth century and the middle of the twentieth, which was not, in whole or in part, either Hegelian or Neo-Thomist.

The overcoming of this dyarchy, in order to succeed in at delineating a medieval (and medievalist) paradigm which claimed to present itself as epistemologically objective could not happen except at the cost of sacrificing the most extreme and vital aspects both of Thomism and of Hegelianism. It was therefore necessary to discuss the human, personal, existential value of the history of philosophy, that is to say, exactly that which united the two systems. Eliminating this prospective meant canceling, from

[46] G. GENTILE, *Il modernismo ed i rapporti tra religione e filosofia*, Bari 1909, p. 125.

Hegelianism, the idea that every successive stage of the process refers to the history of the process itself just as to history itself and from Thomism, on the other hand, the conviction that Thomas was not a simple stage in the history of thought, but the unique true speculative paradigm worthy of the name.

It was in 1959 that Eugenio Garin, in the celebrated collection of essays *La filosofia come sapere storico*, imputes to this bifrontal model of militant historian of philosophy the responsibility for a tradition of non-objective, and therefore fruitless, historiographic studies. Every historical research is, according to Garin, made vain if it is inserted in a metaphysical perspective, or, worse, an individually spiritual one. The attack which Garin makes simultaneously on Idealism and on Neo-Thomism shows by contrast the deep link of method discussed above between the two historiographic perspectives.

> Fu tra la seconda metà del secolo XVIII ed il principio del secolo XIX che alla raffigurazione delle sette filosofiche si sostituì l'esposizione del 'progresso' dello spirito o dell'umanità in genere, e venne affermandosi l'idea dell'unità e continuità del filosofare (...). La rigorosa tesi dell'*unità* come data *a priori* (...), sotto l'influsso combinato delle correnti idealistiche (e variamente storicistiche) e della storiografia neoscolastica (o in genere fondata su presupposti 'teologizzanti'), costituì uno dei canoni interpretativi di più largo uso negli scritti di storia della filosofia in lingua italiana[47].

It is with poorly-hidden irony that Garin stigmatizes the errors of such a double but identical tendency, locating, in the works of its most illustrious representatives, a long sequence of methodological errors. In the reading offered by Garin, Idealism claimed to reduce the different periods of the history of philosophy to simple stages which, since partial reflections of a dialectically homogeneous whole, were able to show, in the singular, the universal. Thus, in 1907, Gentile had claimed to be able to extend to the world of the history of philosophy the method of the naturalist Cuvier, reconstructing the whole from one part.

[47] E. GARIN, *La filosofia come sapere storico*, Bari 1959, pp. 11-12.

> Come «Cuvier da un osso ricostruiva idealmente l'animale», perché l'animale è un'unità, un'entelechia, così lo storico da un frammento può ricostruire l'intero sistema, da una questione speciale la visione totale. E siccome Gentile era, nonostante ogni suo modo retorico, coerente alla sua logica, da quel frammento ricostruire addirittura tutta la filosofia, non di *quel* filosofo, di *quell'*età, di *quella* nazione, ma la Filosofia con la maiuscola, *sic et simpliciter*[48].

In the same way, Garin accuses Neo-Scholasticism of having wanted to find the ideal forms of truth in philosophical notions, to later place them, at their pleasure, into the historical reality analyzed. This is the case of a master researcher like Gilson:

> In *The unity of philosophical experience*, il 'metodo comparativo' applicato alla 'varietà' delle filosofie 'storiche' riesce ad enuclearne le 'essenze' – «nella sua purezza astratta l'essenza del criticismo sussiste per se stessa» – e, quindi, applicato alle 'essenze' spersonalizzate raggiunge *la* filosofia, ossia quella unica filosofia che è la *philosophia perennis*, in cui quel che è il criticismo di Kant non lo apprendiamo più da Kant, ma dal 'criticismo' in sé[49].

A series of «luoghi comuni metafisici» in historiography is born, according to Garin, from the combination of such approximations of method and content, such as «la consuetudine di non dare rilievo, o darne scarsissimo, alla biografia, alla situazione storica, alla cultura effettiva dei filosofi»[50]. Garin is persuaded that the historian's duty is completely different:

> Il lavoro dello storico consiste nello stabilire dei rapporti, ossia nell'unificare, oltreché nel distinguere e differenziare (...). Solo che il rapporto, o il processo di unificazione, non sta nel postulare *sic et simpliciter* 'unità' o 'continuità', ma nel ritrovare connessioni effettive, legami, somiglianze. Che un pensatore abbia letto un altro pensatore, che abbia risposto a certe domande, che abbia fatto certe esperienze, che abbia avuto certi colloqui, che si sia mosso in una società, persona fra certe

[48] *Ibid.*, p. 17.

[49] *Ibid.*, p. 19. Garin refers to É. GILSON, *The unity of philosophical experience*, New York 1947 (London 1948²).

[50] *Ibidem.*

> determinate persone – ecco quello che lo storico deve accertare. Non esiste la Filosofia, davanti al cui tribunale chiamare al *redde rationem* le filosofie ed i filosofi: esistono uomini che hanno cercato di rendersi criticamente conto in modo unitario della loro esperienza e del loro tempo[51].

Garin's conclusion is unambiguous. These men used tools; they had relationships. To understand such relations is the work of the historian: «questi nessi lo storico trova»[52].

In 1915, Martin Heidegger acquired his *Habilitation* at Freiburg with a study on *Die Kategorien- und Bedeutungslehre des Duns Scotus*. Heidegger acknowledged how – in the Middle Ages perhaps more than in other periods – the link between authors and context is essential. For this reason he magnified the efforts produced along these lines by the studies of Baeumker, the founder of the *Beiträge zur Geschichte der Philosophie*, and by the author of *Die Geschichte der scolastischen Methode*, Martin Grabmann. In this matter, Heidegger specified how «Texteditionen, Vollständigkeit des Materials und dessen Verläßlichkeit sind unentbehrliche Grundlagen für jedes weitere Eindringen in den Gedankengehalt der Scholastik», although he was convinced that «mit der bloßen Ansammlung, Registrierung und inhaltlichen Wiedergabe sind noch nicht alle Vorbedingungen für eine Auswertung des mittelalterlichen philosophischen Gedankengutes erfüllt»[53]. It would therefore be desirable – this is the implicit conclusion – that the ones to collect, analyze and comment such documents be scholars who unite historical-critical heft with a meaningful speculative identity; but, «reine philosophische Begabung und eine wirklich fruchtbringende Fähigkeit historischen Denkens sich nur in den allerseltensten Fällen in eine Persönlichkeit zusammenfinden»[54]. For philosophy does not have, for Heidegger, only a cultural value, so that its history can be the erudite description of an *iter*; it has a *Lebenswert*,

[51] *Ibid.*, pp. 29-30.

[52] *Ibid.*, p. 30.

[53] M. Heidegger, *Die Kategorien- und Bedeutungslehre des Duns Scotus*, in Id., *Frühe Schriften*, I, ed. V. Klostermann, Frankfurt a. M. 1978 (*Gesamtausgabe*, 1), pp. 189-412; here, p. 194.

[54] *Ibidem*.

and therefore the study of its history, which should arise from an instinct for philosophizing, is not able to put in parentheses the existential value of the material of which it reconstructs the evolution, separating thus the erudite investigation of the historical fact from the personal reception of the speculative content.

The cultural and methodological inquiry defended by Garin certainly revealed the necessity, for the historian of philosophy, of starting from the rigorous collection of the sources. In the specific case of the search for the *medieval paradigm*, this presupposition cleared the field of prejudicial receptions of Patristic and Scholastic theology, allowing the critical analysis, in the last decades, of a mass of material which contributed to change sensibly the stereotyped image of the Middle Ages. The attention to the sources, the acquisition of better historical-critical techniques borrowed from other disciplinary areas, the capacity of conceiving the Middle Ages as a plurivocal *iter*, extended not only in time but also in space, embracing, that is to say, diverse geographical areas and different cultural identities, has produced research able to amplify the interpretative horizon of the Middle Ages. The multiformity of the realities discovered by such analyses makes it difficult, even more than in the past, but for opposite reasons, as Heidegger makes clear, to delineate a *medieval paradigm* which is not identical with a general and indeterminate listing of all the cultural questions of this period. The prejudicial visions which characterized historical studies from the Renaissance era having been overcome, contemporary medievalistic, precisely in becoming fully critical and, therefore, non-denominational and willfully non-theoretical, has permitted that every soul of the variegated medieval panorama find its right of citizenship in the field of scientific research, sacrificing however, to the effort necessary to give a foundation to such an opening of perspectives, the Hegelian capacity to recount its own present by studying the initial phases of its own history. Free from the duty of following only certain lines of research, useful, at different times, for the demonstration of different paradigms, concordist, anticoncordist, Lutheran, critical, Hegelian or Neo-Thomist, the historical research on the Middle Ages was able to explore regions poorly understood or underestimated previously, amplifying, in extension, the awareness of the different facets of the medieval identity, but renouncing, in depth, to incorporate their different emphases into a single unifying vision.

The construction of a *medieval paradigm* shows, therefore, in its evolution through the centuries, profound limits. In as much as it is a hermeneutical operation, it is aimed at overcoming a gap, and therefore is based on the necessary effort to overcome the differences created by the elapsed time and by the changing of cultural and linguistic contexts; for to delineate the features of a *medieval paradigm* means, at the same time, to set oneself to listen to the voices coming from that specific past and to gather the most general problems and projects and the framework underlying them. In this matter, the historiography which, in the last fifty years, has broadly and analytically amplified the base of knowledge concerning the medieval world, has worked considering it possible (and desirable) to delineate the borders of a Middle Ages as object: applying to the history of the ideas developed between the fifth and fourteenth centuries the same historical-critical method, the rigorous analysis of the sources and the construction of a solid philological articulation, it tried, that is, to produce a narrated Middle Ages which would adhere as closely as possible to the historically existing Middle Ages. This concrete plan of work poses a very strong question of method, founded in turn on a precise epistemological option; i. e., it assumes that it is possible, methodologically, to use universally shared and functional collections of tools, starting from the idea that, epistemologically, an objective reconstruction of texts and contexts of the past can be reached. Assuming that this inquiry is epistemologically founded and can be followed and that, on the contrary, in a certain measure it has already been possible to reconstruct the most objective of the images of certain authors, it is necessary to understand what is the use in view of which this object has been so rigorously reconstructed. The erudite historiography of the sixteenth century, the lack of interest of Renan for the speculative precipitate of Averroism or the appeal of Garin for a historiography not militant but rigorously far from a hypothetical and dangerous tribunal of Philosophy indicate, along these lines, a first option: the history of medieval philosophy reconstructs texts and contexts, with the maximum possible rigor, bringing them into the contemporary world not as present interlocutors, but as objects of cultural archaeology. Hegelian historiography, Gilsonian Neo-Thomism, Gentilian actualism, on the contrary, celebrate the necessity that the historian of philosophy turn himself into history of philosophy, feel himself in communion with the subjects which he studies and recognize, at the same time, his own status as part of the same slow progress.

In the alternation, often polemical, of these two hermeneutical models, the two typologies of the Middle Ages and, in consequence, of medievalistic, the search for the medieval paradigm has remained a programmatic horizon never truly reached, suspended between the affirmation of a predetermined speculative identity and the impersonal reconstruction of erudition and incapable of grasping the possibility of a virtuous reconciliation of the stimuli coming from both approaches. Rather, it is precisely on the richness and the solidity of the acquisitions furnished by the scientific research of the historical-critical approach that it is possible to avoid speaking of the past as if it were irremediably so or as a simple object useful for an exercise in self-affirmation by the interpreter, but imagining it as an interlocutor of the contemporary world, speculatively alive in itself but rendered present and useful for whoever studies its forms, texts and methodologies. It is in this light that it is therefore possible to delineate today, finally, a *medieval paradigm*, that is to say the perimeter of strong (and, as such, atemporal) cultural option born in a determined historical context and from there, consigned to the history of the human visions of the world.

(English translation by Eric HEWETT)

MASSIMO PARODI

UNA RIFLESSIONE SULL'IDEA DI PARADIGMA: AGOSTINO E IL SECOLO XII

Considerare la storia della filosofia in termini di paradigmi che si confrontano, si criticano, si sostituiscono reciprocamente, significa introdurre l'idea decisiva di modelli alternativi nel modo di concepire la ragione umana, i suoi rapporti con diverse forme di conoscenza, le relazioni con altre discipline e quindi la stessa coscienza di sé da parte di quella regione del sapere che di volta in volta si definisce *filosofia*. Si tratta dunque di uno sforzo di relativizzazione, quanto mai prezioso soprattutto in un'epoca come la nostra, quando la storia sembra esigere un impegno formidabile per fare sì che i rapporti tra differenti tradizioni culturali possano assumere appunto l'aspetto e l'andamento di auspicabili confronti tra paradigmi e non di drammatici scontri fra civiltà.

L'idea di 'paradigma', introdotta nel dibattito culturale contemporaneo da Kuhn con il suo famoso studio sulle rivoluzioni scientifiche[1], racchiude naturalmente in sé la possibilità di esiti anche molto radicali, come è emerso dalle discussioni sviluppatesi in particolare nell'ambito della storia e della filosofia della scienza. Non si può tuttavia negare che anche le posizioni più estreme, come quella ben nota della *incommensurabilità dei paradigmi* sostenuta da Feyerabend[2], possano svolgere una funzione positiva di decostruzione di schemi interpretativi troppo rigidi e assestati, che talvolta rischiano di tradursi in vere e proprie filosofie

[1] T. S. KUHN, *The structure of scientific revolutions*, Chicago 1962 (1996[3]) (tr. it., Torino 1969).

[2] P. K. FEYERABEND, *Against Method*, London 1975 (tr. it., Milano 1979).

10.1484/M.NUTRIX-EB.1.101233

della storia. In vari suoi studi Feyerabend riprende la questione sempre aperta su continuità o discontinuità fra scienza medievale e scienza moderna[3], mettendo in discussione fin dalle fondamenta la possibilità di paragonare la dinamica dell'*impetus* con la dinamica successiva e con il principio di inerzia. Se ne possono discutere molte tesi, ma credo non si possa sottovalutare l'importanza di restituire, in termini teorici, al pensiero medievale quanto in esso vi è di medievale, senza dovere sempre inseguire gli apparenti balbettii che anticiperebbero la *vera* scienza dei secoli successivi.

Proprio la storia della filosofia medievale sembra un ambito di ricerca in cui particolarmente utile potrebbe risultare l'applicazione di categorie interpretative tese ad alleggerire la storiografia dal peso di un'idea di sviluppo quasi provvidenziale alla quale si sono qualche volta contrapposte visioni di insieme altrettanto provvidenziali. La presenza, nel millennio che abitualmente si definisce *Medioevo*, di una componente ideologica molto forte rappresentata dalla religione cristiana ha quasi inevitabilmente portato alla costruzione di un oggetto unitario, apparentemente governato nella sua storia da un disegno significativo, da una sorta di sviluppo al tempo stesso storico e razionale. L'idea di un millennio il cui pensiero presenta caratteri coerenti e unitari, che conducono inevitabilmente alle grandi sintesi scolastiche del secolo XIII, è oggi in gran parte superata dalla molteplicità delle prospettive di studio e dalla articolazione di analisi sempre più specialistiche. E tuttavia accade spesso di rendersi conto che, al di sotto della consapevolezza che nessuno oserebbe più sostenere apertamente di sapere che cosa sia il pensiero medievale in quanto tale, continua a vivere un'altra idea secondo cui esistono caratteri comuni, sia pure difficili da indicare con precisione, che comunque costituiscono un insieme di differenze specifiche capace, in linea di principio, di cogliere un oggetto determinato nella storia.

[3] Si vedano P. K. FEYERABEND, *Explanation, Reduction, and Empiricism*, in *Scientific Explanation, Space, and Time*, ed. by H. Feigl – G. Maxwel, University of Minnesota 1962 (Minnesota Studies in the Philosophy of Science, 3), pp. 28-97; ID., *Problems of Empiricism*, in *Beyond the Edge of Certainty: Essays in Contemporary Science and Philosophy*, ed. by R. G. Colodny, Englewood Cliffs (NJ) 1965 (University of Pittsburgh Series in Philosophy of Science, 2), pp. 145-260.

Ulteriore complicazione, per quanto concerne la definizione di caratteri specifici del pensiero medievale, è data dal fatto che quella che si è chiamata *componente ideologica* gioca un ruolo altrettanto decisivo dalla parte di chi studia e interpreta la storia di questo pensiero. Se la questione ermeneutica si pone per ogni periodo e per ogni autore, nel caso del Medioevo sembra esserci qualcosa in più, nei termini di una quasi programmatica opzione iniziale consistente nella condivisione o nel rifiuto, così come nell'intensità e nei modi di tali pre-assunzioni, di fronte al ruolo e al peso della tradizione religiosa cristiana. È abbastanza evidente che quanto più è forte la componente ideologica nelle interpretazioni storiografiche, tanto più risultano definibili gli oggetti di cui ci si occupa, proprio per la necessità di non cadere nella contraddizione di proporre interpretazioni molto determinate e caratterizzate in termini teorici di oggetti invece poco determinati e caratterizzabili in termini storici. Per questi motivi, l'idea di *paradigma* può rendere meno condizionanti i presupposti teorici e metodologici, aiutando a mettere tra parentesi quelli che si potrebbero definire veri e propri *loci* di carattere storiografico.

Un *locus* classico è rappresentato dalla centralità della riflessione filosofica del secolo XIII, comprensibilmente condiviso nel quadro di quella prospettiva neoscolastica che intendeva assumere le grandi *Summae* dei maestri universitari come strumenti ancora utili per le discussioni culturali e politiche dei secoli XIX e XX. Ma la stessa convinzione appare condivisa anche nelle proposte di individuare negli autori del cosiddetto periodo d'oro della Scolastica, nei loro *Commenti alle Sentenze* e nelle loro riflessioni sull'aristotelismo fisico, etico e politico, l'avvio di una effettiva *filosofia medievale* progressivamente sempre più libera da condizionamenti di carattere teologico. Se non esiste *la ragione* o *la filosofia* ma solo modi di concepirle in termini più o meno sistematici nel contesto di un *paradigma*, si può sperare che la grande narrazione riguardante i modi di sviluppo del pensiero medievale superi finalmente il pregiudizio della lunga preparazione, dei primi tentativi, del trionfo della ragione aristotelica e della decadenza del pensiero medievale. L'idea di *paradigma*, che mette certamente in discussione ogni narrazione storica troppo grande o troppo unitaria, può allora essere perfezionata dal ricorso alla nozione di *paradigmi* al plurale, in modo da evitare che gli elementi di relativismo siano compensati da riferimenti unitari a livello sempre più alto.

Una delle più interessanti rielaborazioni del concetto di 'paradigma' è rappresentata dalla cosiddetta *metodologia dei programmi di ricerca*, proposta da Lakatos[4] a partire dagli insegnamenti di Kuhn, e usata in un articolo famoso da Thijssen[5] per analizzare la questione della continuità e delle trasformazioni nell'aristotelismo medievale e rinascimentale. Thijssen fa notare che l'enfasi posta dalla ricerca storica sul «carattere radicalmente differenziato ed eclettico dell'aristotelismo rinascimentale (e medievale) fa sorgere domande sulla continuità e la coerenza di questa tradizione». Se non si vuole abbandonare l'aristotelismo come utile categoria interpretativa, occorre inevitabilmente procedere a una ridefinizione del concetto, in grado in primo luogo di distinguere fra le trasformazioni *nell'*aristotelismo dalle trasformazione *dell'*aristotelismo, fra gli aspetti innovativi che vengono riassorbiti in una prospettiva aristotelica e quelli che invece mettono in discussione la validità di una tale prospettiva. Concentrando la propria attenzione in particolare sulla filosofia naturale, Thijssen rilegge l'aristotelismo nei termini di un *programma di ricerca* che, nella considerazione di Lakatos, consiste essenzialmente di tre elementi. Vi è in primo luogo un *nucleo forte* di leggi o di princìpi generali che non vengono messi in discussione, intorno ai quali opera una *cintura protettiva* entro cui si verificano continui aggiustamenti e riaggiustamenti di ipotesi, in modo da proteggere e difendere il nucleo, sulla base di un'*euristica* che rappresenta l'insieme del-

[4] I. LAKATOS, *Falsification and the Methodology of Scientific Research Programmes*, in *Criticism and the Growth of Knowledge*, Proceedings of the International Colloquium in the Philosophy of Science (London, 1965), ed. by I. Lakatos – A. Musgrave, New York 1970, pp. 91-195 (tr. it. di G. Giorello, *Critica e crescita della conoscenza*, Milano 1976, pp. 164-276). Cfr. inoltre I. LAKATOS, *History of Science and its Rational Reconstructions*, in *In Memory of Rudolf Carnap*, ed. by R. C. Buck – R. S. Cohen, Dordrecht 1971 (Boston Studies in the Philosophy of Science, 8), pp. 91-136 (tr. it. *ibid.*, pp. 366-408).

[5] J. M. M. H. THIJSSEN, *Some Reflections on Continuity and Transformation of Aristotelianism in Medieval (and Renaissance) Natural Philosophy*, in «Documenti e studi sulla tradizione filosofica medievale», 2/2 (1991), pp. 503-528 (tr. it. in *Medioevo in discussione. Temi, problemi, interpretazioni del pensiero medievale*, a c. di G. Briguglia, Milano 2001, pp. 175-200).

le tecniche di soluzione dei problemi accettate dal programma di ricerca.

Nella interpretazione di Thijssen, il *nucleo forte* dell'aristotelismo è costituito da princìpi di carattere generale che non vengono messi in dubbio, come il fatto che siano le forme a determinare l'essere, che i quattro elementi semplici siano i costituenti del mondo sublunare, che la realtà vada considerata nei termini di relazioni fra potenza e atto. Le discussioni, gli aspetti innovativi, i confronti tra ipotesi diverse avvengono nella *cintura protettiva* e assumono spesso l'andamento di una ricerca delle soluzioni migliori per difendere e garantire la validità dei princìpi generali del *nucleo forte*. Fino a che si ripropone questa situazione, il nucleo non viene aggredito e la struttura concettuale complessiva rimane integra.

È evidente che, se il *programma di ricerca* viene esteso a comprendere ambiti storici o teorici troppo vasti, ne consegue che quanto si è definito *nucleo forte*, ciò che permane al di sotto dei cambiamenti, andrà individuato a livello molto alto, per collocarsi, nella nostra considerazione del pensiero medievale, al di sopra delle diverse tradizioni, al di là delle differenze di contenuto culturale, politico, geografico. Se dunque si parla al singolare di *paradigma medievale*, la conseguenza probabile è di configurare un nucleo costituito essenzialmente dalla centralità dell'adesione alla religione cristiana e dai modi per dare conto del rapporto con i contenuti della fede. L'utilità dell'approccio proposto da Thijssen sta tuttavia nel fatto che, anche in questo caso, ci si può in qualche misura rendere conto dei motivi per cui ricompare inevitabilmente una visione unitaria che da altri punti di vista è invece in larga misura superata.

Assumendo nel nostro caso la metodologia di Lakatos come strumento euristico, tradendone quindi consapevolmente il senso specifico, è possibile tuttavia operare per così dire in senso inverso, stabilendo rapporti tra possibili nuclei e relative cinture protettive per verificare in che termini e fino a che punto le reciproche interazioni possano suggerire la determinazione di uno dei possibili paradigmi filosofici medievali. La storia della filosofia non costruisce evidentemente programmi di ricerca, ma tenta di verificare se atteggiamenti di questo genere esistano in certi periodi, a quale livello teorico pongano il proprio nucleo forte, quale sia l'efficacia della cintura protettiva e se sia dunque lecito parlare di un vero e proprio paradigma filosofico.

Si è detto che la funzione relativizzante del concetto di paradigma assume un senso ulteriore se, entro il millennio medievale, se ne riesce a parlare al plurale. Trascurando dunque il paradigma aristotelico, sulla cui esistenza concordano sia quanti possiamo definire ancora per comodità *neoscolastici* sia quanti forse potremmo, certo in modo generico e impreciso, definire *neoaverroisti*, si tratta in primo luogo di verificare se sia lecito ricondurre all'idea di 'paradigma' anche un'altra grande tradizione medievale di pensiero, e cioè quella tradizionalmente indicata come *agostinismo*. O meglio, si tratta di provare a utilizzare lo strumento euristico di cui si è parlato per mettere in evidenza quali elementi facciano di un certo tipo di riflessione filosofica una riflessione agostiniana. Detto in altri termini, occorre verificare se esista e come sia costituito un nucleo forte di un preteso programma agostiniano di ricerca filosofica, come si muovano le cose all'interno di una cintura protettiva, che cosa rimanga invariato e che cosa invece si trasformi nel metodo della ricerca, nella sua euristica[6].

Anselmo, nel *Monologion*, afferma che il Sommo Essere va concepito in termini trinitari perché è questo il modo in cui l'uomo pensa ogni artefice che, per compiere la propria opera, deve esistere, avere un progetto e la volontà di realizzarlo. Negli stessi termini viene quindi concepito anche l'Essere Sommo da cui dipende ed è posto l'essere di tutte le cose volute attraverso l'atto della creazione[7]. Al centro del proprio percorso di ricerca,

[6] Si riprende qui, rielaborandola parzialmente, la proposta di interpretazione avanzata in M. Parodi, *Il paradigma filosofico agostiniano. Un modello di razionalità e la sua crisi nel* XII *secolo*, Bergamo 2006 (Quodlibet. Ricerche e strumenti di filosofia medievale, 14).

[7] Cfr. Anselmus Cantuariensis, *Monologion*, 48, PL 158, 199BC, ed. F. S. Schmitt, *Opera Omnia*, 6 voll., Roma – Edinburg 1946-1961, I, p. 63,13-24: «Equidem cum summa sapientia sui memor esse negari non possit, nihil competentius quam in memoria Pater, sicut in Verbo Filius intelligitur, quoniam de memoria nasci Verbum videtur. Quod clarius in nostra mente percipitur. Quoniam namque mens humana non semper se cogitat, sicut sui semper meminit, liquet, cum se cogitat, quia verbum eius nascitur de memoria. Unde apparet quia si semper se cogitaret, semper verbum eius de memoria nasceretur. Rem etenim cogitare, cuius memoriam habemus, hoc est mente eam dicere; verbum vero rei, est ipsa cogitatio ad eius similitudinem ex memoria formata. Hinc itaque liquido animadverti potest de summa Sapientia, quae sic semper se dicit sicut semper sui memor est, quia de aeterna memoria eius coaeternum Verbum nascitur».

Anselmo pone dunque uno dei contenuti fondamentali della fede cristiana e cioè la concezione trinitaria di Dio, ma ne rivendica con forza la razionalità, in quanto la basa sulla sola ragione e sui criteri che governano la normale conoscenza umana e la riferisce al Sommo Essere, la cui esistenza ha appena dimostrato in termini del tutto filosofici e che non è ancora stato identificato con il Dio della fede. Si condensano in questo passaggio alcuni degli elementi che senza dubbio vanno considerati come costitutivi del nucleo forte di ogni possibile prospettiva filosofica agostiniana.

Compare chiaramente l'idea di un principio della realtà – Sommo Essere o Dio, forse Sommo Essere e Dio – in cui sia presente la dialettica *identità/differenza*, *unità/molteplicità*, che quindi si distingue profondamente, pur mantenendone alcuni caratteri, dalla concezione neoplatonica dell'Uno. La centralità di questo aspetto viene colta soprattutto grazie al modo di operare della conoscenza umana, ed è questo un secondo fondamentale costituente del nucleo agostiniano. Se pure non si cade mai in un soggettivismo che potrebbe avere addirittura esiti scettici, e che anzi li avrà effettivamente in un differente contesto storico e culturale, si afferma con decisione che è il soggetto a porre le relazioni tra le cose, e che quindi la conoscenza è un processo attivo che non subisce l'azione della realtà esterna. Il soggetto pone le relazioni ma, così facendo ne coglie comunque l'esistenza e il senso, dal momento che la sua conoscenza possiede la medesima struttura presente nel principio della realtà. Questo terzo elemento emerge in modo assai efficace proprio in quella specie di circolo, per cui Anselmo afferma che il Sommo Essere è pensato in termini trinitari perché così l'uomo pensa ogni tipo di artefice e, nello stesso tempo, che l'uomo pensa in questo modo perché immagine e somiglianza di un Dio trinitario. Emerge in maniera evidente il quarto costituente del nucleo e cioè l'impossibilità di principio di distinguere un livello della ragione come totalmente altro rispetto a uno specifico livello della fede. Riassumendo: concezione trinitaria di Dio strettamente connessa all'idea di un'originaria dialettica *identità/differenza*, alla centralità di un soggetto attivo del processo della conoscenza, al fondamento nella relazione di somiglianza fra creatore e creatura e, infine, alla stretta connessione fra le dimensioni conoscitive della ragione e della fede. Per rimanere all'interno dell'ipotesi di lettura che si cerca di proporre, si deve osservare in conclusione che tale nucleo viene approfondito e sviluppato nelle proprie conseguenze sulla base di un metodo, di un'euristica, rappresentato essenzialmente dal ragionamento per analogia. Un modo di argomentare che trova le proprie origini nella riflessione di carattere retorico diviene, entro questo 'paradigma', lo strumento fondamentale della conoscenza, ma anche il modo effettivo di strutturarsi da parte della realtà. Il ruolo attivo del soggetto conoscente, unito al suo carattere di immagine e somiglianza con il principio della realtà, rendono in larga misura indistinguibili o comunque sovrapponibili le due dimensioni dell'essere e dell'essere pensato.

Si è assunto, come punto di partenza del nostro ragionamento, Anselmo d'Aosta, in quanto permette di porre una questione essenziale nello schema interpretativo che si ricollega all'idea dei programmi di ricerca. Se gli elementi messi in evidenza possono essere considerati i costituenti fondamentali del paradigma agostiniano, viene allora immediatamente da chiedersi quali siano invece in movimento, quali si siano trasformati entro la cintura protettiva, in modo da fare del pensiero di Anselmo un grande esempio di riflessione agostiniana, ma pur sempre qualcosa di diverso e di distinguibile dalla riflessione di Agostino. Proviamo a isolare tre questioni decisive: il ruolo e il peso del punto di vista della totalità, il modo di procedere della ricerca, il modo di interpretare lo strumento dell'analogia.

In Agostino il procedere analogico della conoscenza e, parallelamente, la struttura analogica del mondo convergono nel segnalare l'esistenza di un punto limite, quello cioè dell'uguaglianza che riconduce a unità tutte le relazioni basate su una somiglianza di rapporti che tende all'identità. La funzione della ricerca è inevitabilmente volta a cogliere forme di unità sempre più elevate che implicano punti di vista successivi più totalizzanti e rappresentano livelli progressivamente più ampi di conoscenza. Di fronte alla rete di relazioni che la struttura del mondo fornisce alla conoscenza, la ricerca di unità e totalità consente di individuare una direzione, un senso della ricerca umana che, appunto in quanto tale, ripropone sempre nuovi inizi su nuovi livelli, senza porsi mai come punto di arrivo definitivo e acquisito. In Anselmo si può cogliere, in taluni passaggi, la stessa spinta a procedere oltre, a trasformare certi punti di arrivo in nuovi punti di partenza, in nuove domande. Tuttavia il limite rappresentato dall'unità si trasforma, si irrigidisce in un vero e proprio dato, in un qualcosa di esistente e definibile, in modo problematico ma preciso. La ragione umana può cogliere il principio unitario e ridurlo, anche se con difficoltà, alla propria misura, riconducendolo alle dimensioni del pensiero come *ciò di cui non si può pensare il maggiore*. Diventa evidente che il principio unitario coincide con il punto di vista della totalità perché esattamente con la totalità del pensiero viene identificato, ma in questo modo si trasforma da spirito animatore della ragione in un suo contenuto, in qualcosa di determinato. Per riprendere i termini con cui si era iniziato, la cintura protettiva si fa più solida, ma perde in elasticità.

La trasformazione del punto di vista della totalità da punto limite e regola della ricerca razionale in prospettiva che può essere assunta in modo stabile per riconsiderare tutto il percorso compiuto modifica inevitabilmente il movimento stesso della riflessione filosofica. In Agostino ogni risultato acquisito, ogni oggetto posto di fronte alla conoscenza, rappresenta al tempo stesso un riferimento unitario che dà senso al cammino compiuto, ma anche il motivo per nuove domande che segnalano la necessità di ulteriori livelli di unità. È come se, nella rete di relazioni che la conoscenza si trova davanti, ogni elemento non potesse che rivelarsi, a un certo punto, imperfetto, incompiuto, in quanto nodo possibile di ulteriori reti di rapporti, probabilmente infiniti. Ogni oggetto si trasforma allora in nuovo problema, ogni punto di arrivo in nuovo punto di partenza, ogni risposta in nuova domanda capace di portare a risposte sempre più complete. Il modello analogico perde in Anselmo gran parte del suo dinamismo interno, come si può notare nel modo stesso in cui procede il famoso argomento del *Proslogion* che trova il proprio fondamento in una concezione più immediata del rapporto analogico tra facoltà della conoscenza umana e persone della Trinità divina, per cui la comprensione piena, a livello di enunciato verbale, della definizione di Dio, accompagnata dalla convinzione, basata sulla fede, che tale enunciato abbia un significato, dà origine alla comprensione intellettuale e consente quindi di costruire l'argomento sulla certezza che di Dio esista un concetto nella mente umana. Anche se l'*unum argumentum* rivela tutta la sua ricchezza, e le sue tonalità profondamente agostiniane, solo in una considerazione complessiva di *Monologion* e *Proslogion*[8] i singoli passaggi esaminati isolatamente rivelano, per riprendere i termini iniziali, che la cintura protettiva perde almeno parzialmente qualcosa della sua trama relazionale e quindi, anche da questo punto di vista, tende a irrigidirsi.

Appare chiaro che è il senso complessivo del procedere analogico a modificarsi e ad assumere accenti diversi rispetto ad Agostino, nel quale difficilmente la somiglianza di rapporti fra i diversi livelli dell'essere o della conoscenza ha necessità di trovare ulteriori giustificazioni di carattere logico. La profonda convinzione che l'analogia consenta di indicare rapporti di somiglianza tra cose che, considerate in sé, rimangono assolutamente dissomiglianti lascia spazio teorico persino alla contraddizione, all'instabilità di quanto per un tratto di cammino sembrava assolutamente certo, a quella componente scettica del pensiero agostiniano che costringe a rimettere sempre tutto in discussione. In Anselmo il ricorso all'analogia, soprattutto dopo il *Proslogion* e in particolare nella *Epistola de incarnatione Verbi*, assume il tono talvolta difensivo di fronte alla sempre più evidente presenza di un diverso modello di razionalità di ispirazione logico-aristotelica[9]. L'argomento stesso del *Proslogion*, considerato isolatamente, risulta basato essenzialmente sul principio di non contraddizione, mentre la ricerca di analogie, nell'*Epistola*, sembra esplicitamente tesa a dare conto della concezione trinitaria in modi che possano resistere alle obiezioni ormai evidenti, per cui i predicati di persona o cadono nella categoria aristotelica di sostanza, per cui risultano essenziali e l'unità divina si spezza, o cadono nella categoria di relazione, per cui risultano accidentali e nella concezione di Dio si viene a perdere l'aspetto trinitario.

Pochi anni dopo, Abelardo critica l'uso disinvolto dell'analogia da parte di Anselmo – soprattutto quando la Trinità viene paragonata alla situazione per cui uno stesso corso d'acqua può essere visto nel suo nascere, nel suo scorrere e nel suo sfociare in un lago – e in tal modo rende evidente quanto il paradigma agosti-

[8] Per questa tesi si veda M. PARODI, *Il conflitto dei pensieri. Studio su Anselmo d'Aosta*, Bergamo 1988 (Quodlibet. Ricerche e strumenti di filosofia medievale, 3).

[9] Per una discussione più approfondita di questa fase del pensiero anselmiano si veda *Fra le due rupi. La logica della Trinità nella discussione tra Roscellino, Anselmo e Abelardo*, a cura di M. Parodi e M. Rossini, Milano 2000.

niano sia stato messo in discussione dal suo ultimo grande difensore. Abelardo non crede di essere ormai fuori dall'ispirazione agostiniana, né intende metterla apertamente in dubbio, e proprio per questo non comprende quanto fosse stato drammatico e, in certo senso, conclusivo l'impegno di Anselmo per rafforzare la cintura protettiva e difendere il nucleo forte del proprio programma di ricerca.

Per un verso Gaunilone, nella sua difesa dello stolto, aveva volto a proprio favore quello che si è definito *irrigidimento* anselmiano, e aveva messo in dubbio la possibilità di passare dalla comprensione delle parole alla generazione del concetto, rendendo in questo modo del tutto infondato il resto del percorso dell'*unum argumentum*. Per parte sua Abelardo propone una concezione trinitaria che rende del tutto evidente quanto ormai il nucleo sia stato aggredito, per cui ci si trova di fronte non più a trasformazioni *nel* paradigma ma a veri e propri mutamenti *del* paradigma. La Trinità viene assunta come dato di fede, non può e non deve essere raggiunta con gli strumenti della sola ragione e non si fonda più sul complesso discorso agostiniano a proposito dell'analogia con le facoltà conoscitive. La stessa proposta di considerare i predicati di persona come collocati sul livello del *proprium* mostra come Abelardo rinunci al tentativo di liberare il discorso trinitario dai legami della logica aristotelica e sposti quindi l'accento dal tipo di predicato – la relazione come categoria non sostanziale ma neppure accidentale – a quel tipo di predicazione che stabilisce un nesso tra il soggetto e una sua proprietà sempre presente, ma non come costituente essenziale della definizione e quindi della sostanza.

Il nucleo forte che si è ipotizzato si sgretola nelle pagine di Abelardo dedicate alla Trinità e non rimane nulla di quel lungo percorso agostiniano di ricerca di analogie sempre più perfette che occupa la seconda parte del *De Trinitate* e rappresenta in un certo senso l'esposizione più significativa del metodo della sua ricerca. Partendo dalla relazione di amore tra un soggetto e un oggetto che rappresenta la forma pura della relazione – si potrebbe dire *in se stessa* – Agostino passa attraverso conoscenza sensibile e conoscenza intellettuale proponendo successive analogie, che di volta in volta si rivelano problematiche e fonti di dubbio, ne trae spunto per salire a livelli successivi di precisione, costruire una nuova analogia, discuterla, superarla e approdare infine alla grandiosa sintesi in cui le relazioni intratrinitarie appaiono accostabili alle relazioni che intercorrono fra memoria, intelligenza e volontà. In Abelardo l'oggetto è dato, non si tratta di costruirlo né di farne la forma di rapporti conoscitivi sempre più comprensivi; si tratta piuttosto di chiarirne i termini senza mai metterlo in discussione, attraverso un uso attento della predicazione del *proprium* e una minuziosa analisi a livello linguistico sui significati di *identico* e *diverso*. La logica aristotelica sostituisce il procedimento analogico e tende quindi a isolare le facoltà dell'intelligenza come livello privilegiato dell'indagine razionale rompendone i nessi, essenziali invece nella ragione agostiniana, con la memoria, cioè con la riflessione sui princìpi di ogni forma di conoscenza umana, e con la volontà, cioè con l'aspetto *intenzionale* e attivo della conoscenza.

L'idea di *paradigma* sembra rivelarsi utile per riportare a una possibile unità la speculazione filosofica di autori differenti, rispettandone tuttavia, con gli strumenti suggeriti dalla struttura dei *programmi di ricerca*, la specificità e le accentuazioni personali. Tale unità, basata su dottrine condivise, e soprattutto su aspetti logico-strutturali comuni, consente di utilizzare criticamente quelle che Giulio Preti, con una indiscutibile punta di ironia, definiva le *essenze* entro la storia della filosofia, i famosi «-ismi» come appunto agostinismo, aristotelismo, realismo, empirismo o scetticismo[10]. Inevitabilmente lo storico propone quadri in qualche misura unitari, ma può mantenere la precisa consapevolezza che essi hanno una funzione eminentemente operativa per il proprio lavoro e mantengono un proprio valore solo entro i limiti di una cultura storicamente data e di linguaggi effettivamente usati. In questo senso la storia della filosofia, come d'altra parte la filosofia di cui si nutre, potrebbe davvero rinunciare a quella che Preti chiama la *millenaria dimensione religiosa*[11] che fonda la pretesa di poter cogliere gli assoluti in se stessi, per dare conto di come il mondo è e di come, nel mondo, si sviluppa il pensiero dell'uomo.

[10] Cfr. G. PRETI, *Continuità e discontinuità nella storia della filosofia*, in ID., *Saggi filosofici*, 2 voll., Firenze 1976, II, *Storia della logica e storiografia filosofica*, pp. 217-243; ID., *Continuità ed «essenze» nella storia della filosofia*, *ibid.*, pp. 245-264.

[11] Cfr. ID., *Il linguaggio della filosofia*, in ID., *Saggi filosofici* cit., I, *Empirismo logico, epistemologia e logica*, [pp. 455-474], pp. 473-474.

L'idea di *paradigma* sembra poter essere strumento efficace proprio per coniugare la ricerca di possibili aspetti unitari, mantenendo chiara al tempo stesso la loro collocazione nella sfera del relativo, con la convinzione che tali aspetti unitari si basano su postulati di carattere sempre ipotetico e sempre rinegoziabili nella comunità degli studiosi. Contemporaneamente consente di rendere più comprensibili i motivi per cui quelle che Preti chiama *tradizioni filosofiche* – cioè complessi di scopi, aspirazioni, tecniche, direzioni di ricerca – possono di fatto costituire punti di partenza, rispetto ai quali il punto di arrivo può risultare anche del tutto diverso.

Nello specifico delle questioni che stiamo discutendo, riuscire a cogliere le trasformazioni che hanno luogo in quella che si è chiamata *cintura protettiva* dovrebbe consentire di verificare quali autori, sia nei secoli alto-medievali sia nelle riprese tardo-medievali di talune linee agostiniane, possano rientrare in una effettiva tradizione in qualche misura unitaria e quali altre tradizioni di pensiero si vengano configurando in termini di paradigmi o programmi alternativi. È probabile che, lungo questa linea di approfondimento, possano emergere anche interessanti considerazioni sulle differenti forme di platonismo che caratterizzano, accanto al paradigma agostiniano, i secoli alto-medievali. Non solo. L'idea di una possibile unità, che viene meno in un certo momento del suo sviluppo, dovrebbe anche essere in grado di delineare, almeno in termini generali, le linee di frattura e quindi le direzioni lungo le quali si può dare un mutamento di paradigma.

In Anselmo si è irrigidita la cintura protettiva che dopo di lui sembra andare in frantumi di fronte alla nuova razionalità di Gaunilone e di Abelardo. Si sta uscendo dal paradigma agostiniano e ci si può domandare che cosa ne sopravviva nel corso del secolo XII e verso quali direzioni ci si stia avviando. Viene quasi da immaginare che proprio il disgregarsi del nucleo forte – strutturato, come si è visto, sulla grande analogia tra facoltà della conoscenza umana e relazioni intratrinitarie – disegni, nello spazio teorico della riflessione del secolo XII, una serie di linee di forza che riportano quasi insensibilmente al confronto con il paradigma in via di dissoluzione[12]. Abelardo, si è detto, sposta il centro della sua

[12] Questa idea è più ampiamente sviluppata nella seconda parte di PARODI,

ricerca filosofica dall'analisi della struttura del mondo a quella della struttura del discorso umano, trasformando di conseguenza l'analogia agostiniana in semplice metafora, che recupera gran parte del valore originario di strumento di espressione linguistica, e suggerisce al tempo stesso una specie di isolamento del livello dell'intelligenza rispetto alla articolazione ternaria delle facoltà conoscitive agostiniane.

Succede allora – e questa è ancora una traccia della forza del paradigma agostiniano sulla stessa lettura che ne danno gli autori del secolo XII – che molti dei tentativi di rinnovare la ricerca filosofica di questo periodo appaiano disporsi quasi naturalmente su una sorta di pentagramma strutturato in termini agostiniani. Sul livello della memoria si muove la proposta di una *teologia assiomatica* da parte di Alano di Lilla e Nicola di Amiens, nella quale il centro della riflessione sta nella individuazione dei princìpi, di quelle regole che, come aveva insegnato Boezio, non appena ascoltate si impongono come autoevidenti alla conoscenza umana. La memoria, in cui Agostino trovava i fondamenti delle scienze mediante le quali l'uomo conferisce un ordine alla propria incerta comprensione del mondo, nel metodo cosiddetto *assiomatico* di questi autori del secolo XII sembra isolarsi dalle relazioni con le altre facoltà, lasciando all'intelletto il compito fondamentale di estrarre dai princìpi quanto in essi è già implicitamente contenuto. La riflessione di Alano si sviluppa anche in molte altre opere impostate in termini completamente diversi rispetto alle *Regulae coelestis iuris*, che dimostrano quanto si sia «voluto coscientemente misurare con tutte le strumentazioni e le metodologie documentabili e disponibili, come per voler verificare quale fosse la più adeguata da trasmettere al futuro della ricerca teologica quale esito di tale vaglio critico»[13]. In queste opere, così come in altri autori, in particolare in Gilberto di Poitiers o Teodorico di Chartres, emerge in modo assai peculiare lo sfor-

Il paradigma filosofico agostiniano cit. (alla nota 6).

[13] G. D'ONOFRIO, *Alano di Lilla e la teologia*, in *Alain de Lille, le Docteur Universel. Philosophie, théologie et littérature au XIIe siècle*, Actes du XIe Colloque international de la S.I.E.P.M. (Paris, 23-25 octobre 2003), éd. par J.-L. Solère – A. Vassiliu – A. Galonnier, Turnhout 2005 (Société Internationale pour l'Étude de la Philosophie Médiévale – Rencontres de Philosophie Médiévale, 12), [pp. 289-337], p. 293.

zo di individuare una possibile mediazione tra il livello dei princìpi – memoria – e i modi in cui se ne possono cogliere conseguenze e sviluppi nell'articolarsi dell'esperienza del mondo – intelligenza –. Le complesse argomentazioni di carattere aritmetico che cercano di dare conto del passaggio dall'unità alla molteplicità rendono evidente la necessità di una mediazione tra livelli della realtà e facoltà della conoscenza che nel paradigma agostiniano erano connessi dalla struttura analogica.

In posizione mediana, sull'ipotetico pentagramma, con cui si tenta di suggerire una qualche struttura per quelle che si sono definite linee di forza provenienti dal paradigma in dissoluzione, si incontra senza dubbio Abelardo e il suo impegno logico-analitico nell'approfondimento di princìpi accettati per fede, come quello della Trinità divina, oppure di tesi di carattere etico, volte essenzialmente a mettere in evidenza come l'uomo sia veramente un essere razionale solo sul livello dell'intelligenza: per un verso, comprensione discorsiva di princìpi che non trova in se stesso e, per altro verso, preparazione delle proprie scelte e delle proprie azioni che tuttavia nulla aggiungeranno alla responsabilità che resta esclusivamente intellettuale. Viene da pensare che princìpi accettati solo per fede potrebbero generare qualche problema di incertezza nel cuore della riflessione intellettuale, sollevare in modo più radicale alcune di quelle domande che, nel *Contra Academicos*, Agostino aveva posto e trasformato in criteri metodologici della ricerca. E infatti non pare un caso che, accanto ad Abelardo, si incontri Giovanni di Salisbury, nella cui riflessione lo scetticismo accademico assume un ruolo del tutto nuovo rispetto alla lezione agostiniana, perdendo il proprio senso essenzialmente metodologico, per assumere invece la funzione di delimitare gli ambiti della certezza, empirica o di fede, attraverso l'individuazione di una zona esclusivamente *probabile* che tende a sovrapporsi e identificarsi proprio con la conoscenza intellettuale.

L'isolamento della facoltà dell'intelligenza, così come accade con l'enfatizzazione della memoria, sacrifica naturalmente la complessa articolazione trinitaria del modello agostiniano di ragione, ma proprio della necessaria complessità della conoscenza umana e del suo stratificarsi in livelli successivi si occupano alcune opere particolarmente lontane, a prima vista, da una sensibilità filosofica moderna, che fioriscono nel secolo XII, ad esempio nella scuola di san Vittore. La capacità con cui Ugo di san Vittore riesce a coniugare indicazioni di carattere enciclopedico con tratti di carattere mistico sembra individuare una nuova zona di mediazione fra il livello dell'intelligenza e quello della volontà, per usare i termini agostiniani. La straordinaria analiticità con cui Riccardo di san Vittore riesce a porre in relazione la storia biblica di Beniamino e dei suoi fratelli con le fasi, le regole, i rapporti interni della conoscenza umana mostra, sia nel contenuto sia nel metodo dei suoi scritti, quanto appaia essenziale, in questo caso, lo sforzo di difendere il nesso tra conoscenza intellettuale e conoscenza mistica, tra ragione e fede, tra intelligenza e amore.

Anche a livello della dialettica tra le facoltà dell'anima è decisiva per Agostino, la relazione, il cui nome è *spirito* nella Trinità divina e *volontà* nella conoscenza umana. È la volontà che, indirizzando l'attenzione sull'oggetto, riesce a coniugare l'aspetto sintetico dei princìpi rintracciabili nella memoria e la funzione analitica dell'attività intellettuale. Se la volontà tende a diventare una facoltà autonoma, risulta evidentemente esaltato il ruolo della direzionalità, dell'intenzionalità, a scapito tuttavia della chiarezza nella individuazione dei princìpi e della distinzione fra i vari passaggi dell'indagine intellettuale. La volontà perde in tal modo la propria funzione di relazione per divenire strumento e, contemporaneamente, oggetto della conoscenza. In autori come Bernardo di Clairvaux e Guglielmo di saint-Thierry, e più in generale in molti autori appartenenti al mondo monastico, l'amore appare come la modalità fondamentale del conoscere e il rapporto tra amante e amato, centrale nelle numerose letture del *Cantico dei cantici*, diviene il riferimento analogico per chiarire il procedere della conoscenza. Le conseguenze principali di questo spostamento di accento rispetto al modello agostiniano sono, da un lato, la tendenziale assimilazione tra soggetto e oggetto della conoscenza che tendono a fondersi in unità, come accade nella realizzazione del rapporto amoroso e, d'altro lato, il progressivo annullamento della distanza fra i diversi livelli della realtà lungo i quali si procede nel perfezionamento della conoscenza. La relazione analogica consentiva di collegare tali livelli, mantenendoli tuttavia distinti e difendendone la dissomiglianza, ma quando l'idea stessa di relazione – l'amore – diviene possibile oggetto di indagine, in quanto nesso non tra aspetti che si danno nei due casi distinti collegati dall'analogia, ma tra aspetti lontani che vengono tuttavia collegati direttamente e progressivamente identificati, allora è l'unità stessa, che funzionava come concetto limite dell'analogia, a divenire oggetto possibile e Dio appare come punto di arrivo di una conoscenza ben condotta.

Si profila, lungo questa strada, lo sviluppo di una conoscenza di carattere mistico e si comprende come sia destinata a diventare, nei secoli successivi, un'esplicita alternativa alla ragione, che invece verrà progressivamente identificata con il procedimento logico questionativo. Naturalmente i problemi sollevati sono molto più numerosi delle risposte che possono venire dalla presentazione rapida della proposta interpretativa formulata in queste pagine, ma dovrebbe risultare almeno credibile l'ipotesi che le principali linee di sviluppo del pensiero del secolo XII siano tutte in qualche misura riconducibili ai frammenti del grande paradigma agostiniano, senza che qualcuna sia in grado di riproporlo nella sua compiutezza né di formulare una consapevole alternativa.

Il venire meno dell'intima relazione tra facoltà dell'anima umana e dialettica trinitaria divina fa sì che si precisi una forma di conoscenza specifica delle realtà divine, una *teologia* in quanto tale, e che proprio su questo terreno, come si è visto, si collochino i diversi tentativi di fondare e mettere alla prova una nuova dottrina della conoscenza. La teologia stessa si viene quindi definendo in termini razionali, recuperando tradizione patristica e alto-medievale[14]. La conseguenza più evidente di questo intreccio di nuovi problemi e di elementi provenienti dal passato è che risulta messa radicalmente in discussione la determinazione e l'articolazione stessa della ragione e quindi della filosofia.

Su ognuno dei diversi livelli, individuati attraverso la metafora delle linee di forza e ricollegabili al paradigma agostiniano, se ne tenta una riformulazione che viene per così dire sperimentata sul terreno di una possibile conoscenza teologica, in quanto terreno privilegiato per definire una sorta di *ontologia regionale* grazie alla quale considerare in termini assoluti gli elementi costi-

[14] Tra gli studi recenti si veda C. MARTELLO, *La dottrina dei teologi. Ragione e dialettica nei secoli XI-XII*, Catania 2005 (Symbolon. Studi e testi di filosofia antica e medievale, 29).

tutivi della teoria. Si è osservato, nel corso di queste pagine, che lo strumento concettuale del *paradigma* aiuta a relativizzare, pur consentendo di indicare forme di unità possibile cui ricondurre posizioni filosofiche che mantengono una loro distinzione e periodi storici che mantengono la loro ricchezza di articolazioni interne. Da questo punto di vista si possono trarre due conclusioni interessanti dall'esempio su cui si è concentrata l'attenzione. Per quanto concerne l'oggetto storico individuato, sembra potersi dire che i diversi tentativi di ricostruire un modello di ragione si collocano gli uni accanto agli altri, con tratti comuni e tratti divergenti, in una situazione in cui ancora non può essere chiaro quale sia destinato ad avere il sopravvento e a rappresentare quindi il modello di ragione dominante nel periodo successivo. Ma questa situazione sposta subito l'attenzione sul piano del soggetto della ricerca storica, ponendo una questione di fondo e cioè quanto il quadro tendenzialmente unitario che si è tratteggiato sia tale in se stesso e quanto invece dipenda dalla nostra incertezza nel saper mettere in evidenza aspetti di sintesi differenti e più forti.

Si può allora immaginare che uno dei compiti ancora aperti di fronte al lavoro storiografico sia proprio di proporre una considerazione autonoma, pur nella consapevolezza della ricchezza di eredità e della complessità del periodo, degli anni che stanno fra la rottura del paradigma agostiniano e l'egemonia di quello aristotelico-scolastico. Una considerazione per così dire *iuxta propria principia*, ma che sappia anche individuare riferimenti unitari, per sottrarre gli autori che si collocano tra i secoli XII e XIII al curioso destino di una continua oscillazione. Mentre la seconda metà del Duecento appare come un terreno perfettamente piano su cui i diversi pensatori si collocano saldamente con un loro significato specifico e in un quadro abbastanza comprensibile, gli ultimi decenni del secolo XII e i primi del XIII sembrano condannati a continue oscillazioni, come si trattasse di un terreno sismico. Gli autori di questo periodo o inclinano verso il passato, e sono *ancora* un po' troppo agostiniani, o inclinano verso il futuro e sono dunque *già* scolastici e aristotelici. Sarebbe interessante prestare attenzione a quale sia o quali siano i programmi di ricerca cui è possibile ricondurre la loro riflessione, intorno a quali nuclei forti si dispongano le diverse posizioni e che cosa avvenga nelle rispettive cinture protettive.

In questo modo potrebbe forse essere accantonata la difesa di un nucleo troppo forte e troppo astratto, che talvolta ricompare nel programma di ricerca sulla storia del pensiero medievale, e potrebbe dunque essere superata la visione unitaria e finalistica di uno svolgimento *razionale* della filosofia nel Medioevo. Il millennio medievale si troverebbe infine a ottenere cittadinanza paritaria nello sviluppo storico del pensiero occidentale, apparendo articolato, contraddittorio, frammentario, riconducibile ad aspetti unitari, ma sempre discutibili e quindi *rinegoziabili* fra gli studiosi, esattamente come ogni altro periodo della nostra storia.

FABIO SELLER

TEMI E PROBLEMI PER LA DEFINIZIONE DI UN PARADIGMA SCIENTIFICO MEDIEVALE

L'individuazione di un *paradigma*, nel senso che tale termine ha assunto nella riflessione epistemologica di Thomas Kuhn, rappresenta il prodotto di un'operazione ermeneutica molto delicata: da un lato, infatti, ogni *paradigma* così inteso è un'ipotesi di lavoro, uno schema interpretativo (ma anche pedagogico) che può consentire allo studioso di racchiudere all'interno di un perimetro definito problemi, mezzi e risultati condivisi da una comunità scientifica in un dato periodo storico; dall'altro, esso riflette in senso pieno il principio per cui, nella ricerca storica, *verum et factum convertuntur*, in quanto si sforza di individuare quei caratteri di condivisione, storicamente ricostruibili, che formano la condizione 'normale' di un sapere scientifico, nella sua interna tensione tra l'aspetto 'convergente' e quello 'rivoluzionario'. Non v'è dubbio che l'assunzione di un *paradigma medievale* che si definisca come condivisione di principi il cui carattere ultimativo pertiene alla sfera del religioso – principi che fungono da sfondo onnipresente ai molteplici 'rompicapo' (uso il termine nella sua accezione kuhniana) a cui i pensatori medievali si dedicarono – appaia dotato di una efficace consistenza e mostri un'indubitabile utilità nella lettura della lunga fase del pensiero umano costituita dal Medioevo latino. All'interno di questo generale quadro interpretativo del pensiero medievale, potrebbe apparire tuttavia alquanto problematica la giustificazione del sapere strettamente scientifico e del suo rapportarsi con una generalizzata ammissione – che dovrebbe essere valida per l'intera epoca medievale e per ogni istanza conoscitiva prodotta entro i suoi confini cronologici –

10.1484/M.NUTRIX-EB.1.101234

della superiore e indiscutibile veridicità delle asserzioni di ordine religioso introdotte dalla Rivelazione.

L'ammissione come *paradigma generale* di quello che presuppone un ultimo, inevitabile confrontarsi con i dettami della fede non sembra potersi tradurre senz'altro quale necessario e sufficiente condizionamento anche per lo studio del pensiero scientifico medievale, che sembra richiedere, invece, un suo peculiare modello speculativo, valido nell'ambito delle indagini naturali ed eventualmente assumibile come un *paradigma particolare* all'interno, o *a latere*, di quello generale. Bisogna, allora, chiedersi se tale sussunzione sia storiograficamente legittimata, se, cioè, il *paradigma generale* del pensiero medievale, inteso come il sistematico confronto di ogni conquista della razionalità con le verità indiscutibili della fede, sia dotato di prerogative tali da imporsi come principio ermeneutico dominante anche nei confronti dei procedimenti propri del pensiero tecnico-scientifico.

Quello del rapporto tra scienza medievale e contesto religioso è stato – ed è ancora – tema assai dibattuto tra gli studiosi del Medioevo e solleva grandi difficoltà già nella definizione di cosa si debba intendere quando si parla di 'scienza medievale'. Per la delineazione di un (eventuale) *paradigma scientifico* nell'ambito di una più ampia ricerca sul *paradigma medievale* in generale occorrerebbe dunque porsi il compito di chiarire i rapporti tra ciò che definiamo 'pensiero scientifico medievale' e l'atteggiamento mentale, condiviso dagli intellettuali di questi secoli, di riferimento assiduo alla Verità rivelata nelle Scritture. Solo a seguito di tale preliminare messa a punto sarà possibile stabilire se ed entro quali limiti si possa parlare di un *paradigma scientifico medievale*, e quanto quest'ultimo debba essere inteso come uno strumento prezioso per la completezza dello studio del pensiero nel Medioevo.

Alla definizione di un *paradigma scientifico medievale* non si può che giungere per tratti progressivi, ponendo sempre maggiore attenzione alle rifiniture e ai contorni, al fine di ottenere un quadro il più vivido possibile, partendo, come inquadramento generale, dalla verifica del suo rapporto con il sapere religioso. Si entra qui in un campo, quello della relazione tra religione e teologia da un lato, scienze esatte e metodologia della ricerca scientifica dall'altro, che presenta dimensioni assai vaste, sia dal punto di vista di una teoresi sincronicamente impostata, sia da quello dell'analisi diacronica sulla genesi e l'evoluzione di concetti e stili di pensiero che hanno caratterizzato entrambi i membri della (dis)equazione.

Come sempre accade in simili situazioni, il ventaglio di possibilità varia tra due estremi, quello dello scontro e inconciliabilità e quello della concordia, all'interno dei quali si estende un'ampia gamma di possibili valutazioni, ciascuna caratterizzata da peculiari concessioni e restrizioni rispetto alla possibilità di un incontro tra religione e scienza. Nella verifica e nello studio di tali tesi bisogna tenere in debita considerazione la componente ideologica, latente o dichiarata, che orienta il discorso degli storici e degli interpreti in una precisa direzione e rischia di renderlo selettivo in modo pregiudiziale e non sempre del tutto giustificato.

È noto che la formula stereotipata di uno scontro aperto tra pensiero scientifico e dogma religioso ha prevalso per secoli come schema interpretativo del rapporto tra indagine volta a scoprire le leggi che regolano il mondo naturale, da un lato, e dominio di una verità incontestabile e dalle pretese onnipervadenti, dall'altro. A questa visione hanno contribuito sicuramente le considerazioni che gli stessi autori umanisti e rinascimentali ebbero del periodo che li precedette e, in misura più intensa e aggressiva, quelle svolte con veemenza dalla storiografia nata e cresciuta sotto l'egida dell'*enlightment*, la cui eredità ancora oggi fa percepire la sua presenza. Su questo tema esiste una nutrita letteratura che, acquisendo diverse colorazioni di epoca in epoca, ha visto il rapporto tra pensiero religioso e pensiero scientifico nel Medioevo come un 'conflitto' tra nemici irriducibili o come un terreno comune di reciproci e proficui scambi, oppure, infine, come mutua indifferenza segnata da qualche incontro casuale e peregrino[1].

Nella prima categoria si possono inquadrare tutte quelle opere che considerano il preponderante atteggiamento religioso del Medioevo come un ostacolo (per sua natura o per precisa volontà 'oscurantista') alla nascita e diffusione della scienza. David Lind-

[1] Una utilissima, sebbene incompleta, bibliografia sul tema è stata realizzata da C. Kren, *Medieval Science and Technology: A Selected, Annotated Bibliography*, New York 1985.

berg ha rintracciato una paternità ideale di tale tesi storiografica nell'opera di due autori attivi nella seconda metà del secolo XIX, John William Draper e Andrew Dickson White, la cui perniciosa influenza, di natura polemica ed ideologica, si sarebbe esercitata fino al tempo presente, condizionando le discussioni su Cristianesimo medievale e scienza, e riecheggiando spesso nelle pubblicazioni non specialistiche[2]. Uno dei corollari più pregiudizievoli della 'tesi' Draper-White consiste nell'opinione che riconosce come vero e unico precedente della scienza moderna la filosofia antica, nella quale si sarebbero incarnati gli ideali di razionalità e oggettività, ripresi e rivivificati successivamente in epoca rinascimentale[3].

Già a partire dagli anni '20 e '30 del secolo scorso, tuttavia, si manifestò una reazione a tale prospettiva storiografica, nella direzione di una posizione conciliante, tesa a sottolineare i modi attraverso i quali la religione aveva rappresentato un fattore favorevole alla nascita e diffusione della scienza, in quanto la convinzione che esista nell'universo un ordine regolare voluto da Dio spronerebbe il ricercatore all'indagine di tali leggi divi-

[2] John William Draper (1811-1882) emigrò negli Stati Uniti, dove ottenne la cattedra di chimica e fisiologia alla New York University. Dietro suggerimento di Edward Youmans – il primo divulgatore scientifico americano – Draper compilò una *Storia dello scontro tra religione e scienza* (1874), fortemente critica nei confronti del Cristianesimo, accusato di aver ostacolato con tutti i mezzi la diffusione della scienza. L'opera vendette moltissimo, ed ebbe più di 50 ristampe e dieci traduzioni. Andrew Dickson White (1832-1918), professore all'Università del Michigan e primo rettore della Cornell University di New York, è autore di una *Storia del conflitto della scienza con la teologia nella Cristianità* (1896), in cui attaccava senza mezzi termini i denigratori della scienza, descrivendo lo scontro teologia/scienza come una vera e propria 'guerra'. L'analisi di White, tuttavia, sembra distinguere, rispetto a quella di Draper, la teologia dalla religione: la prima si intromette con dichiarazioni dogmatiche nello studio del mondo e vede nella Bibbia un testo scientifico, mentre la religione è incentrata sul riconoscimento di un 'potere universale' e sulla moralità della condotta di vita. Contrariamente alla teologia, la religione, come sentimento individuale, avrebbe favorito la scienza. Va notato che l'eco diffusa da queste opere è stata ampia nella considerazione dei rapporti tra scienza e religione all'inizio del secolo scorso e non solo, se è vero che George Sarton lodava l'opera e la posizione di White nel 1955. Su tutto ciò, cfr. l'Introduzione di D. C. LINDBERG a *God and Nature. Historical essays on the Encounter between Christianity and Science*, ed. by D. C. Lindberg – R. L. Numbers, Berkeley – Los Angeles – London 1986, pp. 1-18 (tr. it., Firenze 1994, pp. IX-XXVIII).

[3] Cfr. D. C. LINDBERG, *Science and the early Church*, in *God and Nature* cit., pp. 19-48, in partic. pp. 22-23 (tr. it. cit., pp. 1-38, in partic. pp. 4-5).

namente disposte[4]. A tale proposito c'è da dire che il conflitto della scienza *con la religione* (il Cristianesimo, in quanto termine costante di riferimento) assunse in molti casi un nuovo aspetto, configurandosi come conflitto *di una religione*, quella cattolica, in aperta opposizione alla generosità di una Riforma che, per diverse ragioni, aveva concesso alla nascente scienza i giusti spazi per emergere in tutta la sua specificità. Basti citare il caso di Robert K. Merton, il quale in un celebre articolo dal titolo *Science, Technology and Society in Seventeenth Century England* del 1938, descriveva un Cristianesimo medievale sprezzante nei confronti della natura, fondamentalmente ascetico e incentrato sul sentimento della precarietà di tutto ciò che è connesso alla materia, contrapponendo ad esso l'atteggiamento proprio delle Chiese riformate (ma l'accento è posto, in modo specifico, sull'etica puritana e sull'ideologia del capitalismo), per il quale lo studio della natura è concepito come atto di pietà, sforzo di svelare la gloria del Creatore attraverso l'ordine e l'armonia del creato, ma anche come precisa volontà di migliorare lo stato dell'umanità grazie ai vantaggi offerti dai risultati dell'indagine scientifica[5].

Un vero e proprio cambiamento di prospettiva, fondato su motivazioni che si spingono oltre il mero piano del conflitto ideologico, è però da ascriversi agli studi inaugurati da Pierre Duhem all'inizio del secolo scorso[6]. Com'è noto, Duhem reagì al pregiudizio – mai di fatto sostenuto da prove attendibili – secondo cui nella ricostruzione della storia del pensiero scientifico oc-

[4] Cfr. ad esempio A. N. Whitehead, *Science and the Modern World*, New York 1925.

[5] R. K. Merton, *Science, Technology and Society in Seventeenth Century England*, in «Osiris», 4 (1938), pp. 360-632; cfr. *Puritanism and the Rise of Modern Science: The Merton Thesis*, eds. I. B. Cohen – K. E. Duffin – S. Strickland, New Brunswick 1990.

[6] Sulla figura e l'opera di Duhem, cfr. J. E. Murdoch, *Pierre Duhem and the History of Late Medieval Science and Philosophy in the Latin West*, in *Gli studi di filosofia medievale fra Ottocento e Novecento. Contributo a un bilancio storiografico*, a c. di R. Imbach – A. Maierù, Roma 1991, pp. 253-302; S. L. Jaki, *Uneasy Genius. The Life and Work of Pierre Duhem*, The Hague 1984; alla figura intellettuale di Duhem sono dedicati i volumi 2 e 3 della rivista «Synthèse» (1990), curati da R. Ariew e B. Backer. E si veda dello stesso P. Duhem, *An Account of the Scientific Titles and Works of Pierre Duhem*, in «Science in Context», 1 (1987), pp. 333-348.

cidentale sarebbe del tutto legittimo procedere assecondando l'idea di una diretta confluenza dei significativi risultati raggiunti dalla scienza classica e tardo-antica in quelli sorti nel periodo rinascimentale, senza la partecipazione di alcun termine medio. Partendo dalla semplice quanto coraggiosa convinzione che non si può pensare ad un'assenza di spirito scientifico di cui sarebbero stati affetti ben dieci secoli di storia, Duhem si propose di approfondire l'indagine sugli eventuali fattori che dimostrerebbero la presenza, anche nei secoli medievali, di un pensiero scientificamente definibile, nel senso che la parola *scienza* acquisirà più tardi con Galileo e Newton. Nell'opinione dello studioso francese un punto di svolta in questo processo è individuato nel 1277: le condanne, pronunciate dal vescovo Tempier nei confronti delle 219 proposizioni contrarie alla fede cristiana, avrebbero orientato i pensatori nella direzione di un rifiuto della fisica aristotelica e nella ricerca di direzioni nuove, il che avrebbe condotto alla nascita della scienza moderna. Alla base della continuità tra pensiero scientifico medievale e rinascimentale vi sarebbe la teologia cristiana della creazione, l'idea per cui il mondo, creato da Dio *ex nihilo*, conserverebbe in filigrana l'impronta del Creatore, esibendo i caratteri del bene, dell'ordine e della razionalità, presupposti essenziali per lo sviluppo della scienza.

La tesi di Duhem non incontrò il favore degli ambienti scientifici del tempo, soprattutto in Francia, dove imperava l'impostazione razionalista ed anti-clericale della Terza Repubblica; tutt'altra fu l'accoglienza riservatagli, invece, oltreoceano, grazie soprattutto alla favorevole recensione di George Sarton alla sua opera fondamentale, *Le Système du monde*[7]. Il modello proposto da Duhem, noto agli storici della scienza come 'continuismo', è oggi per molti versi superato, tanto nelle sue linee generali, quanto nell'attendibilità storica di alcuni riferimenti

[7] Per la recensione al primo volume dello scritto di Duhem, si veda «Isis», 2 (1914), p. 203. Alla sua morte, avvenuta nel 1916, Duhem aveva pubblicato solo una parte del suo capolavoro, lasciando il resto in forma manoscritta; fu per interessamento della figlia Hélène e di alcuni suoi discepoli che i restanti volumi furono successivamente pubblicati, fino al 1959, non senza difficoltà. Cfr. S. L. Jaki, *Science and Censorship: Hélène Duhem and the Pubblication of the Système du Monde*, in «Intercollegiate Review», 21 (1985-1986), pp. 41-49; P. E. Hodgson, *Pierre Duhem: Historian of the Christian Origin of Science*, in «Contemporary Review», 264/1538 (1994), pp. 134-139.

testuali[8]. Gli va riconosciuto, nondimeno, l'indubbio merito di aver portato alla luce uno spaccato della vitalità speculativa medievale in precedenza molto o del tutto trascurato. Inoltre la tesi che considera la scienza parte integrante della cultura cristiana del Medioevo e insieme contributo essenziale per l'origine della scienza moderna è stata accolta da diverse generazioni di studiosi a partire dal secondo dopoguerra.

Gli studi di Duhem hanno inferto un colpo vigoroso allo sbarramento formato da vecchi pregiudizi storiografici, lasciando fluire un nuovo corso nella storia del pensiero scientifico, con specifiche ulteriori ramificazioni. I maestri di questa nuova fase sono individuabili in un gruppo di studiosi che hanno raccolto lo spirito duhemiano e lo hanno aggiornato con nuove ricerche e nuovi approcci. L'impostazione 'continuista' è stata raccolta, tra gli altri, da Annalise Maier[9] e, in maniera ancor più convinta, da Alaistir Crombie. In particolare, il saggio di Crombie, *Da Agostino a Galileo. Storia della scienza dal* V *al* XVII *secolo*, pubblicato per la prima volta nel 1952, ha fatto scuola per diversi decenni nella seconda metà del secolo XX, suscitando convinte adesioni e severe critiche[10]. A dispetto del titolo, la parte relativa alla scienza dal quinto secolo fino alla metà del dodicesimo è compendiata nel primo breve capitolo; il secondo capitolo, infatti, insiste sulla centralità dell'atteggiamento proprio dei teologi cristiani nel porre problemi di carattere scientifico. La tesi di Crombie è che la metodologia della ricerca scientifica, che poi confluirà nella rivoluzione scientifica e nella scienza moderna, è rintracciabile già negli scritti di autori del secolo XIII. Contro di essa si sono schierati diversi studiosi, da Marshall Clagett a James McEvoy, ma l'attacco più deciso è venuto da Alexandre Koyré. Quest'ultimo cercò di dimostrare che molte delle grandi scoperte scientifiche avvenute nel Medioevo non hanno nulla a che vedere con l'avanza-

[8] Cfr. L. Bianchi, *Il vescovo e i filosofi: la condanna parigina del 1277 e l'evoluzione dell'aristotelismo scolastico*, Bergamo 1990, pp. 13-15; J. Biard, *Le rôle des condamnations de 1277 dans le développement de la physique selon Pierre Duhem*, in «Revue des Questions Scientifiques», 75 (2004), pp. 15-35.

[9] Cfr. A. Maier, *Metaphysische Hintergründe der spätscholastichen Naturphilosophie*, Roma 1955.

[10] A. Crombie, *Augustine to Galileo: the history of science A. D. 400-1650*, Melbourne – London – Toronto 1957 (tr. it., Milano 1982).

mento della scienza e grandi macchine come gli orologi medievali sono da considerarsi piuttosto le cause che non l'effetto della teoria scientifica; persino gli sviluppi interni alla tradizione dell'ockhamismo sarebbero stati di poco conto per la nascita della nuova scienza[11].

In sintonia con la tesi di Crombie si può collocare quella di John Herman Randall: nel suo studio *The School of Padua and the Emergence of Modern Science* del 1961, Randall cerca di dimostrare – sulla base delle precedenti riflessioni di Ernst Cassirer[12] – come l'Università di Padova sia stata il luogo di accoglienza di una serie di studiosi che, partendo da Pietro d'Abano, e passando per Zabarella, sarebbe giunta fino a Galileo[13]. Anche questa linea interpretativa è stata posta *sub iudice*: Neal Gilbert, ad esempio, ha fatto notare che la metodologia scientifica scandita in *resolutio* e *compositio* Galileo la eredita non dagli studiosi padovani, bensì direttamente dai matematici greci[14], e non mancano studi più dettagliati tesi ad evidenziare la portata innovativa del metodo galileiano rispetto alle riflessioni epistemologiche svolte in ambiente padovano[15].

È stato giustamente osservato che un approccio intelligente ed efficace al problema di una corretta definizione del pensiero scientifico medievale, non può non prendere le mosse da una circostanziata considerazione dei testi che ne sono l'espressione. In questa direzione si sono mossi gli sforzi di quanti, come Marshall

[11] Cfr. A. Koyrè, *The Origins of Modern Science: A New Interpretation*, in «Diogenes», 16 (1956), pp. 14-42; M. Clagett, *The Science of Mechanics in the Middle Ages*, Madison 1959; J. McEvoy, *The Philosophy of Robert Grosseteste*, Oxford 1982.

[12] Cfr. E. Cassirer, *Das Erkenntnisproblem in der Philosophie und Wissenschaft der neueren Zeit*, 2ª ed., 2 voll., Berlin 1911-1923, I, pp. 136-143.

[13] Cfr. J. H. Randall, *The School of Padua and the Emergence of Modern Science*, Padova 1961, in partic. p. 27: «It is possible to trace step by step in rather beautiful fashion the gradual elaboration of the Aristotelian method, in the light of the medical tradition, from first discussion in Pietro d'Abano to its completed statement in the logical controversies of Zabarella, in which it reaches the form familiar to Galileo (...)».

[14] Cfr. N. W. Gilbert, *Galileo and the School of Padua*, in «Journal of the History of Philosophy», 1 (1963), pp. 223-231, in partic. p. 227 e nota 4.

[15] Cfr. C. B. Schmitt, *Experience and Experiment: A Comparision of Zabarella's View With Galileo's in De motu*, in «Studies in the Renaissance», 16 (1969), pp. 80-138.

Clagett e i suoi allievi, hanno ritenuto prioritario il lavoro di edizione dei trattati scientifici, prediligendo un percorso 'internalista', attento cioè al contenuto in tutta la sua estensione e profondità, senza indietreggiare di fronte alle difficoltà derivate dal linguaggio tecnico proprio delle scienze particolari[16], relativizzando così gli aspetti 'esterni' che hanno contribuito alla produzione dell'opera.

Negli ultimi decenni, l'idea di un libero fluire del pensiero scientifico occidentale, senza soluzione di continuità, dal mondo classico all'età di Copernico, Galileo e Newton, ha ceduto il posto ad una più cauta riconsiderazione della specificità della scienza medievale. È stato giustamente osservato che la lettura dei prodotti del pensiero di un'epoca non può essere dominata da un metodo di indagine storica guidata da *a priori* regolativi che diventano, nella concreta realtà storica, *a posteriori*, essendosi formati nel contesto culturale della scienza moderna. In ossequio al principio del *Verstehen* nella ricerca storica, è stato più volte rilevato il pericolo di una conoscenza incentrata su categorie appartenenti a periodi posteriori rispetto a quelli indagati, il rischio di una distorsione che può sorgere da una subordinazione del lavoro proprio dello storico nei confronti di quello di pertinenza dello scienziato[17].

Una delle maggiori difficoltà nello studio del pensiero scientifico medievale consiste proprio nella messa a fuoco dell'oggetto di cui ci si occupa. Il problema di fondo del *quicquid agitur* quando si parli di 'scienza' medievale e si voglia chiarire il senso e la pertinenza dell'aggettivo *scientifico* in relazione ad un *paradigma medievale*, presenta evidenti difficoltà di prospettiva storiografica. È fin troppo ovvio che il termine *scientia* (e i suoi analoghi) ha assunto, da Boezio a Galileo, una gamma assai vasta di signifi-

[16] Cfr. D. C. Lindberg, *Medieval Science and Its Religious Context*, in «Osiris», 10 (1995), pp. 60-79, in part. pp. 64-65. Naturalmente, per il caso che stiamo discutendo, relativo alla definizione di un paradigma scientifico medievale, andrebbe scartata apriori la posizione dell''internalismo forte', che esclude dal proprio ambito di interesse le implicazioni concettuali e culturali derivanti dalla produzione scientifica.

[17] Cfr. J.V. Pickstone, *Past and Present Knowledges in the Practice of the History of Science*, in «History of Science», 33.2 (1995), pp. 203-224, in partic. p. 204.

cati e connotazioni, sia rispetto al contesto storico-culturale in cui si opera, sia anche in riferimento a singoli autori che agiscono in un medesimo contesto (senza considerare che, non raramente, il senso può subire metamorfosi tra scritti diversi di uguale paternità). Questo punto sembrerebbe rappresentare una vera e propria *crux desperationis* nel tentativo di definizione di un *paradigma scientifico medievale*, un *limes* ove i percorsi si interrompono fatalmente. La polivocità e l'*aequivocatio* del termine *scientia* nel Medioevo appare sfuggente e indefinibile per lo storico del pensiero scientifico generalmente educato all'impiego di una categoria – quella della *scienza* in senso moderno – che, per quanto portatrice anch'essa di una interna complessa polisemanticità, si lascia ricondurre ad una struttura che presenta indubbi caratteri di omogeneità. Diversamente, per quanto riguarda il Medioevo la costellazione di significati in cui la *scientia* viene di volta in volta definita sembra avere come esito inevitabile un *dictum de nullo*.

A fronte di tali difficoltà, un dato poco contestabile emerge dalla storia del pensiero medievale: se impieghiamo l'attributo 'scientifico' nel significato ampio di 'pertinente al mondo della natura', sia essa indagata con gli strumenti del pensiero filosofico o con quelli matematici propri delle scienze esatte, dobbiamo riconoscere che, sebbene nell'alto Medioevo non manchino riflessioni in questo ambito (e l'analisi delle opere dedicate alle arti quadriviali è sufficiente a provarlo), tuttavia è solo a partire dall'affluenza nell'Occidente latino dei testi scientifici greco-arabi e dei *libri naturales* di Aristotele che la ricerca si amplia, estendendosi a settori prima trascurati o pressoché assenti[18].

[18] Questa opinione, largamente diffusa tra gli studiosi, non andrebbe però accentuata oltre misura, come sembra fare Edward Grant, il quale attribuisce all'alto Medioevo un livello scientifico molto ridotto, tale da non rappresentare in alcun modo una fonte di conoscenze alternativa o distinta e eventualmente contrapponibile a quelle derivanti dalla dottrina cristiana, proprio perché «most of it was encyclopedic, unintegrated, and frequently confused or contradictory»; cfr. E. GRANT, *Science and Theology in the Middle Ages*, in *God and Nature* cit. (alla nota 2), pp. 49-75, in partic. p. 51 (tr. it. cit., pp. 39-72, in partic. p. 42). Sull'argomento, si vedano anche W. H. STAHL, *Dominant Traditions in Early Medieval Latin Science*, in «Isis», 50.2 (1959), pp. 59-124; E. J. DIJKSTERHUIS, *Demechanisering van het wereldbeeld*, Amsterdam 1950 (tr. it., *Il meccanismo e l'immagine del mondo*, Milano 1980).

Non c'è dubbio che il confronto con il crescente numero di scritti relativi alle «scientiae mediae» e ai problemi sollevati dagli *Analitici Posteriori* e dai commentari ad essi dedicati mutarono sensibilmente l'idea di *scientia* e i criteri epistemologici dei pensatori dei secoli XII, XIII e XIV[19]. Se poi i risultati che ne seguirono siano da leggersi come un'anticipazione del mutamento di paradigma che si avrà in epoca rinascimentale o se invece vada piuttosto sottolineata la specificità di tali riflessioni nel contesto del Medioevo, è questione che sembra non aver trovato un punto di convergenza tra gli studiosi. A partire dalla proposta duhemiana, si è spesso dato risalto ai mutui rapporti che la speculazione orientata sulla natura ha instaurato, nel Medioevo, con altri domini del pensiero, primo fra tutti quello proprio della teologia. Gli stessi studi pionieristici di Annalise Maier prendevano le mosse proprio da tale intreccio, sebbene poi la studiosa abbia dedicato la sua attenzione quasi esclusivamente agli scritti che potremmo definire più 'scientifici'. L'impostazione continuista ha dato origine ad una perplessità di fondo sul significato corretto da attribuire alla 'filosofia della natura' medievale, che ancora oggi contrappone gli studiosi, dimostrando che il fantasma della vecchia controversia continuismo/discontinuità è tutt'altro che dileguato. Emblematica di tale stato di incertezza è la polemica che ha coinvolto due tra i maggiori storici della scienza moderna, Edward Grant e Andrew Cunningham.

Grant – i cui contributi hanno fornito materiale prezioso tanto per la ricerca storica quanto per la discussione sulla metodologia appropriata a tale ricerca[20] – ha rivendicato una sostanziale autonomia del pensiero scientifico medievale dal *milieu* religioso in cui gli autori erano di fatto immersi. Secondo Grant i «naturales» dediti all'analisi e al commento delle opere di Aristotele, di Tolomeo, di Galeno, si imbattevano inevitabilmente in Dio e la

[19] Cfr. A. CORBINI, *La teoria della scienza nel XIII secolo. I commenti agli Analitici Secondi*, Firenze 2006; *La divisione della filosofia e le sue ragioni. Lettura di testi medievali (VI-XIII secolo)*, Atti del VII Convegno della Società Italiana per lo Studio del Pensiero Medievale (S.I.S.P.M.) (Assisi, 14-15 novembre 1997), a c. di G. d'Onofrio, Cava de' Tirreni 2001.

[20] Il volume di E. GRANT pubblicato a Cambridge (Mass.) nel 1974 con il titolo *A Source Book in Medieval Science* ha rappresentato una pietra miliare nello studio della 'scienza' medievale, al di là dei limiti che col tempo gli sono stati riconosciuti.

fede, ma in una misura sicuramente trascurabile, tanto da rendere del tutto marginale l'impatto che tali oggetti potevano avere sulle loro argomentazioni[21]. In un saggio che significativamente reca il titolo *Le origini medievali della scienza moderna* lo studioso individua quelli che ritiene i prerequisiti contestuali e sostanziali che resero possibile la Rivoluzione scientifica e la nascita della scienza in senso moderno, collocandoli cronologicamente negli ultimi secoli del Medioevo. Un ruolo di primo piano nel fornire l'*humus* adatta ad accogliere i semi della futura scienza è svolto dalle successive ondate di traduzioni che hanno messo a disposizione degli studiosi europei una vasta produzione di opere di scienza e filosofia della natura, il cui nucleo fondamentale, costituito dalle opere di Aristotele, si è col tempo arricchito degli apporti di autori arabi, sotto forma di commenti e trattati scientifici originali. Tale materiale, sostanzialmente nuovo, ha poi trovato accoglienza in quei luoghi istituzionali che rappresentano un *unicum* nel mondo medievale, vale a dire le Università. Grant attenua molto la portata delle condanne ecclesiastiche che hanno colpito tali istituzioni a partire dai primi decenni del secolo XIII, ridimensionando la stessa condanna del 1277, concependola unicamente come un fenomeno locale, la cui approvazione da parte del pontefice sarebbe avvenuta solo a cose fatte, e ricorda che già nel 1255 le opere di Aristotele entrarono di fatto a far parte del *curriculum* dell'Università di Parigi[22]. L'incontro della scienza e della filosofia naturale greco-arabe con il mondo cristiano fu favorito da una categoria di filosofi teologico-naturali, i quali, trovandosi nella condizione di essere esperti in entrambe le discipline (la Facoltà delle Arti, com'è noto, era un passaggio quasi sempre obbligato per l'acquisizione del titolo di *magister theologiae*), operarono nel senso di una membrana permeabile per il passaggio dei nuovi saperi. Proprio grazie a tale mediazione, Grant conclude che «alcune occasionali reazioni contro la filosofia naturale (...) quan-

[21] Cfr. ID., *God, Science, and Natural Philosophy in the Late Middle Ages*, in *Between Demonstration and Imagination. Essays in the History of Science and Philosophy Presented to John D. North*, eds. L. Nauta – A. Vanderjagt, Leiden 1999, pp. 243-267.

[22] Cfr. ID., *The foundations of modern science in the Middle Ages: their religious, institutional and intellectual contexts*, Cambridge 1996, pp. 168 e seqq. (tr. it., Torino 2001, pp. 252 e seqq.).

do il vescovo di Parigi pronunciò la condanna del 1277, debbono essere considerate come delle aberrazioni di secondaria importanza nell'arco complessivo della storia della cristianità occidentale»[23]. I prerequisiti sostanziali alla nascita della scienza moderna riguarderebbero il ruolo della filosofia naturale e delle scienze esatte[24]. Grazie a questi presupposti, sia nella Facoltà delle Arti che in quella di Teologia, la lettura dei testi di nuova acquisizione avrebbe avuto come risultato la proposizione di una serie di questioni sulla natura, che aprirono la strada a metodi e soluzioni originali, alla base della scienza moderna[25]. In termini kuhniani è questa la fase di crisi del vecchio paradigma, che spingerà a tentare nuove vie per la soluzione dei 'rompicapo' con cui si confrontavano i filosofi-scienziati medievali.

Appare evidente, da quanto detto, che la posizione di Grant – come, del resto, quella della maggior parte degli storici della scienza medievale – si configuri come una forma di malcelato 'continuismo'; è questa la critica che Andrew Cunningham ha mosso allo studioso, rilevando che, in termini più generali, gli storici della scienza tendono, per lo più, a confondere il piano della scienza moderna con quello della *philosophia naturalis* propria del Medioevo[26]. La carenza di una preliminare specificazione sui caratteri distintivi della filosofia naturale non può che essere fonte di confusione e imprecisione storica[27]. Cunningham è chiaro su questo punto: la *philosophia naturalis* è *scientia* ma in modo pecu-

[23] *Ibid.*, p. 85 (tr. it., pp. 262-263).

[24] Cfr. *ibid.*, pp. 191 e seqq. (tr. it., pp. 286 e seqq.). Secondo Grant le scienze esatte non conobbero significative innovazioni durante il Medioevo, sebbene l'interesse nei loro confronti non sia mai scemato. Questa opinione è però contraddetta dai più recenti studi sullo sviluppo di scienze come la meccanica, soprattutto in ambiente arabo. Cfr. W. R. Knorr, *Ancient Sources of the Medieval Tradition of Mechanics. Greek, Arabic and Latin Studies on the Balance*, Supplemento agli «Annali dell'Istituto e Museo di Storia della Scienza», anno 1982, fasc. 2; *Mechanics and Natural Philosophy before the Scientific Revolution*, eds. W. R. Laird – S. Roux, Dordrecht 2008.

[25] Cfr. Grant, *ibid.*, pp. 194-195 (tr. it., pp. 288-289).

[26] Cfr. A. Cunningham, *The Identity of Natural Philosophy. A Response to Edward Grant*, in «Early Science and Medicine», 5, 3 (2000), pp. 259-278. Il contributo di Cunningham è, nelle intenzioni dell'autore, una risposta alla critica che lo stesso Grant gli aveva rivolto in *God, Science and Natural Philosophy* cit. (alla nota 21).

[27] Cfr. Cunningham, *ibid.*, p. 260: «The meanings we attribute to the term 'science' in our researches and writings as historian of science are crucial, yet are

liare, in quanto raccoglie al suo interno una serie di discipline alle quali anche spetta di diritto tale titolo; ma qui *scientia* ha un significato diverso da quello che gli attribuiranno i teorici della scienza moderna, e considerare la prima meramente come uno stadio iniziale di sviluppo che conduce alla seconda è un errore di valutazione commesso, più o meno consapevolmente, da molti storici della scienza[28]. Spostando i termini del discorso, Cunningham considera la *philosophia naturalis*, in quanto *scientia*, come un'attività pratica ed intenzionale e perciò accompagnata da una considerazione sui fini e l'interpretazione dei risultati prodotti. In buona parte la sua genesi può essere rintracciata nelle speculazioni di pensatori appartenenti ai due maggiori Ordini Mendicanti del Basso Medioevo, il francescano e il domenicano[29]. Non si può non ammettere che la filosofia naturale coltivata dai pensatori medievali abbia a che fare con Dio e la creazione, non nel senso di una appiattita identificazione con la teologia, né di una indifferenziata contaminazione tra le due discipline; la prospettiva in cui Cunningham si pone è quella di chi assume il confronto obbligato con le asserzioni della Rivelazione come contesto sensibile a cui riportare il senso della intenzionalità di cui si è fatto cenno[30]. Diversamente da quanto avverrà per gli scienziati moderni, le questioni di fede non erano per i *naturales* medievali fattori irrilevanti; l'apparente *epoché* a cui i motivi religiosi sembravano essere soggetti può emergere soltanto da una lettura basata esclusivamente sul testo, perdendo di vista il senso più ampio dell'opera stessa e il fine per cui è stata prodotta. Ad una prima

usually uninspected and unspecified by us. This is a potential source of confusion and mistaken identities. (...) It is a very slippery term».

[28] Cfr. *ibid.*, pp. 261-262.

[29] Cfr. *ibid.*, pp. 263-264. Si veda anche R. FRENCH – A. CUNNINGHAM, *Before Science: The Invention of the Friars' Natural Philosophy*, Aldershot 1996. Edith Sylla ha più volte fatto notare quanto i problemi sollevati nell'ambito delle discussioni teologiche avessero contribuito significativamente ad approfondire tematiche pertinenti alla *naturalis philosophia*; questo nesso sarebbe stato molto forte ed avrebbe guidato il singolo pensatore verso percorsi trasversali, dando vita alla figura di 'filosofo della natura-teologo', competente in entrambe le discipline, le quali si presentano in una relazione di reciproca referenzialità, tanto da costituire una sorta di sinolo: cfr. E. D. SYLLA, *Interactions of natural philosophy and theology*, in *The Cambridge Companion to Medieval Philosophy*, ed. by A. S. McGrade, Cambridge 2003, pp. 187-195.

[30] Cfr. CUNNINGHAM, *ibid.*, pp. 267-269.

lettura un testo può apparire orientato esclusivamente ai temi di filosofia naturale e ciò sembra tanto più giustificato dalla presenza di un elevato livello di tecnicismo, ma ciò non esclude che vi possa essere un significato più vasto, sebbene poco evidente: le opere di filosofia naturale si iscrivono in una cornice che va al di là dell'oggetto stesso sottoposto ad indagine, rinviando ad un universo di senso che è parte integrante della produzione scientifica[31]. D'altro canto, come spiegare la ragione per cui uomini che in qualche modo erano legati al mondo religioso del loro tempo avrebbero dedicato i loro sforzi allo studio della natura se ciò non avesse servito un fine più ampio[32]? Non è convincente la tesi di Grant che da un lato parla di una sorta di reciproca intesa tra filosofia naturale e teologia, dall'altro considera il discorso su Dio e sulla Sua creazione come una indebita 'intrusione' (*intrusion*) in un ambito che non è di sua pertinenza.

La *philosophia naturalis* non può essere confinata al ruolo di fase di passaggio tra la scienza antica e quella moderna; per dissipare ogni possibile confusione si dovrebbe utilizzare la parola 'scienza' (senza ulteriori specificazioni) per riferirsi esclusivamente all'impresa scientifica compiuta dai pensatori moderni[33]. Inoltre, la convinzione che la 'secolarizzazione' della scienza (ma sarebbe più corretto dire *le* scienze), intesa come attività di ricerca rivolta esclusivamente all'indagine sulla natura, sia avvenuta nel secolo XVII è, nell'opinione di Cunningham, un *cliché* storiografico non più proponibile. Forgiato negli anni '40 da studiosi come Alexandre Koyré e Herbert Butterfield[34], l'approccio 'internalista'

[31] Cfr. *ibid.*, pp. 273-276.

[32] Cfr. *ibid.*, p. 276.

[33] Cfr. *ibid.*, pp. 277-278, dove si legge: «I would wish us to be referring to a historical sequence of Philosophy (ancient period), natural philosophy (medieval and early modern period), and then science (modern period), disciplines fulfilling different roles in their respective areas».

[34] Cfr. A. CUNNINGHAM – P. WILLIAMS, *De-Centring the 'Big Picture': The Origins of Modern Science and the Modern Origins of Science*, in «The British Journal for the History of Science», 26, 4 (1993), pp. 407-432, in partic. pp. 408-410; H. BUTTERFIELD, *The Origins of Moderns Science 1300-1800*, London 1957. Sulla storiografia cui gli autori fanno riferimento, si vedano J. R. R. CHRISTIE, *The developement of the historiography of science*, in *Companion to the History of Modern Science*, eds. R. C. Olby – G. N. Cantor – J. R. R. Christie – M. J. S. Hodge, London 1996, pp. 5-22; A. THACKARY, *The pre-history of an academic discipline: the study of the history of science in the United States, 1891-1941*, in «Minerva», 18 (1980), pp. 448-473.

ha infatti gettato nuova luce sui debiti che la scienza del Seicento contrae con idee e schemi di pensiero propri della filosofia tradizionale (*in primis* quella aristotelica), nonché sul ruolo, tutt'altro che di secondo piano, assunto da discipline come la metafisica e la teologia nello studio dei fenomeni naturali[35]. Traendo spunto dalla rivalutazione che la storiografia scientifica ha operato, a partire dagli anni '60, nei confronti dei fattori esterni per la ricostruzione della genesi e specificità del pensiero scientifico occidentale, Cunningham ha proposto una nuova «big picture», nella quale la scienza è vista «as historically contingent and embodying the values, aims and norms of a particular social group (...) as limited, bounded in time and space and culture»[36]; con tali presupposti, la nascita della 'scienza' in senso moderno andrebbe post-datata agli anni 1760-1848[37].

La polemica Grant-Cunningham è un riflesso della disputa ancora viva tra gli storici della scienza, fra un atteggiamento «centrato sul tempo presente» e una prospettiva che tende a valorizzare gli aspetti sociali, culturali, politici che formano le condizioni per la nascita di determinati problemi, con le rispettive proposte di soluzione. Nel mondo anglosassone – in cui hanno visto la luce la maggior parte degli studi sulla scienza medievale – tale polemica ha assunto la forma di uno scontro tra la prospettiva storiografica «whiggish» e quella fondata su discipline come la sociologia della scienza e la storia delle idee. Tra i caratteri distintivi della «Whig history of science» – o «present-centred history» – emerge l'idea di un progressivo rischiaramento della verità scientificamente accertabile, vista con gli occhi dello scienziato contemporaneo; ciò comporta, in alcuni casi, una valutazione riduttiva di quelle ipotesi che si sono rivelate, con l'evolversi del pensiero scientifico, sostanzialmente infondate[38]. A partire dall'inizio degli

[35] Cfr. S. SCHAFFER, *Occultism and reason*, in *Philosophy, its History and Historiography*, ed. by A. J. Holland, Dordrecht 1985, pp. 117-143.

[36] CUNNINGHAM – WILLIAMS, *De-Centring the 'Big Picture'* cit. (alla nota 34), p. 418.

[37] Cfr. *ibid.*, pp. 419-420.

[38] L'espressione «Whig history» trova la sua genesi nell'opera di H. BUTTERFIELD, *The Whig Interpretation of History*, Harmondsworth 1973; la formula «present-centred history» è stata invece coniata in T. G. ASHPLANT – A. WILSON, *Present-centred history and the problem of historical knowledge*, in «The Historical

anni '60 l'idea stessa di una uniformità e univocità metodologica della ricerca scientifica fu sottoposta ad attenta analisi: il risultato fu la nascita dell'approccio «externalist», per il quale non si può considerare la scienza come un prodotto trascendentale del pensare, dato che alla sua genesi concorrono, necessariamente, fattori esterni quali la religione, l'economia, la politica[39]. Lo studioso della scienza nel Medioevo non può non essere coinvolto in tali discussioni di carattere storiografico ed epistemologico; se ciò vale in senso generale per lo studio della storia della scienza a partire dal secolo XVII, con maggior forza si impone rispetto ai secoli medievali, in cui il rapporto tra le *scientiae* e i fattori 'esterni' – primo fra tutti quello religioso – sono particolarmente intricati e dunque problematici.

Estremizzando tale posizione, l'applicazione alla produzione scientifica medievale di un paradigma fondato sull'inevitabilità del confronto con le affermazioni della Rivelazione sembrerebbe del tutto giustificata. In effetti, sulla imprescindibilità di riconoscere l'incidenza del contesto religioso sulla produzione del pensiero scientifico nel Medioevo hanno insistito, più di recente, diversi studiosi. Dall'esame di numerose opere a carattere scientifico emerge con chiarezza un'immagine precisa del ruolo che la religione – ovvero la Chiesa come istituzione patrocinatrice e le formule della fede come bussola d'orientamento – ha svolto nei confronti della libertà di formulazione di asserti di ordine naturale, soprattutto nei casi-limite in cui le tesi proposte assunsero evidentemente la forma di dottrine contrastanti con il dogma e che dunque furono stigmatizzate quali *errores philosophorum*, come l'affermazione dell'eternità del mondo[40]. Ad un più approfondito esame, tuttavia, qualora si assuma il termine 'scienza' nel suo senso più tecnico, va riconosciuto che uno studio sui suoi rapporti con il contesto religioso, in termini che superino gli or-

Journal», 31 (1988), pp. 253-273; degli stessi, si veda anche, nello stesso volume, *Whig history and present-centred history*, pp. 1-16.

[39] Un chiaro esempio della revisione operata sul precedente modello epistemologico emerge, ad esempio, nelle opere di Paul Karl Feyerabend e Thomas Kuhn. Cfr. CUNNINGHAM – WILLIAMS, *ibid.*, p. 415.

[40] Cfr. N. STENECK, *Science and Creation in the Middle Ages: Henry of Langenstein on Genesis*, Notre Dame (Ind.) 1976; A. FUNKENSTEIN, *Theology and the Scientific Imagination from the Middle Ages to the Seventeenth Century*, Princeton 1986.

mai datati schemi duhemiani, si è imposta come oggetto di ricerca solo in tempi relativamente recenti[41]. David Lindberg ha sottolineato in più occasioni il ruolo giocato dalla Chiesa quale principale promotrice, diretta o indiretta, dell'attività intellettuale del Medioevo, compresi quegli aspetti che si rivolgono a questioni concernenti lo studio della natura; sarebbe, perciò, controfattuale pretendere di far astrazione da essa nel tentativo di ritrarre una scienza autonoma e laicizzata[42]. Quanto al fattore di natura ideologica che si è accompagnato a tale funzione della Chiesa e della religione, Lindberg ritiene che esso sia fisiologico e rifletta comunque un requisito socialmente e politicamente integrale alla stessa produzione scientifica[43]. In conclusione, il Cristianesimo si costituirebbe, nel Medioevo, come realtà onnipresente, le cui interferenze nell'impresa scientifica sarebbero state meno «intrusive» di quanto si sia per troppo tempo pensato; se vi furono dei contrasti, questi sono da ascriversi ad attriti nati tra i singoli pensatori e non ad un atteggiamento impositivo della Chiesa[44].

Il punto di vista di Lindberg, condiviso nelle sue linee generali anche da altri studiosi[45], illustra con intelligenza e moderazione una realtà storica che sembra ormai fuori discussione: il *milieu* re-

[41] Cfr. LINDBERG, *Medieval Science* cit. (alla nota 16), p. 68: «If you go looking for a book that offers a full, responsible, and reasonably up-to-date analysis of the relationship between science and religion in the Middle Ages, I do not think you will find it (...). This frame of mind can be explained historically as the product both of centuries of abuse (...) over the relative importance of medieval and early modem contributions to the origins of modern science». E cfr. ID., *The Beginnings of Western Science: The European Scientific Tradition in Philosophical, Religious, and Institutional Context, 600 B.C. to A.D. 1450*, Chicago 1992.

[42] Cfr. ID., *Medieval Science* cit., p. 74. Il tema della progressiva «laicizzazione» della scienza medievale, attestato da una letteratura in lingua volgare prodotta al di fuori delle istituzioni universitarie controllate dalla Chiesa, è stato affrontato, tra gli altri, da J. CADDEN, *Charles V, Nicole Oresme, and Christine de Pizan: Unities and Uses of Knowledges in Fourteenth-Century France*, in *Text and Context in Ancient and medieval Science: Studies on the Occasion of John E. Murdoch's Seventieth Birthday*, ed. by E. Sylla – M. McVaugh, Leiden 1997, pp. 208-244.

[43] Cfr. LINDBERG, *ibid.*, p. 74: «(...) most important developments in the history of science have emerged not from autonomous science (certainly not from scientific activity that was viewed by its patrons as autonomous), but from science in the service of some ideology, social program, or practical end (...)».

[44] Cfr. *ibid.*, p. 76.

[45] Cfr. R. HOOYKAAS, *Religion and the Rise of Modern Science*, Grand Rapids 1972; E. KLAAREN, *La riforma protestante e la scienza*, in «Comunità», 28/173

ligiosamente caratterizzato all'interno del quale sono immersi e si muovono, come pesci in una vasca, i singoli filosofi-scienziati, ciascuno scegliendo la propria direzione, ma non varcando mai l'elemento da cui sono avvolti.

Eppure, resta il problema di dove collocare alcuni pensatori, i quali risulterebbero, alla luce di questa generalizzata situazione, come dei *monstra*, dal momento che, pur condividendo con gli altri la *species*, appaiono muoversi in un elemento diverso, una sorta di 'pesci fuor d'acqua'. Questi autori pensano e scrivono in una dimensione che, se non è apertamente refrattaria ad assumere i principi religiosi come *apriori* del pensiero, quantomeno ne prescinde e li 'pone tra parentesi'. Attraverso una più o meno dichiarata ma decisa opzione di distinguere i domini e gli strumenti d'indagine ad essi pertinenti, questi pensatori si impegnano in questioni concernenti la *natura* senza quel processo di gemmazione che caratterizza l'attività del teologo che si lancia in approfondite analisi fisiche per individuare *rationes necessariae* a sostegno della creazione del mondo, della transustanziazione del pane e del vino, del moto degli angeli. Il loro percorso inizia, si dipana e termina restando all'interno di un contesto speculativo che tratta dei corpi, delle sostanze generabili e corruttibili, del possibile *ut frequenter*, considerati nella loro dignità epistemologica; quest'ultima è possibile grazie alla rielaborazione del concetto di *scientia*, alla luce delle nuove categorie rese disponibili dagli *Analitici Secondi*, dal libro VI dell'*Etica Nicomachea*, dalle questioni proemiali di trattati di astrologia e medicina[46].

(1974), pp. 115-159; S. JAKI, *The Road of Science and the Ways to God*, Chicago – Edinburgh 1978 (tr. it., Milano 1988).

[46] Sul contributo fondamentale che la medicina scolastica ha fornito nell'indagine sulla metodologia scientifica, cfr. P.-G. OTTOSSON, *Scholastic medicine and philosophy. A study of Commentaries on Galen's* Tegni *(ca. 1300-1450)*, Napoli 1984; C. CRISCIANI – J. AGRIMI, *Edocere medicos. Medicina scolastica nei secoli* XIII-XV, Napoli 1988. La centralità spettante al libro VI dell'*Etica Nicomachea* nella delineazione della *scientia* come *virtus dianoetica*, è stata rilevata da Graziella Federici Vescovini in relazione alla epistemologia di Pietro d'Abano; cfr. G. FEDERICI VESCOVINI, *La médicine synthèse d'art et de science selon Pierre d'Abano*, in *Les doctrines de la science de l'antiquité à l'âge classique*, éd. par R. Rashed – J. Biard, Leuven 1999, pp. 236-255. Una attenzione particolare, in tale direzione di ricerca, merita senza dubbio il considerevole contributo offerto dagli studi di Guy Beaujouan: cfr., tra altre testimonianze, *Comprendre et maitriser la nature au Moyen*

Un esempio significativo di questa possibile lettura alternativa dei modelli formali cui risponde certa produzione scientifica medievale può essere tratto da una attenta analisi dei criteri metodologici messi in pratica nell'opera di Pietro d'Abano. I suoi trattati di argomento astrologico, medico e fisiognomico vertono su temi ed articoli che non abbandonano mai il terreno degli enti naturali, con tutta la contingenza che essi comportano. In questo caso, però, si tratta di una scelta consapevole ed epistemologicamente fondata o, perlomeno, giustificata. Il termine di riferimento non è più la rigida e rigorosa determinazione dei criteri di scientificità esposti negli *Analitici Secondi*, perché l'oggetto non è più l'*ens necessarium* e *perfectum* della metafisica (teologia), bensì l'*ens in fieri* o l'*ens futurum*: la grande novità sta proprio nell'aver individuato i criteri e i metodi che consentono uno studio meramente 'scientifico' di tali oggetti[47]. Di fatto – argomenta l'Aponense richiamandosi ad un concetto espresso in apertura dell'*Almagesto* – proprio questo sapere scientifico, che si presenta così 'debole' se confrontato con quello metafisico e teologico, è in realtà il più certo per noi, perché le cause che sono in esso indagate non sono tanto remote da apparire quasi inafferrabili, ma sono più proporzionate al nostro intelletto di uomini. Bisogna inoltre ricordare che l'insistenza sulle condizioni storico-politico-sociali, all'interno delle quali si pone il ruolo svolto dalla Chiesa come realtà sostenitrice e promotrice di una cultura cristiana in cui la pratica della scienza ha trovato il giusto accoglimento, non è necessariamente un fattore determinante o con-causante per l'evoluzione del pensiero scientifico[48].

Risulta chiaro da esempi come questo il fatto che una ricerca sul paradigma speculativo, che caratterizza in modo tipicizzato l'universo del pensiero medievale, non può non tenere conto di quanto nell'ambito specifico delle indagini naturali l'autonomia metodologica, congegnata dai filosofi classici per indagare il

Âge: mélanges d'histoire des sciences offerts à Guy Beaujouan, éd. par G. Beaujouan – M. Terrasse, Genève 1994.

[47] Mi sia consentito di rimandare a F. SELLER, Scientia astrorum. *La fondazione epistemologica dell'astrologia in Pietro d'Abano*, Napoli 2009.

[48] Cfr. P. ROSSI, *I ragni e le formiche. Un'apologia della storia della scienza*, Bologna 1986.

vero, potesse trovare la sua più valida conferma proprio in base ad una rigorosa distinzione tra ambiti e strumenti del sapere che consentiva di evitare contaminazioni tanto inutili quanto pericolose. Autori come Pietro d'Abano e Biagio Pelacani da Parma non sono dunque né 'eccezioni' che confermerebbero la regola di una dipendenza dell'intera filosofia medievale dalla teologia, né *outsiders*, più affascinanti per la loro esoticità che non per il fondamentale contributo da essi dato ad una autentica presa di coscienza del significato più autentico del pensare scientificamente nei secoli del Medioevo, ma veri e propri 'scienziati', che hanno posto il loro operare conoscitivo al di qua del margine fissato dalla conoscenza teologica. Questi casi hanno un senso nella misura in cui rendono esplicita l'esigenza di considerare i prodotti del pensiero medievale anche da un altro punto di fuga. Quando lo scienziato medievale (sia esso *anche* e/o *principalmente* teologo) affronta questioni ad un alto livello di tecnicismo, il più delle volte sta pensando da scienziato e non da teologo o da uomo di fede. Per leggerlo e interpretarlo dobbiamo assumere noi stessi quell'*habitus* mentale, provvisorio o caratteristico dell'autore, che ci consenta di seguire la trama dei ragionamenti; in diverse occasioni constateremo che l'ordito non ha nulla a che fare con la religione o la teologia, ma si pone ad un livello di competenza tecnica spesso disorientante. Un argomento cosmologico come la causalità astrale nei suoi effetti di lunga durata può implicare premesse di carattere strettamente astronomico, anche molto dettagliate, che in non pochi casi vengono ridotte ai minimi termini nella lettura 'filosofica' dei testi, con il risultato di lasciare zone grigie nel processo di comprensione e coglimento del senso di un'argomentazione. Lo storico della filosofia antica e medievale che affronti questioni di carattere scientifico non può concedersi il privilegio di non essere anche storico della scienza. Naturalmente, questo è un problema di non poca rilevanza, perché investe difficoltà di ordine pratico, oltre a rappresentare il rischio di ipostatizzare uno dei due termini a scapito dell'altro. È vero che negli ultimi decenni questa divaricazione si è notevolmente ridotta, grazie al paziente e competente contributo di diversi studiosi; nonostante ciò, l'urgenza della formulazione di un modello paradigmatico definito per il pensiero scientifico medievale sembra ancora essere un affare di pertinenza esclusiva dello storico della scienza[49]. Basterebbe, tuttavia, osservare che il filosofo-scienziato medievale non è una finzione letteraria; individuare il *minimum* di competenza tecnica che sta alla base della sua produzione testuale rappresenta un passaggio essenziale e ineludibile per lo storico del pensiero medievale. La multidisciplinarietà – una categoria estranea al Medioevo – può fornire un valido aiuto in tale direzione, come già avviene, nella messa a disposizione di differenti competenze settoriali per lo studio di un'opera scientifica, a patto che si stabilisca tra i diversi soggetti un clima di con-divisione, che nella prassi risulta non sempre così immediato da realizzare[50]. Sotto questo aspetto, il *paradigma scientifico medievale* perde la sua naturale predisposizione ad orientarsi verso gli ultimi secoli del Medioevo, per il prevalere in essi di un impegno in questioni epistemologiche più vasto e articolato, grazie alla disponibilità degli scritti aristotelici sull'argomento e all'apporto delle scienze arabe: la determinazione precisa delle fasi lunari, per portare un esempio astronomico, è un problema che non interessò solo i pensatori dal secolo XII in avanti.

Gli spunti di riflessione sin qui suggeriti in maniera concisa non hanno alcuna pretesa di esaustività, sia *intensive* che *exstensive*. Tuttavia convengo con quanti ritengono la questione della scienza nel Medioevo un tema quanto mai attuale e tutt'altro che determinato, e ciò è dovuto, in parte, alle ragioni sopra esposte. Oggi disponiamo di un discreto numero di studi sull'argomento, tanto rispetto alla focalizzazione su temi particolari, quanto sulle questioni di natura epistemologica e di storia della scienza che ne

[49] Degna di considerazione è la seguente osservazione di A. C. CROMBIE, *What is history of science*, in ID., *Science, Optics and Music in Medieval and Early Modern Though*, London 1990, pp. 441-452, in partic. p. 441 (tr. it., *Stili di pensiero scientifico agli inizi dell'Europa moderna*, Napoli 1992, pp. 11-30, in partic. p. 11): «Some of the best work on the history of scientific as of other thought has been done not surprisingly by historians of philosophy, and also by historians of literature».

[50] Il problema delle distonie e degli incontri mancati è risaltato già nella stessa storia della scienza: le differenze di forme, finalità, provenienze di ambiti disciplinari, può creare difficoltà di ordine pratico di non poco rilievo. Su ciò cfr. J. ROGER, *L'histoire des sciences: problème et pratiques. Histoire des sciences, histoire des mentalités, micro-histoire*, in ID., *Les sciences de la vie dans la pensée française du XVIIIe siècle*, Paris 1993, pp. XIX-XXXIX.

scaturiscono. La produzione scientifica nel Medioevo non è sempre un prodotto secondario di un'attività speculativa rivolta principalmente a questioni il cui fine ultimo o motore primo è rappresentato dalla teologia, intesa come scienza di Dio e del mondo in quanto Sua creatura. L'indubbio peso che la religione e la Chiesa hanno avuto nella produzione, promozione e definizione della cultura medievale non basta ad avvalorare l'ipotesi di una banale e infeconda ancillarità della filosofia naturale e delle scienze particolari alla teologia e ai precetti della fede religiosa, e non può relegare, per ciò stesso, il pensiero scientifico medievale a un ruolo subalternato; anche quando ciò accade, bisogna riconoscere la specificità e l'autonomia – non pretesa, ma naturale – del discorso scientifico, del *naturaliter loqui*, di quell'insieme di procedimenti, strumenti e metodologie che hanno permesso agli scienziati medievali di affrontare e risolvere i loro 'rompicapo'.

ALAIN GALONNIER

LE GESTE INAUGURAL DE LA PHILOSOPHIE MÉDIÉVALE

La question parcourue d'embûches de l'*initium* problématique de la philosophie médiévale, qui tient de la quête sans fin pour l'historien des idées, est particulièrement périlleuse dans la mesure où elle présuppose une périodisation forcément arbitraire, dès lors que toute tentative de cloisonnement fait aussitôt apparaître des failles et immédiatement naître des exceptions. Dans cet environnement défavorable, l'hypothèse de travail que nous allons commencer par synthétiser, pour pallier le risque que la forme de notre exposé n'en dissimule le fond, pose comme préalable qu'il serait vain, car non pertinent, de s'enquérir d'un point de départ du Moyen Âge philosophique sans savoir de quel Moyen Âge on parle, et, corrélativement, tout aussi peu cohérent de chercher cette signification ailleurs que chez ceux qui ont formé le syntagme et lui ont apposé un contenu, à savoir les gens de la Renaissance, et plus particulièrement ceux qui l'ont porté à l'existence pour la contourner ou l'enjamber. Car, on l'aura sans doute compris, le Moyen Âge que nous avons voulu doter d'une origine, fut cette période qui servit à la fois de repoussoir et de tremplin à ce que l'on appellera bien plus tard la Renaissance, cette ère moyenne à laquelle on refusera une considération en raison de ses erreurs et errements. Or, si l'on admet, comme nous l'avons fait ici, que la civilisation renaissante fut toute pénétrée et saturée de christianisme au dire de Lucien Febvre[1], d'idées et de

[1] Voir L. FEBVRE, *Le problème de l'incroyance au* XVI*e* *siècle. La religion de Rabelais*, Paris 1975², pp. 336 et 348.

10.1484/M.NUTRIX-EB.1.101235

sentiments chrétiens, on se disposera à comprendre que c'est dans cette perspective christiano-centrée que le Moyen Âge fut perçu par la Renaissance, et que c'est celui-là même que nous avons tâché de surprendre à sa source. Un Moyen Âge chrétien donc, mais chrétiennement déviant pour le penseur renaissant, sur lequel pèse encore ce reproche fondamental: n'avoir jamais réussi à mettre en harmonie les tendances d'un mysticisme qui affirmait la présence immédiate de Dieu et de la vérité dans l'esprit humain avec les tendances de la philosophie intellectualiste qui, présupposant une réalité au dehors de l'esprit qui la cherche, donnait tous ses soins à la construction, riche formellement mais vide substantiellement, de ce qui ne pouvait être la vérité[2].

Quant à ce point d'ancrage que nous allons traquer à présent, il doit, en tant que tel, se plier à l'exigence de sa condition, c'est-à-dire, et nous insistons sur cette définition, avoir à la fois intégré et dépassé les stades antérieurs et, au regard de celui qui l'incarne, avoir eu doublement conscience d'intervenir en héritier et de participer à une avancée doctrinale.

Au cours d'une récente conférence[3], Pierre Magnard s'est employé à montrer que le Moyen Âge philosophique fut sans auteur, sans événement et sans innovation. Il ignore, a-t-il précisé, la dimension de l'inaugural et la catégorie du révolu. Du coup, la philosophie médiévale ne s'est point développée à partir d'une racine ou d'une souche, mais «en rhizomes». Elle n'a de fécondité que par son commentarisme, comme mémoire des textes, matrice de concepts, génératrice de problèmes, créatrice d'hybrides (au sens où elle mêle des courants de pensée différents) et creuset ou *officina* de la raison disputante. La cause semble donc entendue: l'expression «Moyen Âge», du moins en son acception philosophique, à laquelle sont étrangers et l'«inaugural» et le «révolu», ne se ramène qu'à une provocation de renaissant mettant dix siècles de réflexion entre parenthèses, et corrélativement, se-

[2] Voir *ibid.*, p. 448 in fine.

[3] P. Magnard, *La philosophie médiévale innove-t-elle?*, in *Comment écrire l'histoire de la philosophie?*, éd. Y. Ch. Zarka, Paris 2001, pp. 161-170. Pour suppléer à l'absence d'une définition de la philosophie dans cet article, nous entendrons le terme au sens de savoir construit sur des procédés rationnels visant à l'explication synthétique du moi, du monde et de Dieu.

rions-nous tenté d'ajouter, à un syndrome d'historien. Son point d'ancrage ou, comme le dit encore Pierre Magnard en une heureuse métaphore, son «geste inaugural», à moins d'être nié, ne devrait alors plus se réduire au mieux qu'à une insignifiante et vaine gesticulation.

L'histoire contemporaine de la philosophie confirme ces vues sans les rendre définitives. Certes, aucune tentative pour ramener le Moyen Âge à une unité de perspective, pour lui trouver une visée globalisante et l'organiser harmonieusement, n'est jamais parvenue à susciter le consensus, principalement en raison de l'incapacité à convenir d'un lieu initial[4]. Il ne semble pas que l'on puisse entendre à ce sujet échos plus dissonants que ceux qui retentissent lorsque les spécialistes, et pas seulement ceux de l'histoire événementielle, essayent de périodiser le Moyen Âge. Lambert-Marie de Rijk a recensé[5] pas moins de vingt propositions pour en marquer justement le début, c'est-à-dire sa frontière avec l'Antiquité, ce qui correspond à un éventail de plus de 600 ans, de la mort de Marc Aurèle (180) pour la plus reculée, au début de la renaissance dite carolingienne (ca. 800) pour la plus rapprochée. Pourtant, un exemple, pris dans une littérature encore plus récente, montre la difficulté qu'il y a à se passer en l'occurrence de tout repère d'origine. À supposer que l'on refuse, comme le fit Alain de Libera parcourant la philosophie du Moyen Âge, les découpages mécaniques et stéréotypés, en adoptant une approche thématique et disciplinaire réglée sur une typologie des problèmes, on obtient inévitablement une médiévalité aux contours flous[6]. Car si le jeu des idées fait justement naître le sentiment de la durée, il n'éveille point, à dessein du reste, la notion de période et de limite, que l'esprit réclame néanmoins pour stabiliser en un

[4] Voir entre autres G.-L. Burr, *How the Middle Ages Got their Name*, in «American Historical Review», 20 (1914-1915), pp. 813-814; et D. Norberg, *Au seuil du Moyen Âge: études linguistiques, métriques et littéraires publiées par ses collègues et élèves a l'occasion de son 65. anniv.*, Padova 1974 (Medioevo e Umanesimo, 19). La recherche de ce lieu ne paraît pas, du moins en France, avoir beaucoup intéressé les historiens de la philosophie. Citons quand même J. Jolivet, *Émergences de la philosophie au Moyen Âge*, in «Revue de synthèse», IVe série, 3-4 (1987), pp. 381-416 (= Id., *Philosophie médiévale arabe et latine*, Paris 1995, pp. 11-46).

[5] Voir L. M. de Rijk, *La philosophie au moyen âge*, Leiden 1985, p. 3.

[6] Voir A. de Libera, *La philosophie médiévale*, Paris 1994^{3} («Que sais-je?»); et Id., *La philosophie médiévale*, Paris 1993.

moment fondateur ces nombreux siècles violemment balayés par les vents de l'histoire. Or, conséquence probable de cette déstructuration chronologique, le souffle de la foi ne paraît pas vraiment être passé sur les temps philosophiques qu'Alain de Libera propose de survoler.

Cette situation instable et assez confuse nous a incité, contre toute attente, à vouloir figer le geste inaugural, à la fois chimérique et paradoxal, d'un âge qui se façonna en permanence, mais fut également sclérosé par un autre âge qui le mit entre parenthèses et se détermina lui-même en le niant. C'est sans doute aussi à cause de cette sorte d'antinomie que nous n'avons pas renoncé, en cette remontée à la source hypothétique de la philosophie médiévale, à présupposer une relative organicité, qui la rende pour une part capable de relever d'un idéal commun de vérité et d'une confluence des méthodes suivies pour y parvenir, sans tenter délibérément d'échapper à ce carcan où l'a immobilisé l'ère qui se voulut résurgente.

Dans ces conditions, notre enquête empruntera rapidement deux directions: d'un côté, celle pour isoler non pas une phase consécutive à quelque rupture ou renouveau, mais l'épisode remarquable initialisant un développement continu quoique inégal et cahotique; de l'autre, celle pour appréhender le contenu de ce *tempus* qu'elle ouvre, et qui n'en cherchera volontairement aucun hors du contexte et de l'état d'esprit dans lesquels il a été forgé. Autrement dit, et c'est le parti-pris, peut-être intenable, que nous avons adopté, on ne peut légitimement demander l'un des sens du syntagme «Moyen Âge» qu'à ceux qui l'ont créé et lui en ont donné un, si partiel et hétéroclite fût-il, et seulement à partir de là chercher l'*initium* qui lui corresponde. Sous ce rapport, il nous apparaît – truisme ou vrai programme? – que l'acte de naissance du Moyen Âge philosophique s'identifie au point fusionnel de quatre paramètres, et plus exactement d'une religion, le christianisme, d'une langue, le latin, d'une zone géographique, l'Occident, et d'une problématique, la pénétration rationnelle des contenus de foi. À leur carrefour, il nous faudra ensuite tenter de situer un auteur: Marius Victorinus (ca. 285 - ca. 365) dit *Afer*, en référence à ses origines africaines. Or, et c'est à défendre le bien-fondé de ces lignes de force qu'il convient de travailler, les trois premiers paramètres nous sont imposés par la périodisation qu'amena, à tort ou à raison, une certaine Renaissance, tandis que le quatrième prête bien son épaisseur à ce que le moment originel suppose pour être appelé tel, c'est-à-dire d'avoir à la fois intégré et dépassé les stades antérieurs et, au regard de celui qui l'incarne, d'avoir eu doublement conscience d'intervenir en héritier et de participer à une avancée doctrinale.

Il ne va pas forcément de soi d'admettre que les trois premières charges sémantiques du syntagme «Moyen Âge», dans son acception générale, soient à réclamer au milieu qui l'a inventé pour mieux l'ignorer. Cette expression, telle que nous l'entendrons ici, est, faut-il le rappeler, un critère de périodisation minoratif introduit par la proto-Renaissance[7]. Il s'installe vraisemblablement, dans les textes et les esprits, en 1373 avec le *medium tempus* de Pétrarque, pour désigner la période barbarisante qui le sépare de l'Empire romain[8]. On reconnaît là ce qu'il est convenu d'appeler l'«idéologie de la décadence», fondée sur les notions de «déclin» et de «barbarie». Quel qu'en soit le bien-fondé ou le côté arbitraire, ce coup porté à une histoire dont on découvrait que le devenir n'était ni linéaire ni progressif, par son caractère initial et sa représentativité de l'ère qui s'annonçait, ne resta pas lettre morte. Il allait en effet retentir de deux manières différentes chez ceux qui prônaient d'accomplir un gigantesque bond culturel pour tenter de remédier à toutes sortes de dévoiements. Deux réactions, non concertées au départ et par la suite divergentes, contribuèrent à doter ce critère d'appréciation d'une dimension historiale: l'une fut spéculative, l'autre plus directement confessionnelle.

Avec la première, due à un large courant humaniste, on ambitionna de rejoindre une Antiquité gréco-romaine jugée salutaire, afin d'en réaliser non pas une réplique mais une réappropriation.

[7] Sur le sens de ce terme et sur celui d'«humanisme» que nous utiliserons aussi, voir De Rijk, *ibid.*, pp. 5-7.

[8] Voir Franciscus Petrarcha, *Epistolae metricae*, III, 33 (cité par De Rijk, *ibid.*, p. 2, avec la note). Toutefois, des formes plus tardives, telle que la *media tempestas* chez Giovanni Andrea de Bossi éditant Apulée (voir De Rijk, *ibid.*, p. 219, note 2, qui cite J. Voss, *Das Mittelalter im historischen Denken Frankreichs*, München 1972, p. 41, et P. Magnard, *La philosophie médiévale innove-t-elle?* cit. [à la note 3], p. 162, repris de M. de Gandillac, *Nicolas de Cues. Œuvres choisies*, Paris 1942), remontant à 1469, ne répercuteront pas la même dénonciation.

Il s'agissait notamment de dégager la philosophie du pilori où l'avait clouée la scolastique, à laquelle on imputait surtout d'avoir sacrifié l'homme et la nature qui pouvait être magnifiquement dominée et soumise. Pareil recentrage sur le naturel et l'humain eut de multiples répercussions, entre autres de susciter une critique de la croyance populaire, accusée de les appauvrir, et de la vie recluse, accusée de les déserter. Mais outre les exceptions qui l'entament, cette vue totalisante repose sur trop d'inaperçus. Premièrement, il ne fait guère de doute que la fascination pour la grécité et la latinité classique opérait déjà chez un Boèce ou un Jean de Salisbury. Deuxièmement, la volonté de constituer un savoir non par sédimentation mais par rupture ne fut pas complètement étrangère au penseur médiéval qui cependant ne radicalisera jamais autant sa position. S'il ne put en effet avoir conscience de sa *medietas*, il eut parfois, lui aussi, surtout quand il était philosophe, celle de sa modernité. Le renouveau carolingien n'est point seulement une catégorisation d'historiographe, et ce que l'on nomme la «renaissance du XIIe siècle»[9] repose sur le sentiment, authentiquement éprouvé à l'époque, puisqu'on y évoquait tour à tour une *renovatio*, une *reformatio* et une *restauratio*[10], de participer à un nouvel élan, avec le souci néanmois de reconnaître sa dette, comme en témoigne la trop fameuse sentence prêtée à Bernard de Chartres: «Nous sommes semblables à des nains juchés sur des épaules de géants»[11]. Troisièmement, l'accusa-

[9] Rappelons que l'expression est due à C. H. HASKINS, *Studies in the History of Mediaeval Sciences*, Cambridge 1924, notamment le chap. VIII; puis ID., *The Renaissance of the Twelfth Century*, Cambridge 1927 (1990^7). Pour une critique voir F. CANTOR, *Inventing the Middle Ages. The Lives, Works, and Ideas of the Great Mediavalists of the Twentieth Century*, New York 1991 (1992^2); et M. LEJBOWICZ, *L'historien, son siècle et sa recherche. Recherches sur l'acculturation des enseignants médiévaux (X^e^-XIIe siècles)*, Thèse inédite de Doctorat de l'Université de Lille III, 2002 [pp. 1-147], pp. 53-84. Sur la question voir aussi T. GREGORY, *La nouvelle idée de nature et de savoir scientifique au XIIe siècle*, in *The Cultural Context of Medieval Learning* (Proceedings of the First International Colloquium on Philosophy, Science, and Theology in the Middle Ages, September 1973), eds. J. E. Murdoch – E. D. Sylla, Dordrecht 1975, pp. 193-218.

[10] Voir G. B. LADNER, *Terms and Ideas of Renewal*, in *Renaissance and Renewal in the Twelfth Century*, Actes du Colloque de Cambridge (Mass.), eds. L. Benson – G. Constable – C. D. Lanham, Toronto 1982 (1991^2), pp. 1-33.

[11] Voir IOHANNES SARISBERIENSIS, *Metalogicon*, III, 4, PL 199, 900C, éd. J. B. Hall – K. S. B. Keats-Rohan, Turnhout 1991 (CCCM, 98), p. 116,46-50; et le sentiment d'É. JEAUNEAU, *«Nani gigantum humeris insidentes». Essai d'interpré-*

tion d'avoir négligé l'homme et la nature fait piètre cas des textes médiévaux qui partent à leur découverte, tels ceux de Jean Scot pour l'une et du même Bernard ou d'Alain de Lille pour l'autre[12]. Le moule dans lequel s'est trouvé pris le *medium tempus* l'assimilait donc ici à une ère de braises refroidies, alors qu'elle crépita de plusieurs incandescences.

La seconde réaction, pâtissant des mêmes excès, émana essentiellement des théoriciens protestants, qui préconisèrent un retour à l'authenticité apostolique et évangélique pour juguler les égarements en tous genres de l'Église qu'ils fustigeaient, aussi bien quant aux déviances de ses représentants que quant à l'instauration contestée de divers points d'ecclésiologie, dont la communion *monospecie* et la dérive sacrificielle du rite messianique. La nécessité du saut multi-séculaire répondait cette fois-ci au besoin impérieux de «(revenir à) la Bible sans la compromettre avec quinze cents ans d'accommodement doctrinal»[13]. Mais, là encore, c'est se montrer oublieux d'un précédent en la matière, attendu qu'un objectif semblable, visant à restaurer les idéaux des époques apostoliques et patristiques pour lutter contre la simonie et le nicolaïsme, anima la réforme dite grégorienne, commencée sous le pontificat de Grégoire VII (1073-1085) et achevée sous celui de Calixte II (1119-1124)[14].

Pareils gauchissements attestent que ceux qui forgèrent l'expression «âge intermédiaire» ou avalisèrent l'idée de distanciation qui lui est attachée, globalisèrent les siècles qu'ils désiraient abstraire en fonction de leurs manières de penser et de ressentir, de leurs convictions et aspirations. Nonobstant ces généralisations réductrices[15], il n'est point pertinent, redisons-le, d'interroger un

tation de Bernard de Chartres, in «Vivarium», 5 (1967), pp. 79-99; et ID., *Nains et géants*, in *Entretiens sur la renaissance du XIIe siècle*, éd. par É. Jeauneau et M. de Gandillac, Paris 1968, pp. 21-52.

[12] Voir LEJBOWICZ, *ibid.*, p. 74, qui renvoie aux articles *Homme* et *Nature* du *Dictionnaire du Moyen Âge*, éd. par C. Gauvard – A. de Libera – M. Zink, Paris 2002, pp. 967-973 et 1087-1093.

[13] H. VÉDRINE, *Les philosophies de la Renaissance*, Paris 1971, p. 115.

[14] Voir LEJBOWICZ, *ibid.*, p. 74.

[15] Cfr. l'opposition de DE RIJK, *La philosophie au Moyen Âge* cit. (*supra*, à la note 5), pp. 9-10, qui dénonce ce type de restriction sous l'appellation, déjà évoquée, d'«idéologie de la décadence» (parce qu'elle est fondée sur les notions de «déclin» et de «barbarie»), et plus largement récuse le processus de «périodisation intrinsèque» (défini *ibid.*, à la p. 23) qui la détermine.

autre horizon idéologique que celui des renaissants et le repérage qui en émerge, fût-il partial et molaire, pour appréhender la teneur d'une médiévalité qui rend redondante la qualification du syntagme «Moyen Âge» par les adjectifs «latin», «occidental» et «chrétien».

La ligne réflexive ainsi tracée fait coïncider philosophie chrétienne ou christiano-centrée et philosophie médiévale, écartant par là même de celle-ci la pensée arabo-musulmane, sans nier pour autant l'éventualité d'une renaissance proprement islamique[16]. On ne peut aborder ici les difficultés afférentes à cette autre équation, qui ont suscité d'amples débats. Sa légitimité relève toutefois d'une certaine évidence, au moins sous l'angle choisi par nous. Dans le cas symptomatique de la philosophie sarrasine, il semble aller de soi qu'elle ne saurait accéder au statut du médiéval autrement que par ses vecteurs occidentaux. Il nous paraît en effet dépourvu de sens d'envisager que, aux yeux des auteurs renaissants, Avicenne ou Averroès entre autres aient pu être rangés parmi les médiévaux, si ce n'est pour autant que divers pans doctrinaux à consonance formelle, c'est-à-dire qui n'impliquaient rien de spécifique à leur conviction, s'étaient vus, en fonction de convergences thématiques et méthodologiques, repris et assimilés par des penseurs latins[17]. Et c'est effectivement en se trouvant soumis à la même instrumentalisation qu'ils furent utilisés par la Renaissance. En 1529 et 1530, les *Commentaires* d'Averroès sur la *Métaphysique* et le *De anima* d'Aristote sont traduits en latin pour alimenter la controverse touchant l'immortalité de l'âme, et à la même époque Rabelais, dans son *Pantagruel*, évoque Avicenne uniquement pour contrer le déterminisme des astrologues. D'autre part, l'orientaliste Guillaume Postel ne se

[16] Ce que l'on appelle la «renaissance islamique» ne semble cependant limitée qu'à l'intégration, par assimilation et diffusion, de l'ancien héritage grec. Voir A. METZ, *Die Renaisssance des Islams*, Heidelberg 1922 (traduit en anglais par S. K. Bukhsh et D. S. Margoliouth, London 1937), et J. L. KRAEMER, *Humanism in the Renaissance of Islam: The Cultural Revival during the Buyid Age*, Leiden 1986, et ID., *Philosophy in the Renaissance of Islam: Abū Sulaymān al-Sijistānī and his Circle*, Leiden 1986, en particulier à la p. X: «The philosophic humanism (...) was mainly expressed in a shared devotion to ancient thought, in a dedication to cosmopolitan ideas, and in a cultivated affection for humanity».

[17] Voir l'avis divergent de JOLIVET, *Émergences de la philosophie* cit. (*supra*, à la note 4), où le pluriel renvoie aux deux traditions latine et arabe; et cfr. ID., *La théologie chez les arabes*, Paris 2002.

passionna à l'islamisme qu'afin de servir sa propagande pour une religion naturelle, sorte de christianisme à l'unité élargie, c'est-à-dire qui aurait intégré tout ce qu'il y avait à ses yeux de meilleur dans les religions du Livre[18]. L'indifférence envers la latinité affichée par les écrivains d'expression arabe, entièrement dépendants d'une ère, d'un texte et d'une langue spécifiques, expliquerait d'ailleurs pour une part cette constatation. Il ne manque pas d'intérêt d'observer, en renversant la perspective, que par une attitude apparentée à celle des écrivains renaissants, mais qui tint au hasard et ne fut point revendiquée en dépit de sa systématicité, les représentants du savoir d'expression arabe ont fait totalement abstraction de tout ce qui pouvait toucher de près ou de loin aux productions intellectuelles de leurs prédécesseurs latins, accaparés qu'ils étaient, non pas eux aussi mais eux d'abord, par la volonté de rejoindre pour le compléter ou le renouveler l'héritage des Grecs.

Le comportement réactionnel des renaissants leur fit donc percevoir les médiévaux comme les acteurs du déchiffrement d'un univers qu'eux-mêmes avaient l'intention de repenser et de réorganiser, à savoir faisant effort, pénétrés de christianisme et véhiculant au moyen de la langue latine une spéculation qui se modelait dans le creuset de l'Occident, pour faire émerger d'un monde saturé de Dieu une créature écrasée par lui[19]. Ils imprimèrent de ce fait à la notion de *medietas* une orientation conceptuelle dont nous sommes entièrement tributaires. Plus précisément, cette médiévalité récusée par la mentalité qui l'a produite

[18] Voir, sur l'ensemble de ces points, FEBVRE, *Le problème de l'incroyance* cit. (*supra*, à la note 1).

[19] On pourrait arguer du fait que la tradition gréco-byzantine, qui connut sa propre renaissance au IXe siècle (des écrivains comme Léon le philosophe [né ca. 790] et Photius [né ca. 810] y ont contribué), paraît fournir un exemple de saut culturel tout hellène, en la personne de Georges Gémiste, dit Pléthon († 1452), qui rechercha lui aussi, par une même projection, une complicité avec la pensée antique, sans changer d'aire linguistique. Mais, et nous aurons plus loin à reprendre l'argument, ce dernier aspect fausse pour nous les conditions d'accès au savoir en le rendant immédiat. De plus, il semblerait que ses motivations, particulières car centrées sur la création d'un néo-paganisme d'inspiration platonicienne, conçu par défiance du christianisme, n'aient eu qu'une affinité très restreinte avec les idéaux que nous avons signalés. La question, et sa réponse prudente, ne valent cependant pas, à plusieurs égards, pour des contemporains tels Bessarion, Théodore Gazès, Georges Scholarios ou Georges de Trébizonde.

sans lui donner de contenu suffisamment contrasté fut celle qui, tout en ayant absolutisé les mêmes données de départ qu'étaient la foi et le dogme révélé, avait eu le tort d'être obnubilée par la science du divin et la doctrine de l'Être suprême. Ce théocentrisme avait en quelque sorte entaché de nullité l'effort du *medium tempus*, à la fois primordial et souvent réactualisé, pour intégrer le legs de la grande Grèce, d'abord assimilé par un acte de traduction, afin de satisfaire les attentes scientifiques d'une tendance à l'intelligibilité qui travailla le christianisme primitif[20]. C'est dans cette dimension qu'il nous faut situer notre quatrième paramètre et celui qui serait susceptible de lui conférer quelque pertinence.

Au vu des jalons qui viennent d'être posés et qui doivent baliser notre hypothèse de lecture, on ne sera point surpris que le milieu dans lequel apparut et prit essor la philosophie médiévale ait été marquée par le fait religieux, et plus précisément celui que posa l'avènement de l'Homme-Dieu. Manifesté par la révélation et reçu par la grâce, il s'incarnait dans un monde que le philosophe entreprenait depuis longtemps d'expliquer synthétiquement, à l'aide d'un langage et d'un savoir rationnels, en ses causes et en ses principes, curieux de la réalité ultime des choses. Une rencontre eut lieu, celle du λόγος et de la διάνοια d'un côté, discours organisé d'une pensée courant en jugements qui s'enchaînent, et du message chrétien de l'autre, discours surnaturel, délivré en paraboles plurivoques. Ce rapprochement entre argumentation et témoignage mit en contact deux univers, l'un d'élaboration conceptuelle, l'autre d'édification spirituelle, où répulsion et attraction alternèrent ou composèrent, au cours des trois premiers siècles de l'ère chrétienne, jusqu'au compromis que nous assimilons à une impulsion décisive. Pour tenter de comprendre ce qui a pu se produire à la confluence de ces deux courants de pensée, et quelles en furent les principales conséquences, nous commencerons par envisager succinctement la façon dont se sont répartis quelques-uns des éléments d'affinité et d'incompatibilité, et quelles orientations ils ont déterminé, afin de mieux cerner par contraste celle qui nous occupe.

[20] Voir DE RIJK, *La philosophie au moyen âge* cit. (*supra*, à la note 5), pp. 18-20.

Le principal écueil concerne les tenants et les aboutissants de la prédication du Christ, inconciliable par bien des aspects avec la culture philosophique grecque, dont sont totalement imprégnés à l'époque les milieux où se répand sa parole. Celle-là, dans son souci d'universalité, n'était visiblement pas prête à prendre en charge l'unicité d'un fait historique rapportant qu'en un lieu et un temps donnés Dieu s'est manifesté en son Fils, lequel annonce la bonne nouvelle d'une vie fondée sur l'amour, afin que se réalise la Loi mosaïque et le message des Prophètes. Il y avait antinomie, pour un philosophe hellène, entre une raison visant à l'universalité et une histoire inscrite dans la temporalité, car l'universel (καθόλου) ne peut prendre en charge la singularité d'un événement où s'initie un écoulement temporel, lequel s'accomplit dans ses propres limites, de la genèse à la fin des temps. L'histoire chrétienne, qui fait en se faisant elle-même, n'est pas une histoire hellène, précisément parce que le temps grec, comme règne de l'éphémère et du présent, est assimilé à un processus de défaisance, alors que le temps chrétien s'anime en continuité édificatrice par un moment de création fondée sur une révélation. Ces exemples de distorsion reçoivent d'une certaine manière un écho en plusieurs volets de l'enseignement apostolique. Ainsi, dans sa première *Épître aux Corinthiens* Paul affirme que pour un Grec, qui ne comprend pas le sens d'un Dieu mourant en esclave, la Croix est une folie (1, 18), cela après avoir signalé qu'il annonce l'Évangile sans la sagesse du langage, c'est-à-dire sans la spéculation rationnelle et l'artifice rhétorique (1, 17) – rejet inadmissible pour une civilisation de la parole conquérante. C'est animé des mêmes sentiments que dans son *Épître aux Romains* (12, 2) il prêche une rupture avec la manière de pensée grecque et ses structures mentales. Pareille attitude influencera durablement le courant des opposants à une intellectualisation de la foi; on y récusera toute compromission avec la pensée païenne et tout usage de la raison, pour ne point corrompre la pureté du message christique. Ce renoncement aux valeurs du paganisme montre sans doute que les premiers penseurs chrétiens furent conscients d'une évolution radicale; mais il les exclut par là même d'une démarche philosophique dont nous nous efforçons de trouver le premier point de focalisation.

La réalité historique apparaît cependant davantage nuancée. Ces deux mentalités ne furent point complètement hermétiques l'une à l'autre, et c'est avec la conscience plus ou moins vive de cette inter-réceptivité que beaucoup, privilégiant en outre un langage paulinien tout différent, vont reprendre à leur compte des pans entiers hérités de la culture hellène. Que l'on songe en effet, parmi les notions susceptibles d'être partagées, à celle du καιρός comme moment opportun ou temps favorable qui, appliqué à la venue du Sauveur, devient intelligible même pour un Grec, ou encore à celle d'un salut dans l'éternité bienheureuse, promise assurément par le Christianisme mais aussi par l'Orphisme et le culte de Déméter, dont les mystères étaient célébrés à Eleusis – et jusqu'à celle typiquement chrétienne de la mort de Dieu, qui n'est pas une totale aberration pour un Hellène si l'on se souvient que Dionysos, dieu sauveur manifesté dans le monde, mourut sous les coups acharnés des Titans. Par un phénomène d'écho comparable au précédent, on assiste à un changement profond dans le discours même de Paul, celui prononcé à Athènes et rapporté dans les *Actes des Apôtres* (17, 22-34), où nous l'entendons assurer aux Grecs que ce qu'il leur annonce, ils le révèrent déjà, en d'autres termes que le miracle chrétien prolonge et achève leur tradition, elle-même chrétienne à leur insu. Ces dispositions à l'accueil de la mentalité hellénistique ont probablement facilité le moment décisif d'ouverture qui ne manqua point de se produire. Ici, de nouveau, deux axes sont à distinguer.

Il semblerait que le christianisme demeure la seule religion où la foi soit sous-tendue par un besoin d'intelligibilité, c'est-à-dire la seule qui, en dépit de la part importante de mystère qu'elle doit accepter dans son intangibilité, ait cherché à s'approfondir en répondant aux exigences irréductibles que l'intelligence peut avoir. Or, lorsque les premiers chrétiens lettrés qui souhaitaient dépasser une lecture fruste de la *sacra pagina* ressentirent la nécessité de se doter d'un contenu doctrinal, ils ne purent le faire qu'avec les catégories et le moule de la pensée grecque. Elle seule apparaissait capable de servir à l'expression de la philosophie qui soustend le fonds scripturaire, ne serait-ce que par le discours qu'il véhicule sur Dieu, le monde et l'homme, ainsi que sur leurs relations. D'autre part, l'Église primitive se trouva presque tout de suite confrontée à des hérésies. Dès lors que l'unique appel à la foi ne constitue pas un moyen de lutte infaillible – car comment garantir que ceux qui soutiennent des propositions aventureuses ne sont pas les vrais inspirés? –, il fut indispensable, aux yeux de ceux qui ne s'en tenaient pas à l'argument d'autorité, de recourir à l'organisation conceptuelle et au raisonnement. En résumé, seul le discours rationnel permet de répondre à la fois aux réquisits d'une conviction dont il est de la nature de satisfaire ses propres revendications intellectuelles, et aux attaques de courants déviants, qui rendaient la controverse inéluctable. Pareil matériel dialectique ne pouvait alors être emprunté qu'au λόγος hellénistique. Avec ce recours rendu doublement nécessaire s'ouvrait la marche vers ce que l'on appellera la théologie spéculative, autrement dit, et cette définition est pour nous du plus grand intérêt, la science d'une foi qui organise le don d'une révélation en quelque chose capable de satisfaire aux exigences de la raison: la philosophie médiévale pourrait y être, cette fois-ci, tout entière contenue. Ses prémices ne nous sont pas inconnues.

C'est à partir de Justin, qui se convertit vers 130, que rationaliser sa foi devient une démarche progressivement familière, que l'on y soit ou non favorable. Ceux qui la pratiquent, surtout au début du quatrième siècle, lorsque survient la deuxième des grandes hérésies, celle d'Arius (ca. 256 – ca. 336), usent pour l'essentiel du platonisme, du stoïcisme et du péripatétisme. Mais quand ce n'est pas d'une manière qui dénote une connaissance superficielle et de seconde main de la philosophie, car recueillie dans des manuels de doxographie, c'est par le biais d'une méthode d'exposition et d'argumentation rhétoriques, avec un recours parfois massif à l'allégorisme, au métaphorisme et à l'hermétisme, qui manque la plupart du temps de tout logicisme. Certaines pratiques de logicisation se rencontrent, il est vrai, chez Athanase d'Alexandrie († 373) et dans quelques pages d'Apollinaire de Laodicée († ca. 392), ainsi que dans les fragments d'ouvrages de représentants du néo-arianisme dialectique de ce même siècle, que sont par exemple Eunome de Cyzique et Aèce d'Antioche. Cependant, ces tentatives nous paraissent manquer d'intensité et de systématicité. Quoi qu'il en soit, si intéressant reste-t-il pour l'histoire des idées, le phénomène ne peut bénéficier d'une considération équivalente, dans la mesure où ces écrivains avaient à leur disposition les trésors du corpus philosophique grec.

Il semble donc beaucoup plus significatif de porter l'observation chez des auteurs d'expression latine, même si cela conduit d'abord à un constat identique de carence. Qu'il s'agisse en effet d'Irénée de Lyon (né ca. 125) ou plus tard des trois érudits d'Afrique, Minucius Félix, Arnobe et Lactance, lequel meurt vraisemblablement au cours du premier quart du quatrième siècle, tous font preuve d'un bagage philosophique assez rudimentaire. Ce qui frappe plus particulièrement chez eux, c'est la faiblesse de l'influence d'Aristote et sa quasi-inexistence sur un plan logique. La situation de Marius Victorinus va alors modifier les données de façon assez notable, comme cela ressort dès sa bio-bibliographie, fût-elle lacunaire et parfois incertaine.

Sa vie s'est jusqu'à présent dérobée à l'enquête des historiens, et tout ce que l'on sait sur sa carrière c'est qu'il fut *rhetor urbis Romae* sous l'empereur d'Occident Constance II (337-353); mais ses compétences s'appliquaient à l'ensemble des disciplines du *trivium*, qu'il pratiqua très longtemps. Converti tardivement, à 70 ans à peu près, soit approximativement en 356, il ne rédigea son premier ouvrage chrétien que vers 360, c'est-à-dire cinq années environ avant sa mort. Une traduction paraphrastique de l'*Isagoge* de Porphyre nous a été partiellement conservée sous son nom par Boèce, alors que celles des *Catégories* et du *Peri hermeneias* d'Aristote sont toutes deux perdues, quoique seulement présumées. Perdus également mais attestés un *De syllogismis hypotheticis*, un commentaire sur les *Topiques* de Cicéron, ainsi que les célèbres *Libri platonicorum* dont la lecture bouleversa saint Augustin, lesquels pourraient renvoyer à des écrits de Plotin et de Porphyre traduits en latin. Enfin, le traité *De definitionibus*[21], l'*Ars grammatica* et le commentaire au *De inventione* de Cicéron ont été intégralement préservés. Dans le domaine sacré, trois genres littéraires peuvent être distingués: des écrits de controverse théologique avec l'*Adversus Arium*, et deux opuscules annexes (*Ad Candidum*

[21] Cfr. C. Marius Victorinus, *Liber de definitionibus: eine spätantike Theorie der Definition und des Definierens,* mit Einleitung, Übersetzung und Kommentar, hrsg. von A. Pronay, Frankfurt am Main 1997 (Studien zur klassischen Philologie, 103).

Arrianum et *De homoousio recipiendo*), de la poésie religieuse avec quelques *Hymnes* et de l'exégèse biblique avec trois commentaires sur des épîtres pauliniennes[22]; tous sont en notre possession, bien que dans un état quelquefois incomplet pour les derniers.

Cette présentation fort abrupte suffit pourtant à esquisser le profil de précurseur auquel notre auteur correspondrait à plusieurs titres. Historiquement en effet, Victorinus est sans doute le premier traducteur latin d'un certain nombre de traités aristotéliciens et néoplatoniciens portant sur la philosophie et la dialectique. Sa très longue expérience dans ces domaines en fit un logicien exercé à l'organisation des concepts, aux méthodes d'analyse et à la maîtrise du discours persuasif et de son arsenal lexicographique. Or, c'est avec ce façonnement d'esprit et adossé à ses traductions et monographies qu'il aborda ensuite la controverse religieuse dans son *Adversus Arium* notamment, illustrant, par le fait même et pour la première fois aussi méthodiquement, le second phénomène, appelé théologie spéculative, que nous avons vu naître de la confrontation du λόγος et de la parole évangélique.

Il serait superflu d'examiner dans le détail comment cela se traduisit chez Victorinus. Pierre Hadot s'y est employé à diverses reprises[23]. Ses études donnent à constater que nous assistons bien à l'émergence provoquée d'une procédure logique dans la défense et l'affermissement du dogme catholique. En voici quelques indices.

Les premières lignes du début du livre I de l'*Adversus* qui fixent la méthode victorinienne sont à elles seules révélatrices de l'enjeu et des moyens mis en œuvre. Il s'agit globalement d'établir la consubstantialité en Dieu du Père et du Fils, autrement dit de les manifester comme deux substances non pas semblables (ὁμοιούσιον) mais identiques (ὁμοούσιον), et plus particulièrement ici d'asseoir, contre la position d'Eusèbe de Nicomédie, l'un

[22] Cfr. Marius Victorinus, *In epistolam Pauli ad Ephesios, In epistolam Pauli ad Galatas, In epistolam Pauli ad Philippenses*, ed. critica con introd. trad. ital. note e indici a c. di F. Gori, Torino 1981.

[23] Voir surtout P. Hadot, *Porphyre et Victorinus*, 2 voll., Paris 1968; et Id., *Marius Victorinus. Recherches sur sa vie et ses œuvres*, Paris 1971. Cfr. aussi M. Baltes, *Marius Victorinus. Zur Philosophie in seinen theologischen Schriften*, München-Leipzig 2002.

des points les plus fondamentaux du dogme catholique, à savoir que le Christ a été engendré (*natus*) et non pas créé (*factus*):

> D'abord, que le Fils est né (*nascere*), nous le ferons savoir (*docere*) par l'ensemble de la lecture sacrée, ensuite, la même thèse, c'est-à-dire qu'il est substantiellement Fils, nous la défendrons (*adserere*), comme nous le pourrons (*ut possumus*) (et) avec la permission de l'Esprit[24].

Ce simple plan de travail met en place deux facteurs essentiels. D'une part, la primauté absolue du fidéo-scripturaire, qui sacralise l'enseignement dispensé, de l'autre l'intervention de la preuve rationnellement déduite, qui s'impose deux limites symboliques bien différentes : en premier lieu celle des capacités de l'esprit humain (*ut possumus*), mobilisé par conséquent pour aller jusqu'au bout de lui-même, en second lieu celle que Dieu autorise, laquelle reste de toute façon purement formelle mais justifie que le dernier mot revienne à la prière[25]. Si ce schéma est explicitement appliqué au livre premier, le plus imposant du volume, il court en fait sur sa totalité, stratégiquement réactivé par des rappels, tel celui-ci à propos de l'idée selon laquelle Dieu est l'Esprit qui «et vivit et vivere facit»:

> Ce (point de doctrine) est aussi conforme (*rectum*) (à l'Écriture) que pleinement vrai (*verum*) pour la raison (*ratio*)[26],

ou cet autre à propos de la *consubstantialitas*:

> Qu'il en soit ainsi, nous le ferons savoir (*docere*) d'abord par la lecture (sacrée), ensuite, comme l'ordre (*ordo*) l'exige (et) comme la nécessité (*necessitas*) de ces sujets le réclame, nous (le) rendrons aussi évident (*perspicere*)[27].

[24] C. MARIUS VICTORINUS, *Adversus Arium*, I, 2, 2-3, ed. P. Henry, in ID., *Ad Candidum Arrianum, Adversus Arium, De homoousio recipiendo, Hymni*, ed. P. Henry – P. Hadot 1971, p. 190,41-43. À noter que P. Hadot traduit, non sans pertinence, «docere» et «adserere» de manière plus appuyée, par «établir» et «prouver rationnellement» (p. 191).

[25] Voir les conclusions orantes en *ibid.*, I, 64, ed. Henry, p. 386,28-30; II, 12, p. 430,22-37; IV, 33, p. 602,42-45.

[26] *Ibid.*, IV, 5, p. 512, 23.

[27] *Ibid.*, IV, 8, p. 520,1-2.

Dans le même registre, pour donner à comprendre de quelle façon les énoncés fidéiques ont en quelque sorte besoin de s'épanouir en permanence par l'apport rationnel, Victorinus procède à une comparaison qui rappelle si besoin était qu'il fut et reste un rhéteur. À l'aide d'un langage métaphorique, il fait intervenir une sentence construite sur la bisémie d'un comparatif de supériorité (*posterior*), puis montre par enchaînement l'interpénétration de la foi et de la raison en redisant que la première s'identifie au Christ et la seconde à l'Esprit Saint:

> (Quand la science) seconde (*posterior*) intervient, la foi secondée (*posterior*) commence à œuvrer (*operari*). En effet, après le départ du Christ qui, par des miracles et des préceptes, avait ensemencé (*seminare*) la foi (...), tout a été achevé par l'Esprit, et la foi dans le Christ, mûrie (*adultus*) par la connaissance (*cognitio*), croît de nouveau (*succrescere*), toujours en présence du Christ lui-même[28].

La problématique d'ensemble à présent, est très marquée par l'ontologie trinitaire, à laquelle appartient le thème central de la consubstantialité, et plus particulièrement la question de l'*unum*. Ce dernier, qui à la fois désigne et caractérise Dieu, se scinde, en tant que tel, en « un-monadique » (*unum unum* ou *unum unalitas*), c'est-à-dire l'un avant la venue de l'être, désignant le Père, et en «un-substantiel» (*unum in substantia*), c'est-à-dire l'un ayant surgi dans l'être, désignant le Λόγος, autrement dit le Fils et l'Esprit Saint. Leur rapport à l'*unum* implique alors que le Père et le Fils soient dits *duo unum*, à savoir «deux qui sont un», et le Fils et l'Esprit *in uno duo*, soit «deux qui sont en un»[29]. L'outillage mental mobilisé suit et nourrit cette ligne conceptuelle. Ainsi, la thématique de l'être (*esse*) conduit Victorinus à distinguer entre l'ὂν ou *esse formatum*[30], l'*esse universale* (le Λόγος) et l'*esse supra universale* (le Père)[31], et à jouer sur quatre transpositions pour désigner l'ὀντότης: *existentia* – *existentialitas* – *essentia* – *essentitas*[32]. Ce contexte ontologico-métaphysique souvent centré sur le Λόγος, se prête

[28] *Ibid.*, IV, 18, p. 550,1-6.
[29] Cfr. *ibid.*, I, 49-50, pp. 340-346.
[30] Cfr. *ibid.*, II, 4, p. 406,14.
[31] Cfr. *ibid.*, I, 34, p. 288,23-24.
[32] Cfr. *ibid.*, IV, 5-6, pp. 512-518.

bien à l'exploitation du binôme porphyrien εἶναι ὄν (*esse – existens*)[33], introduit sans doute ici pour la première fois dans la pensée occidentale, et que Boèce a pu adapter en son *De hebdomadibus* par la dyade *esse – id quod est*. Dans le même registre, on recensera les notions d'*identitas* et d'*alteritas*[34], ainsi que l'importante théorie sur le panvitalisme au livre IV[35], déployée autour de la procession, depuis le vivre (le Père), de la vie (le Λόγος) dans le vivant, et préparée par une sorte de cycle d'inspiration néoplatonicienne: *descensio – conversio – ascensio*[36]. Il convient de constater encore, outre la prégnance de la *necessitas* et de la *demonstratio*, ainsi que la recherche du *consequens*[37], l'usage récurrent des catégories aristotéliciennes, dont la *substantia* bien sûr, mais également la *qualitas*, couplée avec la *quantitas*[38], et la *relatio*[39]. À signaler enfin l'intervention de la *definitio* et de la *causalitas*, sans oublier la très ample réflexion sur la *forma*, comme équivalent de μορφή et d'εἶδος, particulièrement au même livre IV.

Ces prélèvements suffiront, du moins l'espérons-nous, à donner une idée de la façon dont Marius Victorinus se présente à l'historien comme le penseur chez lequel la méthode *more dialectico*[40] fait son apparition en contexte théologique. Certes, c'est poussé par son adversaire arien Candidus, vraisemblablement fictif d'ailleurs, qu'il relève le défi d'une élaboration conceptuelle de la foi. Mais il s'y applique de telle manière qu'on le sent persuadé d'accomplir une œuvre parfaitement syncrétique. Se retrouvent ainsi réunies en son recueil les conditions de la transmission d'une cul-

[33] Cfr. *ibid.*, 19, pp. 556-558. Voir P. HADOT, *La distinction de l'être et de l'étant dans le* De hebdomadibus *de Boèce*, in *Die Metaphysik im Mittelalter*, éd. P. Wilpert, Berlin 1963, pp. 147-153; et ID., *Porphyre et Victorinus* cit. (à la note 23), I, pp. 488-493.

[34] Cfr. C. MARIUS VICTORINUS, *ibid.*, I, 54 et IV, 1-3, ed. Henry, pp. 356-358 et 502-508.

[35] Cfr. *ibid.*, IV, 10-13, pp. 530,45 - 536,14.

[36] Cfr. *ibid.*, I, 51, pp. 346-350.

[37] Ce sont ces critères rationnels qui imposent notamment de dire que le Père est dans le Fils et le Fils dans le Père; cfr. *ibid.*, II, 11, pp. 424-428.

[38] Cfr. *ibid.*, I, 21-23, pp. 240-252.

[39] Cfr. *ibid.*, IV, 23, p. 570,35-37.

[40] Sur cette expression due à Jérôme, voir HADOT, *Marius Victorinus* cit. (à la note 23), p. 15, et ID., dans MARIUS VICTORINUS, *Traités théologiques sur la Trinité*, introd. trad. et notes par P. Hadot, Paris 1960 (SC 68-69), pp. 70-72.

ture, du développement d'une authentique tendance spéculative des contenus révélés et de l'illustration d'une conception de la dialectique comme instrument universel de connaissance. C'est à partir de lui que paraît s'amorcer une nouvelle interprétation de la matière scripturaire, pour autant que la conceptualisation à laquelle il procède dépasse et la religion populaire et la foi des Apologistes, mais également ce qui fut tenté auparavant pour que s'harmonisent croire et savoir. À le suivre, il ne s'agit plus seulement d'éclairer la *fides* par la *ratio*, mais de les rendre interdépendantes pour que coïncident la lettre fidéique et le concept philosophique, sans que l'exigence du savoir mette en péril la perspective du salut. Dans cette visée englobante se recueille alors, semble-t-il pour la première fois, l'élan, conscient de l'innovation qu'il introduit, d'une recherche motivée par la foi mais alimentée par la raison.

Au total, si Victorinus peut figurer de la sorte au rang des initiateurs, c'est en un sens parce que s'amorce suffisamment chez lui une nouvelle démarche intellectuelle, promise à un devenir aussi fécond que diversiforme. Elle suppose, comme le résume L. M. de Rijk à propos de la scolastique, le goût pour un système constitué d'argumentation utilisant des notions, des distinctions et des analyses, autrement dit une technique de raisonnements et une méthode de dispute, qui vise à rapprocher les hommes des vérités surnaturelles, à rendre possible leur aperçu systématique et à le défendre contre les objections rationnelles[41]. Par ailleurs, le statut de Victorinus le fait correspondre triplement à la catégorie du médiéval telle que l'orienta le courant renaissant que nous avons privilégié, d'abord parce qu'il n'excède ni la latinité, ni l'Occident, ni la chrétienté, ensuite parce qu'il apparaît comme l'ancêtre des scolastiques, dont il annoncerait et l'idéal et la pratique, enfin, parce qu'il illustre une forme de théocentrisme, bien que le fait de situer la raison à l'origine d'une certaine émancipation de l'homme vis-à-vis du mystère instauré par Dieu, puisse passer pour une valorisation de celui-là.

Nous mesurons parfaitement le caractère périlleux de notre épure où, de concept mal affiné en simplification hâtive, de raccourci abrupt en concordance factice et d'opposition grossière en

[41] Voir DE RIJK, *La philosophie au moyen âge* cit. (*supra*, à la note 5), pp. 21 et 83.

rapprochement réducteur, chaque suggestion peut à tout moment se transformer en faux-pas et s'exposer au démenti. C'est pourquoi une précaution élémentaire consiste à se garder de surinterpréter la portée de l'incidence suggérée. Il n'est nullement question de majorer le rôle intellectuel de Victorinus, en mesurant son influence «à l'aide de citations ou de références explicites ou implicites [que l'on trouve chez les médiévaux] et de la fréquence avec laquelle (s)es ouvrages (...) se présentent dans les anciens catalogues des bibliothèques»[42]. De notre point de vue, cette matérialisation ne rend pas compte du type d'événement auquel nous pensons. Il ne s'agit point de faire de lui le détenteur d'une doctrine normative, d'une clé universelle de lecture pour plus de mille ans de philosophie, ramenée, on s'en souvient, à la théologie raisonnée, mais d'y voir l'éclosion possible de cette dernière par une stratégie inédite. Car la conjecture selon laquelle Victorinus serait en mesure d'assumer le rôle de premier philosophe du Moyen Âge ne tient qu'à la condition d'accepter que la philosophie médiévale soit née fondamentalement de la rencontre du dogme chrétien et de la science grecque du discours, cette rencontre elle-même, nous l'avons dit, étant en quelque sorte inscrite dans la parole divine telle qu'elle fut livrée aux hommes, dont notre penseur a systématisé l'exercice. Il aurait d'une certaine façon incarné ce moment précis où le contenu dogmatique, courant en images et en symboles, passa du statut d'absolu quasi inaccessible à la vérité logique du jugement à celui d'absolu problématisé par un effort rationnel qui l'ouvrit au discours et à une structure conceptuelle réticulée, pouvant tendre à toujours plus d'autonomie dans l'espace qui lui fut concédé. C'est pourquoi on concevra peut-être mieux Victorinus en porteur d'un projet fondateur quand on aura admis, avec Pierre Hadot[43], que le Moyen Âge marque effectivement une rupture, en ce qu'il instrumentalise la philosophie pour en faire un discours de raison mis au service non point du tout de la sagesse, qui disparaît de l'horizon intellectuel médiéval, mais exclusivement de la religion. La démarche qui initialise cette émancipation et ce transfert n'eut pas besoin d'être reconnue par tous ceux qui l'adoptèrent pour s'en

[42] Voir *ibid.*, p. 226, n. 6.

[43] Voir P. Hadot, *Qu'est-ce que la philosophie antique?*, Paris 1995.

trouver légitimée comme telle. De fait, à notre connaissance seul Alcuin, dans son *De fide sanctae et individuae trinitatis*, eut recours à Victorinus comme à une autorité en théologie déductive, et encore s'y montra-t-il davantage compilateur polygraphe que philosophe[44]. En d'autres termes, que le rédacteur de l'*Adversus Arium* ait été fort peu mentionné et utilisé en sa qualité de théologien dialectique au cours d'une tradition dérivant de Boèce[45], qui porta le genre à son paroxysme dans ses *Opuscula sacra*, et se diversifiant chez tous ceux qui firent bon accueil, sans jamais se départir des vérités de foi, aux règles argumentatives de la raison disputante, n'oblitère notre hypothèse de travail que si l'on se trompe d'objectif. Victorinus, nous l'avons vu, pratiqua, de manière intentionnelle et méthodique, l'approfondissement par la *ratio* du substrat scripturaire, à la fois en mobilisant pour eux-mêmes des schèmes théoriques et en adoptant une formulation technique: c'est cette planification, et non point sa capacité à transformer son auteur en modèle unificateur, qui peut passer, aux yeux de l'historiographe, pour un geste inaugural.

[44] Voir P. HADOT, *Marius Victorinus et Alcuin*, in «Archives d'Histoire Doctrinale et Littéraire du Moyen Âge», 21 (1954), pp. 5-19; et J. CAVADINI, *The Sources of Theology of Alcuin's* De fide, in «Traditio», 46 (1991), pp. 123-146.

[45] Victorinus fut loin d'être un inconnu pour Boèce; mais les diverses réactions qu'il afficha à son égard ne concernent que la sphère du *trivium*. Voir L. ADAMO, *Boezio e Mario Vittorino traduttori e interpreti dell'*Isagoge *di Porfirio*, in «Rivista critica di storia della filosofia», 22 (1967), pp. 141-164.

PASQUALE PORRO

FELICITÀ E SALVEZZA: AGOSTINO, IL CRISTIANESIMO E LA TRASFORMAZIONE DELLE PRATICHE FILOSOFICHE

1. *Nulla est homini causa philosophandi, nisi ut beatus sit*[1] – non c'è nessuna ragione, per l'uomo, di praticare la filosofia, se non per essere felice: ciò che nella storiografia contemporanea sembra essere tornato al centro dell'attenzione soprattutto in seguito agli studi e all'approccio di Pierre Hadot[2], era del tutto evidente alla gran parte dei pensatori antichi e tardo-antichi, come testimonia appunto Agostino. La filosofia non è tanto o soltanto un campo disciplinare, una regione epistemica, un *corpus* di dottrine da apprendere o analizzare, ma una *Lebensform*, uno stile di vita, una pratica esistenziale finalizzata al conseguimento della propria felicità. Quando tuttavia Agostino ripete questo luogo, ormai cristallizzatosi perfino in un brocardo di uso scolastico (e utilizzato come tale, ad esempio, da Quintiliano nella sua trattazione dell'epicherema), una rottura epocale si è già consumata; il contesto della citazione agostiniana, quello del libro XIX del *De civitate Dei*, è ormai segnato da una profonda e definitiva sfiducia nei confronti della capacità della filosofia di poter realmente assicurare ciò che essa continuava a promettere: il conseguimento della

[1] AUGUSTINUS HIPPONENSIS, *De civitate Dei*, XIX, 1, PL 41, 624, ed. B. Dombart – A. Kalb, Turnhout 1955 (CCSL, 47-48), II, p. 659,120-125: «Quando quidem nulla est homini causa philosophandi, nisi ut beatus sit; quod autem beatum facit, ipse est finis boni; nulla est igitur causa philosophandi, nisi finis boni: quam ob rem quae nullum boni finem sectatur, nulla philosophiae secta dicenda est».

[2] Cfr. soprattutto, naturalmente, P. HADOT, *Qu'est-ce que la philosophie antique?*, Paris 1995 (tr. it., Torino 1998); ID., *Exercices spirituels et philosophie antique*, nouv. éd., Paris 2002 (tr. it., Torino 2002).

10.1484/M.NUTRIX-EB.1.101236

felicità, appunto. Anche questo, in definitiva, sembra accordarsi con gli schemi storiografici delineati da Hadot, e riproposti in forme diverse da Juliusz Domanski[3] o più recentemente da Christoph Horn[4]: la transizione dalla filosofia come stile di vita alla filosofia come discorso teorico e sistematico sarebbe stata prodotta prevalentemente dal cristianesimo e avrebbe avuto luogo tra la Tarda Antichità e ciò che comunemente denominiamo 'Medioevo'. Volendo sintetizzare in maniera forse un po' semplicistica, se non addirittura brutale, le tesi di Hadot, si potrebbe dire che a un primo periodo in cui anche il cristianesimo si presenta insieme come dottrina e stile di vita, mutuando molti degli «esercizi spirituali» propri della filosofia pagana (ciò che fa sì che il termine greco φιλόσοφος e quello latino *philosophus* possano essere utilizzati per designare chi sceglie la vita monastica, e che perfino nei lessici il verbo *philosophari* venga preso come equivalente di *monachum agere*)[5], abbia fatto seguito una sorta di divorzio – una separazione, cioè, tra i discorsi filosofici e i modi di vita che li ispiravano. Questo iato sarebbe stato determinato essenzialmente, nell'ottica di Hadot, dall'asservimento della filosofia alla teologia, che avrebbe comportato un arretramento della prima a livello di mera propedeutica: in tale ruolo ausiliario e preparatorio, la filosofia sarebbe così venuta ad occupare la stessa posizione che in precedenza le arti liberali avevano tenuto nei suoi confronti. Il compimento di questa traiettoria si sarebbe avuto, nell'Occidente latino, con la fondazione delle Università e la professionalizzazione dell'insegnamento della filosofia[6]: da questo

[3] Cfr. J. DOMANSKI, *La philosophie, théorie ou manière de vivre? Les controverses de l'antiquité à la Renaissance*, avec une préf. de P. Hadot, Fribourg – Paris 1996 (Vestigia, 18).

[4] Cfr. C. HORN, *Antike Lebenskunst. Glück und Moral von Sokrates bis zu den Neuplatonikern*, München 1998 (tr. it. a c. di E. Spinelli, Roma 2004).

[5] Cfr. in proposito studi ormai classici come quelli di J. LECLERCQ, *Pour l'histoire de l'expression «philosophie chrétienne»*, in «Mélanges de science religieuse», 9 (1952), pp. 221-226; ID., *Études sur le vocabulaire monastique du Moyen Âge*, Roma 1961, in partic. pp. 39-67; G. PENCO, *La vita ascetica come 'filosofia' nell'antica tradizione monastica*, in «Studia Monastica», 2 (1960), pp. 79-93; A.-M. MALINGREY, *«Philosophia». Étude d'un groupe de mots dans la littérature grecque des Présocratiques au IVe siècle après J.C.*, Paris 1961; G. MADEC, *«Philosophia christiana» (Augustin,* Contra Iulianum, *IV, 14, 72)*, in *L'art des confins. Mélanges offerts à Maurice de Gandillac*, publ. sous la dir. de A. Cazenave – J.-F. Lyotard, Paris 1985, pp. 585-597 (quindi in ID., *Petites études augustiniennes*, Paris 1994, pp. 163-177).

[6] Cfr. HADOT, *Qu'est-ce que la philosophie antique?* cit., tr. it., p. 248: «(...) Vi è

momento in poi, e fino ai nostri giorni, il compito della filosofia non sarebbe stato più, come nell'Antichità, quello «di formare al mestiere di uomo, ma di formare al mestiere di chierico o di professore, vale a dire di specialista, di teorico, detentore di un certo sapere, più o meno esoterico»[7]. In ogni caso, questo sapere non avrebbe più messo «in gioco l'intera vita», come sarebbe invece accaduto nella filosofia antica.

L'avvento del (o di *un*) 'paradigma' cristiano – per attenerci al titolo di questo volume – non avrebbe così segnato tanto una sostituzione di contenuti o di modelli epistemologici all'interno di un orizzonte destinato a permanere sostanzialmente identico, ma una vera e propria *metabasis eis allo genos*: dalla filosofia come *pratica* alla filosofia come *teoria*. Ora, questo modello merita forse di essere approfondito e qualificato, se non in rapporto alla filosofia antica (per quanto anche a questo proposito ci sarebbe senz'altro qualcosa da osservare), almeno in rapporto a ciò che più ci interessa – il Medioevo.

Una prima cautela molto generale potrebbe in realtà essere avanzata a livello puramente metodologico: così come sembrano essere intese e utilizzate da Hadot, le denominazioni Antichità e Medioevo definiscono periodi ben precisi, con dei tratti distintivi intrinseci facilmente identificabili e discernibili (e una riprova di ciò è data dal fatto che anche Hadot assimila *tout court* in modo spontaneo e automatico la filosofia medievale a quella latina e cristiana, facendola culminare nella Scolastica). Come ho avuto modo di osservare anche in altre occasioni, non credo che il Medioevo possa essere caratterizzato come un'epoca dai confini ben definiti (in base a criteri intrinseci di contenuto) di cui sia possibile provare a individuare l'essenza o lo spirito, in contrasto ad esempio con quello della filosofia antica. In realtà, se, come sostiene de Rijk[8] (e secondo la mia opinione assai giustamente), il Medioevo non è null'altro se non il risultato di una divisione convenzionale del lavoro tra gli storici (e dunque il risultato di

stata dal Medioevo in poi una sorta di causalità reciproca tra la struttura delle istituzioni universitarie e le rappresentazioni che esse hanno elaborato circa la natura della filosofia».

[7] *Ibid.*, p. 249.

[8] Cfr. L. M. de Rijk, *La philosophie au moyen âge*, Leiden 1985, in partic. pp. 1-81.

un'operazione di periodizzazione puramente estrinseca), non ha senso cercare di estrapolarne una caratteristica di fondo, ipostatizzarla, e farne un tratto definitorio da utilizzare in contrasto con altri periodi, definiti in modi diversi ma ipostatizzati in egual maniera. Un primo limite dell'operazione di Hadot è insomma che egli sembra credere nella possibilità di periodizzazioni intrinseche, ovvero che sia possibile considerare la storia come un insieme di oggetti presuntamente naturali di cui lo storico sia chiamato semplicemente a dar conto. Proprio perché un merito indiscusso di Pierre Hadot è stato quello di aver riportato l'attenzione sulla filosofia come pratica, egli avrebbe forse potuto spingersi più oltre fino ad accettare l'idea, sviluppata da Michel Foucault e soprattutto da Paul Veyne, secondo cui la storia intera è sempre il risultato di pratiche, e tutto ciò che a prima vista ci appare come un oggetto – ad esempio, la filosofia medievale – non è in realtà che un'oggettivazione, cioè un prodotto mutevole di pratiche esse stesse mutevoli, circoscritte, «datate» (per usare l'espressione di Veyne)[9], che spesso si sovrappongono ed entrano in competizione o in conflitto tra loro. Compito dello storico, da questo punto di vista, non sembra tanto essere quello di individuare i possibili tratti unificanti, i grandi quadri d'insieme, ma piuttosto quello di censire le differenze, gli slittamenti, gli scarti, le discontinuità, le reduplicazioni – creare un archivio o un inventario delle differenze, per riprendere un'altra formula cara allo stesso Paul Veyne.

La questione della fine della filosofia come *Lebensform* potrebbe pertanto essere così riformulata, e cioè *non:* come e quando è accaduto che la filosofia da pratica esistenziale si sia trasformata in altro (ad esempio in un discorso teorico)? *ma:* come è accaduto il passaggio, in periodi che estrinsecamente e convenzionalmente definiamo come Tarda Antichità e Medioevo, da una serie di pratiche dominanti ad un'altra serie di pratiche dominanti? Si potrebbe in altri termini provare a ipotizzare *non* che *una pratica* abbia ceduto il posto a qualcos'altro – a qualcosa come *un oggetto* – *ma* piuttosto che *una determinata pratica*, in sé non esaustiva e non

[9] Cfr. P. VEYNE, *Foucault révolutionne l'histoire*, Paris 1978 (quindi in appendice all'edizione del 1996 di ID., *Comment on écrit l'histoire*, Paris 1996 [ed. orig. 1971], pp. 383-429); tr. it. in ID., *Michel Foucault. La storia, il nichilismo e la morale*, a c. di M. Guareschi, Verona 1998, pp. 7-65.

isolata, abbia ceduto il posto ad *altre pratiche competitive*, alcune delle quali si sono imposte come dominanti.

Ciò che vorrei cominciare a considerare, in questa sede, è proprio come, nel periodo che ci interessa, la filosofia vada incontro a una trasformazione che la riguarda esattamente in quanto pratica, e non primariamente nel suo aspetto dottrinale ed epistemico (che anche ciò accada, è in qualche modo inevitabile: ma tutto sta nel determinare in modo possibilmente più preciso la direzione causale tra i due fenomeni). Questa trasformazione implica in sostanza che la pratica precedentemente dominante si riveli a un certo punto improponibile, o poco remunerativa, perché inefficace nel raggiungere il fine in vista del quale si era costituita e consolidata – fine che potremmo per brevità e comodità riportare esattamente all'ideale della felicità del sapiente da cui siamo partiti. Perché in definitiva di questo si tratta: di come la filosofia abbia cessato di essere uno strumento di felicità e di salvezza intramondana – riservandoci alla fine di chiederci se questo evento sia poi così negativo e funesto come Hadot lo descrive.

Ed è proprio Agostino ad offrire una prospettiva privilegiata per seguire questa trasformazione. Naturalmente, se si accetta il modello di una storiografia che fa a meno, in linea di principio, di ogni forma di periodizzazione intrinseca, si deve rinunciare anche alla possibilità di identificare eventi-catastrofe che segnino i punti di rottura, così come alla possibilità di indicare in modo inequivocabile singoli, determinati autori che portino realmente a termine una transizione. Non intendo pertanto sostenere che Agostino sia il solo o principale artefice di questa trasformazione, ma che la sua peculiare biografia intellettuale permetta quanto meno di mostrare, come una cartina di tornasole, la coesistenza, il sovrapporsi e infine il conflitto tra pratiche diverse, ovvero tra modi differenti di intendere e praticare la filosofia[10].

[10] Sull'evoluzione del concetto stesso di *philosophia* nella produzione agostiniana si può ora disporre di studi ricchi e documentati. Cfr. in primo luogo (per quanto limitata cronologicamente fino al *De vera religione*) la ricognizione sistematica di G. CATAPANO, *Il concetto di filosofia nei primi scritti di Agostino. Analisi dei passi metafilosofici dal* Contra Academicos *al* De vera religione, Roma 2001, a cui si possono aggiungere naturalmente i numerosi sondaggi di G. MADEC: cfr. soprattutto *Saint Augustin et la philosophie. Notes critiques*, Paris 1996 (Collection des

2. Com'è ben noto, il giovane Agostino, nel ritiro di Cassiciaco, insegue un ideale di vita filosofica che risponde in larga misura ai criteri individuati da Hadot. Nel *Contra Academicos*, Agostino ricorda di aver confidato con passione all'amico Romaniano le sue aspettative relative all'*otium philosophandi*; nessuna prospettiva gli sembrava più prospera, nessun'altra vita, o nessun altro stile di vita, più felice:

> Nam cum praesens praesenti tibi exposuissem interiores motus animi mei vehementerque ac saepius assererem nullam mihi videri prosperam fortunam, nisi quae *otium philosophandi* daret, *nullam beatam vitam, nisi qua in philosophia viveretur*, sed me tanto meorum onere, quorum ex officio meo vita penderet, multisque necessitatibus vel pudoris vel ineptae meorum miseriae refrenari, tam magno es elatus gaudio, tam sancto huius vitae inflammatus ardore, ut te diceres, si tu ab illarum importunarum litium vinculis aliquo modo eximereris, omnia mea vincula etiam patrimonii tui mecum participatione rupturum[11].

Preoccupato dagli impegni e dalle incombenze familiari, Agostino viene liberato da questi affanni grazie all'intervento dello stesso Romaniano, che gli procura le condizioni materiali dell'*otium* e della vita filosofica. Non sorprende pertanto che quando il giovane Agostino affronta direttamente il tema della felicità (nel *De beata vita*, più o meno contemporaneamente al *Contra Academicos*, e cioè verso la fine del 386), non abbia esitazioni nel farla dipendere dalla vita filosofica; solo il porto della filosofia, secondo una metafora ricorrente nei primi scritti, permette di sbarcare sulla terra della felicità, a patto naturalmente di saper evitare le insidie

Études Augustiniennes. Série Antiquité, 149); *Le christianisme comme accomplissement du platonisme*, in Id., *Chez Augustin*, préface de J.-C. Fredouille, Paris 1996 (Collection des Études Augustiniennes. Série Antiquité, 160), pp. 41-69 [una versione appena differente di quest'ultimo saggio (per altro precedentemente pubblicato in ceco: *Aurelius Augustinus, Krestanství jako naplnení platonismu*, in *Krestanství a filosofie*, ed. F. Karfik – V. Nemec – F. Vilím, Praha 1994, pp. 9-26) è stata poi pubblicata con il titolo *Le christianisme comme accomplissement du platonisme selon saint Augustin*, in «Documenti e studi sulla tradizione filosofica medievale», 10 (1999), pp. 109-129]; *Philosophia: secundum Ambrosium – secundum Augustinum*, in «Medioevo», 7 (2003), pp. 7-16.

[11] Augustinus Hipponensis, *Contra Academicos*, II, 2, 4, PL 32, 921, ed. W. M. Green, Turnhout 1970 (CCSL, 29), p. 20,34-44. I corsivi, in questa e in tutte le successive citazioni in latino, nel testo e nelle note, sono miei.

del monte dell'orgoglio e della *iactantia*[12], che alcuni scambiano per la regione stessa della beatitudine. Se qualche riserva viene espressa nei confronti dell'esercizio filosofico, essa riguarda principalmente la sua estensione o la sua incidenza numerica, il fatto cioè che lo stile di vita filosofico sembra poter essere abbracciato solo da un numero esiguo di persone, che sarebbe per altro ancora inferiore se questa scelta dipendesse solo dalla ragione e dalla volontà, e non anche da qualche 'tempesta' o evento fortuito, come appunto nel caso dello stesso Agostino:

> Si ad philosophiae portum, e quo iam in beatae vitae regionem solumque proceditur (...), ratione institutus cursus et uoluntas ipsa perduceret, nescio, utrum temere dixerim multo minoris numeri homines ad eum perventuros fuisse, quamvis nunc quoque, ut videmus, rari admodum paucique perveniant[13].

Non è possibile seguire qui l'intero andamento del dialogo, per altro ben noto[14]; sarà forse sufficiente ricordarne le conclusioni:

[12] Al monte dell'orgoglio Agostino farà riferimento ancora in altre occasioni dopo il *De beata vita*, anche ad esempio in uno dei discorsi nuovi ritrovati da Dolbeau e databile intorno al 404 (e quindi ben successivi alla 'svolta' sulla grazia a cui faremo riferimento in seguito; ma sulla persistenza in Agostino di un'attitudine fortemente critica nei confronti dell'elitarismo filosofico cfr. *infra*, nota 38): cfr. *Sermones Novi* (Dolbeau), 26, 59 (utilizzo in questo caso l'edizione contenuta nella Nuova Biblioteca Agostiniana, XXXV/2, che riproduce il testo dell'ed. Dolbeau: SANT'AGOSTINO, *Discorsi nuovi. Supplemento II: Dolbeau 21-31; Étaix 4-5*, testo, note e appendici di F. Dolbeau, tr. it. di V. Tarulli; indici di F. Dolbeau, F. Monteverde, Roma 2002, p. 722): «Vos autem, fratres mei, qui forte non videtis acie mentis quod illi viderunt, et nondum estis idonei transcendere cogitatione animi universam creaturam, non solum corporalem, sed etiam spiritalem, et videre incommutabilem Deum a quo et per quem et in quo facta sunt omnia, ne trepidetis, ne desperetis, quia ille qui usque ad infimos et infirmos descendere voluit ipsum vobis fecit viam. Quid enim prodest illis quod de longinquo patriam vident superbientes? Non inveniunt viam, quoniam ad illam altitudinem patriae ab humilitate incipit via. Illi quasi de monte superbiae vident patriam, de monte contrario vident eam. Sed nemo ad eam ascendit, nisi prius descenderit. Descendere illi nolunt, ut possint ascendere, id est humiles esse nolunt, ut possint esse christiani. Cum sibi dicunt: 'Et hoc futurus sum quod est ostiaria mea, ac non potius quod fuit Plato, quod Pythagoras?', ore temerato sufflantes inania, nolunt descendere, non possunt ascendere. Dominus enim noster descendit ad nos de altitudine maiestatis suae, et nolunt ad eum isti descendere de tumore superbiae suae».

[13] AUGUSTINUS HIPPONENSIS, *De beata vita*, 1, 1, PL 32, 959, ed. W. M. Green, Turnhout 1970 (CCSL, 29), p. 65,1-6.

[14] Si può rinviare in proposito alla minuziosa analisi di L. F. PIZZOLATO, *Il* De

essere felici significa non soggiacere a privazione, perché i beni di cui possiamo essere privati non possono renderci veramente felici, non foss'altro per il timore di perderli. Ma non avere bisogno di nulla significa essere sapienti:

> Ergo beatum esse nihil est aliud quam non egere, hoc est esse sapientem. Si autem quaeritis, quid sit sapientia, iam et ipsam ratio, quantum in praesentia potuit, evolvit atque eruit; nihil est enim aliud quam modus animi, hoc est quo sese animus librat, ut neque excurrat in nimium neque infra quam plenum est coartetur[15].

È infatti la sapienza ciò che non ci può mai essere sottratto, e se si prova a determinare con maggiore precisione in cosa consista la sapienza, si dovrà convenire che essa non è altro che il perfetto *modus animi*, la perfetta misura che permette all'animo di evitare ogni squilibrio per eccesso o per difetto, ovvero di dilatarsi nella lussuria, nella volontà di dominio, nella superbia, o di restringersi nella cupidigia, nell'avarizia, nel timore, nella tristezza. Anche in questo caso, siamo di fronte all'immagine del filosofo antico come colui che sa dominare le passioni, e sa conservare, in qualunque circostanza esteriore, un perfetto controllo di sé. Essere felici, ovvero essere sapienti, significa possedere la misura di sé: «Habet ergo modum suum, id est sapientiam, quisquis beatus est»[16].

Questo modello si ritrova, come detto, in tutti gli scritti giovanili: per non citare che un solo altro esempio, sarà sufficiente rinviare al passo del *De libero arbitrio* (388-394/395) in cui l'equazione tra sapienza e felicità è ribadita in modo inequivocabile: tutti vogliamo essere felici, e dunque tutti vogliamo essere sapienti, perché nessuno può essere felice senza sapienza («quia nemo sine sapientia beatus est»)[17]. Tuttavia, man mano che la conversione al cristianesimo in senso stretto comincia a distinguersi e a differenziarsi dalla conversione alla filosofia e al neoplatonismo, ad

beata vita *o la possibile felicità nel tempo*, in *L'opera letteraria di Agostino tra Cassiciacum e Milano. Agostino nelle terre di Ambrogio* (1-4 ottobre 1986), Palermo 1987, pp. 31-112.

[15] AUGUSTINUS HIPPONENSIS, *ibid.*, 4, 33, 975, p. 83,232-237.

[16] *Ibid.*, p. 84,247-248.

[17] Cfr. ID., *De libero arbitrio*, II, 9, 26, PL 32, 1254, ed. W. M. Green, Turnhout 1970 (CCSL, 29), p. 254,47-49: «Ut ergo constat nos beatos esse velle, ita nos constat esse velle sapientes, quia nemo sine sapientia beatus est».

essere radicalizzato è proprio il tema dell'efficacia. Ciò che anzi colpisce maggiormente è proprio il fatto che la contrapposizione tra filosofia e vita cristiana non viene per ora impostata né in termini di contenuto, né in termini di finalità, ma appunto in termini di incidenza o pervasività: la liberazione e la felicità promesse dalla filosofia riguardano pochissimi uomini; l'*auctoritas* e la fede hanno invece il potere di liberare popolazioni intere. Questo è il senso del celeberrimo passaggio del *De ordine* (ancora nel 386) in cui Agostino mette in parallelo la *ratio* e l'*auctoritas*:

> Duplex enim est via, quam sequimur, cum rerum nos obscuritas movet, aut rationem aut certe auctoritatem. *Philosophia rationem promittit et vix paucissimos liberat,* quos tamen non modo non contemnere illa mysteria sed sola intellegere, ut intellegenda sunt, cogit, nullumque aliud habet negotium, quae vera et, ut ita dicam, germana philosophia est, quam ut doceat, quod sit omnium rerum principium sine principio quantusque in eo maneat intellectus quidve inde in nostram salutem sine ulla degeneratione manaverit, quem unum Deum omnipotentem, eumque tripotentem patrem et filium et spiritum sanctum, docent veneranda mysteria, *quae fide sincera et inconcussa populos liberant,* nec confuse, ut quidam, nec contumeliose, ut multi, praedicant[18].

Ugualmente, in un altro passaggio altrettanto celebre del *De vera religione* (390-391), si afferma che Dio ha già persuaso tutti i popoli della necessità di disprezzare questo mondo sensibile e di purificare i propri animi con le virtù:

> Qui ergo sensibilem istum mundum contemnere et animam virtute purgandam summo Deo subicere atque subiungere vanum aut malum putant, alia ratione refellendi sunt, si tamen cum his dignum est disputare. Qui autem bonum et appetendum fatentur, cognoscant Deum et cedant Deo, *per quem populis iam omnibus haec credenda persuasa sunt.* Quod utique ab ipsis fieret, si tantum valerent, aut si non fieret, crimen invidentiae vitare non possent. Ergo cedant ei, a quo factum est, nec curiositate aut inani iactantia impediantur, quominus agnoscant, *quid intersit inter paucorum timidas coniecturas et manifestam salutem correctionemque populorum.* Illi enim si revivisce-

[18] Id., *De ordine*, II, 5, 16, PL 32, 1002, ed. W. M. Green, Turnhout 1970 (CCSL, 29), pp. 115,42 - 116,54.

> rent, quorum isti nominibus gloriantur, et invenirent refertas ecclesias, templa deserta, a cupiditate bonorum temporalium atque affluentium ad spem vitae aeternae et bona spiritalia et intellegibilia vocari et currere humanum genus, dicerent fortasse, si tales essent, quales fuisse memorantur: *haec sunt, quae nos persuadere populis non ausi sumus*, et eorum potius consuetudini cessimus quam illos in nostram fidem voluntatemque traduximus[19].

È appena il caso di notare come oggetto della persuasione operata da Dio sia qui ancora l'ideale della vita filosofica descritto da Hadot, i cui principali obiettivi consistono appunto nel distacco dal mondo sensibile e nella purificazione dell'animo attraverso opportuni esercizi spirituali[20]. Se gli antichi filosofi tornassero in vita, come afferma esplicitamente Agostino, non potrebbero non riconoscere che ciò che il cristianesimo realizza non è affatto diverso da ciò che essi propugnavano, ma non avevano avuto il coraggio di diffondere («haec sunt, quae nos persuadere populis non ausi sumus»). La differenza, di nuovo, non sta dunque né nei contenuti (perché poco oltre si precisa in modo inequivocabile che tali filosofi, modificando *poche* espressioni e *poche* dottrine, sarebbero divenuti cristiani: «paucis mutatis verbis atque sententiis Christiani fierent»)[21], né nelle finalità, ma nello scarto che si dà, per riprendere l'espressione dello stesso Agostino, tra le «timide congetture di pochi» e la «salvezza e la correzione manifesta dei popoli». L'*auctoritas* cristiana procura insomma più facilmente ciò che i filosofi si proponevano, ma non erano riusciti a realizzare. Se

[19] ID., *De vera religione*, 4, 6, PL 34, 126, ed. K.-D. Daur, Turnhout 1962 (CCSL, 32), p. 192,1-19.

[20] A ciò si ricollega il tema della coincidenza tra *religio* e *vera philosophia*, esplicitamente affermata, com'è ben noto, nello stesso *De vera religione*. Per un ampio sguardo prospettico sulle vicende di questa identificazione in tutto l'Alto Medioevo latino cfr. ora la ricostruzione di G. D'ONOFRIO, *Quando la metafisica non c'era.* Vera philosophia *nell'Occidente latino 'pre-aristotelico'*, in *Metaphysica – sapientia – scientia divina. Soggetto e statuto della filosofia prima nel Medioevo*, Atti del Convegno della Società Italiana per lo Studio del Pensiero Medievale, Bari 9-12 giugno 2004, a c. di P. Porro, Turnhout – Bari 2006 [= «Quaestio» 5 (2005)], pp. 103-144. Cfr. inoltre *infra*, nel presente volume, il contributo di G. Fioravanti.

[21] Cfr. AUGUSTINUS HIPPONENSIS, *ibid.*, 4, 7, 126, p. 192,20-24: «Ita si hanc vitam illi viri nobiscum rursus agere potuissent, *viderent profecto, cuius auctoritate facilius consuleretur hominibus, et paucis mutatis verbis atque sententiis Christiani fierent*, sicut plerique recentiorum nostrorumque temporum Platonici fecerunt».

Agostino si fosse fermato a questo livello, si sarebbe in definitiva potuto dare una parvenza di verità alla nota affermazione nietzscheana – ripresa non a caso proprio da Hadot – secondo cui il cristianesimo non sarebbe altro che una forma di platonismo per il popolo[22].

Potremmo così riassumere l'essenziale di questa prima fase in due punti fermi principali:

a. Agostino non considera la vita filosofica e la vita cristiana come pratiche irriducibilmente incompatibili o conflittuali, fatti salvi naturalmente i necessari aggiustamenti: la differenza, come detto, è più *quantitativa* che *qualitativa*;

b. Agostino ritiene che la felicità, la *beatitudo* in senso tecnico, sia un ideale ancora concretamente perseguibile in questa vita: ci si può purificare in questa vita, sia pure con l'aiuto divino; si può già essere felici possedendo la sapienza e Dio, come la conclusione del *De beata vita* mostra inequivocabilmente; si può essere liberati, soprattutto dal *pondus* delle passioni e delle immagini sensibili, già in questa vita, come i passi del *De ordine* e del *De vera religione* attestano chiaramente.

3. In modo piuttosto repentino, intorno alla metà degli anni novanta del secolo IV, questo scenario muta radicalmente. La felicità viene sempre più esclusa dall'orizzonte terreno, e risospinta verso quello celeste; non è una più una *res*, ma una *spes*, per adoperare le stesse espressioni utilizzate da Agostino nel *De doctrina christiana* (la cui composizione è, com'è noto, particolarmente tormentata, estendendosi dal 397, se non prima [395?], al 426/427)[23]. Ma chi spera di essere felice, evidentemente *non è* ancora felice («sed qui spe beatus est nondum beatus est»)[24]. Prima di tornare ad occuparci di ciò che accade intorno al 396-397, e

[22] Cfr. HADOT, *Qu'est-ce que la philosophie antique?* cit., tr. it., p. 240.

[23] Cfr. AUGUSTINUS HIPPONENSIS, *De doctrina christiana*, I, 22, 20, PL 34, 26, ed. J. Martin, Turnhout 1962 (CCSL, 32), p. 17,13-16: «Quod enim propter se diligendum est, *in eo constituitur beata vita, cuius etiam si nondum res, tamen spes eius nos hoc tempore consolatur*».

[24] ID., *De Trinitate*, XIII, 7, 10, PL 42, 1021, ed. W. J. Mountain – F. Glorie, Turnhout 1968 (CCSL, 50A), p. 395,32. E di seguito (p. 395,32-36): «Exspectat namque per patientiam beatitudinem quam nondum tenet. Qui vero sine ulla spe tali, sine ulla tali mercede cruciatur quantamlibet adhibeat tolerantiam, non est beatus veraciter sed miser fortiter».

cioè di esaminare le radici o le ragioni di questo mutamento, cerchiamo di comprenderne il senso. In questo orizzonte, cioè nella nostra condizione mortale, la vita beata è irrealizzabile, perché la felicità richiede che si possa vivere come si desidera e si possa avere ciò che si vuole: ciò che appunto ora non si dà mai («quod nunc esse nullo modo potest», scrive esplicitamente Agostino nel libro XIII del *De Trinitate*), nella misura in cui l'uomo o si trova a desiderare ciò che gli manca, o si trova ad esser privo di ciò che desidera. L'ideale filosofico diventa a questo punto, nella sua interezza, pura presunzione: «Nunc vero fecerunt quidem sibi philosophi sicut eorum cuique placuit vitas beatas suas ut quasi propria virtute possent quod communi mortalium conditione non poterant, sic scilicet vivere ut vellent»[25] – di fatto i filosofi, ciascuno a suo modo, si sono costruiti la loro propria vita beata, come se potessero, *con la loro propria virtù*, ottenere quel che è impossibile nella comune condizione di mortali: vivere come si vuole. Lo scarto non potrebbe essere più evidente: il limite della filosofia non è più quello di proporre una via accessibile solo a pochi, in modo poco efficace e elitario, ma è quello ben più radicale di proporre un ideale impossibile, e perciò illusorio e ingannevole: che sia cioè possibile raggiungere la felicità in questa vita attraverso l'esercizio della virtù. Non si può più dire che la filosofia coincida con la vera *religio*, liberando tuttavia solo pochi uomini: la verità è che la filosofia non libera più nessuno, e dunque è sterile e improduttiva *non in quanto dottrina*, ma proprio *in quanto pratica*.

Si può facilmente percepire la portata di questo cambiamento mettendo a confronto i diversi modi in cui, in fasi diverse della propria produzione, Agostino utilizza e commenta gli stessi versi tratti dall'*Andria* di Terenzio (II, 1, 5-6, 305 seqq.): «quoniam non potest id fieri quod vis / id velis quod possis» («poiché non può realizzarsi ciò che vuoi, desidera ciò che puoi», ovvero: «se non puoi fare ciò che vuoi, cerca di volere ciò che puoi»). Questi versi, inutile sottolinearlo, racchiudono ancora l'essenziale di ciò che Hadot ritiene l'atteggiamento del filosofo antico. Quando Agostino cita per la prima volta i due versi nel *De beata vita*, sembra tutto sommato approvarli: come potrà essere infelice, commenta infatti Agostino, un uomo cui nulla accade contro il suo volere, se

[25] *Ibid.*, p. 394,15-18.

è vero che non può volere una cosa che sa non potergli accadere? Ciò che un tale uomo (il saggio, il sapiente) desidera è il bene più certo e sicuro: agire solo secondo virtù e secondo la divina legge della sapienza, un bene che in quanto tale non può essergli tolto. Come ad esempio nell'etica stoica, anche in condizioni estreme il sapiente basta a se stesso; può essere felice perché la sua felicità non dipende da altro, se non dall'esercizio stesso della sua vita e delle virtù:

> Etenim et illa eiusdem comici sententia non minus vera est: «quoniam non potest id fieri, quod vis, / id velis, quod possis». Quomodo erit miser, cui nihil accidit praeter voluntatem, quia, quod sibi videt non posse provenire, non potest velle? Habet enim rerum certissimarum voluntatem, id est ut quicquid agit non agat nisi ex virtutis quodam praescipto et divina lege sapientiae, quae nullo ab eo pacto eripi possunt[26].

Ma nel *De Trinitate* il giudizio è molto meno benevolo, e assai più sarcastico: questa è tutta la felicità, osserva ora Agostino – non si sa se ridicola, o piuttosto degna di compassione –, di alcuni orgogliosi mortali, che si vantano di vivere *come vogliono*, perché sopportano *volontariamente*, con pazienza, quei mali e quelle sventure che tuttavia *non vorrebbero* dover affrontare. I versi di Terenzio sono certo belli, chi potrebbe negarlo? («commode hoc dictum esse quis negat?»). Ma è un consiglio dato ad un infelice, perché non fosse maggiormente infelice. A chi è infatti veramente felice non si può dire: peccato, non può realizzarsi ciò che vuoi. Al contrario, se qualcuno è veramente felice, è tale soltanto perché può realizzare ciò che vuole; ma questa condizione, conclude Agostino, non è propria di questa vita mortale, e si realizzerà solo nell'immortalità:

> Haec est tota, utrum ridenda an potius miseranda, superborum beatitudo mortalium gloriantium se vivere ut uolunt quia volentes patienter ferunt quae accidere sibi nolunt. Hoc est enim aiunt quod sapienter dixit Terentius: «quoniam non potest id fieri quod vis, / id velis quod possis». Commode hoc dictum esse quis negat? Sed consilium est datum misero ne esset miserior. Beato autem quales se esse omnes volunt non recte nec vere dicitur, «non potest fieri quod vis». Si

[26] Id., *De beata vita*, 4, 25, 971-972, ed. Green cit. (alla nota 13), p. 79,53-60.

> enim beatus est, quidquid vult fieri potest quia non vult quod fieri non potest. Sed non est mortalitatis huius haec vita, nec erit nisi quando et immortalitas erit[27].

Nel *De civitate Dei*, il rovesciamento viene portato ancora più oltre: solo chi è felice vive come vuole, ma nessuno, neppure il giusto, può vivere come vuole se non avrà raggiunto quella condizione che non conosce più la morte, l'errore, la sofferenza. Questo è quanto esige la natura, che sarà perfettamente felice solo quando avrà ottenuto quanto richiede. Consideriamo allora quanto proposto da Terenzio, prendiamo cioè il caso di un uomo che non vive di fatto come vuole, e che si è imposto con grande disciplina di non volere ciò che non può, ma solo ciò che può: potrà egli essere ritenuto davvero felice, solo perché accetta con pazienza la sua infelicità?

> Quamquam si diligentius adtendamus, nisi beatus non vivit ut vult, et nullus beatus nisi iustus. Sed etiam ipse iustus non vivet ut vult, nisi eo pervenerit, ubi mori falli offendi omnino non possit eique sit certum ita semper futurum. Hoc enim natura expetit, nec plene atque perfecte beata erit nisi adepta quod expetit. (...) Verum ecce vivat ut vult, quoniam sibi extorsit sibique imperavit non velle quod non potest, atque hoc velle quod potest (sicut ait Terentius: «quoniam non potest id fieri quod vis, / id velis quod possis»): num ideo beatus est, quia patienter miser est? Beata quippe vita si non amatur, non habetur. Porro si amatur et habetur, ceteris omnibus rebus excellentius necesse est ametur, quoniam propter hanc amandum est quidquid aliud amatur. Porro si tantum amatur, quantum amari digna est (non enim beatus est, a quo ipsa beata vita non amatur ut digna est): fieri non potest, ut eam, qui sic amat, non aeternam velit. Tunc igitur beata erit, quando aeterna erit[28].

Ecco in che cosa si è trasformato l'ideale della vita filosofica: non nel conseguimento della felicità, ma nell'accettazione paziente della propria ineluttabile infelicità. Tutte le sette filosofiche, ovunque collochino nello specifico la felicità, sono accomunate dallo

[27] Id., *De Trinitate*, *ibid.*, 1022, pp. 395,54 - 396,65.

[28] Id., *De civitate Dei*, XIV, 25, 433, ed. Dombart – Kalb cit. (alla nota 1), I, pp. 448,1 - 449,25.

stesso errore; quanti hanno creduto che il fine del bene e del male sia in questa vita – ponendo il sommo bene nel corpo o nell'anima o in entrambi, nel piacere o nella virtù o in entrambi, nel riposo o nella virtù o in entrambi, e così via – ebbene, tutti costoro hanno voluto essere felici in *questa* vita e procurarsi *da soli* la felicità con incredibile vanità:

> Illi autem, qui in ista vita fines bonorum et malorum esse putaverunt, sive in corpore sive in animo sive in utroque ponentes summum bonum, atque, ut id explicatius eloquar, sive in voluptate sive in virtute sive in utraque, sive in quiete sive in virtute sive in utraque, sive in voluptate simul et in quiete sive in virtute sive in utrisque, sive in primis naturae sive in virtute sive in utrisque, *hic beati esse et a se ipsis beatificari mira vanitate voluerunt*[29].

Ancora, dopo aver offerto un impressionante catalogo fenomenologico dei mali di questo mondo, Agostino ribadisce che la nostra felicità, come la nostra salvezza, sono solo *in spe*, non *in re*: e d'altra parte come potrebbe essere *felice* la vita che non è ancora *salva*? E invece i filosofi non vogliono credere a questa felicità, perché non la vedono, e si sforzano di fabbricarsene una assolutamente falsa, sulla base di una virtù che appare tanto più orgogliosa, quanto più è illusoria e mendace:

> *Quo modo enim beata est* [*scil.* vita humana], *quae nondum salva est?* (...) Sicut ergo spe salvi, ita spe beati facti sumus, et sicut salutem, ita beatitudinem non iam tenemus praesentem, sed expectamus futuram, et hoc «per patientiam» (cfr. *Rm* 8, 25); quia in malis sumus, quae patienter tolerare debemus, donec ad illa veniamus bona, ubi omnia ‹erunt›, quibus ineffabiliter delectemur, nihil erit autem, quod iam tolerare debeamus. *Talis salus, quae in futuro erit saeculo, ipsa erit etiam finalis beatitudo. Quam beatitudinem isti philosophi, quoniam non videntes nolunt credere, hic sibi conantur falsissimam fabricare, quanto superbiore, tanto mendaciore virtute*[30].

Anche qui, lo iato rispetto alla concezione precedente non potrebbe essere più marcato: la vita virtuosa autosufficiente del sapiente è inutile e falsa; non è più la virtù (o almeno: non è più l'e-

[29] *Ibid.*, XIX, 4, 627, II, p. 664,11-18.
[30] *Ibid.*, pp. 668,186 - 669,202.

sercizio puramente umano della virtù) ad assicurare la felicità: non c'è felicità senza salvezza, e la salvezza di cui si parla non è più quella puramente intramondana propria dell'etica filosofica pagana.

4. Cosa è dunque accaduto in questa traiettoria dal *De beata vita* al *De civitate*? Agostino ci offre un indizio al riguardo nelle *Retractationes*: a proposito del *De beata vita*, si rammarica esplicitamente di aver affermato che la felicità risieda soltanto nell'animo del sapiente, e il motivo che egli stesso adduce è quello di non aver sufficientemente considerato l'ostacolo della corporeità nella condizione mortale. Se l'ideale filosofico antico prevedeva l'assoluto controllo del corpo e delle passioni, bene, è proprio questo che Agostino considera ora di fatto impossibile; solo quando il corpo sarà veramente disciplinato e sottomesso, quando sarà cioè corpo glorioso, allora si potrà essere felici:

> *Displicet* autem illic (...) *quod tempore vitae huius in solo animo sapientis dixi habitare beatam vitam, quomodolibet se habeat corpus eius*, cum perfectam cognitionem Dei, hoc est qua homini maior esse non possit, in futura vita speret Apostolus (cfr. *1Cor* 13, 12), *quae sola beata vita dicenda est, ubi et corpus incorruptibile atque inmortale spiritui suo sine ulla molestia vel reluctatione subdetur*[31].

La rinuncia all'ideale filosofico antico sta dunque nella diversa concezione del corpo? In realtà, quest'ultimo impedimento è ancora più un effetto che la vera causa o radice. Il corpo è un ostacolo solo perché è un corpo corruttibile, mutevole e mortale; ed è tale in conseguenza del peccato. Lo scacco dell'ideale filosofico è così segnato dall'ingresso nello scenario dottrinale del concetto di peccato originale e di quello, simmetrico e corrispondente, della grazia divina come unica possibilità di sottrarsi a tale stato. E ciò ci riconduce esattamente al periodo prima segnalato, e cioè intorno al 396-397, e più precisamente alle *Quaestiones ad Simplicianum*, quando per la prima volta Agostino adotta la propria dottrina della grazia irresistibile, che lo accompagnerà per tutto il re-

[31] ID., *Retractationes*, I, 2, PL 32, 588, ed. A. Mutzenbecher, Turnhout 1984 (CCSL, 57), p. 11,7-15.

sto della sua vita[32]: trentacinque anni circa, dunque lo spazio sicuramente più lungo e intenso della sua attività intellettuale. Non è il caso di soffermarsi su questa svolta, perché è stata già evidenziata, in toni diversi, da Flasch e Lettieri[33]: mi limiterò a ricordare che Agostino ritratta e corregge qui il suo primo tentativo di interpretazione della *Lettera ai Romani*[34], sciogliendo ogni nesso tra prescienza e predestinazione (la predestinazione non dipende in alcun modo dalla prescienza, anzi la *iustificatio* precede l'*electio*, per restare al lessico paolino)[35] e affermando chiaramente che non ci può essere nessun merito umano a fondamento del dono della

[32] Conviene forse ricordare che è lo stesso Agostino ad indicare nelle *Quaestiones ad Simplicianum* un punto di svolta nella propria riflessione; cfr. ad es. *De dono perseverantiae*, 20, 52, PL 45, 1026: «Quod plenius sapere coepi in ea disputatione, quam scripsi ad beatae memoriae Simplicianum episcopum Mediolanensis Ecclesiae, in mei episcopatus exordio, quando et initium fidei donum Dei esse cognovi, et asserui».

[33] Cfr. K. FLASCH, *Logik des Schreckens. Augustins von Hippo* De diversis quaestionibus ad Simplicianum *I, 2*, Mainz 1990 (1995²) (Excerpta classica, 8); G. LETTIERI, *L'altro Agostino. Ermeneutica e retorica della grazia dalla crisi alla metamorfosi del* De doctrina christiana, Brescia 2001. Al volume di Lettieri si rimanda anche per un bilancio critico delle principali posizioni interpretative. Per gli sviluppi dello stesso tema nel confronto con i monaci della Gallia meridionale cfr. invece soprattutto D. OGLIARI, Gratia et certamen. *The Relationship between Grace and Free Will in the Discussion of Augustine with the So-Called Semipelagians*, Leuven – Paris – Dudley 2003.

[34] Cfr. AUGUSTINUS HIPPONENSIS, *Expositio quarundam propositionum ex epistola ad Romanos* (a. 394-395), in partic. 52-55, PL 35, 2071, ed. I. Divjak, Wien 1971 (CSEL, 84), pp. 33-40; *De diversis quaestionibus octoginta tribus*, q. 68, PL 40, 70-74, ed. A. Mutzenbecher, Turnhout 1975 (CCSL, 44A), pp. 174-183. La datazione esatta delle singole questioni che compongono il *De diversis quaestionibus octoginta tribus* (che le *Retractationes* collocano tra il 388 e il 395-397) non è del tutto certa: è tuttavia probabile che il gruppo di questioni (dalla 66 alla 75) relativo all'interpretazione di passi paolini, tratti in particolare dalla *Lettera ai Romani*, possa essere collocato nello stesso biennio (394-395) in cui Agostino aveva cercato di occuparsi sistematicamente del medesimo testo nell'*Expositio quarundam propositionum ex epistola ad Romanos* e nell'*Epistolae ad Romanos inchoata expositio*. La cronologia relativa tra questi tre approcci non è tuttavia ancora perfettamente definita: cfr. in proposito F. COCCHINI, *Dal* De diversis quaestionibus LXXXIII. *Note di esegesi e di storia (qq. LI-LXXXIII)*, in *«De diversis quaestionibus octoginta tribus» – «De diversis quaestionibus ad Simplicianum» di Agostino d'Ippona*, Roma 1996 (Lectio Augustini – Settimana Agostiniana Pavese, 12), pp. 67-91, in partic. p. 69. Sul confronto complessivo di Agostino con Paolo in questi anni cfr. M. G. MARA, *Agostino interprete di Paolo*, Milano 1993.

[35] Cfr. AUGUSTINUS HIPPONENSIS, *De diversis quaestionibus ad Simplicianum*, I, 2, 6, PL 40, 115, ed. A. Mutzenbecher (CCSL, 44), p. 31, 188-189: «Non tamen electio praecedit iustificationem sed electionem iustificatio».

grazia[36]: anche l'*initium fidei* e la volontà di credere, che in un primo momento Agostino aveva riservato al potere o alla potestà umana, vengono ora interamente avocati alla decisione divina[37]. Crederanno soltanto coloro che sono stati predestinati a credere; questi ultimi potranno poi compiere opere buone e, perseverando, essere sottratti alla *massa damnationis* determinata dal peccato originale.

Ecco dunque perché la filosofia è una pratica inefficace: non perché erronea nei contenuti o nel modello proposto, ma ben più semplicemente, e radicalmente, perché *qualunque pratica umana*, anche la più virtuosa, è di per sé inefficace ad assicurare felicità e salvezza. La felicità e la salvezza sono solo un dono gratuito di Dio: non c'è una pratica esclusivamente umana che possa condurre a esse, o anche solo che ci possa rendere meritevoli di essere felici e salvi.

Se così è, almeno in Agostino, si comprende come le tesi di Hadot descrivano soltanto un aspetto, parziale, di questa transizione: il tramonto della filosofia come *Lebensform* non è dovuto solo al fatto che il cristianesimo si presenta come un altro stile di vita, come un'altra pratica esistenziale più efficace, ma al fatto che qualsiasi pratica umana finalizzata a una felicità e a una salvezza intramondane non ha ormai in realtà più alcun senso.

In secondo luogo, si dovrà osservare che anche la comparazione in termini di diffusione e incidenza tra filosofia e fede cristiana, così come l'avevamo considerata nel giovane Agostino, è anch'essa ormai svuotata di ogni significato. Se il giovane Agostino poteva ancora dire che la filosofia ha il limite di liberare solo pochi uomini, mentre il cristianesimo libera interi popoli, lo scena-

[36] Cfr. *ibid.*, 2, 7, 115, pp. 31,204 - 32,211: «Nemo enim credit qui non vocatur. Misericors autem Deus vocat nullis hoc vel fidei meritis largiens, quia merita fidei sequuntur vocationem potius quam praecedunt. (...) Nisi ergo vocando praecedat misericordia Dei, nec credere quisquam potest, ut ex hoc incipiat iustificari et accipere facultatem bene operandi. Ergo ante omne meritum est gratia (...)».

[37] Sullo scarto introdotto nell'*Ad Simplicianum* a proposito dell'*initium fidei* cfr. D. Marafioti, *Il problema dell'*initium fidei *in Sant'Agostino fino al 397*, in «Augustinianum», 21 (1981), pp. 541-565; N. Cipriani, *L'autonomia della volontà umana nell'atto di fede: le ragioni di una teoria prima accolta e poi respinta da S. Agostino*, in *Il mistero del male e la libertà possibile: linee di antropologia agostiniana*, Atti del VI Seminario del Centro di Studi Agostiniani di Perugia, a c. di L. Alici – R. Piccolomini – A. Pieretti, Roma 1995 (Studia Ephemeridis Augustinianum, 48), pp. 7-17.

rio, a partire dalle *Quaestiones ad Simplicianum*, diventa assai più restrittivo: in realtà, come visto, la filosofia non libera assolutamente nessuno, ma anche il cristianesimo, a sua volta, non libera tutti, e neppure le grandi masse – non più nazioni intere, ma solo i predestinati[38]. Da questo punto di vista, il cristianesimo non può più essere considerato, in alcun modo, platonismo per il popolo, con buona pace di Nietzsche e dello stesso Hadot. Non si comprende forse la portata di questo gesto agostiniano di destituzione *complessiva* della validità delle pratiche salvifiche, prima fra tutte la filosofia, se non si presta attenzione al risvolto forse più inquietante della dottrina agostiniana della grazia: anche la salvezza cristiana non è più universale, non è più alla portata di tutti, ma è riservata solo agli eletti. Poiché la chiamata di Dio è irresistibile (non si può infatti immaginare, secondo Agostino, che Dio non sappia come richiamare a sé le proprie creature), si deve concludere che la *vocatio*, l'appello alla fede, non è in sé veramente uni-

[38] E tuttavia, come proprio la laboriosa esegesi di *1Tm* 2, 4 proposta da Agostino dimostra (cfr. *infra*, note 39-42), la salvezza cristiana rimane 'universale' – a differenza di quella filosofica o di quella dei pelagiani e semi-pelagiani – perché non è riservata ai soli dotti, ma è accessibile a coloro che provengono da tutti i ceti e tutte le condizioni sociali, dunque anche (se non soprattutto) ai semplici, purché ovviamente scelti e predestinati da Dio: non tutti insomma si salveranno dal punto di vista numerico, ma tutte le classi di uomini saranno rappresentate nel regno dei cieli. In questo senso, perfino la tarda polemica con Giuliano prolunga quella giovanile contro l'elitarismo filosofico; alcuni esempi saranno sufficienti: AUGUSTINUS HIPPONENSIS, *Contra Iulianum*, V, 1, 2, PL 44, 783: «Exaggeras quam sit 'difficilis paucisque conveniens eruditis sanctarum cognitio Litterarum'; videlicet, 'ut Deus hominum, sicut universi conditor, et justus et verax ac pius, idem donorum suorum in homines cumulator probetur; quia una est – ut fateris – optima causa studiorum bonorum, ut honoretur Deus'. Quem tamen sic honoras, ut parvulorum liberatorem neges per Christum Jesum, id est, Salvatorem, cujus eos Baptismate sic ablui dicitis, ut non consequantur salutem, tanquam medico non indigeant Christo; humanae originis venam sagaciter inspiciente, et eos sanos pronuntiante Juliano. Quanto melius nihil omnino didicisses, quam per istam velut scientiam legis, in qua te turgidus jactas, non sane duce Dei lege, sed vestra potius vanitate, ad hanc impiam praesumptionem inimicam fidei christianae et tuae animali pervenisses». ID., *Contra Iulianum opus imperfectum*, II, 51, PL 45, 1163, ed. M. Zelzer, Wien 1974 (CSEL, 85/1), pp. 199,6 - 200,13: «Promiseras te intellegentiam suggesturum esse lectori et loqueris de omonymis et aequivocis; quomodo ergo te ipsi saltem Pelagiani intellecturi sunt, nisi prius ad scolas dialecticorum, ubicumque terrarum poterint inveniri, propter haec discenda mittantur? An forte categorias Aristotelis, antequam tuos libros legant, eis exponens ipse lecturus es? Cur non et hoc facias, homo ingeniosissimus, quandoquidem a deceptis miseris pasceris otiosus?». *Ibid.*, V, 3, PL 45, 1434: «Haec est enim vestra praeclara scientia, nulli hominum comprehensibilis, nisi prudentibus raris, nec ipsis nisi laborantibus miseris».

versale. Per sostenere questa tesi, Agostino non esita a proporre un'esegesi piuttosto ardita di *1Tm* 2, 4 («qui omnes homines vult salvos fieri, et ad agnitionem veritatis venire»)[39], enfatizzando soprattutto la valenza antignostica del versetto: la salvezza non può essere raggiunta attraverso i meriti (e dunque, neppure tramite la conoscenza), ma dipende essenzialmente dal *volere* divino. Il senso assoluto del *velle* («qui vult») qualifica così in modo essenziale la portata di «omnes»: Dio salva *tutti* coloro che *vuole salvare*. O ancora, si dovrà invertire la costruzione del versetto, prendendo «omnes» come indice dell'unicità ed esclusività della via per la salvezza: tutti coloro che si salvano, si salvano *solo* attraverso la volontà divina (cioè: non c'è salvezza al di fuori del volere divino). Il fatto che Dio compaia come soggetto della frase non è per Agostino significativo: se in una città c'è un solo maestro di lettere o grammatica, si potrà dire che egli insegna a *tutti* gli abitanti di quella città, non perché davvero tutti effettivamente abbiano studiato, studino o studieranno lettere o grammatica, ma perché coloro che hanno avuto, hanno o avranno la possibilità di farlo, potranno farlo solo con quel maestro. O infine – poiché per Agostino è certo che non tutti si salvino, ed è altrettanto certo che ciò non possa accadere contro la volontà divina – si dovrà attribuire ad «omnes» un valore per così dire distributivo: Dio *non salva tutti gli uomini*, ma salva uomini appartenenti *a tutti i ceti e tutte le classi*. L'*Enchiridion* (a. 421/422) ci offre congiuntamente un chiaro esempio della prima e della terza soluzione:

> Ac per hoc cum audimus et in sacris litteris legimus quod velit omnes homines salvos fieri, quamvis certum sit nobis non omnes homines salvos fieri, non tamen ideo debemus omnipotentis Dei voluntati aliquid derogare, sed ita intellegere quod scriptum est: «Qui omnes homines vult salvos fieri» (*1Tm* 2, 4), tanquam diceretur nullum hominem fieri salvum nisi quem fieri ipse voluerit; non quod nullus sit hominum nisi quem salvum fieri velit, sed quod nullus fiat nisi quem velit, et ideo sit rogandus ut velit, quia necesse est fieri si vo-

[39] Cfr. L. DOUCET, *L'exégèse augustinienne de I Tim. 2, 4: «Dieu veut que tous les hommes soient sauvés»*, in «Bulletin des Facultés catholiques de Lyon», 73 (1984), pp. 43-61; A. SAGE, *La volonté salvifique universelle de Dieu dans la pensée de saint Augustin*, in «Recherches Augustiniennes», 3 (1965), pp. 107-131; OGLIARI, *Gratia et certamen* cit. (alla nota 33), pp. 357-366.

luerit. (...) Aut certe sic dictum est: «Qui omnes homines vult salvos fieri», non quod nullus hominum esset quem salvum fieri nollet qui virtutes miraculorum facere noluit apud eos quos dicit acturos fuisse paenitentiam si fecisset, sed ut «omnes homines», omne genus hominum intellegamus per quascumque differentias distributos, reges privatos, nobiles ignobiles, sublimes humiles, doctos indoctos, integri corporis debiles, ingeniosos tardicordes fatuos, divites pauperes mediocres, mares feminas, infantes pueros adulescentes iuvenes seniores senes, in linguis omnibus, in moribus omnibus, in artibus omnibus, in professionibus omnibus, in voluntatum et conscientiarum varietate innumerabili constitutos, et si quid aliud differentiarum est in hominibus. (...) Isto locutionis modo et Dominus est usus in evangelio, ubi ait Pharisaeis: «Decimatis mentam et rutam et omne holus» (*Lc* 11, 42); neque enim Pharisaei et quaecumque aliena et omnium per omnes terras alienigenarum omnia holera decimabant. Sicut ergo hic «omne holus» omne holerum genus, ita et illic «omnes homines» omne hominum genus intellegere possumus. Et quocumque alio modo intellegi potest, dum tamen credere non cogamur aliquid omnipotentem voluisse fieri, factumque non esse; qui sine ullis ambiguitatibus, si in caelo et in terra, sicut eum veritas cantat, omnia quaecumque voluit fecit, profecto facere noluit quodcumque non fecit[40].

[40] AUGUSTINUS HIPPONENSIS, *Enchiridion ad Laurentium de fide et spe et caritate*, 103, PL 40, 280-281, ed. E. Evans, Turnhout 1969 (CCSL, 46), pp. 104,1-9, 105,14-26 e 105,39 - 106,50. Analogamente, entrambi questi modelli esplicativi sono presenti nell'*Epistola* 149 (a. 415?), in cui si insiste sia sulla figura di Cristo come unico mediatore e unica possibilità di salvezza (tutti coloro che si salvano, si salvano in virtù di Cristo), sia sul fatto che le membra della Chiesa-corpo di Cristo debbano essere tratte da tutti i generi di uomini; cfr. ID., *Epistolae*, 149, 2, 17, PL 33, 637, ed. A. Goldbacher, Wien – Leipzig 1904 (CSEL, 44), pp. 363,17 - 364,12: «Haec autem causa praecipua fuit ista dicendi, ut his breviter perstrictis atque significatis non putaretur neglegendum esse, quod sequitur: 'Pro omnibus hominibus, pro regibus et his, qui in sublimitate sunt, ut quietam et tranquillam vitam agamus in omni pietate et caritate' (*1Tm* 2, 1-2), ne quisquam, sicut se habet humanae cogitationis infirmitas, existimaret non esse ista facienda pro his, a quibus persecutionem patiebatur ecclesia, cum membra Christi ex omni essent hominum genere colligenda. Unde adiungit et dicit: 'Hoc enim bonum et acceptum est coram salvatore Deo nostro, qui omnes homines vult salvos fieri et in agnitionem veritatis venire' (*ibid.* 2, 3). Et ne quisquam diceret posse esse salutis viam in bona conversatione et unius Dei omnipotentis cultu sine participatione corporis et sanguinis Christi, 'unus enim Deus', inquit, 'et unus mediator Dei et hominum homo Christus Iesus' (*ibid.* 2, 5), ut illud, quod dixerat 'omnes homines vult salvos fieri', nullo alio modo intellegatur praestari nisi per mediatorem non Deum, quod semper erat Verbum, sed hominem Christum Iesum, cum 'Ver-

La seconda ipotesi interpretativa e il relativo esempio ricordato in precedenza si ritrovano invece nel *De praedestinatione sanctorum* (a. 428/429):

> Cur ergo non omnes docet, ut veniant ad Christum, nisi quia omnes quos docet, misericordia docet, quos autem non docet, judicio non docet? Quoniam 'cujus vult miseretur, et quem vult obdurat' (*Rm* 9, 18): sed miseretur, bona tribuens; obdurat, digna retribuens. (...) Et tamen secundum quemdam modum, omnes Pater docet venire ad suum Filium. Non enim frustra scriptum est in Prophetis: 'Et erunt omnes docibiles Dei' (*Jo* 6, 45, cfr. *Is* 54, 13). Quod testimonium cum praemisisset, tunc subdidit: 'Omnis qui audivit a Patre et didicit, venit ad me' (*Jo* 6, 45). Sicut ergo integre loquimur, cum de aliquo litterarum magistro, qui in civitate solus est, dicimus: Omnes iste hic litteras docet, non quia omnes discunt, sed quia nemo nisi ab illo discit, quicumque ibi litteras discit, ita recte dicimus: omnes Deus docet venire ad Christum, non quia omnes veniunt, sed quia nemo aliter venit. Cur autem non omnes doceat, aperuit Apostolus, quantum aperiendum judicavit: quia 'volens ostendere iram, et demonstrare poten-

bum caro factum est et habitauit in nobis' (*Jo* 1, 14)» (i corsivi sostituiscono qui, come nelle successive citazioni, gli spaziati dell'edizione Goldbacher). Per un'altra significativa attestazione della prima ipotesi interpretativa cfr. *ibid.* 217 [a. 426/428], 6, 19, PL 33, 985-986, ed. A. Goldbacher, Wien – Leipzig 1911 (CSEL, 57), pp. 417,17 - 418,4: «Unde manifestum est eos, qui huic resistunt tam perspicuae veritati, non intellegere omnino, qua locutione sit dictum, quod 'omnes homines vult Deus salvos fieri', cum tam multi salvi non fiant, non quia ipsi sed quia Deus non vult, quod sine ulla caligine manifestatur in parvulis. Sed sicut illud, quod dictum est: 'omnes in Christo vivificabuntur', cum tam multi aeterna morte puniantur, ideo dictum est, quia omnes, quicumque vitam aeternam percipiunt, non percipiunt nisi in Christo, ita, quod dictum est: 'omnes homines vult Deus salvos fieri', cum tam multos nolit salvos fieri, ideo dictum est, quia omnes qui salvi fiunt, nisi ipso volente non fiunt, et, si quo alio modo illa verba apostolica intellegi possunt, ut tamen huic apertissimae veritati, in qua videmus tam multos volentibus hominibus sed Deo nolente salvos non fieri, contraria esse non possint». Per altri due esempi del terzo modello cfr. invece Id., *De correptione et gratia*, 14, 44, PL 44, 943, ed. G. Folliet, Wien 2000 (CSEL, 92), p. 272,1-6; «Et quod scriptum est, quod 'omnes homines vult salvos fieri', nec tamen omnes salvi fiunt, multis quidem modis intelligi potest, ex quibus in aliis opusculis nostris aliquos commemoravimus, sed hic unum dicam. Ita dictum est: 'omnes homines vult salvos fieri', ut intelligantur omnes praedestinati quia omne genus hominum in eis est». Id., *Sermo* 304, 3, 2, PL 38, 1396: «Prorsus, dilectissimi, nullum genus hominum de sua vocatione desperet: pro omnibus passus est Christus. Veraciter de illo scriptum est: 'Qui vult omnes homines salvos fieri, et in agnitionem veritatis venire'».

> tiam suam, attulit in multa patientia vasa irae quae perfecta sunt in perditionem, et ut notas faciat divitias gloriae suae in vasa misericordiae, quae praeparavit in gloriam' (*Rm* 9, 22-23). Hinc est quod 'verbum crucis pereuntibus stultitia est; his autem qui salvi fiunt, virtus Dei est' (*1Cor* 1, 18). Hos omnes docet venire ad Christum Deus; *hos enim 'omnes vult salvos fieri, et in agnitionem veritatis venire'*. Nam si et illos quibus stultitia est verbum crucis, ut ad Christum venirent, docere voluisset, procul dubio venirent et ipsi. Non enim fallit aut fallitur qui ait: 'Omnis qui audivit a Patre et didicit, venit ad me'. Absit ergo ut quisquam non veniat, qui a Patre audivit et didicit[41].

Dio *non vuole* che tutti si salvino: ma quelli che si salvano, si salvano *solo* per il volere divino e la mediazione di Cristo. È questo dunque l'errore dei filosofi e della filosofia: contando di poter fare affidamento sulle sole proprie forze, i filosofi si mostrano per quel che sono – per dei pelagiani che rendono vana la croce di Cristo! L'errore dei pelagiani (o dei semi-pelagiani) e dei filosofi pagani è per Agostino il medesimo: ritenere sufficiente l'autocontrollo, l'*askesis* come pratica di disciplinamento del Sé, come tutela e protezione della cittadella del libero arbitrio[42]. Come è detto esplicitamente nell'*Epistola* 186 (a. 417), difendendo la natura e il libero arbitrio, i filosofi hanno fatto di tutto per persuadere se stessi e gli altri che ci si può procurare la felicità con le sole forze della propria volontà («...argute defendendo naturam et liberum arbitrium, quemadmodum philosophi hujus mundi, qui vehementer egerunt ut putarentur vel putarent sibi beatam vitam virtute propriae voluntatis efficere»)[43]. E a ciò fa riferimento

[41] Id., *De praedestinatione sanctorum*, 8, 14, PL 44, 971 (è stata qui leggermente modificata l'interpunzione).

[42] Cfr. P. Brown, *Augustinus of Hippo*, London – Berkeley 1967 (2000²), p. 366 (tr. it., n. ed. ampliata, Torino 2005, p. 374), in riferimento a Pelagius, *Epistula ad Demetriadem*, 4, PL 30, 20B.

[43] Augustinus Hipponensis, *Epistolae*, 186, 11, 37, PL 33, 830, ed. Goldbacher, pp. 76,14 - 77,13: «Sed quid plura? Non solum ad istos vitandos cauti esse debemus, verum etiam ad docendos vel monendos, si patiantur, pigrescere non debemus. Plus eis tamen sine dubitatione praestamus, si, ut corrigantur, oremus, ne cum tantis ingeniis vel pereant vel alios perdant praesumptione damnabili, quia 'zelum Dei habent sed non secundum scientiam; ignorantes' autem 'Dei iustitiam', id est, iustitiam, quae ex Deo est, 'et suam volentes constituere, iustitiae Dei non sunt subiecti' (*Rm* 10, 2-3). Quibus utique, quoniam Christiani appel-

Agostino anche nelle pagine conclusive del *De civitate*: dall'inferno di questa vita ci libera solo la grazia di Cristo. Qualcuno dice che la filosofia potrebbe essere d'aiuto, ma la vera filosofia è concessa a pochissimi, ed è anch'essa un dono divino: praticare la vera vita filosofica non è pertanto qualcosa che ci renda meritevoli della salvezza, ma è già un dono gratuito, un dono divino[44] – dunque un segno della salvezza, e non una via per la salvezza.

Se dunque il cristianesimo, almeno nel modello agostiniano, gioca un ruolo decisivo nella trasformazione delle pratiche filosofiche, non è tanto perché suggerisce una pratica di salvezza più efficace (questo era appunto ciò che aveva creduto solo il *primo* Agostino), ma perché mette più radicalmente in dubbio l'efficacia di qualsiasi pratica eudaimonologica e soteriologica: da questo momento, la salvezza e la felicità non sono più in potere dell'uomo, e dunque si sottraggono alle pratiche esclusivamente umane. Privata della sua finalità originaria, la filosofia (anche la filosofia cristiana) sarà dunque gradualmente costretta a ripensarsi nella sua funzione, e a presentarsi come una pratica del tutto diversa: una pratica fondamentalmente *interpretativa*, in cui l'approccio al mondo è mediato dall'analisi di ciò che è stato già *scritto* (dai filosofi antichi, e dai loro commentatori) sul mondo.

lantur, magis observandum est quam Iudaeis, de quibus hoc dixit apostolus, ne offendant in lapidem offensionis velut *argute defendendo naturam et liberum arbitrium quem ad modum philosophi huius mundi, qui vehementer egerunt, ut putarentur vel putarent sibi beatam vitam virtute propriae voluntatis efficere*. Caveant ergo isti, ne per sapientiam verbi evacuent crucem Christi et hoc sit eis 'offendere in lapidem offensionis' (*Rm* 9, 32). Natura enim humana etiam si in illa integritate, in qua condita est, permaneret, nullo modo se ipsa creatore suo non adiuvante servaret. Cum igitur sine Dei gratia salutem non posset custodire, quam accepit, quo modo sine Dei gratia potest reparare, quam perdidit?».

[44] Id., *De civitate Dei*, XXII, 22, 4, 786-787, ed. Dombart – Kalb cit. (alla nota 1), II, p. 845, 111-112 e 121-133: «Ab huius tam miserae quasi quibusdam inferis vitae non liberat nisi gratia Salvatoris Christi, Dei ac Domini nostri (...). Ad quam rem *etiam philosophiam prodesse dicunt docti huius saeculi, quam dii quibusdam paucis*, ait Tullius, veram dederunt; nec hominibus, inquit, ab his aut datum est donum maius aut potuit ullum dari. Usque adeo et ipsi, contra quos agimus, *quoquo modo compulsi sunt in habenda non quacumque, sed vera philosophia diuinam gratiam confiteri*. Porro si paucis divinitus datum est verae philosophiae contra miserias huius vitae unicum auxilium, satis et hinc apparet humanum genus ad luendas miseriarum poenas esse damnatum. Sicut autem hoc, ut fatentur, nullum divinum maius est donum, sic a nullo Deo dari credendum est, nisi ab illo, quo et ipsi qui multos deos colunt nullum dicunt esse maiorem».

5. Restano forse, in conclusione, almeno altre due piccole cose da considerare. In primo luogo, ci si potrebbe chiedere quanto le decisioni agostiniane abbiano realmente influenzato gli sviluppi del pensiero nell'Occidente latino e cristiano. In modo estremamente sommario, si potrebbe osservare da una parte che la storia dell'agostinismo è in effetti anche la storia dell'edulcorazione e della parziale neutralizzazione della sua dottrina della grazia[45], e dall'altra che la riacculturazione filosofica dell'Occidente a partire dal secolo XII ha riportato parzialmente in luce l'antico modo di concepire e praticare la filosofia – ciò che per altro sia Hadot che Domański almeno in certa misura concedono. È ad esempio interessante rilevare come il nodo cruciale dell'efficacia della filosofia come pratica salvifica non sia stato affatto dissimulato nel dibattito scolastico: sarà sufficiente ricordare il caso del più celebre manifesto medievale in difesa della filosofia, il *De summo bono* di Boezio di Dacia, che attira l'attenzione dei censori e dei teologi non tanto perché in esso venga negata la subordinazione della beatitudine naturale a quella soprannaturale (tesi che è anzi esposta nell'opuscolo in termini non troppo dissimili da quelli adoperati ad esempio da Tommaso d'Aquino), ma perché in esso torna a riaffacciarsi l'ideale della sapienza che basta a se stessa, e che in quanto tale salva e redime: solo il filosofo non pecca, scrive in effetti Boezio[46]. È questa, senza dubbio, la tesi più scandalosa del *De summo bono*, ed è una tesi che rimette in gioco proprio

[45] Mi sono soffermato su alcuni aspetti della ricezione scolastica della dottrina agostiniana del merito e della grazia in P. PORRO, *Predestinazione e merito: Agostino e la teologia medievale*, in *Il mistero del male e la libertà possibile (IV): ripensare Agostino.* Atti dell'VIII Seminario del Centro di Studi Agostiniani di Perugia, a c. di L. Alici – R. Piccolomini – A. Pieretti, Roma 1997 (Studia Ephemeridis Augustinianum, 59), Roma 1997, pp. 249-278.

[46] Cfr. BOETHIUS DE DACIA, *De summo bono*, ed. N. J. Green-Pedersen, København 1976 (Corpus Philosophorum Danicorum Medii Aevi, 6/2), p. 372,75-78: «Qui enim perfectior est in beatitudine, quam in hac vita homini possibile esse per rationem scimus, ipse propinquior est beatitudini quam in vita futura per fidem expectamus». E cfr. *ibid.*, p. 374,135-148: «Et inter operationes virtutis intellectivae, si aliqua est optima et perfectissima, omnes naturaliter sunt propter illam. Et cum homo est in illa operatione, est in optimo statu qui est homini possibilis. *Et isti sunt philosophi, qui ponunt vitam suam in studio sapientiae.* (...) *Omnes autem alii homines* qui vivunt secundum virtutes inferiores eligentes operationes earum et delectationes, quae sunt in illis operibus, innaturaliter ordinati sunt et *peccant contra ordinem naturalem.* Declinatio enim hominis ab ordine naturali peccatum est in homine, et *quia philosophus ab hoc ordine non declinat, propter hoc contra ordinem naturalem non peccat*».

l'efficacia salvifica di una pratica puramente umana. È soprattutto il ritorno in Occidente dei testi aristotelici, e in particolare dell'*Etica Nicomachea* (insieme alle tesi sulla felicità intellettuale elaborate dai *falāsifa*), a riaprire almeno in parte (o provvisoriamente) la prospettiva di una felicità conseguibile (almeno in *questo* mondo) con le proprie forze – e cioè, appunto, con la scelta della filosofia come stile di vita[47]. L'accusa di 'pelagianesimo' rivolta ad alcuni Maestri delle Arti della seconda metà del secolo XIII appare così meno astrusa e anacronistica di quanto possa apparire a prima vista[48]. E inversamente, si può ricordare come proprio Agostino (con un'inconsapevole e altrettanto anacronistica profezia) abbia fatto riferimento a un ipotetico «consiglio degli aristotelici» come ultima corte di appello dei pelagiani[49]. Ma l'aristote-

[47] Sull'ideale della felicità speculativa (o «mentale», per usare la fortunata espressione di Maria Corti) nel Medioevo, e in particolare nel secolo XIII, esiste ormai una copiosa letteratura: sarà sufficiente rinviare al volume *Le felicità nel Medioevo*, Atti del Convegno della Società Italiana per lo Studio del Pensiero Medievale (Milano, 12-13 settembre 2003), a c. di M. Bettetini – F. D. Paparella, Louvain-la-Neuve 2005 (Féderation Internationale des Instituts d'Études Médiévales – Textes et Études du Moyen Âge, 31), e in particolare ai contributi, in esso contenuti, di G. Fioravanti (*La felicità intellettuale: storiografia e precisazioni*, pp. 1-12) e L. Bianchi (*Felicità intellettuale, «ascetismo» e «arabismo»: nota sul «De summo bono» di Boezio di Dacia*, pp. 13-34). Il volume comprende anche un interessante contributo di M. Parodi (*Agostino e il desiderio*, pp. 35-51), che tocca molti dei temi e dei testi da me sfiorati in queste pagine, ma che tende invece a ridimensionare (nella prospettiva di una logica non *lineare*, ma *relazionale*) la portata della dottrina della grazia 'immeritata' all'interno dei percorsi agostiniani sulla ricerca della felicità.

[48] È appena il caso di ricordare a questo proposito come i nomi di Agostino e di Pelagio compaiano in esplicita contrapposizione nella condanna del 1277, e in particolare nel celebre art. 130 (nella numerazione del *Chartularium Universitatis Parisiensis*) o 166 (nella numerazione di Mandonnet e Hissette), che è il vero punto cruciale dell'intero dibattito negli ultimi decenni del Duecento sul cosiddetto 'determinismo psicologico', ovvero sul primato della ragione (e della conoscenza) sulla volontà. Cfr. R. Hissette, *Enquête sur les 219 articles condamnés à Paris le 7 mars 1277*, Louvain – Paris 1977 (Philosophes médiévaux, 22), p. 257: «Quod si ratio recta, et voluntas recta. – Error, quia contra glossam Augustini super illud Psalmi: 'Concupivit anima mea desiderare' (*Ps* 118, 20) etc., et quia secundum hoc, ad rectitudinem voluntatis non esset necessaria gratia, sed scientia solum, quod est error Pelagii». Per una ricostruzione d'insieme del dibattito sul 'determinismo psicologico', cfr. F.-X. Putallaz, *Insolente liberté. Controverses et condamnations au XIIIe siècle*, Fribourg – Paris 1995 (Vestigia, 15).

[49] Cfr. Augustinus Hipponensis, *Contra Iulianum*, II, 10, 37, PL 44, 700: «De reliquis sane non habes omnino quod dicas. Numquid Irenaeus, et Cyprianus, et Reticius, et Olympius, et Hilarius, et Gregorius, et Basilius, et Ambrosius, et Joannes, 'de plebeia faece sellulariorum', sicut Tulliane jocaris, 'in vestram invi-

lismo scolastico rimane anch'esso un'opzione fondamentalmente interpretativa: gli stessi Maestri della Facoltà delle Arti cercheranno pur sempre di presentarsi come 'professionisti' dell'interpretazione e dell'insegnamento dei testi aristotelici, senza la pretesa assoluta di reintrodurre la filosofia stessa come via *esclusiva* verso la felicità (la beatitudine soprannaturale, come già ricordato, non viene praticamente mai messa in discussione).

In secondo luogo, ci si potrebbe infine chiedere se il tramonto della filosofia come stile di vita e pratica di salvezza intramondana debba necessariamente essere considerato come qualcosa di negativo, così come sembra a più riprese suggerire lo stesso Hadot. Il fatto è che se Hadot, più ancora che Domanski, considera questa trasformazione – il fatto cioè che la filosofia da *Lebensform*, da pratica su di sé e sul Sé, si sia trasformata in disciplina teoretica (Hadot) o in pratica testuale (come qui suggerito) – come un peggioramento, è in definitiva perché egli sembra avere in mente un tipo ideale della filosofia, un quadro prescrittivo, un dover-essere dell'esercizio filosofico: la vera filosofia dovrebbe per Hadot ancora oggi essere qualcosa in grado di trasformare la propria vita, come già ricordato, e non una disciplina da studiare. A questa convinzione si potrebbe replicare che agisce forse anche qui, almeno implicitamente, la tentazione ricorrente di far riferimento a essenze atemporali, e di omettere dati storici che invece non dovrebbero essere trascurati: ad esempio, che la filosofia come stile di vita è forse possibile fino in fondo solo in una società in cui gli uomini liberi sono esentati dai rapporti di produzione, in cui il lavoro è organizzato su base schiavistica, e in cui non esistono né mestieri intellettuali né conseguentemente intellettuali di professione. Ma neppure solo di questo si tratta: si dovrebbe forse riconoscere che dietro la trasformazione della filosofia in pratica testuale, in pratica esegetica o ermeneutica (che

diam concitati sunt?'. Numquid 'milites?' numquid 'scholastici auditoriales?' numquid 'nautae, tabernarii, cetarii, coqui, lanii?' numquid 'adolescentes ex monachis dissoluti?' Numquid postremo 'de qualiumcumque clericorum turba' isti sunt, quos urbana exagitatos dicacitate, vel potius vanitate contemnis, 'quia non possunt secundum categorias Aristotelis de dogmatibus iudicare?' Quasi tu, qui maxime quereris 'examen vobis et episcopale iudicium denegari', *Peripateticorum possis invenire concilium, ubi de subjecto et his quae sunt in subjecto contra originale peccatum dialectica sententia proferatur*». E cfr. *ibid.*, VI, 20, 64, 862: «Ad hoc enim redacta est haeresis vestra, ut *gemant sectatores vestri non inveniri dialecticos judices in Ecclesia, de scholis Peripateticorum sive Stoicorum, a quibus possitis absolvi*».

è quello che è accaduto in questi secoli), sta certamente la certezza, cristiana e soprattutto agostiniana, che la salvezza sia ormai fuori dall'orizzonte delle capacità umane in quanto tali, e dunque anche della filosofia (che non può più garantire, nel mondo, la piena e assoluta felicità), ma anche la consapevolezza più generale, estesa anche agli autori non-latini e non-cristiani, di non vivere più in un mondo aurorale, in un mondo virginale, in cui ciascuno possa trovare il proprio posto attraverso idonei esercizi spirituali e un'adeguata pratica di vita. Il mondo dei commentatori bizantini, dei *falāsifa* arabi o dei *magistri* cristiani è un mondo già storicizzato, già interpretato: che la filosofia divenga a sua volta soprattutto pratica ermeneutica o interpretativa è una conseguenza di questo modo di entrare in relazione con il mondo. E proprio questa graduale espulsione della filosofia dal campo delle pratiche di salvezza ci permette forse anche di considerare sotto una luce diversa alcuni degli assunti tradizionali che accompagnano la nostra percezione della filosofia medievale. Se si guarda ad esempio alla tensione tra la pratica progressivamente declinante della filosofia come strumento di salvezza intramondana e la pratica sempre più dominante della filosofia come interpretazione di libri e del libro/mondo, improvvisamente la classica coppia ragione/fede con cui si è soliti leggere la filosofia medievale perde la sua insostituibilità, o almeno gran parte della sua drammaticità: al suo posto (inaspettatamente, sorprendentemente – esattamente come i 'gingilli' rari, d'epoca, di cui parla ancora Paul Veyne) compare tutt'altra possibilità, e cioè che proprio in virtù di questo sganciamento essenziale della filosofia da ogni pratica soteriologica, da ogni strategia di salvezza, si possa dire che nel periodo che convenzionalmente definiamo medievale abbia avuto luogo non tanto un processo di teologizzazione, ma esattamente al contrario, un processo di *secolarizzazione* della filosofia[50]. La filosofia non ci salva più: può anche essere che ciò sia una perdita per noi, ma non è affatto detto che sia un male per la filosofia stessa, che alla fine è forse sopravissuta proprio in quanto secolarizzata e professionalizzata.

[50] Mi permetto di rinviare a quanto osservo a questo stesso proposito in *La filosofia medievale come (presunto) oggetto storiografico*, in corso di pubblicazione negli Atti (a c. di C. Trottmann e A. Vasiliu, Leuven) della giornata di studi *La philosophie médiévale: historiographies d'hier et de demain* (Paris, 23 octobre 2004).

GIANFRANCO FIORAVANTI

LA 'VERA RELIGIONE' DI AGOSTINO, OVVERO DELL'INUTILITÀ DEI FILOSOFI

Vera religio. Cosa significa? Come vanno insieme i due termini? Nel pensiero antico il termine *religio* sembra indicare essenzialmente il culto degli dei, in tutte le sue manifestazioni. Di esse si poteva dire che fossero corrette o non corrette, ma non vere o false. Il contrario della *religio*, la *superstitio*, non era più falsa di quanto la *religio* fosse vera. Anche da un punto di vista rigorosamente filosofico (quello del *De interpretatione* aristotelico[1]) le formule, le invocazioni, le lodi del rito non fanno parte del discorso 'apofantico'. Solo all'interno dell'apologetica cristiana, in cosciente polemica con la tradizione, si è cominciato ad usare questa terminologia. Non sempre però il termine 'vero' ha un significato tecnicamente filosofico. Per esempio nell'*Apologeticum* di Tertulliano esso equivale a 'sincero', non «fictus»: a proposito dei *sollemnia* del genetliaco degli Imperatori, i Cristiani preferiscono celebrarli «in conscientia» senza tribuir loro onori «vani et mentientes»; in questo sono *homines verae religionis*[2]. Più complesso il caso di Lattanzio il quale condanna il culto pagano «qui non habet inquisitionem aliquam veritatis et non officio mentis sed ministerio corporis constat». Ma la *veritas* di cui si parla non sembra avere carattere teoretico: essa consiste piuttosto «in iustitiae virtu-

[1] Cfr. ARISTOTELES, *De interpretatione*, 4, 17a[1] seqq.

[2] TERTULLIANUS, *Apologeticum*, 35, 1, PL 1, 452AB, ed. A. Kroymann, in ID., *Opera*, I, Turnhout 1954 (CCSL, 1), p. 144,1-4: «Propterea igitur publici hostes Christiani, quia imperatoribus *neque vanos neque mentientes* neque temerarios honores dicant, quia *verae religionis homines* etiam solemnia eorum, *conscientia* potius quam lascivia celebrant».

10.1484/M.NUTRIX-EB.1.101237

tisque praeceptis»[3]. Anche Agostino, nel *De vera religione*, identifica almeno in parte la *religio* con il culto. I termini usati sono: «templa», «sacra», adoperati in genere per il paganesimo; per il cristianesimo Agostino preferisce «sacramenta», così come nel *De beata vita* e nel *De ordine*[4] aveva usato «mysteria», con più precisione «divina mysteria» (nel linguaggio liturgico sia «sacramentum» che «divina mysteria» indicano in generale la celebrazione eucaristica). In che senso dunque, per il vescovo di Ippona, si può parlare di vero e di falso?

Il *De vera religione* si apre con una breve dimostrazione della falsità della religione pagana che a prima vista può risultare intrigante:

> Hinc evidentius error deprehenditur eorum populorum qui multos deos colere quam unum verum Deum et Dominum omnium maluerunt quod eorum sapientes, quos philosophos vocant, scholas habebant dissentientes et templa communia. Non enim vel populos vel sacerdotes latebat de ipsorum deorum natura quam diversa sentirent (...) omnes tamen cum sectatoribus suis diversa et adversa sentientibus ad sacra communia nullo prohibente veniebant[5].

La verità della religione cristiana risulta proprio dalla mancanza di questo *vitium*:

> Quod si hoc unum tantum vitium Christiana disciplina sanatum videremus ineffabili laude praedicandam esse neminem negare oporteret. Haereses namque tam innumerabiles a regula Christianitatis aversae testes sunt non admitti ad communicanda sacramenta eos qui de Patre Deo et Sapientia eius et munere divino aliter sentiunt et hominibus persuadere conantur quam veritas postulat[6].

Per Agostino non è dunque possibile avere concezioni diverse di Dio e praticare la medesima *religio*, il medesimo culto. Questo di-

[3] Lucius Caelius Firmianus Lactantius, *Divinae Institutiones*, IV, 3, PL 2, 452D-453A, edd. E. Heck – A. Wlosok, Berlin – New York 2005, II, p. 316.

[4] Cfr. Augustinus Hipponensis, *De beata vita*, 1, 4, PL 32, 961, ed. W. M. Green, Turnhout 1970 (CCSL, 29), p. 67,101; *De ordine*, II 5 16, PL 32, 1016, ed. W. M. Green, *ibid.*, p. 116,52.

[5] Id., *De vera religione*, 1, 1, PL 34, 123, ed. Kl.-D. Daur, Turnhout 1962 (CCSL, 32), p. 187,4-13.

[6] *Ibid.*, 5, 8, 126, p. 193,6-12.

vieto ha senso solo se della vera conoscenza di Dio e della sua natura si fa la condizione stessa per l'esistenza di una *religio* che non sia *superstitio*.

> Illud cuivis intelligere facile est religionem ab eis non esse quaerendam qui eadem sacra suscipiebant cum populis et de suorum deorum natura ac summo bono diversas contrariasque sententias in scholis suis (...) personabant[7].

Solo in questo contesto è spiegabile l'applicazione del termine *superstitio* alle eresie[8].

In questo modo Agostino ribalta la concezione 'pagana' del rapporto tra *religio* pubblica e concezioni 'private' del divino. La prima è accettabile solo se portatrice di quel medesimo valore di verità su cui le altre, pur nella loro diversità e perfino nella loro opposizione, si fondano. Non si possono venerare in comune Dei non solo diversi, ma opposti (accanto all'aggettivo «diversa» Agostino si premura di mettere gli aggettivi «adversa» e «contraria»). Il valore della stessa *religio* 'personale', per quanto soggettivamente intensa e fervorosa, dipende dall'aver colto o meno la verità oggettiva della natura divina. Le *Confessioni* ne sono la testimonianza più evidente: il marchio negativo di ogni esperienza religiosa di Agostino prima della conversione, dal Dio passibile e limitato del Manicheismo al panteismo 'stoico', ma anche molto personale, del mare infinito e della spugna è dato dalla incapacità 'concettuale' di distaccarsi dal mondo della corporeità, di non essere ingannato dai *phantasmata*[9].

Conseguenza di questo atteggiamento è l'identificazione tra *religio* e *philosophia* che Agostino presenta come una caratteristica del Cristianesimo:

> Sic enim creditur et docetur, quod est humanae salutis caput, non aliam esse philosophiam, id est sapientiae studium, et aliam religionem, cum hi quorum doctrinam non approbamus, nec sacramenta nobiscum communicant[10].

[7] *Ibidem*, p. 193,2-6.

[8] Cfr. *ibid.*, 5, 9, 126-127, p. 194,26.

[9] Cfr. Id., *Confessiones*, VII, 1, 2, PL 32, 733-734, ed. L. Verheijen, Turnhout 1981 (CCSL, 27), pp. 92,28 - 93,53.

[10] Id., *De vera religione* 5, 8, 126, ed. Daur cit. (alla nota 5), p. 193,12-16.

Che il Cristianesimo si identificasse con la *vera philosophia* era stato un *topos* dell'apologetica cristiana, ma proprio quel 'vera' spesso voleva significare una estraneità ed una contrapposizione alla filosofia 'normale' così come incontrata dalla nuova religione nel suo movimento espansivo. Senza voler ripercorrere tutta questa storia (già delineata dal libro di Anne Marie Malingrey[11]) basterà ricordare la posizione di Lattanzio, particolarmente significativa per il tema qui trattato. Egli infatti aveva condannato la separazione tra *religio* e *philosophia* nel paganesimo ed esaltato la loro unione nel Cristianesimo in termini che sembrano anticipare la posizione di Agostino:

> Deorum cultus non habet sapientiam (...) quia nihil ibi disseritur quod proficiat ad mores excolendos (...) nec habet inquisitionem aliquam veritatis, sed tantummodo ritum colendi qui non officio mentis, sed ministerio corporis constat. Et ideo non est illa vera religio iudicanda (...) Ita philosophia quia veram religionem, id est summam pietatem non habet, non est vera sapientia. (...) Ubi autem sapientia cum religione inseparabili nexu cohaeret utrumque verum esse necesse est, quia et in colendo sapere debemus, id est scire quid nobis et quomodo sit colendum, et in sapiendo colere, id est re et actu quod scierimus implere. Ubi ergo sapientia cum religione coniungitur? Ibi scilicet ubi Deus colitur unus[12].

Ma questa unione avveniva scartando *in toto* la tradizione filosofica così come storicamente si era data. Tutto il terzo libro delle *Institutiones* è infatti dedicato a dimostrare l'assoluta inattendibilità della filosofia in generale, delle singole scuole e dei singoli filosofi in particolare. Argomento principe, quello della contraddittorietà delle loro teorie. Un argomento che sarebbe stato ripreso e sfruttato da un autore assai più vicino ad Agostino: Ambrogio. Il vescovo di Milano, infatti, costantemente oppone le «simulatoriae disputationes», le «opiniones diversae» dei filosofi «qui sibiipsis constare non possunt» alla *regula veritatis* cristiana che si fonda non sulla dialettica, ma sugli «oracula divini sermonis» e sulla «ostensio spiritus et virtutis». Del resto, in questa tradizione, alme-

[11] A. M. MALINGREY, *«Philosophia». Étude d'un groupe de mots dans la littérature grecque, des présocratiques au IVe siècle après J.-C.*, Paris 1961.

[12] LUCIUS CAELIUS FIRMIANUS LACTANTIUS, *Divinae Institutiones*, IV, 3, 452D-453C, ed. Heck – Wlosok cit. (alla nota 3), pp. 315-317.

no fino da Tertulliano le eresie erano viste come una diretta conseguenza dell'introduzione nel discorso cristiano delle diverse e contraddittorie dottrine filosofiche[13]. Come abbiamo visto, anche nel *De vera religione* i filosofi sostengono, sulla natura divina e sul sommo bene, posizioni «diversae et adversae». Per Agostino, però, non si tratta di una condizione normale della filosofia ma piuttosto di un suo stato patologico. Come ci dicono le *Confessioni* già la lettura dell'*Hortensius* gli aveva insegnato a distinguere tra le varie «sectae» e la *philosophia-sapientia* in se stessa[14]. Questa *vera philosophia* non era rimasta un semplice ideale. Nel *Contra Academicos* Agostino l'aveva identificata con il pensiero di Platone. Esso si era difeso dal dilagare delle posizioni materialiste nascondendosi dietro lo scudo dello scetticismo accademico, ed era riapparso, come un fiume carsico, nella persona di Plotino, «platonicus philosophus ita [Platoni] similis iudicatus, ut (...) in hoc ille revixisse putandus sit»[15]. Constatando la scomparsa di Stoici ed Epicurei, l'esistenza esclusivamente di filosofi platonici e peripatetici («nunc philosophos non fere videmus nisi [...] aut Peripateticos aut Platonicos») e sottolineando come fosse stata ormai dimostrata una perfetta concordia tra Platone ed Aristotele Agostino poteva concludere che dopo molti secoli e molte discordie era stata finalmente prodotta (ma il termine usato è «eliquata»: filtrata, come l'«oleum» viene purgato dalla «amurca», dalla feccia) «una verissimae philosophiae disciplina»[16].

Questa è la *philosophia* scoperta appunto nei *libri Platonicorum* e che egli ritrova «non quidem his verbis», ma pur sempre identica per contenuti («hoc idem omnino») nella Scrittura (cioè in Giovanni e in Paolo)[17]. Quali sono dunque questi contenuti? In genere si ricorre al famoso testo delle *Confessioni* cui si è appena accennato, con la conosciutissima contrapposizione degli «ibi legi», «ibi non legi». Ma particolarmente istruttivo mi sembra pro-

[13] Cfr. TERTULLIANUS, *De praescriptione haereticorum*, 7, PL 2, 19A-21A, ed. A. Kroymann, in ID., *Opera*, I cit. (alla nota 2), pp. 192,1 - 193,40.

[14] Cfr. AUGUSTINUS HIPPONENSIS, *Confessiones*, III, 4, 7-8, 685-686, ed. Verheijen cit. (alla nota 9), pp. 29,29 - 30,37.

[15] ID., *Contra Academicos*, III, 18, 41, PL 32, 956, ed. W. M. Green, Turnhout 1970 (CCSL, 29), p. 60,43-46.

[16] *Ibid.*, 19, 42, 956, p. 60,1-10.

[17] Cfr. ID., *Confessiones*, VII, 9, 13, 740, ed. Verheijen cit., p. 101,1-19.

prio il testo del *De vera religione* in cui Agostino dicendoci come Platone, tornato sulla terra, potrebbe vedere la sua filosofia predicata nelle chiese e messa in pratica dalle folle cristiane, ne elenca indirettamente i capisaldi. Si tratta di una breve riassunto del 'dogma' platonico. Qui la contrapposizione tra ciò che è «unum et idem, eodem modo semper se habens» e ciò che «nascitur, occidit, fluit, labitur», ma che, «in quantum est», riceve dal primo forma ed esistenza si unisce all'indicazione del percorso per cui l'anima deve abbandonare le *imagines* che la tengono prigioniera per raggiungere la perfetta felicità aderendo alla verità incorporea[18]. In maniera più succinta ed incisiva l'unione di religione e di filosofia platonica era già stata formulata nel *De ordine*. Qui Agostino aveva affermato che la madre, Monica, proprio perché profondamente religiosa, era anche inconsapevolmente 'filosofa': infatti la Scrittura non comanda di evitare tutti i filosofi, ma quelli 'di questo mondo'. Questo significa che esistono filosofi che conoscono ed amano un altro mondo «ab istis oculis remotissimum, quem paucorum sanorum intellectus intuetur», e a questi due mondi si riferisce Cristo quando dice «regnum meum non est de hoc mundo» (*Jo* 18, 36) (non semplicemente «de mundo», precisa Agostino)[19]. Non si tratta di una notazione incidentale. Nel *Contra Academicos* proprio la «verissima philosophia» («eliquata» alla fine del lungo percorso iniziato con Platone) viene definita, in contrapposizione alla «philosophia huius mundi, quam sacra nostra meritissime detestantur», come «philosophia alterius mundi intelligibilis»[20]. La proiezione della dottrina platonica dei due mondi, sensibile ed intelligibile, sulla contrapposizione scritturistica (essenzialmente giovannea, ed in parte paolina) tra mondo posto in potere del Maligno e regno divino, costituisce a mio avviso una svolta di fondo per il Cristianesimo occidentale e ne orienterà la autopercezione per i secoli futuri, anche in quegli anni e in quegli ambienti per cui Platone sarebbe diventato poco più che un nome.

[18] Cfr. Id., *De vera religione*, 3, 3, 123-124, ed. Daur cit. (alla nota 5), pp. 188,1 - 190,46 (si veda la citazione integrale e traduzione di questo testo nel saggio di G. d'Onofrio nel presente volume, *supra*, pp. 23-25, nota 14).

[19] Cfr. Id., *De ordine*, I, 11, 32, 993, ed. Green cit. (alla nota 4), p. 106,46-48.

[20] Cfr. *supra*, alla nota 16.

Se le cose stanno così, conclude Agostino, è necessario che chi è religioso sia anche filosofo e chi è filosofo sia anche religioso, «repudiatis (...) qui neque in sacris philosophantur nec in philosophia consecrantur»[21]. Ma cosa significa più precisamente «philosophari in sacris» e «consecrari in philosophia»?

Nei dialoghi di Cassiciaco, parlando della lettura dei *libri Platonicorum*, Agostino non aveva dato indicazioni di contenuto: di essi ci dice semplicemente che avevano riacceso definitivamente l'amore per la filosofia nato molti anni prima con la lettura dell'*Hortensius*. Nel *De vera religione*, la dottrina platonica è essenzialmente, lo abbiamo visto, quella dei due mondi. Nel racconto delle *Confessioni*, invece, i *libri Platonicorum* contengono l'equivalente della dottrina della Trinità, uno dei nuclei centrali della dottrina cristiana che più si presta ad una riflessione razionale (per Agostino l'altro, l'Incarnazione, non sembra filosoficamente tematizzabile, ma solo da accettare nell'umiltà). Proprio riflettendo su questo mistero, cioè cercando di analizzarlo e comprenderlo fin dove sia possibile, la filosofia può veramente diventare «consecrata». È quello che ci dice il *De ordine*:

> Philosophia rationem promittit et vix paucissimos liberat, quos tamen non modo non contemnere illa mysteria, sed sola intelligere ut intelligenda sunt cogit[22].

I *mysteria* sono appunto la fede nella Trinità che la filosofia in qualche modo deve trascrivere nel suo registro terminologico ed argomentativo. Come prosegue immediatamente il testo del *De ordine*:

> Nullumque aliud habet negotium quae vera (...) philosophia est quam ut doceat quod sit omnium rerum principium sine principio quantusque in eo maneat intellectus quidve inde in nostram salutem sine ulla degeneratione manaverit, quem unum Deum omnipotentem eumque tripotentem, Patrem Filium et Spiritum sanctum docent veneranda mysteria[23].

In questa *philosophia consecrata*, però, non trovano posto i filosofi in carne ed ossa, uomini cioè caratterizzati da una specifica forma di

[21] Cfr. Id., *De vera religione*, 7, 12, 128, ed. Daur cit., p. 196,6-7.

[22] Id., *De ordine*, II, 5, 16, 1002, ed. Green cit., pp. 115,43 - 116,46.

[23] *Ibid.*, p. 116,46-52.

esercizio della razionalità e da una peculiare e riconoscibile forma di vita. Se mai la loro attività ha avuto un senso, essa lo ha comunque avuto solo fino all'avvento dei *tempora Christiana*. Qui anche coloro che hanno contribuito all'elaborazione di una «verissima philosophia», i Platonici, cessano la loro funzione. Nel 410 Agostino riceve una lettera (non pervenutaci) in cui un giovane greco, Dioscoro, appassionato di filosofia, gli chiedeva spiegazioni di passi del *De natura deorum* di Cicerone relativi alla 'teologia' di Anassimene, Anassagora e Democrito. Nella sua lunga risposta (l'*Epistola* 118) il vescovo di Ippona traccia una breve storia delle scuole filosofiche e dello scontro tra Stoici, Epicurei e Platonici sulla falsariga di quanto già detto nel *Contra Academicos*, traendone però una conclusione che nello scritto giovanile rimaneva implicita:

> Satis mihi videtur esse demonstratum errores gentium, sive de moribus, sive de natura rerum, sive de ratione investigandae veritatis, (...) expugnantibus doctis et tanta disserendi subtilitate atque copia subvertentibus durasse (...) usque in tempora Christiana. (...) Ex quo intelligitur ipsos quoque Platonicae gentis philosophos paucis mutatis quae Christiana improbat disciplina, invictissimo uni regi Christo pias cervices oportere submittere[24].

I *tempora Christiana*, i tempi dell'avvento della *verissima philosophia*, non hanno più bisogno di 'filosofi', almeno nel senso classico del termine. Come ha giustamente più volte sostenuto Goulven Madec, per Agostino nel Cristianesimo essi trovano il proprio compimento ed il proprio approdo, ma anche, aggiungerei io, la propria scomparsa, sublimata quanto si vuole, ma pur sempre scomparsa. Rimane per la filosofia, oltre alla possibilità di gettare luce sui *mysteria* della vera religione, il compito di difenderla dalle eresie, cioè, nell'idea del vescovo di Ippona, dalla molteplicità di forme in cui continua a manifestarsi una *ybris* filosofica sia pure introiettata dal Cristianesimo. È quello che Agostino chiede a Dioscoro: dopo avergli spiegato l'assurdità dei suoi interessi dossografici da un punto di vista strettamente documentario

[24] Id., *Epistula ad Dioscorum*, 3, 21, in Id., *Epistolae*, 118, PL 33, 442, ed. A. Goldbacher, 5 voll., Praha – Wien – Leipzig 1895-1923 (CSEL, 34/1-2, 44, 57, 58), II, pp. 684,17 - 685,7.

e 'filologico' («[tu] Graecorum philosophorum dogmata, vel potius dogmatum particulas quasdam discerptas atque dispersas in Latinis dialogis quam in ipsorum auctorum libris Graecis tota atque contexta discere maluisti»)[25], il vescovo di Ippona afferma che in ogni caso questo tipo di conoscenze è del tutto inutile. L'unica possibile giustificazione sarebbe quella che è necessario conoscere gli errori contrari alla dottrina cristiana per meglio combatterli. Ma in questo caso «de haereticis potius qui se Christianos vocant, quam de Anaxagora et Democrito nobis cogitandum fuit»[26]. Tutti gli eretici, infatti, «audent imperitos quasi ratione traducere» ed è per questo che il «fidei clementissimus imperator (...) pauciores pie doctos (...) copiosissimis apparatibus etiam invictissimae rationis armavit». Purché, però, ci si ricordi sempre che il giusto ordine consiste nell'usare questi *apparatus* solo in aiuto dei molti deboli accolti e protetti nella rocca della fede: «Verum illa rectissima disciplina est in arcem fidei quam maxime recipi infirmos, ut pro eis iam tutissime positis, fortissima ratione pugnetur»[27]. E per far questo, dice infine Agostino al suo giovane corrispondente, non c'è bisogno di ripercorrere e discutere gli scritti dei filosofi: bastano le *regulae veritatis* della dialettica (che evidentemente sono uno strumento neutro, non compromesso con nessuna particolare scuola di pensiero): «Quanto enim melius atque salubrius (...) ipsas veritatis regulas multo certius et brevius accipis (...), si multorum annosas et decrepitas falsitates studio iactantiore quam prudentiore didiceris»[28].

Questi testi di Agostino, accanto al carattere prescrittivo ne hanno uno descrittivo: gli *errores* dei Gentili, vale a dire in termini meno spregiativi le discussioni condotte da uomini in carne ed ossa che fanno concretamente filosofia sono per lui effettivamente terminate: «nostra aetate obmutuisse conspicimus, ut vix iam in scholis rhetorum commemoretur tantum, quae fuerint illorum sententiae». Questi inutili «certamina» sono stati ormai eliminati anche dai luoghi che dovrebbero essere la loro sede di elezione: «Certamina tamen etiam de loquacissimis Graecorum gymnasiis

[25] *Ibid.*, 2, 10, 437, pp. 674,25 - 675,2.
[26] *Ibid.*, 2, 12, 438, p. 677,6-8.
[27] *Ibid.*, 5, 32, 448, p. 696,7-21.
[28] *Ibid.*, 1, 7, 435, pp. 671,22 - 672,2.

eradicata et compressa sunt»[29]. La prima affermazione assume per noi un senso quasi profetico: il Medioevo, o almeno l'Alto Medioevo, avrebbe ricevuto le poche reliquie delle grandi scuole post-aristoteliche proprio attraverso le glosse di grammatici e retori. La seconda ricorda alcuni testi in cui Ambrogio e Girolamo si rallegrano della progressiva scomparsa dei 'filosofi' di contro al trionfo della Chiesa:

> In ipsis gymnasiis suis iam dialectica tacet. (...) Soli in suis gymnasiis philosophi remanserunt. (...) Illi cottidie a suis consortibus deseruntur, qui copiose disputant, isti cottidie crescunt, qui simpliciter credunt. Non creditur philosophis, creditur piscatoribus, non creditur dialecticis, creditur publicanis[30].
>
> Quotusquisque nunc Aristotelem legit? Quanti Platonis vel libros cognovere vel nomen? Vix in angulis otiosi eos senes recolunt. Rusticanos vero et piscatores nostros totus orbis loquitur, universus mundus sonat[31].

Resta il problema di quanto queste affermazioni descrivano un fenomeno reale e di quanto non siano debitrici di un *topos* elaborato da intellettuali cristiani che, come Girolamo, erano rotti a tutti gli artifici retorici e magari leggevano anche Aristotele e Platone. O come Agostino che, nel momento stesso in cui condanna la *vana curiositas* di Dioscoro, dimostra una ottima conoscenza in materia. Per dirla in termini più brutali, è difficile determinare quanto sia il peso esercitato dalla propaganda e sia pure dalla «propaganda fide». Per smentire Agostino si potrebbe osservare come più di mezzo secolo dopo Sidonio Apollinare dimostrava ancora un qualche interesse per Talete, Pitagora, Democrito ed Eraclito[32]. La scomparsa in Occidente dei filosofi come gruppo riconoscibile sia dallo stile di vita che da specifici modelli di sapere (per non usare il termine troppo 'foucaultiano' prati-

[29] *Ibid.*, 3, 21, 442, p. 684,24-26.

[30] AMBROSIUS MEDIOLANENSIS, *De fide*, I, 13, ed. O. Faller, Wien 1962 (CSEL, 78), p. 37,44-50.

[31] HIERONYMUS STRIDONIUS, *Commentaria in epistolam Pauli ad Galatas*, III, PL 26, 401B, ed. G. Raspanti, Turnhout 2006 (CCSL, 74A), pp. 159,77 - 160,81.

[32] Cfr. SIDONIUS APOLLINARIS, *Carmina*, 2, vv. 156 seqq., ed. Ch. Luetjohann, in MGH, *Auctores antiquissimi*, VIII, Berlin 1887, pp. 177-178; 15, vv. 44 seqq., p. 235.

che intellettuali) è un fenomeno che si conclude solo nel secolo VI. Ma quando, sempre nella lettera a Dioscoro, il vescovo di Ippona, afferma che ora se qualche scuola filosofica (nel suo linguaggio si tratta di «erroris secta») vuole uscire allo scoperto contro la verità («hoc est contra Ecclesiam Christi») – cioè, diremmo noi, vuol essere ancora attiva – non osa farlo «nisi nomine cooperta Christiano»[33], descrive, sia pure dal suo particolare punto di vista, quello che rimarrà un atteggiamento speculativo costante almeno fino al secolo XIII.

[33] Cfr. AUGUSTINUS HIPPONENSIS, *Epistula ad Dioscorum*, 3, 21, 442, ed. Goldbacher cit. (alla nota 24), p. 685,2-3.

CARLA CASAGRANDE – SILVANA VECCHIO

ALLE ORIGINI DEL MODELLO CRISTIANO DELLE PASSIONI

AGOSTINO, CASSIANO, GREGORIO MAGNO

1. *Agostino*

> Da noi, i cittadini della santa città di Dio, che nel pellegrinaggio della vita su questa terra vivono secondo Dio, provano paura e desiderio, dolore e gioia secondo la sacra Scrittura e la sana dottrina; e poiché retto è il loro amore per Dio tutti questi loro affetti sono retti[1].

Queste parole di Agostino, tratte dal libro XIV della *Città di Dio*, sintetizzano la sua riflessione sulle passioni, così come si sviluppa attraverso una serie di osservazioni contenute nei libri IX e appunto XIV[2]. Ma soprattutto queste parole segnano un confine

[1] AUGUSTINUS HIPPONENSIS, *De civitate Dei*, XIV, 9, 1, PL 41, 413, edd. B. Dombart – A. Kalb, Turnhout 1955 (CCSL, 47-48), II, p. 426,4-8: «Apud nos autem iuxta scripturas sacras sanamque doctrinam cives sanctae civitatis Dei in hujus vitae peregrinatione secundum Deum viventes metuunt cupiuntque, dolent gaudentque et quia rectus est amor eorum, istas omnes affectiones rectas habent».

[2] Cfr. *ibid.*, IX, 4-5, 258-261, pp. 251-255, e XIV, 5-9, 408-417, pp. 419-430. Queste pagine della *Città di Dio* presentano l'ultima formulazione della riflessione agostiniana sulle passioni, una formulazione per molti versi distante da quelle precedenti. Per un quadro complessivo delle posizioni di Agostino sul tema delle passioni, vedi innanzitutto l'ampia rassegna dei passi agostiniani sul tema in G. O'DALY – A. ZUMKELLER, s.v. *Affectus (passio, perturbatio)*, in *Augustinus-Lexikon*, hrsg. C. Meyer, I, Basel 1986, pp. 166-180; quindi i contributi critici di: F.-J. THONNARD, *La vie affective de l'âme selon Saint Augustin*, in «L'année théologique augustinienne», 13 (1953), pp. 33-55; I. BOCHET, *Saint Augustin et le désir de Dieu*, Paris 1982, pp. 70-77; M. L. COLISH, *The Stoic Tradition from Antiquity to the Early Middle Ages*, 2 voll., Leiden 1985 (Studies in the History of Christian Thought,

10.1484/M.NUTRIX-EB.1.101238

culturale: le passioni non sono malattie dell'anima dalle quali guarire o movimenti irrazionali e impetuosi da moderare in vista di un ideale di saggezza, ma sono strumento di salvezza. La diffidenza che i filosofi pagani avevano variamente manifestato verso i fenomeni passionali è scomparsa: quelle stesse passioni, che prima impedivano o, nel migliore dei casi, rallentavano il conseguimento della perfezione e della felicità, ora presso i cristiani, «da noi» (*apud nos*), come rivendica quasi con orgoglio Agostino, si impongono come mezzi necessari per ritornare a una beatitudine originaria, dalla quale peraltro non sono completamente escluse: se nella vita beata non c'è posto per il dolore e il timore, la gioia e l'amore invece vi resteranno per sempre[3]. L'affermazione agostiniana che la felicità è possibile solo attraverso e nelle passioni delimita dunque una linea di confine dal quale prende le mosse la storia delle passioni nel Medioevo[4].

Cosa sono e quali sono, per Agostino, le passioni? Sono almeno quattro i nomi che nel lessico agostiniano designano ciò che i greci chiamano, più semplicemente, *pathe*: turbamenti, affezioni, affetti, passioni. Una terminologia molteplice e fluida che fa capo a tradizioni diverse, ma che non preoccupa Agostino il quale di fatto considera quei quattro termini sostanzialmente equivalenti[5].

35), II, pp. 207-219 e 221-225; R. Bodei, *'Ordo amoris'. Conflitti terreni e felicità celeste*, Milano 1991; O. Grassi, *Passioni, desiderio e ragione in Sant'Agostino*, in *La passione della ragione*, a c. di G. Dalmasso, Milano 1991, pp. 41-55; E. Bermon, *La théorie des passions chez Saint Augustin*, in *Les Passions antiques et médiévales*, dir. B. Besnier – P.-F. Moreau – L. Renault, Paris 2003, pp. 173-197; M. C. Nussbaum, *L'intelligenza delle emozioni*, Bologna 2004, pp. 623-656 (ed. or. Cambridge 2001); C. Casagrande, *Agostino, i medievali e il buon uso delle passioni*, in *Agostino d'Ippona. Presenza e pensiero. La scoperta dell'interiorità*, a c. di A. Marini, Milano 2004, pp. 65-75; S. Knuuttila, *Emotions in Ancient and Medieval Philosophy*, Oxford 2004, pp. 152-172; D. Boquet, *L'ordre de l'affect au Moyen Âge. Autour de l'anthropologie affective d'Aelred de Rievaulx*, Caen 2005, pp. 77-91.

[3] Cfr. Augustinus Hipponensis, *ibid.*, XIV, 9, 6, 416, p. 429,143-145: «Beata vero eademque aeterna (vita) amorem habebit et gaudium non solum rectum, verum etiam certum; timorem autem ac dolorem nullum».

[4] Si tratta indubbiamente di un confine convenzionale. Quella di Agostino è solo una delle voci del dibattito sul valore delle passioni nel processo di perfezionamento spirituale, che vede schierati su fronti opposti i Padri greci e quelli latini; un dibattito che certamente, come si vedrà più avanti, non si chiude con Agostino, la cui posizione, tuttavia, per radicalità e autorevolezza, costituisce un punto di svolta e fonte di continua ispirazione per la successiva riflessione medievale.

[5] Cfr. Augustinus Hipponensis, *ibid.*, IX, 4, 1, 258, p. 251,1-6: «Duae sunt sententiae philosophorum de his animi motibus, quae Graeci πάθη, nostri autem qui-

Più complicato è se mai mettere bene a fuoco l'oggetto designato tanto esso appare molteplice e svariato. Una consolidata classificazione di origine stoica, alla quale Agostino si rifà senza esitazioni individua quattro passioni principali (desiderio, timore gioia, dolore) cui possono essere ricondotte tutte le altre, che sono molte e diverse, come notava con un certo stupore lo stesso Agostino nelle *Confessioni*: «È più facile contare i capelli di un uomo che gli affetti e i moti del suo cuore»[6]. Ancora più impegnativo, ed è questo l'obiettivo che anima le pagine della *Città di Dio*, è valutare da un punto di vista etico quei movimenti interiori; stabilire cioè se, come e quanto ciò che viene chiamato ora passione, ora perturbazione, ora affetto, ora affezione, sia un bene o un male in vista del raggiungimento della felicità. Questo significa infatti fare i conti con le risposte che a questa domanda hanno dato le più autorevoli scuole filosofiche pagane.

Agostino non si sottrae alla sfida. La prima mossa consiste nel ridurre i suoi molti avversari a uno solo. A platonici e aristotelici viene attribuita la comune idea che le passioni possono convivere con la saggezza, purché controllate e moderate dalla ragione. Gli stoici, sostenitori di una dottrina secondo la quale passioni e saggezza sono tra loro radicalmente incompatibili, sembrerebbero invece irriducibili a ogni tentativo di assimilazione. Ma le cose, spiega Agostino, non stanno proprio così: lo scandalo stoico di una felicità senza affetti non ha fondamento poiché in realtà gli stoici sostengono, con altre parole, le stesse opinioni dei platonici e degli aristotelici. Tutti infatti propongono un ideale di saggezza in cui la ragione domina, senza esserne dominata, passioni che, se non possono essere eliminate, sono però moderate al punto da essere ininfluenti[7]. Di fatto le differenze tra i pagani sul tema delle passioni sono irrilevanti rispetto a quella fondamentale che divide i pagani dai cristiani.

dam, sicut Cicero, perturbationes, quidam affectiones vel affectus, quidam vero, sicut iste [*scil.* Apuleius], de Graeco expressius passiones vocant. Has ergo perturbationes sive affectiones sive passiones quidam philosophi dicunt (...)». Nelle opere precedenti Agostino preferisce usare *affectus*, *affectiones*, *perturbationes*; nella *Città di Dio*, usa prevalentemente, nel l. IX, *passiones* nel l. XIV, *affectus* e *affectiones*.

[6] Id., *Confessiones*, IV, 14, 22, PL 32, 702, ed. L. M. Verheijen, Turnhout 1981 (CCSL, 27), p. 51,28-29: «Et capilli eius [i.e. hominis] magis numerabiles quam affectus eius et motus cordis eius».

[7] Cfr. Id., *De civitate Dei*, IX, 4, 1-3, 258-260, pp. 251-253.

Agostino è convinto che l'avvento del cristianesimo abbia comportato una frattura radicale rispetto al passato e che uno degli effetti di quella frattura sia anche una diversa concezione e un diverso uso dell'affettività. In che consiste questa 'diversità' cristiana sulle passioni? Nel fatto che il governo che la mente, la parte superiore dell'anima, esercita sui movimenti affettivi, è a sua volta governato da Dio. Questo fa sì che le passioni «siano convertite alla giustizia», che acquistino cioè una direzione, una finalità, un senso che prima non avevano. E infatti «nel nostro ordinamento non si vuole sapere se, ma perché l'animo devoto si adiri; non se sia triste, ma per quale motivo, non se ha paura, ma di che cosa». Insomma le passioni, se provate per un giusto fine sono lodevoli e virtuose. È il caso dell'ira verso i peccatori, della tristezza per gli afflitti, della paura per quanti sono in pericolo. È il caso della misericordia che non è, come ritenevano gli stoici, capacità di aiutare il prossimo senza alcun coinvolgimento affettivo, ma compassione dell'altrui miseria[8]. La mente dunque esercita la funzione di governo che i filosofi le hanno sempre riconosciuto; ma il governo questa volta non consiste più solo nel moderare e contenere. Per i cristiani governare le passioni significa prima di tutto 'convertire', cioè dirigere il movimento passionale verso una giusta direzione. La moderazione interviene eventualmente solo dopo che la conversione è stata operata.

Agostino conosce troppo bene lo stretto rapporto che lega la passione al peccato per dimenticare quanto passioni non 'convertite' al bene possano essere pericolose. Prima tra tutte, il desiderio, che, dopo il peccato originale, si declina facilmente in *libido*, *cupiditas*, *concupiscentia*, cioè in un desiderio incontrollabile e perverso capace a sua volta di volgere in senso negativo tutti gli altri affetti. Ma quale è la causa, quale il percorso che porta le passioni ad essere virtuose o peccaminose? Il peso della colpa ricade tutto sulle parti superiori dell'anima: sulla ragione, cui spettava il riconoscimento dell'ordine, e soprattutto sulla volontà che, nella sua assoluta libertà, ha scelto di destituire la ragione dalla sua funzione. Certo, il peccato consiste nella concupiscenza, nel desiderio disordinato, ma il disordine di quella passione non è l'espressione di una irrefrenabile e irrazionale forza emotiva che

[8] Cfr. *ibid.*, IX, 5, 260-261, pp. 254-255.

proviene dal corpo o dalle parti inferiori dell'anima ma la conseguenza e la pena di un uso mancato della ragione, a sua volta dovuto a un uso perverso della volontà[9]. Allora, se la passione disordinata è in definitiva il frutto della volontà perversa e non di una naturale e incontrollabile impetuosità della passione stessa, se ne può dedurre che là dove la volontà è retta la passione sarà ordinata. Le passioni insomma trovano nello stretto rapporto che le lega alla volontà i motivi della loro dannazione come della loro redenzione.

Nelle pagine della *Città di Dio* quel legame si fa strettissimo al punto che le passioni vengono definite volontà (*voluntates*), volontà di assenso a ciò che vogliamo, volontà di dissenso da ciò che non vogliamo: «Quando l'assenso consiste nella ricerca di ciò che vogliamo, si chiama desiderio, mentre quando consiste nel godimento di ciò che vogliamo, prende il nome di gioia. Ugualmente, il dissenso da ciò che non vogliamo che accada è una volontà chiamata paura, mentre il dissenso da ciò che accade contrariamente dal nostro volere, è una volontà chiamata tristezza»[10]. Modi della volontà, le passioni sono anche modi dell'amore, dato che è l'amore a muovere la volontà e a deciderne la direzione: «l'amore proteso a possedere il suo oggetto è desiderio, mentre quello che lo possiede e gode è gioia; l'amore che rifiuta ciò che lo contrasta è timore, quello che ne soffre se accade è tristezza». Se le passioni sono declinazioni della volontà e dell'amore, esse sono dunque lodevoli o riprovevoli a seconda della qualità della volontà e dell'amore[11]. Una volontà perversa,

[9] Cfr. Id., *De libero arbitrio*, I, PL 32, 1221-1240, ed. W. M. Green, Turnhout 1970 (CCSL, 29), pp. 211-235. Cfr. Bermon, *La théorie*, cit., pp. 175-179.

[10] Augustinus Hipponensis, *De civitate Dei*, IX, 6, 409, p. 421,3-13: «Voluntas est quippe in omnibus; immo omnes nihil aliud quam voluntates sunt. Nam quid est cupiditas et laetitia nisi voluntas in eorum consensione quae volumus? Et quis est metus atque tristitia nisi voluntas in dissensione ab his quae nolumus? Sed cum consentimus appetendo ea quae volumus, cupiditas; cum autem consentimus fruendo his quae volumus, laetitia vocatur. Itemque cum dissentimus ab eo quod accidere nolumus, talis voluntas metus est; cum autem dissentimus ab eo quod nolentibus accidit, talis voluntas tristitia est».

[11] Cfr. *ibid.*, XIV, 7, 2, 410, p. 422,40-45: «Recta itaque voluntas est bonus amor et voluntas perversa malus amor. Amor ergo inhians habere quod amatur, cupiditas est, id autem habens eoque fruens laetitia, fugiens quod ei adversatur, timor est, idque si acciderit sentiens tristitia est. Proinde mala sunt ista, si malus amor est; bona, si bonus».

mossa da un amore disordinato, che privilegia l'amore di sé e del prossimo all'amore per Dio, si declina in passioni malvagie; una volontà retta, mossa da un amore ordinato, cioè da un amore che ama Dio per se stesso e il prossimo, la propria anima e il proprio corpo solo in funzione di Dio, dà luogo a passioni buone: la grazia di Dio converte le passioni verso il bene facendone un efficace strumento di salvezza. «Gli affetti della volontà buona», spiega Agostino con una metafora felice alla quale ricorre più volte, «sono per l'anima piedi, scale e ali: camminiamo, dunque, innalziamoci e voliamo grazie ad essi»[12].

Fondamento ed esempio di questa «via passionale» alla salvezza è il Cristo. Agostino non è certo il primo a porre il problema: alle spalle delle pagine delle *Città di Dio* si intravede il lungo dibattito, teologico e morale insieme, nel quale i primi intellettuali cristiani si sono variamente divisi sull'impassibilità divina e sulle passioni del Cristo. In questo dibattito Agostino interviene con una posizione netta: Cristo non ha finto, come ritenevano alcuni, di provare passioni, e nemmeno, come ritenevano altri, ha subito le passioni del corpo senza provare alcuna passione nell'anima. Cristo, in quanto uomo, ha veramente provato tutti i turbamenti dell'anima umana: il desiderio, la tristezza, la gioia, il timore, l'ansia, l'ira. Ma, a differenza dell'uomo, che prova passioni a causa della sua debolezza, il Cristo, in cui la debolezza è volontaria (*infirmitas voluntaria*), prova passioni perché lo vuole. E lo vuole per mostrare agli uomini la forza delle loro deboli passioni e per insegnare loro come usarle. Non ci può essere niente di indegno nelle passioni dell'uomo se quelle stesse passioni hanno turbato il loro Signore, nei cui turbamenti noi dobbiamo vedere noi stessi per non disperarci quando siamo turbati. Nessun disprezzo, nessuna paura, nessuna diffidenza per tutti i turbamenti dell'animo. Le passioni, se mosse, come lo furono quelle del Cristo, dall'amore per Dio e per il prossimo, sono per l'uomo una ri-

[12] Id., *Enarrationes in Psalmos*, 38, 2, PL 36, 413, edd. E. Dekkers – I. Fraipont, Turnhout 1956 (CCSL, 38), pp. 402,19-21: «Intus autem et pedes, et scalae, et pennae affectus sunt bonae voluntatis. His ambulemus, his adscendamus, his volemus». Per altri passi cfr. M. Fiedrowicz, *'Cives sanctae civitatis Dei omnes affectiones rectas habent' (Civ. 14,9): Terapia delle passioni e preghiera in Sant'Agostino*, in *L'etica cristiana dei secoli* III *e* IV*: eredità e confronti*, XXIV Incontro di studiosi dell'Antichità cristiana nei secoli III e IV (Roma, 4-6 maggio 1995), Roma 1996, pp. 431-440, in partic. p. 439.

sorsa preziosa. «Si turbi completamente l'animo del cristiano, non per miseria ma per misericordia; tema che gli uomini periscano allontanandosi dal Cristo; si rattristi se qualcuno perisce allontanandosi dal Cristo; desideri che gli uomini siano guadagnati dal Cristo; e si rallegri quando lo sono; si rattristi per essere lontano dal Cristo, desideri di regnare con lui e si rallegri mentre spera di regnare con lui»[13].

Nel loro insieme le pagine agostiniane appaiono nello stesso tempo inaugurali e programmatiche. Inaugurali perché istituiscono un legame tra passioni e salvezza, sconosciuto e impensabile nel mondo antico, perché fondato sulla figura del Cristo; programmatiche perché contengono in forma abbreviata e si potrebbe quasi dire 'profetica' le tematiche, il contesto, l'intenzione e le finalità che caratterizzeranno il discorso su ciò che i medievali, con la stessa fluidità che caratterizza il lessico agostiniano, chiameranno ora *passiones*, ora *affectiones*, ora *affectus*.

Eppure il discorso medievale sulle passioni non è totalmente riconducibile al modello agostiniano. E questo non solo perché ci saranno altre definizioni e classificazioni, altre concezioni dell'anima e delle sue facoltà, una diversa idea del rapporto tra anima e corpo, una più complessa analisi psicologica e scientifica sui movimenti passionali, ma anche perché quella rottura nei confronti del modello filosofico antico che il discorso agostiniano presuppone non rappresenta l'unica via attraverso la quale la riflessione antica si trasmette ai secoli medievali. Altre voci autorevoli provenienti dalla patristica greca e latina sembrano riproporre proprio quel modello stoico contro il quale Agostino ha polemizzato.

[13] AUGUSTINUS HIPPONENSIS, *In Iohannis Evangelium*, 60, 1-5, PL 35, 1797-1799, ed. R. Willems, Turnhout 1954 (CCSL, 36), pp. 478-480; per il passaggio citato: 3, 1798, p. 479,4-10: «Turbetur plane animus christianus, non miseria, sed misericordia; timeat ne pereant homines Christo, contristetur cum perit aliquis Christo; concupiscat adquiri homines Christo, laetetur cum adquiruntur homines Christo; timeat et sibi ne pereat Christo, contristetur peregrinari se a Christo; concupiscat regnare cum Christo, laetetur dum sperat se regnaturum esse cum Christo». Cfr. P. GONDREAU, *The Passions of Christ's Soul in the Theology of St. Thomas Aquinas*, Münster 2002 (Beiträge zur Geschichte der Philosophie und Theologie des Mittelalters, N. F., 61), pp. 51-58.

2. *Cassiano*

Cassiano rappresenta la prima importante alternativa al modello agostiniano; ed è sufficiente scorrere le pagine delle *Collazioni* per trovarne la conferma: fine precipuo della vita monastica è la purezza del cuore, ed è in vista di tale obiettivo che il monaco affronta le asperità della vita solitaria: digiuni, veglie, preghiere continue e faticose hanno come obiettivo di «sgomberare il cuore e mantenerlo libero da tutte le passioni». La purificazione del cuore rappresenta al tempo stesso lo strumento principale di questo processo e il punto d'arrivo dell'intero percorso, il culmine della virtù monastica[14]. E in questo percorso non c'è posto per le passioni. Come una cittadella arroccata su se stessa, il cuore puro è isolato e difeso dall'assalto delle passioni.

Affermazioni di questo tipo segnano una distanza assai netta dalla riflessione agostiniana e alludono ad una concezione delle passioni profondamente diversa da quella del maestro di Ippona. Nell'ideale monastico della purezza del cuore proposto da Cassiano sembra riprendere forma l'immagine del saggio stoico esente dalle passioni contro la quale Agostino aveva apertamente polemizzato.

In effetti la 'purezza del cuore' di Cassiano traduce esattamente quello che nei testi monastici della tradizione orientale viene designato come *apateia*, e sullo sfondo delle *Collazioni* si intravede l'intenso dibattito che proprio sul tema delle passioni ha attraversato la cultura alessandrina e si è in qualche modo cristallizzato negli scritti di un altro grande monaco, che di Cassiano è stato il maestro, Evagrio Pontico[15]. Sul ruolo che l'*apateia* svolge nelle

[14] Cfr. IOHANNES CASSIANUS, *Conlationes*, I, 5-7, PL 49, 487A-489A, ed. E. Pichery, 3 voll., Paris 1955, I, (SC, 42), p. 82-84: «'Habentes quidem scopon vestrum in cordis puritate, finem vero vitam aeternam' (cfr. *Rm* 6, 22). (...) Quidquid ergo nos ad hunc scopon, id est puritatem cordis potest dirigere, tota virtute sectandum est, quidquid autem ab hac retrahit, ut perniciosum ac noxium devitandum. (...) Pro hac solitudo sectanda est, pro hac ieiunia, vigilias, labores, corporis nuditatem, lectionem ceterasque virtutes debere nos suscipere noverimus, ut scilicet per illas ab universis passionibus noxiis inlaesum parare cor nostrum et conservare possimus et ad perfectionem caritatis istis gradibus innitendo conscendere».

[15] Al tema dell'impassibilità, ai modi per raggiungerla e ai segni per riconoscerla è dedicato il *Practicus*, il principale trattato di Evagrio: *Traité Pratique ou Le moine*, éd. par A. e C. Guillaumont, 2 voll., Paris 1971 (SC, 170-171); per un'ana-

opere di Evagrio non ci possono essere dubbi: l'*apateia* è il fiore della *practikè*, di quella scienza morale e religiosa che costituisce la pedagogia indispensabile della vita monastica e alla quale Evagrio ha dedicato buona parte della sua produzione letteraria. Discepolo di Clemente Alessandrino, Evagrio ha sviluppato sul tema dell'*apateia* una profonda riflessione che in un certo senso esprime tutta la distanza che separa la tradizione cristiana orientale da quella occidentale. A differenza da quanto accade in occidente, infatti, la nozione di 'impassibilità' che la filosofia greca ha consegnato al cristianesimo dei primi secoli, rielaborata dalle dottrine gnostiche e origeniane e recepita dal monachesimo egiziano, continua a rappresentare per Evagrio e per tutta la tradizione orientale un ideale di virtù somma, al quale i monaci soprattutto debbono tendere[16]. L'apatia è per Evagrio il segno della salute dell'anima, contrapposta a quello stato di malattia che è costituito dalle passioni[17]; ma è anche il culmine della virtù, dal momento che, liberando l'anima dal turbamento delle passioni, ricostituisce quella perfetta armonia tra le sue diverse parti che consente a ciascuna di esse di esercitare la virtù sua propria, e a tutte insieme di cooperare nella realizzazione della giustizia.

Il trasparente riferimento alle dottrine stoiche conferma la distanza culturale che separa la concezione evagriana dalla rilettura che, quasi negli stessi anni, Agostino sta conducendo sul tema dell'impassibilità. Distanza che non è sfuggita a Girolamo, il quale non ha esitato ad attaccare Evagrio proprio sul tema dell'apatia, rimproverandogli di proporre un ideale disumano o comunque irraggiungibile:

lisi del tema cfr. l'*Introduction* di A. GUILLAUMONT, *ibid.*, I, pp. 98-112. Più in generale sul tema dell'*apateia* nella patristica greca e latina, cfr. G. BARDY, s.v. *Apatheia*, in *Dictionnaire de Spiritualité, Ascétique et Mystique*, I, Paris 1937, coll. 727-746; M. SPANNEUT, *Le stoïcisme dans l'histoire de la patience chrétienne*, in «Mélanges de sciences religieuses», 39 (1982), pp. 101-130; G. VERBEKE, *The Presence of Stoicism in Medieval Thought*, Washington 1983, p. 48 seqq.

[16] Cfr. J.-C. LARCHET, *Thérapeutique des maladies spirituelles. Une introduction à la tradition ascétique de l'Église orthodoxe*, Paris 1997; D. N. BELL, *«Apateia»: The Convergence of Bizantine and Cistercian Spirituality*, in «Citeaux», 38 (1987), pp. 141-163; KNUUTTILA, *Emotions* cit. (alla nota 2), pp. 136-151.

[17] EVAGRIUS PONTICUS, *Practicus*, 56, ed. Guillaumont – Guillaumont cit. (alla nota 15), pp. 630-631.

> Evagrio ha pubblicato un libro sulla *apateia*, termine che noi possiamo tradurre con 'impassibilità' o 'imperturbabilità', cioè lo stato in cui l'animo non è turbato da nessun pensiero e da nessun vizio, e, per dirla in breve, o è un sasso, o è un Dio[18].

L'accusa di Gerolamo, schierato su questo tema a fianco di Agostino nel denunciare la disumanità dell'apatia stoica, risente evidentemente, come del resto le affermazioni di Agostino stesso, del clima acceso della polemica antipelagiana, e finisce per travisare almeno in parte quello che è l'autentico pensiero di Evagrio. Ma la distanza che su questo tema separa i due Padri della Chiesa occidentale dai monaci della tradizione orientale appare comunque netta e rinvia a due concezioni dell'universo passionale difficilmente omologabili.

Tale distanza ci impone in qualche modo di tornare indietro per verificare quanto le concezioni orientali abbiano interferito con la cultura del monachesimo occidentale e come si siano variamente intrecciate con la lezione agostiniana nel determinare la spiritualità dell'occidente medievale. In questa ottica la figura di Cassiano appare davvero centrale; l'esperienza monastica condotta tra la Palestina e l'Egitto che ha segnato la prima parte della sua vita lo ha messo in contatto con un mondo che rappresenta agli occhi della cristianità intera un ideale di perfezione[19]: le imprese eroiche dei monaci egiziani costituiscono un modello difficilmente superabile e gli insegnamenti dei padri del deserto condensano tutta la sapienza accumulata nel corso di due secoli da questi uomini forti nella ricerca della perfezione cristiana. È questa esperienza e questa sapienza che Cassiano, trasferitosi dall'Egitto in Gallia all'inizio del v secolo vuole proporre a quanti, anche in occidente, hanno fatto la scelta monastica. Per loro, per i monaci dei monasteri da lui fondati a Lérins e a Marsiglia, Cassiano scrive le *Collazioni*, una raccolta di conferenze che sintetiz-

[18] Hieronymus Stridonius, *Epistolae*, 133, ed. I. Hilberg, 3 voll., Wien – Leipzig 1910-1918 (CSEL, 54-56), III, p. 246,1-6. Cfr. R. Sorabji, *Emotions and the Peace of Mind. From Stoic Agitation to Christian Temptation*, Oxford 2000, pp. 395-397.

[19] Cfr. M. Olphe-Galliard, s.v. *Cassien*, in *Dictionnaire de Spiritualité*, II, Paris 1953, coll. 214-276; O. Chadwick, *John Cassian*, Cambridge 2008; A. De Vogüé, *De Saint Pachome à Jean Cassien. Études littéraires et doctrinales sur le monachisme égyptien à ses debuts*, Roma 1996.

zano le dottrine apprese in Egitto circa trent'anni prima, mettendo in scena direttamente i Padri del deserto e facendoli parlare in latino[20]. Il cammino della santità che essi hanno compiuto rimane per Cassiano un ideale proponibile anche in un ambiente così diverso come quello della Gallia merovingia. Si tratta in qualche modo di ricostruire il deserto, non tanto come luogo fisico, quanto come esperienza psicologica di solitudine e di allontanamento dal mondo. Il viaggio dell'anima si configura allora come un percorso di progressiva eliminazione di tutto quanto si frappone tra il monaco e Dio; inizia con la spoliazione dai beni materiali ed esteriori, per poi passare alla purificazione interiore dell'uomo, alla rinuncia a tutto ciò che lo ingombra: abitudini, vizi, passioni, e, da ultimo, il ricordo stesso del mondo. Solo a questo punto il cuore 'puro' e perfetto, svuotato dall'ascesi, tranquillo e immobile, è pronto per la preghiera, è in condizione di conoscere Dio e di unirsi a lui nella contemplazione[21].

Il riferimento alla pratica squisitamente monastica della rinuncia si intreccia con le dottrine filosofico-teologiche di provenienza origeniana per mettere a punto una nozione di impassibilità che si distacca comunque dalla *apateia* stoica. La purezza del cuore di cui parla Cassiano infatti non è fine a se stessa; come l'*apateia* di Evagrio essa è al tempo stesso una pratica ascetica e un percorso di conoscenza, ed è inconcepibile al di fuori del nesso strettissimo che la lega da una parte alla carità, che è e rimane la virtù fondamentale del monaco, dall'altra alla gnosi, la conoscenza dei misteri di Dio, nella quale soltanto l'anima può trovare il suo appagamento e la sua pace. Svuotare il cuore da ogni impurità è operazione preliminare per consentire che esso si lasci totalmente invadere dall'amore per Dio e si acquieti in uno stato di contemplazione/unione con lui.

La natura progressiva di questo percorso scandisce le tappe dell'ascesi monastica e fa sì che la purezza del cuore/*apateia* si configuri più come un obiettivo da conquistare continuamente che come uno stato di reale impassibilità, di fatto irraggiungibile per l'uomo. Cassiano sa bene che «solo Dio è perfettamente im-

[20] Cfr. IOHANNES CASSIANUS, *Conlationes*, prol., 477A-482A, ed. Pichery cit., I, p. 76,1-4.

[21] Cfr. *ibid.*, IX, 2-3, 771A-774B, ed. Pichery, II, Paris 1967 (SC, 54), pp. 40-43.

mutabile», e che l'imperturbabilità alla quale l'uomo aspira è continuamente minacciata, più ancora che dalle pulsioni del corpo dalla natura stessa dell'anima e dalla sua strutturale mobilità, che la porta necessariamente a vagabondare, volteggiando da una parte e dall'altra[22]. Grazie a questa naturale mobilità, l'anima, come una piuma, potrebbe volare leggera verso l'alto, ma la sua 'rettitudine' originaria è ormai compromessa dal peccato e la sua stessa incontrollata vitalità le impone continue deviazioni dal percorso che la conduce a Dio. Gli affetti che perennemente la ingombrano, il desiderio, il timore, la gioia, la tristezza, rischiano, se non sono correttamente imbrigliati, di trascinarla verso il basso, determinando uno stato patologico di tutte le sue parti. Le passioni, malattie dell'anima, hanno dunque un'unica causa, ma, proprio come accade per il corpo, assumono nomi diversi in relazione alle singole parti dell'anima che vengono colpite, e che Cassiano descrive secondo il modello platonico: «Quando la passione cattiva attacca una di queste facoltà, a seconda dell'alterazione che determina, prende il nome di un vizio specifico. Se infatti la peste del vizio attacca la parte razionale, genera vanagloria, gonfiore, invidia, superbia, presunzione, contesa, eresia. Se colpisce la parte irascibile, produce furore, impazienza, tristezza, accidia, pusillanimità, crudeltà. Se corrompe la parte concupiscibile, dà vita a gola, lussuria, avidità, avarizia, desideri perversi e terreni»[23].

I moti che continuamente agitano l'anima si sono trasformati in passioni cattive[24]; trascinata sempre più verso il basso e verso il 'mondo', l'anima è preda di numerosi vizi, otto per la precisione, gli otto vizi principali, che riprendono gli otto 'pensieri' o gli otto spiriti malvagi di cui parlava Evagrio, ma dai quali scaturiscono innumerevoli vizi secondari[25].

[22] Cfr. *ibid.*, VII, 4, 671C-673B, ed. Pichery, I, pp. 247-249.

[23] *Ibid.*, XXIV, 15, 1306A-1307A, ed. Pichery, III, Paris 1971 (SC, 64), pp. 186,26 - 187,27.

[24] Cfr. *ibid.*, XII, 5, 875C-876A, ed. Pichery, II, pp. 126,25 - 127,4: «Nullatenus enim valet vivacitas mentis absque alicuius desiderii vel timoris, gaudii vel maeroris affectione subsistere, nisi haec eadem in bonam partem fuerint inmutata. Et idcirco si carnales concupiscentias de cordibus nostris desideramus extrudere, spiritales in earum locis plantemus protinus voluptates, ut his animus noster semper innexus et habeat quibus iugiter inmoretur et inlecebras praesentium ac temporalium respuat gaudiorum». Cfr. OLPHE-GALLIARD, s.v. *Cassien* cit., coll. 237-239.

[25] Cfr. IOHANNES CASSIANUS, *ibid.*, V, 609D-642C, ed. Pichery, I, pp. 188-217;

Nella contrapposizione tra malattie dell'anima e purezza del cuore, passioni e vizi indicano allora la stessa cosa, e Cassiano finisce per usare i due termini in maniera interscambiabile; di fatto il sistema degli otto vizi principali costituisce l'unico schema all'interno del quale è possibile classificare e descrivere le diverse passioni dell'anima[26].

3. *Gregorio Magno*

Anche Gregorio Magno parla, con un lessico che echeggia da vicino espressioni di Cassiano e della tradizione monastica orientale, di passioni carnali da mortificare e da reprimere, di affetti e desideri della carne dai quali occorre liberarsi[27].

Che cosa sono le passioni 'carnali' e cosa indica propriamente nel lessico gregoriano la 'carne'? Passioni della carne, affetti carnali, affetti terreni sono tutti sinonimi che indicano la stessa cosa: una patologia della parte spirituale dell'uomo che subisce il peso del corpo, un sovvertimento dei rapporti tra dentro e fuori, tra celeste e terreno, tra alto e basso: «I desideri celesti, le virtù dello spirito, le buone opere stanno in alto; gli affetti terreni, i desideri mondani, i vizi e i peccati stanno in basso»[28]. Nell'ambiguo rap-

EVAGRIUS PONTICUS, *Practicus*, 6-14, ed. Guillaumont – Guillaumont cit. (alla nota 15), pp. 506-534; cfr. GUILLAUMONT, *Introduction* cit., pp. 63-98. Per le origini del sistema dei vizi capitali si veda anche M.W. BLOOMFIELD, *The Seven Deadly Sins. An Introduction to the History of a Religious Concept, with Special Reference to Medieval English Literature*, East Lansing (Mich.) 1952, pp. 43-67; SORABJI, *Emotion and the Peace* cit. (alla nota 18), pp. 359-371; C. STEWART, *Evagrius Ponticus and the 'Eight Generic Logismoi'*, in *In the Garden of Evil. The Vices and Culture in the Middle Ages*, ed. by R. Newhauser, Toronto 2005, pp. 3-34.

[26] Sull'assimilazione vizi/passioni, cfr. A. SOLIGNAC, s.v. *Passions et vie spirituelle*, in *Dictionnaire de Spiritualité*, XII/1, Paris 1984, coll. 342-348.

[27] Cfr. GREGORIUS MAGNUS, *Expositiones in librum primum Regum*, IV, 175, PL 79, 292B, ed. P. Verbraken, Turnhout 1963 (CCSL, 144), p. 390,3630-3631: «Cum coelestia noscimus, si ad ea pervenire volumus, necesse est ut passiones carnis mortificemus»; ID., *Regula Pastoralis*, I, 10, PL 77, 23A, ed. B. Judic, Paris 1992 (SC, 381), pp. 160,1 - 162,3: «Ille igitur, ille modis omnibus debet ad exemplum vivendi pertrahi qui cunctis carnis passionibus moriens iam spiritaliter vivit»; ID., *Moralia in Iob*, XIV, 56, 72, PL 75, 1078C, ed. M. Adriaen, 3 voll., II, Turnhout 1979 (CCSL, 143A), p. 744,43-45: «Quia passiones carnalium desideriorum vicerant, iam liberi per virtutem spiritus in carne non erant».

[28] ID., *Expositiones in librum primum Regum*, V, 72, 350D, ed. Verbraken cit., p. 465,1820-1822: «Caelestia quidem desideria, spiritales virtutes, bona opera in sublimi sunt; affectus terreni, concupiscentiae saeculares, vitia et peccata in infimis».

porto che le lega al corpo, un corpo ormai irrimediabilmente segnato dal peccato, le passioni e gli affetti esprimono le esigenze di una carne non più sottomessa allo spirito e incapace di cogliere le realtà celesti. La colpa contratta con il peccato di Adamo ha reso l'uomo corruttibile dalle passioni, che si manifestano ormai come vizi[29].

Con un percorso analogo a quello seguito da Cassiano, anche Gregorio finisce per approdare ad una concezione delle passioni che ripropone, sia pure in forma asistematica, l'idea di fondo del modello stoico: l'identificazione delle passioni con i vizi. I vizi, tutti i vizi, pur manifestandosi in forme diverse, esprimono un identico patire dello spirito sottomesso alla carne. Certo la fenomenologia dei vizi è pressoché infinita, e anche Gregorio cerca di distinguerli e contrassegnarli con nomi diversi: rielaborando e semplificando il modello di Cassiano, lascia cadere ogni riferimento alle parti dell'anima e mette a punto un sistema semplice ma efficace che descrive la genealogia dei diversi vizi a partire da quella che è la passione principale, la superbia. Passando progressivamente da una dimensione più spirituale e interiore ad una carnalità sempre più esasperata, i vizi si generano l'uno dall'altro secondo uno schema settenario destinato a un enorme successo: vanagloria, invidia, accidia, ira, avarizia, gola, lussuria[30].

L'analisi psicologica con cui Gregorio segue il proliferare del male è funzionale soprattutto all'esigenza di approntare gli strumenti per debellare i vizi. Si tratta per il monaco di estinguere uno ad uno i singoli vizi combattendo la sua personale battaglia contro ciascuno di essi. Ma, al di là dei diversi nomi che li contraddistinguono, si tratta di ripetere sostanzialmente sempre la stessa operazione: reprimere le 'passioni' ristabilendo una corretta gerarchia tra carne e spirito, tra celeste e terreno, tra umano e divino. Tutte in qualche modo 'carnali', anche quando si presentano sotto la forma di vizi spirituali, le diverse passioni devono es-

[29] Cfr. *ibid.*, VI, 52, 442D, p. 582,1253-1255: «Ex illa quidem culpa quam ex vitiosa naturae nostrae radice contrahimus, habemus, ut corrumpi vitiorum passionibus valeamus».

[30] Cfr. ID., *Moralia in Iob*, XXXI, 45, 87, 620CD, ed. Adriaen cit., III, Turnhout 1985, (CCSL, 143B), p. 1610,2-21. Cfr. C. CASAGRANDE – S. VECCHIO, *I sette vizi capitali. Storia dei peccati nel Medioevo*, Torino 2000; C. STRAW, *Gregory, Cassian and the Cardinal Vices*, in *In the Garden of Evil* cit. (alla nota 27), pp. 35-58.

sere 'mortificate', cioè letteralmente uccise nel loro aspetto carnale, per poter recuperare la dimensione spirituale dell'uomo[31].

Non diversamente da quanto sosteneva Agostino, dunque, si tratta di rimpiazzare gli affetti carnali con affetti celesti; ma questa operazione, che per Agostino era totalmente affidata alla volontà, trova in Gregorio un potente alleato proprio nel corpo. Diventato carne a causa del peccato, il corpo costituisce il tratto specifico di un'umanità corrotta; è il marchio della fragilità e dell'insufficienza dell'uomo, ma è anche il punto di partenza del suo riscatto[32]. Dal corpo infatti può iniziare quell'opera di repressione delle passioni e dei vizi che è indispensabile per risalire alle realtà spirituali. Si tratta, sul modello del Cristo, di fare leva sul dolore del corpo per riscattare e redimere i vizi dell'anima; come i primi cristiani che hanno gioiosamente affrontato il martirio abbandonando beni terreni e affetti carnali[33], per tutti i cristiani e per i monaci in particolare, la 'mortificazione della carne' rappresenta la via per ristabilire il primato dello spirito.

In questo senso la repressione delle passioni si salda con un nuovo e diverso senso del patire stesso, un patire salvifico, che trova la sua espressione in una specifica virtù, la pazienza. La pazienza è la 'nuova' virtù del cristiano e del monaco in particolare. Nuova nella misura in cui, prendendo le distanze dalla pazienza/apatia della tradizione stoica, si colloca in un imprescindibile orizzonte teologico che ne specifica il contenuto e le conferisce un senso completamente diverso da quello che aveva nel mondo classico[34].

Già Cassiano aveva riconosciuto nella pazienza la virtù del monaco che rimpiazza l'apatia del saggio stoico[35]; ma è Gregorio

[31] Cfr. S. Vecchio, *Vizi 'carnali' e vizi 'spirituali': il peccato tra anima e corpo*, in «Etica & Politica / Ethics & Politics», Rivista di filosofia on-line, 2 (2002) (http://www2.units.it/~etica/2002_2/indexvecchio.html). Per i rapporti carne spirito in Gregorio cfr. P. Daubercies, *La théologie de la condition charnelle chez les Maîtres du haut Moyen Age*, in «Recherches de Théologie Ancienne et Médiévale», 36 (1963), pp. 5-54.

[32] Cfr. C. Straw, *Gregory the Great. Perfection in Imperfection*, Berkeley – Los Angeles – London 1988, pp. 141 seqq.

[33] Cfr. Gregorius Magnus, *Moralia in Iob*, XXIX, 23, 48, ed. Adriaen cit., III, p. 1466,35-37.

[34] Cfr. M. Spanneut, s.v. *Patience*, in *Dictionnaire de Spiritualité*, XII/1, Paris 1984, coll. 438-476.

[35] Cfr. Iohannes Cassianus, *Conlationes*, XVIII, 13, 1113AB, ed. Pichery cit.,

che, nei *Moralia in Iob*, fissa nella figura di Giobbe il prototipo di questa virtù, leggendo l'intera sua vicenda come un'enorme lezione sul dolore. Giobbe è colui che soffre; il suo stesso nome, che Gregorio, riprendendo un'indicazione di san Gerolamo, interpreta come *dolens*, allude alla sofferenza che improvvisamente e inopinatamente irrompe nella sua vita e scandisce le tappe di un percorso che si fa via via più duro e insopportabile[36].

Il destino di Giobbe appare tanto più crudele in quanto Giobbe è un uomo giusto, le cui sofferenze risultano inspiegabili in termini di punizione per eventuali colpe commesse. Il dolore che prostra la sua carne e il suo spirito è un dolore innocente, nel quale non è possibile leggere, come altre volte accade nel testo biblico, la conseguenza di un peccato. Ma è innocente anche perché tale rimane nel corso della prova: Giobbe sopporta la sofferenza senza peccare, non inveisce contro Dio, non si dispera, anzi continua, a dispetto delle insinuazioni degli amici e degli insulti della moglie, a rendere grazie a Dio, accettando pazientemente la prova estrema. E davvero di prova si tratta: Giobbe infatti è al centro di una sorta di scommessa che contrappone Satana a Dio; è l'oggetto inconsapevole di una sfida che il diavolo ha lanciato contro Dio prima ancora che contro Giobbe stesso, per misurarne la fedeltà e metterne alla prova la devozione. La sofferenza è dunque il banco di prova della sua vita e la manifestazione più completa della sua integrità morale; con un percorso inverso rispetto a quello del dolore, man mano che le tribolazioni penetrano nella sua interiorità, la virtù di Giobbe si manifesta all'esterno e i suoi meriti, dapprima conosciuti solo da Dio, si espandono co-

III, pp. 24-25: «Patientia vera atque tranquillitas absque profunda cordis humilitate nec adquiritur nec tenetur: quae si de hoc fonte descenderit, nec beneficio cellae nec perfugio solitudinis indigebit. (...) A passionibus enim ac sustentatione patientiam dici nullus ignorat, ideoque constat patientem pronuntiari neminem posse nisi eum, qui universa quae sibi fuerint inrogata absque indignatione tolerarit». Cfr. C. Casagrande, *Il dolore virtuoso. Storia medievale della pazienza*, in *Piacere e dolore. Materiali per una storia delle passioni nel Medioevo*, Atti del Convegno (Pavia, 7-8 ottobre 2005), a c. di C. Casagrande – S. Vecchio, Firenze 2009, pp. 31-47.

[36] Cfr. Gregorius Magnus, *ibid.*, Praef., 7, 16, 525D-526A, ed. Adriaen cit., I, Turnhout 1979 (CCSL, 143), pp. 20-21: «Nam quia beatus Iob venturi Redemptoris speciem teneat, etiam nomine demonstrat. Iob quippe interpretatur dolens. Quo nimirum dolore vel Mediatoris passio vel sanctae ecclesiae labor exprimitur, quae multiplici praesentis vitae fatigatione cruciatur». Cfr. anche *ibid.*, III, 14, 26, 612C, p. 131,2-3.

me profumi e gli conferiscono la fama della virtù: la sua pazienza, cioè il suo patire senza peccare, si manifesta come forza e gli conferisce un merito più alto[37].

Tale è in definitiva la lezione che Gregorio trae dal libro di Giobbe: il dolore, le tribolazioni, le 'passioni', sopportati con pazienza, si trasformano in altrettanti meriti accumulati agli occhi di Dio. Il patire 'impassibile' non è una virtù fine a se stessa, che si esaurisce e trova il suo premio nell'ostentazione di una straordinaria forza d'animo, come accadeva per la pazienza stoica, ma è eminentemente segno della gloria di Dio e strumento di santificazione. Questo perché il dolore di Giobbe, prototipo di un dolore che è al tempo stesso innocente e salvifico, acquista il suo senso pieno solo sullo sfondo teologico che legge nell'intera sua vicenda una prefigurazione della passione del Cristo. Nella lettura tipologica della Sacra Scrittura tutti i giusti vissuti prima dell'Incarnazione profetizzano l'evento centrale della storia dell'umanità, anticipando nella propria persona e nella propria vita quella che sarà la vicenda umana del Cristo. «Fu dunque necessario che anche il beato Giobbe (...) mostrasse con le proprie sofferenze ciò che il Cristo avrebbe sofferto e predicesse i misteri della passione con tanta maggiore verità in quanto li profetava con le sue sofferenze più che con le sue parole»[38]. Il dolore di Giobbe è il dolore di Cristo; i patimenti dell'uomo giusto sono figura della Passione del Mediatore. È il Cristo infatti che patisce innocente e che con la sua sofferenza e con la sua morte riscatta il peccato di Adamo: figlio di Dio e vero Dio, come manifestano i suoi miracoli, egli è nondimeno pienamente uomo e proprio i suoi patimenti sono il marchio della sua umanità[39].

[37] Cfr. *ibid.*, Praef., 2, 6, 519B, pp. 11,42-12,50; *ibid.*, 5, 12, 523CD, p. 18,52-55.

[38] *Ibid.*, 6, 14, 524D-525A, p. 19,32-37: «Unde et necesse fuit ut etiam beatus Iob (...) per ea quae [*scil.* Christus] pertulit, quae passurus esset ostenderet tantoque verius passionis illius sacramenta praediceret quanto haec non loquendo tantummodo, sed etiam patiendo prophetaret».

[39] Cfr. Id., *Homiliae in Hiezechielem prophetam,* II, I, 15, PL 76, 945B-946A, ed. M. Adriaen, Turnhout 1971 (CCSL, 142), pp. 219,439-445 e 220,463-467: «Nam miracula eius videntes trahebantur ut crederent, sed rursus passiones illius perpendentes dedignabantur Deum credere, quem carne mortalem videbant; unde factum est ut de eius cognitione dubitarent. Videbant enim esurientem, sitientem, comedentem, bibentem, lassescentem, dormientem, et purum hunc hominem esse aestimabant. (...) Sed quia et divina fecit, et humana pertulit, quasi per

Se il riferimento alle passioni del Cristo riscattava per Agostino le passioni e le coinvolgeva nel discorso della salvezza, l'esplicito riferimento alla passione del Cristo contenuto nei testi gregoriani segna in maniera definitiva lo stacco dalla tradizione antica: qualunque discorso sulle passioni non può più prescindere dal riferimento a quella che è la passione per eccellenza. Mediato dalla pazienza di Giobbe, il cortocircuito tra la passione del Cristo e le passioni umane costituisce il tratto specifico che, in forma più o meno esplicita, caratterizzerà ogni tentativo di riflessione in epoca medievale sul tema delle passioni. Per il cristiano non è possibile parlare di passioni al di fuori del quadro teologico che individua nella passione di Cristo l'inizio di una nuova storia[40].

Soggetto e protagonista di questa nuova storia è una nuova umanità, che, riscattata dal sacrificio di Cristo, fa ormai tutt'uno con lui: la dottrina paolina del corpo mistico consente di individuare nella Chiesa il corpo di cui Cristo è il capo, e la prefigurazione profetica di Giobbe si trasferisce immediatamente sulla Chiesa intera: «la sua sofferenza esprime tanto la passione del Mediatore quanto le tribolazioni della santa Chiesa»[41]. La passione del Cristo non si esaurisce cioè nell'evento storico della sua morte, ma si perpetua e si ripete nelle continue 'passioni' che flagellano il suo corpo, cioè la Chiesa. Ingiustificato e 'scandaloso' fuori dalla Chiesa, il dolore, soprattutto il dolore innocente trova una spiegazione e acquista un valore nell'unione mistica tra Cristo e i fedeli: nella Chiesa e solo nella Chiesa l'accettazione del dolore come strumento di perfezionamento in vista di una ricompensa conferisce al patire un senso nuovo e diverso, destinato a segnare profondamente la cultura medievale.

fenestras vel per cancellos ad homines prospexit, ut Deus et appareret ex miraculis, et lateret ex passionibus, et homo cerneretur ex passionibus, sed tamen esse ultra hominem ex miraculis agnosceretur».

[40] Cfr. E. Auerbach, *«Passio» come passione*, in Id., *San Francesco Dante Vico ed altri saggi di filologia romanza*, Bari 1970, pp. 155-176.

[41] Gregorius Magnus, *Moralia in Iob*, Praef., 7, 16, 525D-526A, ed. Adriaen cit., p. 21,3-4: «Quo nimirum dolore vel Mediatoris passio vel sanctae Ecclesiae labor exprimitur».

***

L'intenso dibattito sul tema delle passioni che, tra i secoli IV e VI, coinvolge i Padri della Chiesa segna il punto di partenza della riflessione 'medievale' sull'affettività[42]. I tre modelli analizzati, espressione di momenti storici e di istanze culturali assai diversi, appaiono comunque segnati dalla specificità che il cristianesimo introduce nel discorso delle passioni. Variamente ripresi in tempi e contesti diversi, gli spunti di Agostino, di Cassiano e di Gregorio, non necessariamente contrapposti, anzi a tratti intrecciati e difficilmente isolabili l'uno dall'altro, alimentano per molti secoli la riflessione psicologica medievale; e anche quando, a partire dal secolo XII, la circolazione di nuovi testi modificherà radicalmente il paradigma dell'affettività, rimangono comunque punto di riferimento imprescindibile per un discorso 'cristiano' sulle passioni.

[42] Su questo tema abbiamo avviato una ricerca di ampio respiro alla quale stiamo lavorando da qualche tempo; per una sorta di indice del lavoro, cfr. CASAGRANDE, *Agostino, i medievali* cit. (alla nota 3), pp. 71-75; alcuni studi specifici sono già stati pubblicati o sono in corso di stampa: cfr. EAD., *Guglielmo d'Auvergne e il buon uso delle passioni nella penitenza*, in *Autour de Guillaume d'Auvergne († 1249)*, Actes du Colloque de Genève (17-19 mai 2001), a c. di F. Morenzoni e Y.-J. Tilliette, Turnhout 2005 (Bibliotheque d'histoire culturelle du Moyen Âge, 2), pp. 189-201; S. VECCHIO, *'Passio', 'affectus', 'virtus': il sistema delle passioni nei trattati morali di Guglielmo d'Alvernia*, *ibid.*, pp. 173-187; C. CASAGRANDE, *'Motions of the Hearth' and Sins. The 'Specchio de' peccati' by Domenico Cavalca O.P.*, in *In the Garden of Evil* cit. (alla nota 27), pp. 128-144; EAD., *'Specchio di Croce'. Domenico Cavalca e l'ordine degli affetti*, in *Il corpo passionato. Modelli e rappresentazioni medievali dell'amore divino*, a c. di C. Bino – M. Gragnolati, in «Comunicazioni Sociali», 25 (2003), pp. 221-230; S. VECCHIO, *Introd.* a TOMMASO D'AQUINO, *Le passioni dell'anima*, Firenze 2002, pp. 5-18; EAD., *Passioni e virtù nella tradizione medievale*, in «Annali Chieresi», 2004, pp. 55-66; EAD., *Le passioni dell'anima*, in *Letture e interpretazioni di Tommaso d'Aquino oggi: cantieri aperti*, Atti del Convegno Internazionale (Milano, 12-13 settembre 2005), a c. di A. Ghisalberti –A. Petagine – R. Rizzello (Quaderni di Annali Chieresi), Torino 2008, pp. 163-174; EAD., *Passions de l'âme et péchés capitaux: les ambiguités de la culture médiévale*, in *Laster in Mittelalter / Vices in the Middle Ages*, ed. by C. Flüeler – M. Rohde, Berlin 2009 (Scrinium Friburgense, 23), pp. 45-64.

JOHN GAVIN, S. J.

LA «FEDE NUDA» E IL «REGNO» DI DIO

LA RAGIONE, LA FEDE E LA DIVINIZZAZIONE DELL'UOMO SECONDO MASSIMO IL CONFESSORE

Massimo il Confessore non tratta il rapporto fra la *fede* e la *ragione* secondo le linee del pensiero occidentale. Questo non significa, d'altra parte, che Massimo non abbia visto alcun rapporto fra queste due facoltà umane. Il pensiero di Massimo si sviluppa in una visione diversa dall'occidente in cui lo *skopos* – il piano di Dio per la divinizzazione della creazione – guida ogni elemento del suo ragionamento sulla persona umana. La 'fede' e la 'ragione' per Massimo si incontrano principalmente al livello della 'pratica' e della divinizzazione. Sono due potenze che contribuiscono alla redenzione e all'elevazione della persona e del cosmo.

In questa presentazione vorrei dimostrare come questi due poteri sono coinvolti nella realizzazione della creatura razionale.

1. *La ragione e la contemplazione*

La ragione contribuisce alla divinizzazione dell'uomo a due livelli: la pratica e la contemplazione (*praxis*, *theoria*)[1]. Nell'ordine del «progresso» della vita spirituale, la pratica (l'esercizio delle virtù e la purificazione della mente) prende il primo posto, seguito dalla contemplazione (la percezione delle cose immateriali nei *logoi*).

[1] Cfr. P. M. Blowers, *Exegesis and Spiritual Pedagogy in Maximus the Confessor: An Investigation of the «Questiones ad Thalassium»*, Notre Dame (Ind.) 1991, p. 136: «Anthropologically the coherence of the two phases (*praxis*, *theoria*) is founded on the very foundation of reason (*logos*) itself, which not only supervises the practice of virtue, but also, since it is conjoined with the mind, supports the mind's higher contemplative activity».

10.1484/M.NUTRIX-EB.1.101239

In questa presentazione, i due livelli li esaminiamo nell'ordine inverso per capire meglio la fondazione della razionalità.

Il fondamento intellegibile del cosmo è basato sullo *skopos* di Dio: la divinizzazione di tutte le cose nell'Incarnazione del *Logos*-Figlio di Dio. «Questo è il piano divino del principio di tutte le cose, concetto valido prima della creazione, che noi definiamo il fine 'preconcepito'. Tutte le cose esistono per questo fine; ma questo fine non esiste per nessuna cosa. Vedendo questo fine Dio ha creato le essenze di tutte le cose»[2]. Significa che Dio ha creato tutto nella sua libertà e che tutta la creazione si muove verso un fine previsto[3]. Per le creature razionali, c'è la possibilità di comprendere questo ordine preconcepito e razionale, e di collaborare alla realizzazione di questo piano tramite la propria volontà.

La comprensibilità di questo piano per la creatura razionale dipende dalla dottrina del *Logos-logoi*[4]. Il *Logos* principale, la fonte di tutto, è Dio, «il *Logos* di Dio il Padre, esistente in Dio in sostanza e in ipostasi, in quanto principio e causa dell'universo»[5]. I *logoi* di tutte le cose o della natura – *logoi tou einai*, *logoi tes fuseos* – definiscono le essenze di tutte le cose e il loro entrare nell'esistenza secondo la volontà di Dio. Non sono cose preesistenti (contro tendenze tipiche dell'Origenismo), e, nonostante il fatto che siano espressioni della volontà di Dio, non sono uguali a Dio stesso (contro una certa tendenza immanentistica nel pensiero dello pseudo-Dionigi, per cui i *logoi* sono anche i *thelemata* di Dio). Sono le fisse intenzioni unite nell'unico *Logos* che mantengono l'ordine delle varie cose e, specialmente, esprimono la presenza dell'unico *Logos* nel mondo. Massimo sostiene che «i molti

[2] MAXIMUS CONFESSOR, *Quaestiones ad Thalassium* (in seguito, solamente: *Thal.*), q. 60, PG 90, 621A, ed. C. Laga – C. Steel, 2 voll., Leuven 1980-1990 (CCSG, 7 e 22), II, p. 75,34-38.

[3] Cfr. P. SHERWOOD, *The Earlier Ambigua of St. Maximus the Confessor*, Roma 1955, p. 168.

[4] Per una presentazione sintetica cfr. L. THUNBERG, *Microcosm and Mediator: The Theological Anthropology of Maximus the Confessor*, Chicago 1995, pp. 72-79.

[5] MAXIMUS CONFESSOR, *Ambigua ad Iohannem* (in seguito, solamente: *Amb. Io.*), 7, PG 91, 1077C. Uso la traduzione di C. Moreschini (MASSIMO IL CONFESSORE, *Ambigua: Problemi Metafisici e Teologici su Testi di Gregorio di Nazianzo e Dionigi Areopagita*, Milano 2003); qui, p. 221. Gli *Ambigua ad Iohannem* corrispondono ai nn. 6-71 della raccolta complessiva degli *Ambigua* di Massimo, mentre i nn. 1-5 sono noti come *Ambigua ad Thomam*; il testo riprodotto in PG, coll. 1032-1417, segue l'ed. di F. Oehler, Halle 1857.

logoi sono uno solo, perchè essi sussistono non confusi, in quanto tutti vengono ricondotti a quel *Logos* per causa sua»[6].

Massimo ha un concetto molto elevato della presenza del *Logos* nel mondo naturale nei *logoi*. Per Massimo «il *Logos* in modo ineffabile per causa nostra si nasconde nei *logoi* delle cose e secondo l'analogia viene indicato mediante ciascuna cosa visibile, come fosse una lettera»[7]. La legge naturale, iscritta nella creazione, e la legge divina, rivelata nelle Scritture, sono completemente uguali per Massimo[8]. Quindi l'umanità ha avuto accesso al *Logos* prima della legge nella creatura (i patriarchi) e dopo la legge nella rivelazione delle Scritture[9]. Si puo parlare di tre incarnazioni del *Logos* nella creazione: nella legge naturale (i *logoi*), nella rivelazione (le Scritture), e nella legge della grazia (un'incarnazione storica nella persona di Gesù Cristo e, in seguito, nella creatura tramite la divinizzazione delle persone in cooperazione con la grazia di Dio). L'ordine e la salvezza del cosmo si sostengono sulla base della volontà del *Logos* di incarnarsi[10]. Con questa visione, Massimo può dire che la natura «è dunque nelle mani di Dio un altro mezzo per rivelarsi e mediante il quale ci è possible conoscere qualcosa di Lui»[11].

Massimo parla della capacità umana di ragionare sulla creazione e sulla rivelazione di Dio. La ragione – il *logos* umano – è una potenza (*dynamis*) data da Dio come la facoltà che guida la persona verso il fine inteso dal Padre. La ragione si esercita correttamente affinché «si possano agevolmente conoscere i modi in cui soddisfare l'amore e non fallire, per sbaglio, l'oggetto che cerchiamo di raggiungere»[12]. La ragione umana cerca una guida pratica per la persona verso il raggiungimento del Sommo Bene, portan-

[6] *Amb. Io.*, 7, 1077C (Moreschini, p. 221).

[7] *Ibid.*, 33, 1285D (Moreschini, p. 431).

[8] Cfr. *ibid.*, 10, 1129A. Paul Blowers parla della «fundamental reciprocity, and indeed interchangeability, established between creation (natural law) and scripture (written law) in virtue of their underlying symbolic structure and their common access to the intelligible mystery of the incarnate *Logos*»: BLOWERS, *Exegesis* cit. (*supra*, alla nota 1), p. 161.

[9] Cfr. *Amb. Io.*, 25, 1152C.

[10] Cfr. THUNBERG, *Microcosm* cit. (*supra*, alla nota 4), p. 77.

[11] V. CROCE, *Tradizione e ricerca: il metodo teologico di San Massimo il Confessore*, Milano 1974, p. 132.

[12] *Amb. Io.*, 48, 1361B (Moreschini, p. 511).

do l'uomo verso la soglia della conoscenza divina. Il termine ultimo «è il bene, in cui cessando dal movimento la ragione si ferma, poiché Dio è il bene, in cui è stabilito che trovi fine ogni potenza di ogni ragione»[13].

Il *logos* umano funziona anche come l'intermediario fra i sensi (*aistheseis*) e la parte più elevata della persona, la mente (*nous*)[14]. La ragione penetra la varietà delle cose sensibli per scoprire i *logoi* come cause e offre questi alla mente per la contemplazione naturale che si muove verso i *logoi* puri e verso l'unico *Logos*[15]. La ragione, nella sua analisi rigorosa della natura, si applica alla creazione sensibile tramite le arti, come la logica e la matematica[16]. La ragione disciplina i sensi nel vedere i *logoi*, che sono le cause originarie di tutte le cose[17]. Il metodo logico di Massimo risulta, secondo Vittorio Croce, «una delle più vigorose e coerenti sistemazioni di 'ontologia cristiana' dell'antichità»[18].

Si evidenzia questa fiducia Massimiana nella fondazione razionale del cosmo nella sua difesa della dottrina cristiana. Massimo è convinto che la formulazione precisa del dogma sostenga la purezza della mente nella percezione del mondo e nello svolgimento della vita spirituale. La sua lotta per la dottrina delle due volontà di Cristo, per esempio, condotta su un livello molto alto per

[13] Maximus Confessor, *Mystagogia* (in seguito, solamente: *Myst.*), 5, PG 91, 677C. Uso, adattandola in certi casi, la traduzione di R. Cantarella (S. Massimo il Confessore, *La Mistagogia ed altri Scritti*, Firenze 1931); qui, p. 152. Il testo riprodotto in PG 91, coll. 657-717, segue l'ed. di F. Combéfis, Paris 1675.

[14] Mentre il potere della ragione soggiace alla mente, entrambe hanno il loro scopo nella divinizzazione della persona: la ragione cerca il Bene, la mente cerca la Verità, «l'ultimo conosciuto», cioè, Dio. Cfr. *Myst.*, 5, 673D. Per l'antropologia tripartita di Massimo, cfr. Thunberg, *Microcosm* cit. (*supra*, alla nota 4), pp. 104-113.

[15] Cfr. *Amb. Io.*, 10, 1113A (Moreschini, p. 255): l'anima ha tre movimenti: «quello secondo l'intelletto, quello secondo la ragione, e quello secondo la sensazione»; la ragione «è conforme alla causa che definisce quello che si ignora, per cui l'anima, muovendosi per sua natura in modo corrispondente ad esso, si procura, con un'attività conforme alla scienza, tutti i *logoi* di quello che è conosciuto solamente in quanto è causa, e a cui i *logoi* danno la forma». La ragione coinvolge la pratica e la prudenza. L'intelletto coinvolge la contemplazione, la sapienza. Cfr. anche *ibid.*, 1109C.

[16] Cfr. *ibid.*, 14, 1212C-1213D; 15, 1216D. Quello delle arti non è un tema molto sviluppato nel pensiero di Massimo, ma se ne possono rintracciare frequenti applicazioni dottrinarie nelle sue opere.

[17] Cfr. *ibid.*, 10, 1108AB.

[18] Croce, *Tradizione e ricerca* cit. (*supra*, alla nota 11), p. 145.

quanto riguarda l'espressione filosofica e la chiarezza dei termini principali (*thelesis, boule, gnome, proairesis*)[19], dimostra l'importanza dell'uso della razionalità nel mantenere una visione giusta dello *skopos* di Dio. L'analasi della facoltà delle volontà ci offre un grande contributo alla comprensione dell'antropologia filosofico-teologica.

Un altro esempio è offerto dalla contemplazione del mondo naturale, che conduce l'uomo verso Dio. Tramite la ragione e la contemplazione naturale l'uomo può, in un atto di sintesi, raggiungere l'esistenza di Dio e la sua presenza nella creazione. In una riflessione importante, nel decimo *Ambiguum*, Massimo spiega come l'uomo possa analizzare la creazione sensibile nei suoi cinque modi:

> Conosceremo anche quei *logoi*, evidentemente gli ultimi da noi raggiungibili, dei quali ci è stata data come maestra la creazione, e i cinque modi della contemplazione ad essi congiunti, con i quali i santi hanno diviso la creazione raccogliendo devotamente i cinque mistici *logoi* che sono in essa. Essi hanno diviso la creazione in sostanza, movimento, diversità, unione e collocazione[20].

La riflessione dell'uomo su questi modi – o categorie con radici platoniche – può scoprire: 1) tramite la sostanza, l'esistenza di Dio come causa (ma non la sua essenza), 2) tramite il movimento, la provvidenza divina per tutte le cose (cioè, il mantenere la loro individualità), 3) tramite la diversità, il giudizio divino (cioè, come le cose si distinguono), 4) tramite l'unione, l'esercizio della volontà per sviluppare le virtù, e 5) tramite la collocazione, la necessità di mantenere la volontà conforme al Bene ed alla ragione. Con un atto di sintesi, l'uomo riduce questi modi all'unico modo nel *Logos*, che porta l'uomo alla soglia della contemplazione teologica[21]. Mentre la mente si inoltra nella contemplazione che porta l'uomo verso l'ultima conclusione, è il potere della ragione

[19] Cfr. MAXIMUS CONFESSOR, *Opuscula theologica et polemica*, 17, PG 91, 212C-D; 18, 213A-216A; 23, 260D-268A; 3, 45B-56D. Il testo riprodotto in PG 91, coll. 9-273, segue l'ed. Combéfis cit. (*supra*, alla nota 13).

[20] *Amb. Io.*, 10, 1133A (Moreschini, p. 274). Per una fonte possibile, cfr. PLATO, *Sophista*, 254d-255c (dove le cinque categorie sono l'*essere*, il *riposo*, il *moto*, lo *stesso*, l'*altro*).

[21] Cfr. *Amb. Io.*, 10, 1133B-1137C.

che analizza la creazione – anche tramite le arti – per superare la confusione dei sensi e delle passioni per offrire alla mente la fonte purificata per la contemplazione naturale, che è la contemplazione dei *logoi* nella creatura[22]. Quando «volgiamo verso le cose la nostra intelligenza mediante gli strumenti della ragione», troviamo la causa (ma non l'essenza) di tutto, Dio[23].

2. *La ragione e la pratica*

Il secondo ruolo attribuito alla ragione per la deificazione dell'uomo consiste nell'esercizio della pratica e nell'accrescimento nelle virtù[24]. Infatti, per Massimo, la pratica è il campo specifico della ragione perchè la ragione si ordina sempre verso il Sommo Bene nelle azioni umane. La ragione, purificata dagli inganni dei sensi, deve guidare la volontà umana nelle sue scelte. Massimo parla di una volontà razionale (*boule logike*) che persegue l'attuazione delle virtù che abbelliscono la persona umana[25]. L'uomo deve sempre agire con il «retto ragionamento» (*orthos logos*) per adornare la sua persona con le virtù e per crescere nel suo modo (*tropos*) di esprimere Cristo[26].

La persona non crea le virtù, che sono insite in Dio, ma le manifesta nelle azioni del corpo e dell'anima[27]. Le virtù sono riflessi delle qualità di Dio e il Cristo/*Logos* è la somma delle virtù[28]. La ragione, quindi, è «l'esegeta delle virtù», la facoltà che confor-

[22] Cfr. *ibid.*, 45, 1356B (Moreschini, p. 504): «Senza dubbio, quindi, coloro che con ragionamento filosofico vogliono destarsi dalla caduta del nostro primogenitore per prima cosa cominciano a spogliarsi totalmente delle passioni, poi del dedicarsi ai principi razionali delle arti, e infine oltrepassano la contemplazione naturale per affacciarsi alla gnosi immateriale, la quale non possiede assolutamente una forma caratterizzata dalla sensazione o un pensiero contenuto nella parola profferita».

[23] *Ibid.*, 10, 1189B (Moreschini, p. 326).

[24] Il tema dello stretto rapporto fra la «teoria» e la «pratica» è fondamentale per Massimo; cfr. P. Renczes, *Agir de Dieu et Liberté de l'Homme: recherches sur l'anthropologie théologique de saint Maxime le Confesseur*, Paris 2003, pp. 282-286; W. Völker, *Maximus Confessor als Meister des Geistlichen Lebens*, Wiesbaden 1965, pp. 238-242.

[25] Cfr. *Amb. Io.*, 10, 1108AB.

[26] Cfr. *ibid.*, 1109B.

[27] Cfr. *ibid.*, 1109A.

[28] Cfr. *ibid.*, 7, 1081D; 10, 1133D.

ma il corpo alla bellezza di Dio[29]. La ragione, invece, ha i suoi limiti e, in questa vita, è spesso ingannata e corrotta dai sensi. Nella sua *Mystagogia,* per esempio, Massimo dimostra il progresso della persona verso il Sommo Bene, che è Dio. L'uomo comincia dalla sua ragione e con la sua intelligenza (prudenza) guida le sue azioni secondo le virtù. Ma questo progresso non finisce con la 'divinizzazione', che equivale all'identificazione perfetta con Dio[30]. Massimo sottolinea il fatto che la conoscenza razionale di Dio (*logos*) non può coesistere con l'esperienza di Dio (*peira*), e che la divinizzazione è, di fatto, oltre la nostra capacità naturale[31]. Senza aiuto, l'uomo non è capace di oltrepassare la contemplazione naturale per raggiungere la contemplazione teologica e avere l'esperienza più alta di Dio. Non può avere una esperienza della Verità che è Dio e che fonda le virtù nella persona. È indispensabile a questo scopo il contributo di un dono divino, la fede.

3. *La fede e la divinizzazione*

L'uomo deve oltrepassare (*diabainein*) il mondo fisico e i concetti razionali per avere una conoscenza delle cose che sono oltre i sensi e che sono necessarie per la sua salvezza. L'uomo ha bisogno di accogliere il dono della fede da Dio, che gli offre la conoscenza e l'esperienza delle cose spirituali: «La salvezza delle anime certamente è il fine della fede. Il fine della fede è la vera rivelazione di una cosa creduta»[32]. Con questo dono è possibile aver contatto con le cose al di sopra della natura e del sapere[33]. La fede contribuisce alla conoscenza dei veri principi delle cose (*archai*) che

[29] Cfr. MAXIMUS CONFESSOR, *Capita theologica et oeconomica* (in seguito, solamente: *Th. Oec.*), I, 14, PG 90, 1088C. Il testo riprodotto in PG 91, coll. 1084-1176, segue l'ed. Combéfis cit. (*supra*, alla nota 13).

[30] Per la struttura di questo progresso, cfr. V.-L. DUPONT, *Le Dynamisme de l'Action Liturgique: une étude de la Mystagogie de Saint Maxime le Confesseur*, in «Revue de Sciences Religieuses», 65 (1991), [pp. 363-387], p. 370.

[31] Cfr. *Thal.*, q. 60, 624A, II, p. 77,77-78. Cfr. P. MIQUEL, Πεῖρα: *Contribution à l'étude du vocabulaire de l'expérience religieuse dans l'oeuvre de Maxime le Confesseur*, Berlin 1963 (Studia Patristica, VII), [pp. 355-361], p. 360: «Cette distinction entre la connaissance expérimentale et la connaissance discursive est capitale chez Maxime».

[32] *Thal.*, 59, 608X, II, p. 53,122-124.

[33] Cfr. *Amb. Io.*, 41, 1313D.

superano la mente (*nous*) e la ragione (*logos*): una forma di conoscenza «qualificata»[34]. La fede, quindi, è il termine della ragione e funziona come un mediatore fra la mente e l'esperienza divina[35].

Allo stesso tempo la fede è un dono dinamico. È un potere (*dynamis*)[36], ed una «chiamata/vocazione»[37]. Come la ragione, la fede si svolge nello *skopos* di Dio. Guida l'uomo non ai *concetti* di Dio, ma verso la vera esperienza di Dio nell'unità del *Logos*[38]. La mente, condotta dalla fede, può oltrepassare i suoi limiti e accedere a Dio: fino ad acquisire in tale modo una forma di conoscenza e certezza più forte della conoscenza naturale[39]. Con la fede, vediamo – entro i limiti delle possibilità umane – la verità di Dio. «Perchè tutte le cose sono cresciute insieme e sono collegate l'una all'altra secondo un semplice e indiviso potere e dono della fede»[40].

La fede, secondo Massimo, crea il regno di Dio «interiore» nella persona (*Lc* 7, 21). «Quindi la fede è la stessa cosa come il regno di Dio. La fede è distinta dal regno soltanto nei concetti intellettuali. La fede è il regno di Dio senza forma; e il regno è la fede formata divinamente»[41]. La fede è una conoscenza delle cose divine all'interno della persona, un dono divino e vivente che è un'esperienza anche dell'amore di Dio impresso nella mente. Quest'amore cerca di esprimersi e non vuole rimanere semplicemente il regno di Dio «senza forma». Ma questo «regno» come si realizza?

Nella sua polemica contro l'Origenismo, Massimo sottolinea che l'uomo è una creatura composta di corpo e di anima dall'inizio[42]. La divinizzazione, quindi, comprende *tutto* l'uomo per farsi uno con Dio[43]. In questa vita la divinizzazione si svolge non soltan-

[34] Cfr. *Th. Oec.*, I, 9, 396B; *Amb. Io.*, 71, 1408D.

[35] Per il *nous* inteso come costitutivo dell'anima, e quindi come equivalente alla persona umana chiamata ad essere sopra la propria natura, cfr. THUNBERG, *Microcosm* cit. (*supra*, alla nota 4), p. 112.

[36] Cfr. *Myst.*, 1, 668A.

[37] Cfr. *ibid.*, 24, 705B.

[38] Cfr. *Thal.*, 33, 373B, I, p. 231,32-35; *Amb. Io.*, 71, 1408D.

[39] Secondo A. COOPER, *The Body in Maximus the Confessor: Holy Flesh, Wholly Divinized*, Oxford 2005, p. 229, il concetto *sola fide* per Massimo è una «epistemological assertion», che conduce ad una «silent adoration and doxological confession».

[40] Cfr. *Myst.*, 1, 668A.

[41] *Thal.*, 33, 373B, p. 229,13-17.

[42] Cfr. *Amb. Io.*, 7, 1100C; *Myst.*, 7, 685AB. L'enfasi è, invece, sempre sull'anima come mediatore.

[43] Cfr. *Th. Oec.*, I, 46, 1100B.

to nelle facoltà interiori dell'uomo (l'anima, la mente), ma anche nella pratica e nell'ascesi (il corpo). Anzi, la divinizzazione non cambia la natura umana, ma si sviluppa nel «modo di essere» dell'uomo, al livello «esistenziale». Con la grazia interiore l'uomo si abbellisce con le virtù per diventare un'espressione di Cristo, il *Logos* incarnato. In un'altra immagine, la fede pianta il Signore – la fonte delle virtù – nell'anima e cresce nell'espressione delle virtù[44].

Una persona particolare «incarna» Cristo interiormente e esteriormente nella grazia e nelle virtù, fino alla divinizzazione completa dopo la morte. Massimo esprime questa «doppia» incarnazione del *Logos* nella persona umana come l'incarnazione «sottile» e l'incarnazione «spessa». «Nella pratica, il *Logos* reso 'spesso' dai modi delle virtù diventa la carne. Ma nella contemplazione, il *Logos* reso 'sottile' dai concetti spirituali, diventa come era all'inizio, *Logos-Dio*»[45].

Quindi la fede – il regno di Dio senza forma – non può rimanere un regno interiore per l'uomo. La fede è la divinizzazione «in potenza» e deve realizzarsi in questa vita fino alla sua consumazione nell'eternità[46]. Uno *scholium* per *Ad Thalassium* 33 che tratta il tema della fede come il regno di Dio, e che certi studiosi credono appartenga a Massimo stesso, distingue la «fede nuda» o «la fede semplice» (*psile pistis*) – la fede che non ha la somiglianza divina tramite le virtù – dal vero Regno di Dio – la fede con la forma del Bene nelle opere[47]. Certamente questo *scholium* esprime il pensiero di Massimo – la fede, un dono divino, si esprime nelle azioni per divinizzare la persona. Una persona deve «vestirsi» con l'espressione di Cristo nelle virtù per avere il vero Regno di Dio. Un altro *scholium* parla di Cristo come la fede «ipostasizzata». Come il *Logos* divino si è ipostatizzato in un uomo, la fede deve ipostasizzarsi nella persona, nella pratica[48]. Nel suo commentario sul Padre Nostro, Massimo sottolinea questa realizzazione del regno di Dio nella persona intera: Il potere del regno è presente quando la persona porta la forma del grande re, Cristo,

[44] Cfr. *ibid.*, II, 11, 1130B.

[45] *Ibid.*, II, 37, 1141CD.

[46] Cfr. *Thal.*, 22, 320BC, I, p. 139,60-65.

[47] Cfr. *ibid.*, 33 (schol., 1), 376B, I, p. 231,1-4.

[48] Cfr. *ibid.*, 25 (schol., 2), 336D, p. 167,2-7.

secondo la grazia (frutto della fede). Ma questo potere del regno, formato nella fede, deve realizzarsi e mantenersi nelle virtù, specialmente l'umiltà e l'amore[49].

Dunque, in questa vita la fede interiore deve tornare alla pratica. La conoscenza data da Dio diventa virtù nell'uomo. La fede, infatti, offre la conoscenza di che cosa dobbiamo cercare nella vita per conoscere Dio: la liberazione dalle passioni, la pazienza, i modi di applicare le virtù, il separarsi dalle cose materiali, l'amore per il prossimo, ecc.[50]. La fede offre la conoscenza di tutte le cose necessarie per raggiungere Dio.

Ma la ragione è il potere che ci conduce al Bene (Dio) nella pratica. La ragione esprime la fede in un modo concreto nelle azioni, «per mezzo della manifestazione delle opere»[51]. La fede non si impone sull'uomo, ma sempre lavora con la ragione e la volontà ragionevole per realizzare la divinizzazione della persona. Massimo interpreta il viaggio di Abramo nella terra promessa come allegoria del viaggio della persona verso Dio. Il credente diventa un altro Abramo quando segue Cristo, abbandonando la vita materiale e le passioni, esercitandosi nelle virtù. Va, tramite «la fede pura» verso «il sommo Bene», ma guidato dalla «ragione»[52]. La fede e la ragione coinvolgono la persona intera affinché possa divinizzarsi con la grazia nel suo modo di essere. Senza l'esercizio della ragione, la fede rimane invece «nuda» o «semplice».

4. *Conclusione*

Massimo non si preoccupa di affrontare e risolvere problemi epistemologici (come il superamento dello scetticismo e dei limiti che la fede potrebbe imporre al sapere scientifico), né si impegna nel problema di poter esprimere i contenuti della fede mediante concetti razionalmente costruiti. Questo non significa, d'altra parte, che le sue opere non siano rigorosamente rispettose dei

[49] Cfr. MAXIMUS CONFESSOR, *Orationis Dominicae brevis expositio*, PG 90, 885C, ed. P. Van Deun, Leuven 1991 (CCSG, 23), [pp. 27-73], p. 29,46-47. Il testo riprodotto in PG 90, coll. 871-910, segue l'ed. Combéfis cit. (*supra*, alla nota 13).

[50] Cfr. *Thal.*, 34, 376D-377A, I, pp. 235,10 - 237,37.

[51] *Myst.*, 5, 677C (Cantarella, p. 153).

[52] Cfr. *Amb. Io.*, 10, 1152D.

procedimenti della logica e della razionalità. Nel suo orizzonte mentale, tuttavia, la creazione e la scrittura, intese entrambe come «rivelazioni di Dio», sono anche misteri che devono insegnare all'intelligenza la loro verità. E i misteri non si intendono, ma si contemplano e si mettono in pratica[53].

Massimo apprezza pienamente il valore della ragione, cui affida il compito di scoprire la presenza dei *logoi* (o del *logos*) nella creatura, affinché l'uomo possa entrare nella contemplazione naturale e, eventualmente, nella fede. Ma il ruolo principale della ragione è collocato nella pratica, nel cui ambito l'uomo razionale è invitato a lavorare congiuntamente con la fede per diventare un altro Cristo nel proprio modo di essere. La ragione e la fede sono per Massimo poteri dinamici, che consentono che l'uomo sia impegnato come autentico attore in un grande dramma in cui il fine è la sua elevazione nella divinità. Vorrei concludere con le parole di Hans Urs von Balthasar, il cui libro *Kosmische Liturgie* ha iniziato lo studio moderno di Massimo. Secondo von Balthasar, la dottrina basilare del Confessore può essere sintetizzata nel modo seguente:

> L'essere è essenzialmente realizzazione dinamica, *Logos* attualizzato e atto tendente al *Logos*, natura che si fa ipostasi e ipostasi che si dispiega attraverso la natura. (...) Certo, si dà anche una teologia senza prassi, ma è la teologia dei demoni. Equivale alla fede senza amore, quale regna nell'inferno[54].

Nella visione di Massimo, la fede non rimane «nuda» o «semplice», ma, congiungendosi con la ragione e perfezionandosi attraverso l'esercizio delle virtù, conduce l'uomo verso l'attuazione definitiva delle sue autentiche potenzialità, verso la realizzazione del vero Regno, nel quale è chiamato a diventare Dio.

[53] Cfr. H. U. von Balthasar, *Kosmische Liturgie. Maximus der Bekenner: Höhe und Krise des griechischen Weltbilds*, Freiburg im Breisgau 1941, pp. 295-296 (tr. it. Milano 2001, pp. 288-289).

[54] *Ibid.*, p. 332 (tr. it., p. 287).

ANNA MORELLI

TEORIA E SPIRITUALITÀ DEL CANTO

ASPETTI DELLA *MUSICA DISCIPLINA* NELL'ALTO MEDIOEVO TRA PENSIERO SCIENTIFICO E PRATICA LITURGICA

Seconda fra le discipline quadriviali, la musica medievale è la scienza speculativa che studia il numero *relatus ad aliquid*[1] in quanto principio d'ordine e d'armonia cosmica, secondo l'eredità pitagorica e platonica. D'altra parte, l'attenzione per il suono nella sua dimensione materiale e precipuamente vocale segna l'originalità del pensiero alto-medievale sulla musica rispetto alle elaborazioni antiche e allo stesso Boezio, palesando il mutamento del 'paradigma' originario secondo un'impostazione squisitamente cristiana, che in questo lavoro si cercherà di evidenziare.

Quando si considera lo studio speculativo della musica nel Medioevo, una è l'*auctoritas* che spicca fra le altre: Boezio, l'uomo eccezionale che fu giustamente riconosciuto come l'ultimo dei Romani e il primo degli Scolastici, poiché pose a fondamento sia della filosofia che della teologia scolastica la tradizione degli studi classici (che ormai si stava sgretolando), volgendo a essi gli occhi dell'uomo già 'medievale', che rimpiange la grandezza antica e vede in quella cultura ormai al tramonto un tutto unitario e omogeneo[2]. Formatosi alle scuole neoplatoniche del suo tempo, Boezio concepisce il sapere come comprensione integrale, ove ogni disciplina trova il suo posto in armoniosa relazione con

[1] Cfr. ANICIUS MANLIUS SEVERINUS BOETHIUS, *De institutione arithmetica*, I, 1, PL 63, 1081B, ed. G. Friedlein, Leipzig 1867 (repr. Frankfurt 1966), p. 9,1-3: «Illam multitudinem, quae per se est, arithmetica speculatur integritas, illam vero, quae ad aliquid, musicis modulaminis temperamenta pernoscunt».

[2] Cfr. J. WEISHEIPL, *Classification of the Sciences in Medieval Thought*, in «Mediaeval studies», 27 (1965), pp. 54-90.

10.1484/M.NUTRIX-EB.1.101240

le altre e prepara l'intelletto ad accogliere conoscenze via via più alte fino alla Sapienza, che, agostinianamente, è contemplazione della Verità, dono di Dio, che l'uomo può tuttavia chiarire e definire razionalmente. La via è tracciata nelle due classificazioni delle scienze che egli ci ha lasciato[3], dove le dottrine sia di Platone che di Aristotele trovano posto in fragile equilibrio: nel primo commentario all'*Isagoge* di Porfirio la filosofia è bipartita in speculativa e attiva[4]; quindi nel *De trinitate* la speculativa è divisa in naturale, matematica e teologia: la prima esamina le forme non separate dal movimento e dalla materia, la seconda le forme astratte dal movimento anche se non dalla materia, mentre la terza le forme totalmente astratte sia dal movimento che dalla materia. La logica, posta fuori dal quadro classificatorio, serve da strumento a ogni scienza. Ciascun ambito della filosofia ha un metodo suo proprio. Così, la fisica procede *rationabiliter*, cioè per mezzo dell'indagine scientifica, dimostrativa; la matematica procede *disciplinaliter*, cioè sfruttando il ragionamento ipotetico, che deve presumere certi assiomi senza investigare il loro fondamento ontologico; la teologia procede *intellectualiter*, cioè attraverso l'intuizione, che le consente di contemplare la pura forma[5]. E benché da una parte l'attribuzione dello status di scienza alla fisica e la valutazione del processo conoscitivo nel suo complesso come un processo astrattivo siano decisamente aristotelici[6], dall'altra la considerazione delle matematiche come discipline capaci di elevare lo spirito alla conoscenza del vero è chiaramente platonica. Esse, aritmetica, musica, geometria e astronomia, costituiscono quella quadruplice via che così viene descritta nel *De institutione arithmetica*:

[3] Cfr. *ibid.*, pp. 58-62. Cfr. anche M.T. FUMAGALLI, *Le Enciclopedie dell'Occidente Medievale*, Torino 1981, pp. 19-21.

[4] Cfr. ANICIUS MANLIUS SEVERINUS BOETHIUS, *In Isagogen Porphirii, editio prima*, I, 3, PL 64, 71A-75A, ed. S. Brandt, Wien – Leipzig 1906 (CSEL, 48), pp. 7-9.

[5] Cfr. ID., *De Trinitate*, 2, PL 64, 1250A-1251A, ed. C. Moreschini, München – Leipzig 2000, pp. 168,68 - 169,80. Cfr. G. D'ONOFRIO, *La scala ricamata. La* philosophiae divisio *di Severino Boezio tra essere e conoscere*, in *La Divisione della Filosofia e le sue Ragioni. Lettura di testi medievali (VI-XIII secolo)*, a c. di G. d'Onofrio, Atti del Settimo Convegno della Società Italiana per lo Studio del Pensiero Medievale (S.I.S.P.M.) (Assisi, 14-15 novembre 1997), Cava dei Tirreni 2001 (Schola Salernitana. Studi e Testi, 5), pp. 11-63.

[6] Cfr. ARISTOTELES, *Metaphysica*, VI, 1, 1025b-1026a.

> Perciò questo è quel quadrivio, per il quale devono avanzare coloro il cui spirito superiore procede dai sensi creati con noi alle certezze più alte dell'intelligenza. Ci sono infatti certi gradi e misure di progressioni sicure, per i quali si può salire e progredire, affinché quell'occhio dello spirito, che, come dice Platone, è maggiormente degno di essere salvaguardato e irrobustito rispetto a molti occhi corporei (poiché la verità può essere investigata e osservata da quella sola luce), dico quest'occhio, chiuso e privato dei sensi corporei, venga nuovamente illuminato proprio da queste discipline[7].

Un tale orientamento, di chiara radice neopitagorica e platonica, permea di sé anche il *De institutione musica*[8], benché in esso si trovino pure elementi aristotelici[9], che però furono trascurati per tutto il Medioevo, mancando ai filosofi, almeno fino al secolo XIII, il paragone con le fonti originarie. Se pure dunque non siano assenti riferimenti alla concretezza fisica del suono e alla sua rilevanza percettiva, infine la musica si caratterizza innanzitutto come disciplina matematica e, in quanto tale, resta platonicamente intesa come parte della conoscenza dianoetica, gradino propedeutico alla *noesis*, comprensione integrale del mondo delle Idee[10]. Pertanto, lo scopo

[7] ANICIUS MANLIUS SEVERINUS BOETHIUS, *De institutione arithmetica*, I, 1, PL 63, 1081D-1082A, ed. Friedlein cit. (alla nota 1), p. 10,1-7: «Hoc igitur illud quadruvium est, quo his viandum sit, quibus excellentior animus a nobiscum procreatis sensibus ad intellegentiae certiora perducitur. Sunt enim quidam gradus certaeque progressionum dimensiones, quibus ascendi progredique possit, ut animi illum oculum, qui, ut ait Plato, multis oculis corporalibus salvari constituique sit dignior, quod eo solo lumine vestigari vel inspici veritas queat, hunc inquam oculum demersum orbatumque corporeis sensibus hae disciplinae rursus inluminent». Su Boezio, cfr. H. CHADWICK, *Boethius: The Consolations of Music, Logic, Theology and Philosophy*, Oxford 1981 (tr. it., Bologna 1986).

[8] Cfr. ANICIUS MANLIUS SEVERINUS BOETHIUS, *De institutione musica*, PL 63, 1167-1300, ed. G. Friedlein, Leipzig 1867 (repr. Frankfurt 1966).

[9] Boezio raccoglie importanti elementi della teoria musicale aristotelico-aristossenica, tra i quali la teoria del moto della voce (il continuo e il discontinuo, ai quali egli aggiunge l'intermedio, tipico della declamazione dei poemi, asserendo di seguire in ciò Albino: cfr. *ibid.*, I, 12, 1177D-1178D, p. 199) e le definizioni di suono («definitur sonus percussio aeris indissoluta usque ad auditum», derivata dal *De anima*: cfr. *ibid.*, 3, 1173A, p. 189,22-23; «sonus igitur est vocis casus emmeles, id est aptus melo, in unam intensionem»: cfr. *ibid.*, 8, 1175D, p. 195,2-3) e di intervallo («intervallum vero est soni acuti gravisque distantia»: cfr. *ibid.*, 1175D-1176A, p. 195,6).

[10] Cfr. PLATO, *Respublica*, VI, 508d-511e, e VII, 533d-534e. Per Platone inoltre, la teoria musicale (*armonica*), in quanto scienza dei rapporti, fornisce la chiave per comprendere le leggi che reggono il cosmo, plasmato dal Demiurgo sul model-

ultimo dell'analisi delle relazioni numeriche che sottendono alle consonanze rimane fondamentalmente quello di giungere alla comprensione delle armonie cosmiche, la *musica mundana*, prodotto della simmetria dell'universo, preparando così l'intelletto al coglimento puro delle Idee. La *musica mundana* trova il suo parallelo nella *musica humana*, riflesso delle ordinate proporzioni del corpo umano e dei suoi rapporti con l'anima. La *musica de quibusdam instrumentis*, che ogni *cantor* può eseguire con la lira, o la cetra, o con qualsiasi altro strumento, è solo la loro più imperfetta sorella, che va studiata non ai fini della produzione musicale in se stessa, ma per la comprensione delle leggi sulle quali si fonda l'armonia universale. Da qui, l'approfondimento della teoria musicale pitagorico-platonica, che indaga la costituzione di quegli intervalli che ancora oggi sono detti perfetti, e cioè l'ottava, la quinta e la quarta, espressione sonora della perfezione del cosmo[11]. Questo dunque il fine dell'intero trattato: portare l'intelletto all'attenta valutazione del numero come principio ordinatore dell'universo.

Con Boezio la musica si conferma come disciplina speculativa. Successivamente, nei lunghi secoli che precedono la rinascita carolingia, lo studio della musica speculativa mantiene il suo spazio fra le arti liberali, e, disperse le fonti tardo antiche, fra cui anche il *De institutione musica*, ai monaci non restò altro che affidarsi alle sommarie compilazioni enciclopediche di Cassiodoro e Isidoro di Siviglia. Nelle sue *Institutiones*, Cassiodoro non muta il quadro epistemologico della musica rispetto a Boezio: essa rimane scienza matematica, inerente alla filosofia *inspectiva* (cioè teorica). Tuttavia la sua definizione come studio dei rapporti numerici si trovano «nei suoni»[12] palesa un certo interesse nei confronti dei suoi risvolti pratici: essa riguarda i rapporti che si determina-

lo del Bene attraverso la mediazione degli Enti matematici e animato da un'anima che ha struttura geometrico-dimensionale e armonica e avvolge tutto il mondo; cfr. ID., *Timaeus*, IV, 34b-37c. Per un approfondimento sulla processione dell'armonia descritta nel *Timeo*, cfr. L. BRISSON, *Le même et l'autre dans la structure ontologique du Timée de Platon*, Sankt Augustin 1998; e B. CERCHIO, *Il suono filosofale. Musica e alchimia*, Lucca 1993.

[11] Fonti principali di Boezio sono Nicomaco, Tolomeo e la *Sectio canonis*. Cfr. CHADWICK, *Boethius* cit. (alla nota 7), pp. 78-101 (tr. it., pp. 117-139).

[12] Cfr. CASSIODORUS SENATOR, *Institutiones divinarum et saecularium litterarum*, II, 3, 6, PL 70, 1168D, ed. R. A. B. Mynors, Oxford 1937, p. 111, 17-19: «Musica est disciplina quae de numeris loquitur, qui ad aliquid sunt his qui inveniuntur in sonis».

no tra suoni percepibili con l'udito, verso i quali punta il maggior interesse dell'autore, il quale infatti, dopo aver ricordato la profonda influenza dei suoni sulla psiche umana, passa ad illustrare nel dettaglio le tre divisioni della musica: l'*harmonica*, che si occupa dello studio delle altezze, la *rithmica*, che studia la corretta unione di parola e suono, e la *metrica*, che analizza i diversi metri[13]. Sulla stessa via prosegue Isidoro. Egli da una parte divide la filosofia in tre sezioni, fisica, etica e logica (una classificazione che deriva da Agostino, nella quale l'assimilazione delle scienze matematiche alla fisica trova spiegazione nella lettura matematica della cosmologia data dal *Timeo*[14]), e riconosce nella musica una delle quattro discipline del quadrivio, nel quale la filosofia naturale è suddivisa[15]; dall'altra, definisce la musica non solo come «disciplina che tratta dei numeri che si trovano nei suoni»[16], ma anche come *peritia modulationis, sono cantuque consistens* (abilità di modulare, che si realizza nel suono e nel canto)[17], addentrandosi poi in una minuta descrizione della musica pratica, anticipatamente divisa in armonica, organica e ritmica, a seconda della fonte sonora:

[13] Cfr. F. D'Elia, *Senso e dimensione della «reductio ad philosophiam» delle discipline matematiche nelle* Institutiones *di Cassiodoro*, in *Knowledge and the Sciences in Medieval Philosophy*, Proceedings of the Eighth International Congress of Medieval Philosophy, S.I.E.P.M. (Helsinki, 24-29 August 1987), 3 voll., Helsinki 1990, II, ed. by S. Knuuttila – R. Tyorinoja – S. Ebbesen (Publications of Luther Agricola Society, Series B, 19), pp. 43-52.

[14] Cfr. Augustinus Hipponensis, *De civitate Dei*, VIII, 4, PL 41, 227-228, ed. B. Dombart – A. Kalb, 2 voll., Turnhout 1955 (CCSL, 47-48), I, pp. 219,1 - 220,33. Agostino chiama tale tripartizione della filosofia «divisione platonica» poiché aveva come fonte Cicerone, il quale l'aveva attribuita direttamente a Platone; in realtà, essa fu strutturata non dallo stesso Platone ma dal suo seguace Senocrate, e fu poi riproposta da stoici e neoplatonici.

[15] Cfr. Isidorus Hispalensis, *Etymologiae*, I, 24, 3-4, PL 82, 141BC, ed. W. M. Lindsay, Oxford 1911 (senza indic. delle pagine): «Philosophiae species tripertita est: una naturalis, quae Graece Physica appellatur, in qua de naturae inquisitione disseritur: altera moralis, quae Graece Ethica dicitur, in qua de moribus agitur: tertia rationalis, quae Graeco vocabulo Logica appellatur, in qua disputatur quemadmodum in rerum causis vel vitae moribus veritas ipsa quaeratur. In Physica igitur causa quaerendi, in Ethica ordo vivendi, in Logica ratio intellegendi versatur. Physicam apud Graecos primus perscrutatus est Thales Milesius, unus ex septem illis sapientibus. Hic enim ante alios caeli causas atque vim rerum naturalium contemplata ratione suspexit, quam postmodum Plato in quattuor definitiones distribuit, id est Arithmeticam, Geometricam, Musicam, Astronomiam».

[16] Cfr. *ibid.*, III, 1, 7-8, 142C: «Musica est disciplina quae de numeris loquitur, qui inveniuntur in sonis».

[17] *Ibid.*, 15, 1, 19-20, 163A.

> Triplice è la natura di ogni suono, elemento materiale della melodia. La prima è l'armonica, la quale si compone dei canti delle voci. La seconda è l'organica, che consiste nel fiato. La terza è la ritmica, che recepisce il ritmo dalla percussione delle dita. (...) Ed infatti il suono è prodotto o dalla voce, attraverso la bocca, o dal soffio, attraverso strumenti come la tuba o la tibia, o dal tocco, come nel caso della cetra o di qualsivoglia altro strumento che, percuotendolo, produce una melodia[18].

Va rilevato inoltre il continuo riferimento di Isidoro alla Bibbia e la sua considerazione della scienza del numero come chiave di interpretazione del significato spirituale della Scrittura[19].

È, specificamente, l'interesse per il suono nella sua veste concreta di melodia vocale a costituire l'elemento di originalità del pensiero musicale alto-medievale. Nell'azione liturgica cristiana infatti, il canto è un momento privilegiato dell'esperienza di incontro tra l'uomo e Dio. Il testo, mutuato in massima parte dalle Scritture, è accolto nel cuore dell'uomo come Parola Vivente e rivolto a Dio come preghiera intonata che eleva alla contemplazione, alla comunione con Lui[20].

Ne troviamo conferma nelle parole di Girolamo (345-420 ca.), che consegna il canto al suo giusto dominio, quello della preghiera:

> Che i giovani adolescenti lo comprendano e lo comprendano coloro il cui compito è di salmodiare (la lode di) Dio in chiesa, cantando non con la voce ma con il cuore (...), nel timore, nel lavoro e nella conoscenza delle Scritture[21].

[18] *Ibid.*, 19, 1-2, 10-17, 164BC: «Ad omnem autem sonum, quae materies cantilenarum est, triformem constat esse naturam. Prima est harmonica, quae ex vocum cantibus constat. Secunda organica, quae ex flatu consistit. Tertia rythmica, quae pulsu digitorum numeros recipit. Nam aut voce editur sonus, sicut per fauces, aut flatu, sicut per tubam vel tibiam, aut pulsu, sicut per citharam, aut per quodlibet aliud, quod percutiendo canorum est».

[19] *Ibid.*, III, 4, 155D-156B.

[20] Sull'argomento, cfr. i seguenti studi di G. B. Baroffio: *La mistica della Parola*, in *La mistica, fenomenologia e riflessione teologica*, a c. di E. Ancili – M. Paparazzi, 2 voll., Roma 1984, II, pp. 31-46; *Bibbia Liturgia Bibbie. Dalle tradizioni orali alla trasmissione scritta*, in *Le Bibbie Atlantiche. Il libro delle Scritture tra monumentalità e rappresentazione*, a c. di M. Maniaci – G. Orofino, Carugate 2000, pp. 81-85; *Die theologischen Grundlagen der Kirchenmusik*, in *Brixner Initiative Musik und Kirche*, Erstes Symposion (Brixen Oktober 1988), hrsg. J. Lanz, Brixen 1989, pp. 17-25; *La liturgia: fonte e culmine della vita cristiana*, in «Iter. Ricerche fonti e immagini per un territorio», 4 (2005), [pp. 29-38], pp. 37-38; *Il canto gregoriano*, *ibid.*, [pp. 39-61], pp. 41-44.

[21] Cfr. Hieronymus Stridonius, *Commentarius in Epistulam Pauli ad Ephesios*,

Oppure in quelle di Agostino, il quale ad esempio, nell'interpretare le parole del Salmo 46 *psallite intelligenter*, consiglia di non cercare «il suono dell'orecchio, ma la luce del cuore»[22]. Anche Benedetto ricorda ai suoi confratelli la presenza di Dio nella comunità orante e sprona a prender parte alla salmodia «in modo tale che l'intima disposizione dell'animo si armonizzi con la nostra voce»[23].

Inoltre, la musica, come è in grado di sollevare l'anima alla contemplazione, così è capace di indirizzarla al bene, come rileva Rabano Mauro parlando del cantico e della salmodia:

> 'Cantico' allude alla scienza spirituale, come nel salmo 'Cantate al Signore un canto nuovo'; 'cantare i salmi' invece significa esercitare la virtù. Il cantico si riferisce alla vita contemplativa, cantare i salmi alla vita attiva[24].

III, 5, 19, PL 26, 562A: «Audiant haec adolescentuli: audiant hi quibus psallendi in ecclesia officium est, Deo non voce, sed corde cantandum (...), in timore, in opere, in scientia scripturarum».

[22] Cfr. AUGUSTINUS HIPPONENSIS, *Enarrationes in Psalmos*, Ps. 46, 9 [v. 8], PL 36, 529, ed. E. Dekkers – J. Fraipont, 3 voll., Turnhout 1956 (CCSL, 38-39-40), I, p. 534,10-13: «QUONIAM REX OMNIS TERRAE DEUS: PSALLITE INTELLIGENTER. Docet nos et admonet nos ut psallamus intelligenter: non quaeramus sonum auris, sed lumen cordis».

[23] Cfr. Cfr. BENEDICTUS CASINENSIS, *Regula*, 19, *De disciplina psallendi*, PL 66, 475A-476A, ed. A. Lentini, Montecassino 1947 (1980²), pp. 238,1 - 240,7: «Ubique credimus divinam esse praesentiam et oculos Domini in omni loco speculari bonos et malos, maxime tamen hoc sine aliqua dubitatione credamus cum ad opus divinum assistimus. Ideo semper memores simus quod ait propheta: 'Servite Domino in timore' (*Ps* 2, 11), et iterum: 'Psallite sapienter' (*Ps* 46, 8), et: 'In conspectu angelorum psallam tibi' (*Ps* 137, 1). Ergo consideremus qualiter oporteat in conspectu divinitatis et angelorum eius esse, et sic stemus ad psallendum ut mens nostra concordet voci nostrae».

[24] Cfr. HRABANUS MAURUS, *De rerum naturis* (*De universo*), XVIII, 4, PL 111, 496C: «'Canticum' significat scientiam spiritalem ut in Psalmo: 'Cantate Domino canticum novum'. 'Psallere' est opus bonum exercere. Canticum ad contemplativam, psallere refertur ad activam vitam». Il richiamo al canto nuovo è frequente nella Bibbia (cfr. *Ps* 95,1; *Ps* 97,1; 149,1; *Is*, 42,10; *Ap* 5,9; *Ap* 14,3), ma in questo caso si spiega attraverso il capitolo 14 dell'Apocalisse, che raffigura la totalità degli eletti in contemplazione del Cristo sul monte Sion, mentre un cantico celeste risuona ovunque: «Et vidi et ecce agnus stabat supra montem Sion et cum illo centum quadraginta quattuor milia habentes nomen eius et nomen Patris eius scriptum in frontibus suis. et audivi vocem de caelo tamquam vocem aquarum multarum et tamquam vocem tonitrui magni et vocem quam audivi sicut citharoedorum citharizantium in citharis suis. Et cantabant quasi canticum novum ante sedem et ante quattuor animalia et seniores et nemo poterat discere canticum nisi illa centum quadraginta quattuor milia qui empti sunt de terra» (*Ap* 14, 1-3).

Il fondamento sacro del canto liturgico risulta anche nel primo trattato di teoria musicale che ci è giunto dall'alto Medioevo, scritto verso la metà del secolo IX da un monaco dell'abbazia di Saint-Jean di Réôme di nome Aureliano, il *Musica disciplina*. Già nel primo capitolo Aureliano ne rammenta la natura di preghiera gradita a Dio:

> Da ciò dunque va dedotto quanto sia grato a Dio l'ufficio del canto, se è eseguito con la dovuta concentrazione, dal momento che in ciò imitiamo i cori angelici che si narra cantino senza interruzione le lodi del Signore[25].

Più avanti, nel XX capitolo, egli indica nella musica sacra una via di salvezza[26] e un'opportunità di raccoglimento contemplativo[27].

Se dunque da una parte la musica è, e resta, la disciplina speculativa del *philosophus*, dall'altra non se ne può trascurare il versante pratico, per la sua natura sacra e la sua valenza etica. Lungo i secoli dell'alto Medioevo matura la consapevolezza dell'importante compito del cantore, che durante l'azione liturgica si deve dedicare con sapienza e perizia ad un'arte così rilevante, sforzandosi di esprimere nel canto la fede che custodisce nel suo cuore,

[25] AURELIANUS REOMENSIS, *Musica disciplina*, 1, ed. L. Gushee, Neuhausen – Stuttgard 1975 (Corpus scriptorum de musica, 21), p. 59, 11: «Hinc ergo colligendum est quam gratum sit Deo officium cantandi, si intenta mente peragatur, quando in hoc angelorum choros imitamur quos sine intermissione Domini laudes concinere traditur». Nell'esortazione a mantenere la *mens intenta*, va visto un richiamo al giusto atteggiamento di raccoglimento e meditazione, per poter accogliere la Parola nel profondo del cuore, come si legge in San Paolo. Cfr. *1Cor* 14, 15: «Orabo spiritu orabo et mente psallam spiritu psallam et mente»; e cfr. anche *Col* 3, 16: «Verbum Christi habitet in vobis abundanter in omni sapientia docentes et commonentes vosmet ipsos psalmis hymnis canticis spiritalibus in gratia cantantes in cordibus vestris Deo».

[26] Cfr. *ibid.*, 20, p. 130, 12: «Et sic tandem laetania finita qua Deus Christusque vocatur ut populo suo misereatur, imitans sacerdos angelum qui gloriam Deo in caelis pacemque in terra hominibus adnunciavit, idem canticum voce intonat salutari».

[27] Cfr. *ibid.*, p. 131, 22: «Communicantibus etiam primum canitur canticum *Agnus Dei qui tollis peccata mundi, misere*[*re*] *nobis*, ut fideles quique corpori et sanguini Domini communicantes, quem percipiunt ore, hauriant vocis modulatione ut scilicet quem gustant, quoddammodo versum incorporalem cybum, recolant ex se crucifixum et mortuum atque sepultum, et eum exorent sua tollere peccata quem ad hoc venisse omnis confitetur ecclesia. Canitur etiam illi adiunctum aliud carmen quod communio vocatur, ut quamdiu populus fidelis suscipit caelestem benedictionem dulcissima modulatione mens eius trahatur et suspendatur in sublimissimam contemplationem».

come è scritto negli *Statuta ecclesiae antiqua*[28]. Nella *Regula canonicorum* di Crodegango di Metz si legge che il contegno dei cantori dev'essere umile, sobrio e casto, poiché il loro canto solleva lo spirito di coloro che li ascoltano all'amore per le cose celesti, non solo in virtù delle parole pronunciate ma anche per la dolcezza della melodia. La loro voce dev'essere eccellente e la loro preparazione severa, cosicché il diletto per tale soavità sproni gli animi della comunità in preghiera[29]. In effetti, la funzione del canto sacro (e di conseguenza la responsabilità sociale di chi lo esegue) viene ancor più esaltata a partire dal secolo VIII, grazie all'opera di riforma liturgica inerente al progetto di unificazione culturale dell'Impero carolingio. Essa fu perseguita da Pipino il Breve e dai suoi discendenti, e conclusa da Ludovico il Pio, che sostenne vivamente Benedetto di Aniane nella sua volontà di rinnovamento spirituale e morale del monachesimo benedettino e di tutta la chiesa franca. Nei Concili di Aquisgrana dell'816 e dell'817 (al quale parteciparono tutti gli abati dell'Impero) fu discussa la sua riforma monastica, che fu infine ratificata dal *Capitulare monasticum* del 10 luglio dell'817; essa ripristinò il pieno valore spirituale dell'Ufficio divino e produsse i suoi effetti più fortunati nei successivi quarant'anni. In tale contesto si colloca la revisione dei libri liturgici, alla quale lavorarono uomini come l'abate di Sant'Albino di Angers, Elisarco, il vescovo di Metz, Amalario, e

[28] Cfr. BAROFFIO, *Il canto gregoriano* cit. (alla nota 20), p. 59.

[29] Cfr. CHRODEGANGUS METTENSIS, *Regula canonicorum*, PL 89, 1079A-B: «Studendum summopere cantoribus est, ne donum sibi divinitus collatum vitiis foedent, sed potius illud humilitate, castitate, et sobrietate, et caeteris sanctarum virtutum ornamentis exornent: quorum melodia animos populi circumstantis ad memoriam amoremque coelistium, non solum sublimitate verborum, sed etiam suavitate tonorum, quae dicuntur, erigat. Cantorem autem, sicut traditum est a sanctis Patribus, et voce et arte praeclarum, illustremque esse oportet, ita ut per oblectamenta dulcedinis, animos incitent audientium, etc. (...)». La preoccupazione di un canto bello, dolce e suadente spinge addirittura Crodegango a chiedere agli inesperti di tacere; cfr. *ibid.*, 1079B: «Hi vero, qui huius artis minus capaces sunt, donec erudiantur, melius convenit ut sileant, quam cantare volendo quod nesciunt, aliorum voces dissonare compellant». Fonte di Crodegango sembra essere Isidoro. Cfr. ISIDORUS HISPALENSIS, *De ecclesiasticis officiis*, II, 12, 2, PL 83, 972B: «Psalmistam autem et voce et arte praeclarum illustremque esse oportet, ita ut oblectamento dulcedinis animos incitet auditorum». Ciò giustificherebbe l'uso dell'«etc.» nel testo di Crodegango, evidentemente riferito al testo di Isidoro che prosegue. L'intero brano di Crodegango verrà in seguito trascritto da AMALARIUS METTENSIS, *De institutione canonicorum*, 37, PL 105, 929AB.

l'arcivescovo di Lione, Agobardo. Nei loro scritti, l'onorevole e delicata funzione del cantore è costantemente rilevata.

Elisarco, in una lettera degli anni 814-822[30], comunica al vescovo Nebridio di Narbona di aver emendato l'antifonario dell'Ufficio, spinto in ciò dal degrado di alcuni responsori, privi di autorità e di logicità[31], e di aver collaborato con eccellenti cantori e lettori[32], nell'intento di restituire ai responsori corrotti la loro correttezza formale, testuale e forse anche musicale[33]. Egli è persuaso della necessità di questo lavoro proprio per i cantori[34], ai quali lo consegna affinché essi possano disporre convenientemente i versetti e ordinarli secondo le modalità dell'arte del canto (*secundum artis cantilenae modum*), intonandoli decorosamente e adattandoli ai responsori nei punti appropriati[35]. E' evidente dalle sue parole l'importanza che viene riconosciuta al ruolo del cantore. Amalario, approvando il serio lavoro di Elisarco[36], ammette di voler pro-

[30] Cfr. HELISACHAR ANDEGAVENSIS, *Epistola ad Nidibrium Narbonensem*, ed E. Dümmler, MGH, *Epistolae*, 5 (*Karolini aevi*, 3), Berlin 1899, pp. 307-309. Sulla questione, cfr. K. LEVY, *Abbot Helisachar's Antiphoner*, in ID., *Gregorian chant and the Carolingians*, Princeton – New York 1998, pp. 176-186.

[31] Cfr. HELISACHAR ANDEGAVENSIS, *ibid.*, p. 307, 28-30: «Sed ut referre solebatis, responsoria auctoritate et ratione carentia, versusque qui in quibusdam responsoriis a nostris vestrisque cantoribus incovenienter aptabantur, animum vestrum magna ex parte obnubilarent».

[32] Cfr. *ibid.*, pp. 307,37 - 308,1: «Adgrediens itaque hoc opus, aggregatisque hinc inde antiphonariis cantoribusque, adhibita etiam librorum copia et peritis lectoribus, coepimus diligenter concordiam probare antiphonariorum».

[33] Cfr. *ibid.*, p. 308, 22-24: «(...) Quodque vitio scriptorum, insolentia cantorum, aliquibus in locis depravatum erat aut quorundam imperitorum demptum vel additum fuerat, artis studio corrigeretur limaque rectitudinis poliretur».

[34] Cfr. *ibid.*, p. 308, 25-27: «(...) Hoc opus (...) nostris tamen vestrisque cantoribus precipue necessarium (...)».

[35] Cfr. *ibid.*, pp. 308,41 - 309,1: «Quia autem sicut premisimus nostris vestrisque cantoribus hoc opus oportunum esse iudicavimus, oportet ut sive ab his sive ab illis summopere observetur, quatinus versus convenienter positi atque ordinati secundum artis cantilenae modum honeste canantur et in responsorium convenientibus locis aptentur».

[36] Cfr. AMALARIUS METTENSIS, *Prologus de ordine Antiphonarii*, PL 105, 1244B: «In versibus (...) laboravit et sudavit sacerdos Dei Elisagarus, apprime eruditus, et studiosissimus in lectione et divino cultu, necnon et inter priores primus palatii excellentissimi Ludovici imperatoris. Non solum ille, sed et quoscumque de eruditis viris ad se potuit convocare, in praesenti negotio sudaverunt». Il Prologo all'antifonario, unico frammento sopravvissuto dell'intero scritto, è databile tra l'831 e l'834. Cfr. M. HUGLO, *Les remaniements de l'antiphonaire grégorien au* IX*e* *siècle: Hélisachar, Agoberd, Amalaire*, in *Culto cristiano e politica imperiale carolingia*, Atti

seguire sulla stessa strada. Nel *Liber de ordine antiphonarii*[37], egli evidenzia il significato teologico del testo intonato, adatta le parole dei canti alla festività in cui sono inseriti, coordina opportunamente la melodia con le parole, mettendo così in risalto l'essenza sacra del canto liturgico, la cui incombenza va affidata a cantori che non devono appagarsi della sola melodia, trascurando il contenuto dottrinale del testo[38], poiché la loro responsabilità nei confronti della comunità orante è grande: la loro voce infatti innalza le menti di chi ascolta a Dio e le sospinge al bene[39]. Un analogo zelo riformatore risalta anche nella lettera pastorale che Agobardo scrive nell'838 per presentare al clero e ai cantori della sua diocesi il nuovo antifonario, che egli ha purgato dai pezzi teologicamente dubbi. Il vescovo da una parte sottolinea la ragione del suo lavoro, riconsegnare ai testi la loro purezza originaria in virtù della trascendenza e della verità in essi contenuta[40], dall'altra spiega quale deve essere il giusto contegno dei cantori, affidandosi in ciò alle parole di Girolamo[41] e ricordando, con abbondanza di citazioni dai Padri, che essi devono mantenere timor di Dio e gravità di spirito, per far sì che la dolcezza delle melodie volga l'animo degli ascoltatori a Dio e non lo turbi tentandolo con musiche molli e suadenti, più adatte al teatro che alla chiesa[42].

del XVIII Convegno Internazionale di Studi sulla spiritualità medievale (Todi, 9-12 ottobre 1977), a c. di G. Fornasari, Todi 1979, pp. 89-120.

[37] Di qualche anno posteriore al Prologo, ma per Huglo precedente all'844.

[38] Cfr. AMALARIUS METTENSIS, *Liber de ordine Antiphonarii*, 18, PL 105, 1274D: «Maxima pars cantorum studet sono placere, tanto minus imbuitur de intellectualibus rebus». Cfr. anche R. MONTEROSSO, *Il «Liber de ordine antiphonarii» di Amalario*, in *Culto cristiano e politica imperiale carolingia* cit. (alla nota 36), pp. 45-59.

[39] Cfr. AMALARIUS METTENSIS, *ibid.*, 1, 1248BC: «Per psalmos opus praedicatorum monstratur, per lectiones doctrina. (...) Doctrina namque praedicatorum quaerit imitatores. Ad hoc enim surgit cantor a sede, et exaltat vocem in responsorio, ut excitet mentes quae audierunt doctrinam ad actiones bonas. Surgunt nacque devotae mentes per devotionem bonorum operum in responsorio (...)».

[40] Cfr. AGOBARDUS LUGDUNENSIS, *Liber de correctione antiphonarii*, PL 104, 329-340. Agobardo è drastico nella scelta dei testi; cfr. *ibid.*, 2, 330B: «Non ergo cuiuscumque figmentis, sed Spiritus sancti eloquiis maiestas divina laudanda est». E cfr. *ibid.*, 3, dove, in nome di tale principio, viene precisato: «(...) Antiphonarium pro viribus nostris magna ex parte correximus, amputatis his quae superflua, vel levia, vel mendacia aut blasphema videbantur».

[41] Cfr. *supra*, il testo cit. alla nota 21.

[42] Cfr. AGOBARDUS LUGDUNENSIS, *ibid.*, 12-17, 334A-337D.

Rabano Mauro è assai chiaro nell'indicare la responsabilità dei cantori:

> È doveroso che il salmista/cantore abbia una buona voce e possegga pienamente la sua arte, affinché possa sollecitare l'animo degli uditori con il fascino e la dolcezza della musica. La sua voce (...) esprima un suono e una melodia adeguati alla santa religione (...), e nel canto stesso riveli la semplicità cristiana e (...) incrementi la compunzione in chi ascolta[43].

In effetti, la dignità e il prestigio dei cantori, unite alla loro grande responsabilità, spingono lo stesso Aureliano a scrivere il suo trattato proprio per la loro elevazione culturale. Egli è cosciente che, nonostante l'abilità e la competenza tecnica di molti cantori, a nessuno di essi spetti il titolo di *musicus* che era stato degli antichi, a causa della loro fragile competenza nelle arti quadriviali; pertanto, redige un «novum opus»[44], attinente a «quibusdam regulis modulationum quas tonos seu tenores appellant[45] sed et de ipsorum vocabulis[46]», che affida al suo abate Bernardo affinché lo

[43] HRABANUS MAURUS, *De institutione clericorum*, II, 48, PL 107, 362AB: «Psalmistam autem et voce et arte praeclarum illustremque esse oportet, ita ut oblectamento dulcedinis animos incitet auditorum. Vox autem eius (...) habens sonum et melodiam sanctae religionis congruentem, (...) quae Christianam simplicitatem in ipsa modulatine demonstret, (...) quae compunctionem magis audientibus faciat». La fonte di Rabano è Isidoro: cfr. ISIDORUS HISPALENSIS, *De ecclesiasticis officiis*, 12, PL 83, 972BC.

[44] L'espressione *novum opus* sembra assunta da Girolamo, che nella Lettera a Papa Damaso premessa al Nuovo Testamento scrive: «Novum opus facere me cogis ex veteri...». Cfr. B. HAGGH, *Aurelian's Library*, in *Cantus Planus papers read at the 9th meeting Esztergom & Visegrád* (1998), ed. by L. Dobszay, Budapest 2001 [pp. 271-300], p. 273.

[45] Sul significato del termine *tonus* nell'epoca carolingia cfr. C. ATKINSON, '*Tonus' in the Carolingian Era: A Terminological* Spannungfeld, in *Quellen und Studien zur Musiktheorie des Mittelalters III*, hrsg. M. Bernhard, München 2001 (Bayerische Akademie der Wissenschaften, Veröffentlichungen der Musikhistorischen Kommission, 15), pp. 19-46.

[46] Il termine *vocabulis* si riferisce alle formule «Noeane – Noeagis». Si tratta di 'parole', chiamate da Aureliano anche *litteraturae*, che sono costituite da sillabe di vocalizzazione che hanno la funzione di riportare alla memoria dei cantori i tratti melodici costitutivi dei canti appartenenti ad uno stesso modo ecclesiastico. Cfr. J. PONTE, *«Aureliani Reomensis musica disciplina». A Revised Text, Translation and Commentary*, 3 voll., Ph. D. Diss., Brandeis University 1961 (University Microfilms, Ann Arbor, 1967), III, p. 9; e cfr. M. HUGLO, *Les formules d'intonations «noeane noeagis» en Orient et en Occident*, in *Aspects de la musique liturgique au Moyen Age*, Actes des Colloques de Royaumont de 1986, 1987 et 1988, éd. C. Meyer, Paris 1991, pp. 43-53; cfr. anche ID., *Grundlagen und Ansätze der Mittelalterlichen Mu-*

valuti, poiché nessuno infatti ha pari autorevolezza e fama nell'*armonica philosophia*[47]. Aureliano parla di *novum opus* poiché nutre l'ambizione di dare a un'opera tecnica indirizzata ai cantori una veste disciplinare: il trattato infatti si divide in due parti, delle quali la seconda, ovvero il tonario costituito dalle conoscenze specialistiche tramandate oralmente dai maestri di coro, è anticipata e introdotta dalla prima, che espone la teoria trasmessa dagli scritti dei *primi doctores*, tra i quali vi sono, oltre che i Padri della Chiesa, Cassiodoro, Isidoro, Boezio (il cui *De institutione musica*, sconosciuto nei primi secoli dell'alto medioevo, ritorna in alcuni frammenti proprio nel *Musica disciplina*), e probabilmente Macrobio. Aureliano non abbandona la classica contrapposizione tra *musicus* e cantor; anzi, la ribadisce più volte, come alla fine del capitolo IV, che si chiude citando letteralmente Boezio:

> Infatti musico è colui che ha la capacità giudicare senza errore, secondo il ragionamento e stabilite regole e secondo la convenienza musicale, modi e ritmi, generi dei canti e loro mescolanze, ma anche i carmi dei poeti[48].

Ma l'espressione «sine errore» apporta al passaggio una sfumatura non marginale: il *musicus* infatti, dovendo valutare 'senza errore' la

siktheorie von der Spätantike bis zur ottonischen Zeit, in *Die Lehre vom einstimmigen liturgischen Gesang*, hrsg. T. Ertelt – F. Zaminer, Darmstadt 2000 (Geschichte der Musiktheorie, 4), [pp. 18-102], pp. 69-75.

[47] Cfr. Aurelianus Reomensis, *Musica disciplina*, Praef., ed. Gushee cit. (alla nota 25), pp. 53,3 - 55,7: «Quoniam genuino ingenio prepollentem et artificali doctrina cluentem pre ceteris vosmet solum agnovi in armonica philosophia, rogatus a fratribus ut super quibusdam regulis modulationum quas tonos seu tenores appellant sed et de ipsorum vocabulis rerum laciniosum praescriberem sermonem; ac ideo seriem harum litterarum ad censuram vestrae nobilitatis direxi vestroque nomini dedicavi, ut si conspectui digna videntur, memoriae commendentur. Sin autem aliter, oblivioni ducantur. Scio enim quia nobilissimi valde inveniuntur cantores. Huius autem fateor nisi vos solum me neminem artis vidisse peritum. Quidam et enim nostorum multa musice norunt statuta, tamen ut fuerunt prisci nusquam, ut arbitror, invenitur musicus. Ac per hoc [haec] quae sparsim in veterum dictis invenire potui sed et quae a vobis et ab aliis audivi, ipse novum opus condere studui, illo iuvante qui donavit et sine quo nihil possumus, cui et devotus gratias ago».

[48] *Ibid.*, 4, p. 68, 14: «Is est enim musicus cui secundum speculationem propositamve rationem ac musicam convenientiam, de modis ac rithmis, deque cantilenarum generibus ac permixtionibus, sed et de poetarum carminibus adest facultas sine errore iudicandi». Cfr. Boethius, *De institutione musica*, I, 34, 1196A, ed. Friedlein cit. (alla nota 8), p. 225,11-15.

convenienza delle composizioni poetiche e musicali, non può prescindere dalla conoscenza delle regole del canto o della poesia. Ne consegue un nuovo, seppur ancora solo abbozzato, concetto della teoria musicale come di una disciplina che enuncia norme per la prassi, cioè individua categorie nella musica del tempo e le propone come regole[49]. Un altro passaggio emblematico a questo proposito è un ulteriore estratto dal *De institutione musica*, il cui inizio allontana dall'originale pensiero boeziano:

> Vi è tanta distanza tra il musico e il cantore, quanta tra il grammatico e il semplice lettore, e quanta tra l'artificio corporale e la ragione. (...) Ed infatti ogni *ars* e *disciplina* ha naturalmente maggiore onorevolezza nella ragione che nel mestiere, il quale si esaurisce nel lavoro manuale[50].

La musica è paragonata alla grammatica[51]; pertanto, si può dedurre che il musico di Aureliano sia di fatto il grammatico della musica, competente circa le strutture regolative del canto e capace di scrivere, come il grammatico, un manuale. Il suo compito, fondato sulla sua preparazione tecnica, è giudicare se le cose sono fatte bene o male. Aureliano continua:

> E in tanto appaiono distare fra loro il musico e il cantore, quanto il maestro e il discepolo. Infatti questi rivolge la sua attenzione ai poemi, mentre quegli li analizza[52].

Il *musicus* deve dunque esaminare e studiare gli elementi della musica, come il *grammaticus* quelli delle lettere, per estrarne principi e regole ancora non ben definiti[53].

[49] Cfr. M. Bielitz, *Musik und Grammatik. Studien zur mittelalterlichen Musiktheorie,* München – Salzburg 1977 (Beiträge zur Musikforschung, 4), pp. 20-23.

[50] Cfr. Aurelianus Reomensis, *ibid.*, 7, p. 77, 1-3: «Tantum inter musicum distat et cantorem, quantum inter grammaticum et simplicem lectorem, et quantum inter corporale artificium et rationem. Etenim artificium corporale quasi serviens famulatur; ratio vero quasi domina imperat, quia nisi a ratione vegetetur opus manus operantis inaniter laborant. Nam omnis ars atque disciplina honorabiliorem naturaliter habet rationem quam artificium quod manu opereque expletur». Cfr. Boethius, *ibid.*, pp. 223,28 - 224,25.

[51] Cfr. Bielitz, *ibid.*, pp. 20-23.

[52] Cfr. Aurelianus Reomensis, *ibid.*, p. 77, 10: «Etenim in tantum distare videntur inter se musicus et cantor quantum magister et discipulus, verbi gratia: is poematibus insistit, ille autem discernit».

[53] La strada verso la definizione di una nuova figura di *musicus* è ormai aperta e

D'altra parte, Aureliano non muta il quadro classificatorio delle scienze: la musica è una delle quattro discipline matematiche che costituiscono la *philosophia naturalis*, prima delle tre parti della filosofia individuate da Isidoro[54]. Essa dunque si connota propriamente come scienza speculativa: la pratica infatti non può trovare, fino all'irruzione del pensiero arabo-aristotelico in Occidente, una giustificazione teoretica[55]. Bisognerà aspettare la diffusione nel secolo XII dei testi di Aristotele, mediati attraverso gli autori arabi, per ottenerne un ripensamento dello statuto epistemologico. Esso porterà ad indicare e determinare, accanto al versante speculativo, quello applicativo non solo della filosofia nel suo complesso ma anche di ciascuna sua disciplina, individuando nella *sapientia* il nuovo fine dell'*utilitas*[56]. Rappresentativo il caso di Domenico

si svilupperà, nei secoli X e XI, in due differenti direzioni, l'una eminentemente didattica, l'altra decisamente speculativa. La prima è perseguita con vivacità da Guido d'Arezzo, il quale, animato dall'intento di preservare e chiarificare la pratica tradizionale, mira ad articolare la teoria modale in sintesi e in forma elementare, adottando efficaci strumenti didattici e proponendola come una semplice verità, necessaria per aiutare a risolvere dubbi e confusioni nell'esecuzione del canto. Pertanto, mentre Aureliano aveva auspicato nel *musicus* competenze sia nell'*armonica philosophia* sia nelle strutture regolative del *cantus planus*, Guido giunge a distinguere tra *philosophus*, *musicus* e *cantor*, ravvisando nel primo lo speculativo, nel secondo il cantore competente nelle regole fondamentali della musica, nel terzo infine, come d'altra parte Aureliano stesso, il cantore incompetentec; cfr. A. Rusconi, *Introduzione*, in Guido d'Arezzo, *Le opere*, intr., tr. e comm. a c. di A. Rusconi, Firenze 2005, pp. LXXV-LXXVIII. La seconda direzione si esplicita invece nella scuola di Reichenau (e in particolare nel suo più grande maestro, Ermanno il Contratto), che indaga la *disciplina* musicale con lo scopo principale di giustificare teoricamente e coordinare perfettamente i vari elementi della teoria modale.

54 Cfr. Aurelianus Reomensis, *ibid.*, 8, p. 80, 29-30: «Nam philosophiam in tres partes distinguere maluerunt, id est phisicam, ethicam, logicam, quae latine dicuntur, naturalis, moralis, rationalis. Naturalis autem disciplina IIII traditur artibus, id est arithmetica, geometrica, musica, astronomia, in quibus vel de numeris disputatur vel de terrae mensuris, vel sonis, vel certe stellarum dispositionibus; sed earum vis et causa omnis in numeris est». Per la divisione della filosofia di Isidoro, cfr. *supra*, alla nota 15.

55 Sulle classificazioni delle scienze nel Medioevo, cfr. Weisheipl, *Classification of the sciences* cit. (alla nota 2). Va però ricordato che l'alto Medioevo non trascurò l'aspetto 'applicativo' delle quattro arti matematiche, come ben mostra G. Beaujouan, *L'enseignement du* Quadrivium, in *'Par raison de nombres'. L'art du calcul et les savoirs scientifiques médiévaux*, éd. par G. Beaujouan, Aldershot 1991, pp. 639-667.

56 Cfr. F. Alessio, *La filosofia e le* artes mechanicae *nel secolo XII*, in «Studi Medievali», 6.1 (1965), pp. 71-161 (oggi in Id., *Studi di storia della filosofia medievale*, a c. di G. Francioni, Pisa 2003, pp. 121-144).

Gundisalvi, che, pur fissando la musica come seconda disciplina del quadrivio, la bipartisce in attiva e speculativa, e divide quest'ultima in cinque grandi parti, che abbracciano sia l'analisi dei principi sui quali si fonda la scienza dei suoni sia lo studio delle applicazioni delle regole compositive nel discorso e nella pratica[57].

Ma, più specificamente, Aureliano definisce la musica come l'*ars* che studia i rapporti fra numeri intelligibili ma mobili: la sua natura quantitativa è pensata quindi come non separata dal movimento, secondo un'idea del *melos* come moto della voce, di radice aristossenica (e presente poi in Boezio e Marziano Capella), e la successiva definizione agostiniana di musica come «scientia bene movendi»[58], ordine e misura del movimento[59]. Inoltre, altrove Aureliano la definisce anche «scienza del modulare rettamente, conveniente al suono e al canto»[60], espressione che compone sia l'agostiniana «musica est scientia bene modulandi»[61], laddove «modulor» significa 'regolare', 'disporre secondo misura'[62], sia l'isidoriana «musica est peritia modulationis sono cantuque consistens»[63], assai più orientata alla pratica, sebbene anch'essa ispirata alle parole di Agostino[64]. Egli quindi, pur riconoscendo alla musica lo status di *scientia speculativa*, ne ravvisa la dimensione fattiva

[57] Cfr. DOMINICUS GUNDISSALINUS, *De scientiis*, 3, ed. P. M. Alonso Alonso, Madrid – Granada 1954, pp. 104,3 - 107,14. Franco Alessio indica con precisione le fonti non solo arabe ma anche latine di Domenico Gundisalvi; cfr. F. ALESSIO, *ibid.*, pp. 129-135.

[58] Cfr. AUGUSTINUS HIPPONENSIS, *De musica*, I, 3, 4, PL 32, 1085 (tr. it. a c. di M. Bettetini, Milano 1997, p. 12).

[59] Cfr. AURELIANUS REOMENSIS, *Musica disciplina*, ed. Gushee cit. (alla nota 25), p. 81, 31: «Arithmetica quippe de illis constat numeris qui stabiles sunt et intelligibiles. Geometrica vero stabiles et sensibiles habet numeros. Musica autem equae intelligibiles, mobiles tamen, et ad aliquid pertinentes. Astronomia quoque mobili, et semper sensibili ratione versatur».

[60] *Ibid.*, p. 61, 1: «Musica autem est scientia recte modulandi, sono cantuque congrua».

[61] Cfr. AUGUSTINUS, *ibid.*, 2, 2, 1083 (tr. it. cit., p. 6). Aureliano ha presente la definizione che Cassiodoro riprende da Agostino: cfr. CASSIODORUS, SENATOR, *Institutiones divinarum et saecularium litterarum*, II, 5, 2, PL 70, 1209A, ed. Mynors cit. (alla nota 12), p. 143,12-13.

[62] Come spiega bene M. BETTETINI, tr. it. cit. (alla nota 58), p. 382, nota 16.

[63] Cfr. ISIDORUS HISPALENSIS, *Etymologiae*, III, 15, 1, PL 82, 163A, ed. Lindsay cit. (alla nota 15), ll. 19-20.

[64] Cfr. AUGUSTINUS, *ibid.*, 2, 3, 1084 (tr. it. cit., p. 8): «Ergo modulatio non incongrue dicitur movendi quaedam peritia (...)».

del canto, i cui principi e regole vorrebbe ricondurre entro la sfera speculativa della scienza armonica, come si legge in apertura del tonario, dove, preoccupato di individuare norme capaci di spiegare l'articolazione melodica dei toni, è spinto a riconoscere nel quadrivio la sede adatta allo studio teorico della musica:

> Circa queste cose, lo spirito del lettore si chiede perché uno e un solo tono abbia tante *varietates*, e talvolta l'ultima sillaba del versetto vada sospinta verso l'alto, mentre talaltra è spinta verso il basso, ed ancora è spesso pronunciata con enfasi (...). Del resto, rimandiamo colui che vorrà conoscere la totalità di questa scienza alla disciplina della musica, e se ad essa vorrà dedicarsi, volga gli occhi alla consonanza delle proporzioni, alla contemplazione degli intervalli e alla certezza dei numeri; ed allora potrà conoscere per quale ragione in una stessa *litteratura* si produca una diversa concordia sonora, e molte altre cose che è lungo dire[65].

Aureliano cerca dunque, per quanto gli è possibile, di stabilire fra la musica come arte quadriviale e il canto liturgico un legame, che nelle intenzioni vorrebbe percorrere l'intero trattato. Certamente, la sezione disciplinare e quella tecnica dell'opera sono per moltissimi aspetti ancora slegate. Nondimeno, va considerato che negli stessi anni, altri teorici della musica si sforzeranno di impostare teoricamente i toni ecclesiastici proprio attraverso la dottrina musicale boeziana[66], ordinando gradualmente le strutture mo-

[65] Aurelianus Reomensis, *ibid.*, 10, pp. 85, 5 - 86, 5: «Qua de re animus movetur lectitantis, quur unus solummodo tonus tot habeat varietatum modos, ut aliquando ultima versiculi sillaba sursum erigatur, nonnumquam iosum deprimatur, plerumque etiam graviter enuntietur (...). Ceterum qui plenitudinem huiusce vult nosse scientiae, ad musicam eum mittimus, et si in ipsa voluerit versari, ad consonantiam proportionum ac speculationem intervallorum necne ad certitudinem oculos vertat numerorum; et tunc nosse poterit, quam ob rem in una eademque litteratura diversus efficiatur [sonoritatis concentus], et cetera plura quae longum est edicere». Le *varietates* sono cadenze salmodiche, che venivano chiamate dai teorici anche *differentiae*, *diffinitiones*, *divisiones*, più raramente *figurae* o *modi*, o anche *formulae* (nelle fonti italiane). Sono cadenze non definitive, che hanno la funzione di riportare, alla fine del versetto salmodico, alla reintonazione 'armoniosa' dell'antifona. Costituiscono l'elemento variabile della salmodia; per una spiegazione complessiva, cfr. M. Huglo, *Les tonaires. Inventaire, analyse, comparation*, Paris 1971, Introd., pp. 11-21. Per il termine *litteraturae*, cfr. *supra*, alla nota 46.

[66] I teorici alto-medievali appresero dalle fonti tardo-antiche, e in primis da Boezio, il concetto di altezza del singolo suono; i concetti di intervallo e di consonanza; l'idea di 'scala', cioè di sistema ordinato di suoni legati tra loro da stabi-

dali del *cantus planus* sulla base delle dimostrazioni armonico-matematiche soprattutto del *De institutione musica* e, viceversa, adattando queste a quelle, come si verifica nelle riuscite sintesi di Ucbaldo di Saint Amand[67] e dell'*Alia musica*[68].

Ma la grande rilevanza del canto nella vita liturgica della comunità cristiana, la sua sacralità, il suo slancio contemplativo e il suo rilievo etico, spingono anche ad una originale interpretazione della boeziana tripartizione dei generi della musica in cosmica, umana e strumentale.

Ancora una volta, è il *Musica disciplina* a mostrare elementi di originalità. Aureliano infatti, che pur trascrive in modo abbastanza fedele e completo da Boezio il famoso capitolo secondo del libro I sui tre generi della musica[69], ne dà poi una lettura nuova. Da una parte infatti accenna ad una connessione tra l'armonia cosmica e i toni della musica liturgica: l'armonia cosmica, ammette, si riconosce nel cosmo intero, nella molteplicità degli elementi e nell'alternarsi delle stagioni così come nei moti dei sette pianeti e del cielo superiore detto zodiaco, i quali otto producono «la dolcissima armonia del canto» che Dio stesso, parlando a Giobbe, chiamò *concentus caeli*, e che sembra trovare espressione nei corri-

lite relazioni armoniche. Per un inquadramento generale sulla teoria armonica platonica e sulla conseguente dottrina boeziana cfr. E. Mainoldi, *Ars musica*, Milano 2001, pp. 120-153 e pp. 192-199; su Marziano Capella cfr. M. E. Duchez, *Le savoir théorico-musical dans les commentaires de Martianus Capella. La tradition erigenienne*, in *Giovanni Scoto nel suo tempo. L'organizzazione del sapere in età carolingia*, Atti del XXIV Convegno Storico Internazionale (Todi, 11-14 ottobre 1987), Spoleto 1989, pp. 553-592; su Macrobio, cfr. C. Meyer, *La théorie des symphoniae selon Macrobe et sa diffusion*, in «Scriptorium», 53 (1999), pp. 82-107. Sull'uso delle fonti tardo-antiche, cfr. anche N. Phillips, *L'enseignement de la théorie des modes du IXe au XIIe siècle*, in *L'enseignement de la musique au Moyen Âge et à la Renaissance*, Colloque (Royaumont, 5-6 Juillet 1985), Royaumont 1987, pp. 96-107, e N. Phillips, *Classical and Late Latin Sources for Ninth-Century Treatises on Music*, in *Music theory and its sources: Antiquity and the Middle Ages*, Notre Dame Conference in Medieval Studies, I (Notre Dame, 30 April – 2 May 1987), ed. by A. Barbera, Notre Dame (Ind.) 1990, pp. 100-135.

67 Cfr. Y. Chartier, *L'oeuvre musicale d'Hucbald de Saint-Amand, Les compositions et le traité de musique*, Bellarmin 1995 (Cahiers d'études médiévales, Cahier spéc. 5).

68 Cfr. *Alia musica*, ed. J. Chailley, Paris 1965.

69 Cfr. Aurelianus Reomensis, *ibid.*, 3, pp. 64 seqq. Il capitolo è un estratto da Boethius, *De institutione musica*, I, 2, 1117AD, ed. Friedlein cit. (alla nota 8), pp. 187-189. Le varianti al testo sono minime, anche se Aureliano omette o abbrevia singoli passi oppure aggiunge brevi interpolazioni esplicative.

spondenti otto toni gregoriani (anche se poi Aureliano ammette: «non spetta a me definire se queste cose siano pertinenti alle regole [modali] predette», poiché gli scriptores di questa scienza sostengono che i principi che ordinano la musica risultano nei numeri)[70]. Dall'altra, decide di trascurare lo studio della musica strumentale, considerata biasimevole perché separata dalla scienza[71], e di esaminare l'articolazione, nel canto, della voce, giudicata estrinsecazione dell'*humana*[72]. La *musica humana*, egli afferma assegnandole la tradizionale divisione di Cassiodoro, si tripartisce in armonica, ritmica e metrica[73]; un pensiero che probabilmente conserva l'impronta di due passi, l'uno dello stesso Cassiodoro, l'altro di Isidoro. Cassiodoro infatti aveva affermato:

[70] Cfr. AURELIANUS REOMENSIS, *ibid.*, 8, pp. 79, 22 - 80, 29: «Quod autem octo sint [i toni della musica liturgica] caelestes motus videntur imitari. Tradunt namque philosophi superiorem esse circulum caeli qui zodiacus nuncupatur (...) Subter hunc autem circulum septem sidera sunt (...): Saturnus, Iupiter, Mars, Sol, Venus, Mercurius, Luna, que sicut amplitudine circuitus ita temporum differunt quantitate (...). Igitur isti astrorum motus VIII sunt, videlicet VII errantium et illius qui dicitur aplanes, quos omnes dicunt dulcissimam cantus armoniam, id est consonantiam efficere; quam etiam Dominus in ea responsione quam de turbine fecit ad sanctum Iob 'concentum celi' (*Jb* 38, 37) nominat. Sed ista utrum ad praefatas regulas pertineant meum non est definire. Ceterum alie sunt quas scriptores huius artis invenerunt. Dicunt enim omnes musice artis rationes ex numeris constare».

[71] Cfr. *ibid.*, 3, p. 66, 19-20: «Tercia est musica, quae in quibusdam consistit instrumentis, videlicet ut sunt organa, cithare, lire, et cetera plura. Sed istud quod in instrumentis positum est, a musice scientia intellectuque seiuncta est; a[d]ministraturque aut intentione, ut nervis, aut spiritu, ut tibiis vel his quae aqua moventur ut organa, aut percussione quadam, ut in his quae ad concava erea feriuntur atque inde diversi efficiuntur soni». Cfr. BOETHIUS, *De institutione musica*, I, 2, 1171D, ed. Friedlein cit. (alla nota 8), p. 89,5-7, e I, 34, 1196B, pp. 224,28 - 225,1. Nell'edizione critica il termine «seiuncta» è trascritto diviso («se iuncta»), come nel manoscritto di riferimento (Valenciennes, Bibliothèque Municipale, 148). Bernhard ne auspica la correzione. Cfr. M. BERNHARD, *Textkritisches zu Aurelianus Reomensis*, in «Musica Disciplina», 40 (1986) [pp. 49-61], p. 53. Si noti che per Boezio è in realtà la musica strumentale l'unica della quale sia possibile lo studio armonico-matematico, perché l'unica percepibile dai sensi.

[72] Ho approfondito l'argomento in A. MORELLI, *Armonia cosmica,* musica humana *e canto liturgico nel pensiero musicale alto-medievale*, in Harmonia mundi. *Musica mondana e musica celeste fra Antichità e Medioevo*, Atti del Convegno internazionale di studi (Roma, 14-15 dicembre 2005) a c. di M. Cristiani – C. Panti – G. Perillo, Firenze 2007 (Micrologus' Library), pp. 145-166.

[73] Cfr. AURELIANUS REOMENSIS, *ibid.*, 4, pp. 66, 1 - 67, 2: «Hactenus de musicae disputavimus generibus, tresque esse musicas enunciavimus, mundanam scilicet, humanam, et eam quae in multis constat instrumentis. Iterum autem humane musice partes, Opifice iuvante, ut possumus adnotemus. Sunt ergo tres: videlicet, armonica, rithmica, metrica». Cfr. CASSIODORUS, SENATOR, *Institutiones divinarum et*

> Anche Agostino scrisse sei libri *De musica*, nei quali mostrò che la voce umana può naturalmente avere suoni ritmici e un'armonia modulabile in sillabe lunghe e brevi[74].

Isidoro, invece, nelle *Etymologiae* aveva scritto:

> La prima divisione della musica, che è detta armonica, cioè modulazione della voce, riguarda gli attori di commedie e tragedie, i cori e tutti coloro che cantano. Anima e corpo producono un movimento, ed esso un suono, dal quale deriva la musica, che nell'uomo è chiamata voce[75].

Considerazioni di questo genere si possono in realtà fare anche per opere dello stesso periodo. Nel manoscritto della seconda metà del secolo IX Paris, Bibliothèque Nationale, lat. 7200, autorevole testimone della *Glossa maior in institutionem musicam Boethii*, un'annotazione spiega la *musica humana* come «vox hominis»; essa verrà poi copiata sei volte in codici più tardi, fino al se-

saecularium litterarum, II, 5, 5, PL 70, 1209B, ed. Mynors cit. (alla nota 12), p. 144, 5-11: «Musicae partes sunt tres: armonica, rithmica, metrica. Armonica est scientia musica quae decernit in sonis acutum et gravem. Rithmica est quae requirit incursionem verborum, utrum bene sonus an male cohaereat. Metrica est quae mensuram diversorum metrorum probabili ratione cognoscit, ut verbi gratia heroicon, iambicon, heleiacon et cetera». Questa tripartizione della musica risente delle parole di Agostino; cfr. AUGUSTINUS HIPPONENSIS, *De ordine*, II, 14. 40, PL 32, 1014, ed. W. M. Green, Turnhout 1970 (CCSL, 29), p. 129,20-34: «Videbat autem hanc materiam esse vilissimam, nisi certa dimensione temporum et acuminis gravitatisque moderata varietate soni figurarentur. Recognovit hinc esse illa semina quae in grammatica, cum syllabas diligenti consideratione versaret, pedes et accentus vocaverat. (...). Quod autem non esset certo fine moderatum, sed tamen rationabiliter ordinatis pedibus curreret, rhythmi nomine notavit, qui latine nihil aliud quam numerus dici potuit»). La medesima tripartizione fu poi trascritta da Isidoro: cfr. ISIDORUS HISPALENSIS, *Etymologiae*, III, 18, PL 82, 164B, ed. Lindsay cit. (alla nota 15), ll. 3-9. Qualche riga più avanti (p. 68,12) Aureliano afferma: «Igitur secundum Nichomacum tertia pars *humanae musicae*, quae metrica nuncupatur (...)», consentendoci così di escludere la possibilità di un errore di trascrizione del copista.

[74] CASSIODORUS, SENATOR, *ibid.*, II, 5, 10, 1212C, p. 149, 20-23: «Scripsit etiam et Pater Augustinus *de Musica* sex libros, in quibus humanam vocem rithmicos sonos et armoniam modulabilem in longis syllabis atque brevibus naturaliter habere posse monstravit».

[75] Cfr. ISIDORUS HISPALENSIS, *ibid.*, III, 20, 1, 164C, ll. 19-23: «Prima divisio Musicae, quae harmonica dicitur, id est, modulatio vocis, pertinet ad comoedos, tragoedos, vel choros, vel ad omnes qui voce propria canunt. Haec ex animo et corpore motum facit, et ex motu sonum, ex quo colligitur Musica, quae in homine vox appellatur».

colo XII[76]. Inoltre, in corrispondenza della famosa affermazione boeziana, che asserisce che la *musica humana* può essere intesa da chiunque discenda in se stesso, poiché è essa stessa che unisce al corpo «illam incorpoream rationis vivacitatem»[77], l'espressione *rationis vivacitas* è interpretata così:

> Haec est vivacitas rationis: ipsa vis rationis animae quae sub silentio in animo latet, tunc autem miscetur corpori, quando formabiliter per sonos foras egreditur[78].

Anche tale annotazione si ripresenta ripetutamente in manoscritti successivi. Essa rimarca il fatto che il potere razionale dell'anima, nascosto nel silenzio nell'anima stessa (poiché non è percepibile dall'esterno con i sensi), quando si unisce al corpo viene alla luce attraverso i suoni; lo si coglie sensibilmente nei suoni, che possono essere quelli delle parole o quelli del canto, che sono un riflesso della musica umana, in quanto unione di corpo e anima. La *vox hominis* è dunque uno dei modi in cui la *musica humana* si manifesta.

La connessione tra *vox humana* e *musica humana* ritorna, con sfumature diverse, in altri autori ed anche in alcuni dei rari scritti musicali posteriori al *Musica disciplina* che prendono in esame la musica speculativa[79]. La continuità di trasmissione di tale pensiero è provata da testimonianze che affiorano qua e là anche ben oltre il secolo XIII, quando la riscoperta del *De anima* aristotelico comporterà il profondo ripensamento delle teorie sull'anima e sulla percezione e produzione del suono[80]. Queste testimonianze,

[76] Cfr. *Glossa maior in institutionem musicam Boethii*, 3 voll., ed. M. Bernhard – C. Bower, München 1993-1996, I, p. 85.

[77] Cfr. BOETHIUS, *De institutione musica*, I, 2, 1172C, ed. Friedlein cit. (alla nota 8), pp. 188,26 - 189,1: «Humanam vero musicam quisquis in seipsum descendit intelligit. Quid est enim, quod illam incorpoream rationis vivacitatem corpori misceat, nisi quaedam coaptatio et veluti gravium leviumque vocum, quasi unam consonantiam efficiens temperatio?».

[78] *Glossa maior in institutionem musicam Boethii*, ed. Bernhard – C. Bower cit. (alla nota 76), I, p. 102. L'annotazione è di una mano diversa dalla precedente.

[79] Purtroppo, nell'alto medioevo i teorici mirano principalmente a sistematizzare il repertorio liturgico e a elaborare un'efficace didattica musicale, trascurando la musica speculativa. Tuttavia, talvolta venivano redatte o compilate brevi esposizioni, con l'intento didattico di riassumere i principi fondamentali della scienza musicale. Di esse restano una sola o poche copie, che però possono servire a chiarire almeno in parte i contenuti della musica speculativa, che la trattatistica musicale perlopiù tralascia. Cfr. C. MEYER, *Les traités de musique*, Turnhout 2001, p. 21.

[80] Cfr. C. PANTI, *Suono interiore e* musica humana *fra tradizione boeziana e ari-*

seppur poche, sparse e a volte sin troppo laconiche, impongono tuttavia di ipotizzare che la boeziana *musica humana* abbia, lungo l'alto Medioevo, parzialmente modificato il suo significato: da movimento naturale dell'anima teso alla realizzazione di un rapporto commisurato tra le sue parti e tra sé e il corpo, ad armonia interiore capace di esplicitarsi attraverso la voce; o anche, direttamente e solamente, a voce, canto.

Nella letteratura monastica dei secoli X e XI si possono ricordare i casi della sassone Rosvita, badessa di Gandersheim, e di Ildegarda, badessa di Bingen. La prima asserisce che la voce, emessa ora gravemente ora acutamente, fa parte della *musica humana*, insieme all'equilibrata corrispondenza delle parti del corpo e alla stretta unione del corpo e dell'anima, facendo proprio uno schema compositivo che si discosta lievemente da quello di Aureliano e delle glosse al *De institutione musica*[81]. Due secoli più tardi, la seconda sosterrà che l'anima umana, che per sua natura è *symphonialis* (sinfonica), è in grado di manifestare la sua lode a Dio attraverso la voce[82].

Considerando la trattatistica musicale dei secoli XI-XIII, vanno citati i casi di Adalboldo di Utrecht, di Enrico di Augusta, di Guglielmo Roffredi e di un manoscritto del secolo XIII, proveniente dalla facoltà delle arti di Parigi. Nella sua *Epistola cum tractatu de musica*, Adalboldo di Utrecht identifica la *musica humana* con le *voces concordes*, assimilandola in parte alla musica strumentale, della quale è in grado di imitare l'artificiosa bellezza[83]. Nel suo *De*

stotelismo: le glosse dello Pseudo-Grossatesta al De institutione musica, in *Parva Naturalia. Saperi medievali, natura e vita*, Atti dell'XI Convegno della Società Italiana per lo Studio del Pensiero Medievale (Macerata, 7-9 dicembre 2001), ed. by C. Crisciani – R. Lambertini – R. Martorelli Vico, Pisa – Roma 2004, pp. 219-245.

[81] Cfr. HROTSVITHA GANDERSHEIMENSIS, *Paphnutius*, II, 17, in EAD., *Dramata*, PL 137, 1031B, éd. P. De Winterfeld, MGH, *Scriptores rerum Germanicarum in usum schol.*, 34 (*Hrotsvitae Opera*), Berlin, 1903, pp. 165,35 - 166,2: «[Humana musica percipiatur] Non solum, ut dixi, in compagine corporis et animae, necnon in emissione nunc gravis, nunc clarae vocis, sed etiam in pulsibus venarum atque in quorumdam mensura membrorum (...)».

[82] Cfr. HILDEGARDIS BINGENSIS, *Epistolarum Liber*, *Epistola* 47, PL 197, 221B: «(...) corpus vero indumentum est animae, quae vivam vocem habet, ideoque decet ut corpus cum anima per vocem Deo laudes decantet».

[83] Cfr. ADALBOLDUS ULTRAIECTENSIS, *Epistola cum tractatu de musica instrumentali humanaque ac mundana*, Introd., ed. J. Smits van Waesberghe, Buren 1981, p. 14: «Humana vero musica dicitur, eo quod humani gutturis fistulis, mirabili quadam

Musica, Enrico di Augusta, citando i tre generi boeziani della *musica mundana, humana* e *artificiosa*, li determina nella musica cosmica, vocale, strumentale, benché egli conosca approfonditamente e tenga sempre presente il *De institutione musica*[84]. Analogamente, nella sua *Summa musicae artis*, Guglielmo Roffredi scrive che la *musica humana* è il canto[85]. Infine, nel manoscritto della facoltà delle Arti di Parigi, viene attribuita direttamente a Boezio la definizione di *musica humana* come modulazione della voce:

> La musica umana si percepisce nel melodioso innalzamento o abbassamento della voce secondo i vari canti[86].

habilitate et artificio, instrumentorum consonantias imitatur». Waesberghe attribuisce l'*Epistola* e il trattato ad Adalboldo, ma il recente studio di Ilnitchi li ripensa come un prodotto anonimo del secolo XIII: cfr. G. ILNITCHI, *Musica mundana, Aristotelian Natural Philosophy and Ptolemaic Astronomy*, in «Early Music History», 21 (2002), pp. 37-74.

[84] Cfr. HENRICUS AUGUSTENSIS, *Musica*, ed. J. Smits van Waesberghe, Buren 1977, [pp. 35-53], p. 35: «Incipit Musica Domni Heinrici Augustensis magistri. Discipulus: Estne musica genus an species? Magister: Species est et subalternum genus. D: Quomodo? M: Scientia artificialis, cum in multa, etiam in musicam [speciem] dividitur. Est autem subalternum genus, quia in tres species subdividitur, quarum prima est mundana, secunda humana, tertia artificiosa. D: Quae est mundana? M: Quam VII planetae, mundi videlicet partes, sua volubi(li)tate efficiunt. D: Quae est humana? M: Quam vivae voces hominum efficiunt. D: Quae est artificiosa? M: Quae arte hominum composita, aut tactu, ut in fidibus, aut flatu, ut in organis, aut percussione, ut in cymbalis et tibiis perficitur». Su Enrico di Augusta, cfr. anche M. HUGLO, *Un théoricien du XIe siècle: Henri d'Augsbourg*, in «Revue de Musicologie», 53 (1967), 53-59.

[85] Cfr. GUILLELMUS LUCENSIS (GUILLELMUS DE DOMO ROFFREDI), *Summa musicae artis, Proemium*, ed. in A. Seay, *Guglielmo Roffredi's 'Summa musicae artis'*, in «Musica disciplina», 24 (1970), [pp. 71-77], p. 71: «Tria autem sunt genera musicae, mundanum, humanum, etiam instrumentale. Mundanum quidem est quod ex caeli volubilitate et spherae superioris collisione conficitur; haec harmonia nuncupatur. Humanum est quod ex hominis capite canori voce profertur. Tertium quod in instrumentis est constitutum, ut in cymbalis, organis, lyra et monochordo, et a Pythagora magistro philosopho per instrumenta et exercitia repertum. Et haec tria uniformiter divisa quodammodo sunt providentia copulata divina». Su Guglielmo Roffredi, vescovo di Lucca dal 1174 al 1190, cfr. anche M. HUGLO, *A propos de la 'Summa artis musicae' attribuée a Guglielmo Roffredi*, «Revue de Musicologie», 58 (1972), pp. 90-94.

[86] Cfr. M. HAAS, *Studien zur mittelalterlichen Musiklehre. I. Eine übersicht über die Musiklehre im Kontext der Philosophie des 13. Jahrhunderts*, in «Forum Musicologicum», 3 (1982), [pp. 323-456], p. 354: «Humana percipitur in modulata elevacione et depressione vocis secundum diversas cantilenas. (*in margine*) Auctor musice Boecius».

Ma ormai il contesto è profondamente mutato. La riscoperta dei *libri naturales* di Aristotele comporta infatti un graduale mutamento epistemologico nella definizione della musica, il cui soggetto, il suono, la pone come *scientia media* fra la fisica e la matematica. La musica è la scienza «de sono», o meglio del «contractus numerus in proportione sonoritatis», o anche «de numero secundum aptitudinem sue proportionis» o infine del «numerus proportionatus», che è il «numerus contractus in sonoritate»[87]. È dunque lo studio numerico del suono. Ne deriva in primo luogo che, essendo un fenomeno fisico-acustico, il suono può altresì essere studiato dalla fisica (e sarà soprattutto nei commenti al *De anima*[88], oltre che nei commenti alla *Fisica* o al *De caelo*, che si troveranno ampie analisi del suono); in secondo luogo che, secondo l'insegnamento degli *Analytica posteriora* di Aristotele, la musica va subalternata all'aritmetica, come specifica anche il manoscritto parigino[89].

Siamo già troppo lontani dal 'paradigma' alto-medievale, che, ravvisando nella scienza musicale e nel canto liturgico un dono della Sapienza divina, li giudica un'unica via di ritorno alla sorgente originaria di ogni bene, che è Dio, delineando in questo modo anche una 'nuova' teoria della musica pratica indirizzata ai *cantores*, per la loro elevazione sia culturale che spirituale. Non resta dunque che chiudere ricordando ancora una volta le parole di Aureliano:

> Senza dubbio la compagine e il naturale accordo di codesto mondo contiene un'armonica proporzione. Infatti, se tu esaminassi come ogni altra cosa gioisca mentre il sole sale più in

[87] *Ibid.*, p. 358.

[88] Cfr. M. WITTMANN, «*Vox atque sonus*»*: Studien zur Rezeption der Aristotelischen Schrift* «*De Anima*» *und ihre Bedeutung für die Musiktheorie*, Ph. D. diss. Universität Freiburg im Br. 1986, Pfaffenweiler 1987 (Musikwissenschaftliche Studien, 4); lo studio espone la storia della recezione del *De anima* dalla tarda antichità fino al secolo XIII e presenta una scelta di glosse al *De anima*.

[89] Cfr. HAAS, *Studien* cit., p. 358: «Item in musica determinatur de numero contracto in proportione sonoritatis, in arismetica vero determinatur de numero simpliciter. Ergo musica subalternatur arismetice». Oltre allo studio di Haas, riferimenti bibliografici sul tema sono: J. GAGNÉ, *Du* Quadrivium *aux* scientiae mediae, in *Arts Liberaux et Philosophie au Moyen-Age*, Actes du Quatrième Congres International de Philosophie Médiévale (27 aout – 2 sept. 1967), Montréal – Paris 1969, pp. 975-986; *Musik und die Geschichte der Philosophie und Naturwissenschafen im Mittelalter*, ed by F. Hentschel, Leiden 1998; PANTI, *Suono interiore e* musica humana cit. (alla nota 80).

alto, e come evidentemente l'aria diventi più pura, e il volto della terra si rivesta della bellezza dei fiori, e il mare si plachi dal suo impeto, capiresti che ogni creatura, unita da una mirabile armonia, si accorda con se medesima. Con quanta congruenza l'uomo stesso si adatti a questa disciplina non potrà non comprenderlo colui che avrà capito di avere tutte le cose che di solito si attribuiscono a quest'arte. Infatti egli ha in gola un condotto per cantare, nel petto una sorta di cetra, distinta per così dire in corde dalle fibre del polmone, e nell'alterna mutazione delle vene e delle pulsazioni l'elevarsi e l'abbassarsi [della voce] Una mente saggia potrà facilmente riconoscere che tutte queste cose si accordano tra loro, al punto da non poter dubitare che la disciplina musicale manifesta in tutte le cose che sono state create la Sapienza del Creatore, e pertanto ogni creatura deve lodare con un canto senza fine il proprio Autore, poiché tramite il profeta si esorta : 'Lodate il Signore dai cieli' e via di seguito fino alla fine del salterio. Nei quali tre salmi, per così dire tutti partecipi di questa disciplina, nessuno è esonerato dall'essere spronato a ripetere degne lodi di Dio[90].

[90] Cfr. AURELIANUS REOMENSIS, *Musica disciplina*, ed. Gushee cit. (alla nota 25), 1, pp. 59,12 - 60,18: «Nempe mundi istius compago convenientiaque naturalis, armonicam quodammodo continet congruentiam. Si enim rimeris qualiter sole altius procedente cetera congaudeant, qualiter scilicet aer purior fiat, terrae facies florum venustate pubescat, mare a suo fervore requiescat, deprehendis quod omnis creatura mira armonia sociata sibi conveniat. Homo etiam ipse quanta congruentia huic aptetur discipline non dubitabit qui scierit omnia se habere quae solent huic arti tribuere. Habet enim cantandi fistulam in gutture, quandam cytharam in pectore, pulmonis fibris quasi quibusdam distinctam cordis, elevationes atque gravationes in venarum pulsuumque reflua mutatione. Haec omnia convenienter sobria mens sibi convenire ita facile poterit cognoscere, ut non dubitet hanc disciplinam in omnibus quae sunt condita, Auctoris sapientiam effulgere ideoque cuncta quae sunt condita conditorem proprium continua cantione predicare debere, cum per prophetam precipiatur: 'Laudate Dominum de caelis' (*Ps* 148, 1), et cetera usque in finem psalterii. In quibus tribus psalmis tamquam omnes huius discipline participes nullus excipitur, qui non ad dignas Creatori laudes referendas provocetur. Huius ergo artis qui primi doctores effulserint tangam, post vero quibus regulis astringatur, Domino annuente, paucis astringam».

FRANCESCO PAPARELLA

IL LINGUAGGIO DEL SIMBOLO IN GIOVANNI ERIUGENA

LA SFIDA DELLA RELIGIONE ALLA RAZIONALITÀ FILOSOFICA

La filosofia eriugeniana, riprendendo e rielaborando la precedente tradizione del pensiero neoplatonico, concepisce la sostanza divina come una realtà ineffabile la cui natura non può essere adeguatamente descritta dal linguaggio e dal pensiero creaturali. Il tema, religioso e insieme metafisico, della natura di Dio celata nell'abisso del suo mistero ipersostanziale costituisce per la ricerca filosofica del maestro palatino una stimolante sfida speculativa che conduce a rinnovare l'indagine sui confini dello stesso pensiero razionale.

La risposta più interessante che Eriugena fornisce quale conseguenza di tale sollecitazione speculativa è rappresentata dalla riflessione sul linguaggio simbolico e sulla natura della conoscenza teologica che esso promette all'uomo: il simbolo appare come uno strumento cognitivo in grado di superare lo iato tra finito e infinito, conducendo a una particolare rivelazione della natura divina. L'analisi della dottrina eriugeniana sul simbolo permette, quindi, di comprendere la centralità per il pensiero del maestro palatino del tema dell'ineffabilità del divino. Tale analisi dovrà prendere le mosse da un preliminare studio delle ragioni metafisiche che portano Eriugena ad affermare l'indicibilità della sostanza divina, in modo tale da ricostruire le conseguenze che una simile dottrina ha sul pensiero finito e sulla sua capacità di produrre una conoscenza adeguata della natura creante e non creata[1]; si potranno a questo punto indicare le strategie linguistico-

[1] Cfr. Iohannes Scotus Eriugena, *Periphyseon*, I, PL 122, 441B, ed. É. Jeauneau, 5 voll., Turnhout 1996-2003 (CCCM, 161-165), I, pp. 3,19 - 4,22.

10.1484/M.NUTRIX-EB.1.101241

concettuali di tipo simbolico sviluppate da Eriugena al fine di superare le aporie prodotte dalla dottrina dell'ineffabilità divina e precisare la tipologia di sapere che queste stesse strategie rendono possibile.

1. *Il problema dell'ineffabilità divina*

La ragione metafisica della natura indicibile e trans-sostanziale della realtà divina viene indicata da Eriugena nel primo libro del *Periphyseon*[2]. Qui, indagando la natura del Principio creatore universale, il maestro palatino afferma l'impossibilità per la ragione finita di produrre una qualsiasi descrizione adeguata della natura divina: l'essenza trinitaria non può essere descritta autenticamente mediante nessuno strumento linguistico-concettuale. La radicalità di questa condizione di misteriosa trascendenza propria di Dio è tale da rendere inefficaci per una corretta descrizione della sostanza trinitaria anche i più universali predicati dell'essere: Dio, infatti, osserva il maestro palatino, è al di là anche delle dieci categorie aristoteliche[3]. Di Dio, quindi, non può essere predicato l'attributo dell'essere[4] o quelli della quiete e del moto[5].

La causa metafisica di tale condizione di ineffabilità della natura divina è individuata dal maestro palatino nell'interna strutturazione dello stesso essere divino: la sostanza trinitaria, infatti, osserva Eriugena, è libera da ogni forma di opposizione[6]. L'opposizione, infatti, è intrinsecamente connessa con una condizione di finitezza[7]: ogni realtà che si trova in una relazione di opposizione con un

[2] Cfr. *ibid.*, 458A, pp. 26,674 seqq.

[3] Cfr. *ibid.*, 452B, pp. 17,430 seqq.

[4] Cfr. *ibid.*, 459C, p. 28,748-749.

[5] All'interno della ipersostanziale essenza trinitaria, questi due stati non rappresentano modi di essere radicalmente contrapposti. Quiete e moto, infatti, possono essere contemporaneamente predicati della volontà divina in quanto facoltà attraverso la quale viene decretata la creazione del mondo: l'atto del decidere di porre in essere l'universo rinvia alla sfera del movimento, mentre la perfezione del progetto creazionistico e la sua inalterabilità rimandano all'idea di stabilità. Uguali considerazioni vengono fatte da Eriugena per tutte le altre categorie aristoteliche; cfr., ad esempio, *ibid.*, 504B, pp. 86,2654 seqq. (per il caso dell'agire e del patire).

[6] Cfr. *ibid.*, 459A-460B, pp. 27,714 - 29,776.

[7] Eriugena individua in questo caso tre tipologie di opposizione: per privazione, per relazione e per contrarietà; cfr. *ibid.*, 458D, p. 27,709-710.

altro ente è, per ciò stesso, limitata e definita. Eriugena, tuttavia, interpreta l'opposizione al proprio altro come un meccanismo metafisico che fonda l'auto-identità di una realtà con se stessa: l'ente 'deve' all'alterità alla quale si contrappone il proprio essere, in quanto solo nel rapporto di opposizione ciascuna realtà diviene se stessa. Il maestro palatino enuncia questo principio speculativo in modo molto chiaro: «opposita ita sibi semper opposita sunt ut simul et inchoare incipiant et simul esse desinant». Gli opposti sono costantemente legati e l'esistenza, in termini di conoscibilità logico-concettuale, dell'uno dipende dall'altro quale suo negativo. L'esempio che Eriugena porta per chiarire questa sua dottrina, ovvero quello del 'semplice' e del 'doppio', è molto significativo: l'idea di 'semplice' richiama immediatamente quella di doppio cosicché l'una non si può dare se non si dà l'altra.

L'impossibilità per l'essenza divina di essere inserita all'interno di una dialettica di opposizione al proprio negativo ha la sua ragione teologico-metafisica in quello che Eriugena considera il più importante fra gli attributi divini, ovvero l'*aeternitas*. Il maestro palatino, da un lato, pone tale attributo in stretta relazione con l'area semantica dell'infinità e, dall'altro, descrive la stessa *aeternitas* come semplicità e perfetta individualità («aeternitas... tota per totum in se ipsa una simplex individuaque subsistit»[8]). La sostanza trinitaria in quanto eterna non può essere coinvolta in nessuna relazione di opposizione: l'infinità, infatti, esclude l'opposizione differenziale dei termini poiché realtà infinite e semplici non possono venir limitate da nessuna alterità.

Tale irriducibilità alla dimensione dell'opposizione dialettica deve essere considerata la radice metafisica dell'ineffabilità della natura divina. Se la relazione di opposizione con il negativo costituisce il principio fondante dell'identità con sé di ogni realtà e, quindi, la causa prima della conoscibilità di questa realtà medesima, l'impossibilità di una data essenza di entrare in un rapporto d'opposizione con il proprio negativo deve coincidere con l'impossibilità che di tale essenza si produca una qualsiasi descrizione; l'assenza di relazione oppositionale produce, infatti, il superamento dell'orizzonte dell'identità determinata.

[8] Cfr. *ibid.*, 459A-459B, p. 27,723-724.

La conseguenza che discende da tale ineffabilità divina quale superamento della dimensione dell'opposizione all'altro da sé è la relativizzazione delle capacità denotativo-descrittive del linguaggio creaturale: nessuno degli attributi che la ragione umana può predicare di Dio è in grado di definire adeguatamente l'indeterminata essenza divina in quanto essa è al di là di ogni definito modo d'esistenza. Eriugena giunge così ad asserire la superiorità della teologia apofatica su quella catafatica. La catafasi rappresenta il tentativo creaturale di fornire una descrizione della natura divina; tale tentativo è sempre destinato a un finale scacco in quanto ogni attributo determinato predicato di Dio costringerebbe la sua eterna sostanza all'interno di una contrapposizione differenziale con il proprio negativo[9]. L'apofasi teologica, invece, consiste nella sospensione di ogni discorso sulla natura divina e, quindi, nel silenzio mistico di fronte all'Assoluto: solamente la cessazione di ogni tentativo linguistico e concettuale di parlare di Dio rappresenta l'atteggiamento epistemologicamente più corretto di fronte alla natura non-opposizionale del Principio primo.

Tale dottrina trova una chiara anticipazione all'interno del *De praedestinatione*, l'opera con la quale Eriugena interviene nell'851, su invito di Incmaro di Reims, nella controversia predestinazionista. In quell'opuscolo, infatti, il filosofo irlandese afferma che l'ineffabile sostanza trinitaria non è descrivibile mediante i concetti finiti della ragione umana; per tale motivo nulla può essere detto del Creatore in senso proprio:

> Bisogna osservare innanzitutto che, poiché nulla può essere detto di Dio in modo adeguato, nessun segno, sia che consista in un nome, in un verbo o in un'altra parte del discorso, può essere predicato a Dio in senso proprio. In che modo infatti dei segni sensibili, ossia relativi a dei corpi, potrebbero significare con certezza quella natura lontana da ogni senso corporeo, che trascendendo ogni intelletto viene colta a stento da una mente assolutamente purificata?[10]

[9] Eriugena fornisce qui alcuni esempi per chiarire la sua dottrina metafisica: la bontà, la verità, la sapienza ma anche l'eternità e lo stesso nome 'Dio' (del quale viene fornita una interpretazione etimologica che lo riconduce alle proprietà del vedere e del correre) devono essere considerati inadeguati per descrivere autenticamente il divino in quanto ciascuno di essi si contrappone al proprio negativo. Cfr. *ibid.*, 459D-460B, pp. 28,750 - 29,776.

[10] Cfr. Id., *De praedestinatione*, 9, 1, PL 122, 390AB, ed. G. Madec, Turnhout

La peculiare natura di Dio rende ogni espressione finita inadeguata, incapace, cioè, di attingere al livello di un discorso *proprie*, che descriva la sostanza trinitaria in modo non ambiguo. La condizione nella quale il linguaggio creaturale, opposizionale e finito, si viene a trovare nel suo aporetico tentativo di fornire una descrizione della sostanza divina, semplice ed eterna, è definita da Eriugena come traslativo-metaforica[11]. Attribuire a Dio, la quiete e il moto, l'essere oppure la bontà e la verità è possibile solo *per quadam divina metaphora*[12]; in modo analogo l'agire e il patire possono essere predicati di Dio unicamente mediante *similitudines* e *translata verba*[13], così come la presenza in Dio di attività cognitive superiori quali il pensiero razionale o quello intellettivo si può dare solo *per metaphoram* in quanto l'essenza trinitaria è 'spoglia' di ogni qualità determinata («nudam siquidem omnique propria significatione relictam divinam essentiam talibus vocabulis vestit»[14]). Il termine *metaphora*, qui impiegato da Eriugena, sta a indicare un procedimento, al tempo stesso semiotico e metafisico,

1978 (CCCM, 50), pp. 55,11 - 56,18; ed. E. Mainoldi, Firenze 2003, pp. 88,24 - 90,3 (la traduzione è mia): «Ubi primo notandum, quoniam nihil digne de Deo dicitur, omnia paene sive nominum sive verborum aliarumque orationis partium signa proprie de Deo dici non posse. Quomodo enim signa sensibilia, id est corporibus adhaerentia, remotam illam omni sensu corporeo naturam ad liquidum significare possent, quae vix purgatissima mente attingitur omnem transcendens intellectum?». Madec, nella sua edizione critica del *De praedestinatione*, osserva su questo punto la dipendenza di Eriugena dal secondo capitolo *De diversis quaestionibus ad Simplicianum* dove il vescovo di Ippona afferma la trascendenza divina e l'impossibilità per il linguaggio umano di conoscere adeguatamente la natura del Creatore; cfr. *ibid.*, ed. Madec cit., p. 56,12, app. Il passo, tuttavia, sembra essere molto vicino alla dottrina dionisiana sull'ineffabilità apofatica della potenza divina e, in particolare, a quanto l'Areopagita dice nel primo capitolo del *De divinis nominibus*. La presenza di una influenza dionisiana nel *De praedestinatione* è stata, d'altronde, suggerita da Édouard Jeauneau (cfr. in ed. di IOANNES SCOTUS ERIUGENA, *Commentarius in evangelium Iohannis*, Paris 1972 [SC, 180], p. 126, nota 21) e poi confermata da Giulio d'Onofrio (cfr. G. D'ONOFRIO, *La nuova edizione del 'De divina praedestinatione liber' di Giovanni Scoto*, in «Studi storico religiosi», V/2 [1981], [pp. 267-288], pp. 271-272, nota 14) e da Concetto Martello (cfr. C. MARTELLO, *Simbolismo e neoplatonismo in Giovanni Scoto Eriugena*, Catania 1986, cap. 3, pp. 63-91). Nel passo in questione, quindi, può essere individuata anche una ripresa eriugeniana degli stilemi di pensiero dell'Areopagita.

[11] Cfr. IOHANNES SCOTUS ERIUGENA, *Periphyseon*, I, 460C, p. 29,787, e 461C, p. 31,832-833.

[12] *Ibid.*, 453B, p. 19,468-469.

[13] Cfr. *ibid.*, 509A, pp. 92,2877 - 93,2878.

[14] *Ibid.*, 461C, p. 31,833-835.

attraverso il quale attributi e qualità finite vengono trasferite dal mondo creaturale, al quale propriamente appartengono, alla dimensione iper-sostanziale divina: la metafora eriugeniana è, quindi, quel μεταφέρειν, quel «portare al di là» (il maestro palatino, riprendendo una terminologia di sapore agostiniano, parla di «verba translata»), le determinazioni della concettualità creaturale per farne strumenti di denotazione dell'essenza trinitaria[15].

Il valore di tali proprietà attribuite metaforicamente a Dio viene chiaramente sottolineato dallo stesso Eriugena nel *De praedestinatione*, trattando delle diverse forme di 'segni verbali' («signa verbalia»)[16]. Oltre ai segni *quasi propria* (ad esempio 'essere' o 'vero') che sembrano essere adeguati a esprimere la natura divina (pur non essendo in grado di dire l'autentica essenza trinitaria), Eriugena individua in questo testo la tipologia dei *signa aliena* o *translata*; tali espressioni sono palesemente incapaci di descrivere correttamente la natura divina e, quindi, possono essere attribuite alla sostanza trinitaria in maniera solamente 'indiretta' e 'parziale', secondo un fenomeno di traslazione appunto. Eriugena, tuttavia, approfondisce ulteriormente la questione dei *signa translata* articolandoli in tre ulteriori sotto-specie; tali sotto-categorie possono essere interpretate come altrettanti meccanismi retorico-linguistici che permettono il passaggio dal predicato *alienus* all'oggetto del discorso teologico (l'essenza divina)[17]. Il maestro

[15] Sul concetto di metafora in Eriugena si può vedere P. DRONKE, *Eriugena's Earthly Paradise*, in *Begriff und Metapher. Sprachform des Denkens bei Eriugena*, Vortrage des 7. Internationalen Eriugena-Colloquiums (Werner, 26-29 Juli 1989), hrsg. von W. Beierwaltes, Heidelberg 1990 (Abhandlungen der Heidelberger Akademie der Wissenschaften. Philosophisch-historische Klasse. Jahrgang 1990. 3. Abhandlung), pp. 213-229; e W. BEIERWALTES, *Eriugena. Grundzüge seines Denkens*, Frankfurt a. M. 1994, pp. 52-82 (tr. it. *Eriugena. I Fondamenti della sua metafisica*, Milano 1998 [Pubblicazioni del centro di ricerche di metafisica. Platonismo e filosofia patristica. Studi e testi, 13], pp. 63-82). Beierwaltes mette in relazione la significazione metaforica con il processo di dispiegamento dell'unità somma nella varietà delle determinazioni molteplici associando questo fenomeno con quello che si sviluppa nel passaggio dal puro pensiero (*intellectus*) all'articolata enunciazione dello stesso (*vox*). Lo stesso Eriugena, d'altronde, nelle *Expositiones* avvicina il funzionamento del simbolo alla relazione tra *vox* e *intellectus*; cfr. IOHANNES SCOTUS ERIUGENA, *Expositiones super Hierarchiam caelestem sancti Dionysii*, 15, ed. J. Barbet, Turnhout 1975 (CCCM, 31), p. 211,915-944.

[16] ID., *De praedestinatione*, 9, 2, 390C, ed. Madec p. 56,25; ed. Mainoldi, p. 90,9.

[17] Nello sviluppare questa dottrina Eriugena riprende quanto dice Marziano Capella in un passaggio del quarto libro del *De nuptiis Philologiae et Mercurii*, in cui l'erudito romano introduce la triplice modalità di formazione dei traslati: *per simili-*

palatino distingue così il genere della *translatio* per similitudine (*similitudo*), per contrario (*contrarium*) e per differenza (*differentia*)[18].

È, tuttavia, al genere dei *signa e contrario* o κατ'ἀντίφρασιν, antifrastici, che Eriugena dedica l'analisi più dettagliata. L'antifrasi, ovvero quel procedimento retorico in base al quale un certo asserto deve essere inteso come avente un significato diametralmente opposto a quello espressamente enunciato, è ulteriormente suddivisa da Eriugena in antifrasi assoluta e antifrasi congiunta; queste due categorie di dire antifrastico sembrano, d'altra parte, ricomprendere al loro interno anche i precedenti generi dei *signa translata per similitudinem* e *per differentiam*. La prima tipologia di espressione *e contrario*, infatti, è relativa a quella categoria di attributi che sono palesemente difformi dalla natura divina (l'esempio eriugeniano è tratto da *1Cor* 1, 19: «Perdam sapientiam sapientum et prudentiam prudentum reprobabo», passo che può essere correttamente interpretato, osserva il maestro palatino, rovesciando radicalmente il suo significato manifesto e intendendolo come promessa dell'abbattimento di ogni falsa verità e di ogni presunta grandezza[19]); in questo modo l'antifrasi assoluta è del tutto simile alla *translatio* secondo *differentia* che riferisce alla sostanza divina attributi a essa dissimili per far fronte alla «necessitas significationis»[20]. La seconda tipologia di discorso *e contrario* viene descritta

tudinem, *per contrarium* e *per differentiam*: cfr. Martianus Capella, *De nuptiis Mercurii et Philologiae*, IV, 360, 6-22, ed. A. Dick – J. Preaux, Stuttgard 1978, p. 165. Costantino Marmo nota, d'altronde, che l'espressione utilizzata da Eriugena per indicare i termini impropri costruiti mediante queste tre vie è non solo *aliena* (termine impiegato dallo stesso Marziano) ma anche *translata*; questo elemento può far supporre che qui il maestro palatino faccia riferimento non solo al *De nuptiis* ma anche al *De doctrina christiana* che sviluppa una complessa riflessione proprio sui *signa translata*; cfr. C. Marmo, *Il 'simbolismo' altomedievale. Tra controversie eucaristiche e conflitti di potere* in *Comunicare e significare nell'Alto Medioevo*, LII Settimana di studio della Fondazione Centro Italiano di Studi sull'Alto Medioevo (Spoleto, 15-20 aprile 2004), 2 voll., Spoleto 2005 (Settimane di Studio della Fondazione C.I.S.A.M., 52), II, [pp. 765-814], pp. 797-798. Marmo nota anche che poco dopo Eriugena fa riferimento ad Agostino come «propriae translataeque locutionis doctor».

[18] Cfr. Iohannes Scotus Eriugena, *ibid.*, 9, 2, ed. Madec, p. 57,37-38; ed. Mainoldi, p. 90,18.

[19] Il passo paolino sottolinea la relazione che lega antifrasi e ironia; cfr. *ibid.*, 15, 7, ed. Madec, p. 91,143-147, ed. Mainoldi, p. 152,21-24, dove Eriugena cita un passaggio ciceroniano che Marziano Capella aveva inserito nel quinto libro del *De nuptiis* come esempio di ironia.

[20] *Ibid.*, 9, 2, ed. Madec, p. 57,53; ed. Mainoldi, p. 92,9.

da Eriugena come una antifrasi che agisce in virtù di una similitudine: alcune qualità o attributi possono essere predicati a Dio in ragione di una sorta di somiglianza anche se l'attribuzione che ne deriva è sempre *abusiva*[21]. Eriugena in questo modo afferma chiaramente l'esistenza di un legame tra antifrasi e *similitudo*.

L'antifrasi diviene così, nella complessa dottrina dei *signa translata* del *De praedestinatione*, il cardine concettuale della riflessione eriugeniana sul rapporto tra linguaggio finito e Dio. L'ineffabilità divina rende ogni tipologia di predicato inadeguata a descrivere autenticamente l'essenza trinitaria; i *signa quasi propria* e i *signa translata* permettono all'uomo di attingere un'identica tipologia di conoscenza teologica la quale non è mai in grado di restituire pienamente la natura del Creatore. La presenza di una *similitudo* (sia essa quella dei *signa quasi propria* oppure quella presente nella *translatio per similitudinem* e nell'antifrasi congiunta) tra realtà divina e attributo a essa predicato risulta sempre parziale e, come tale, deve essere 'corretta' mediante un ragionamento antifrastico. In quanto rovesciamento ironico del significato di un dato enunciato, l'antifrasi riafferma sempre la totale differenza tra natura divina e qualità determinata a essa attribuita, divenendo procedimento intrinsecamente connesso con ogni tentativo della ragione finita di conoscere l'essenza trinitaria: poiché la natura divina non è simile a nessuna determinazione finita e non possiede in realtà alcuna delle qualità che le possono venir attribuite è necessario rovesciare antifrasticamente ogni sua descrizione[22].

Se ogni sforzo catafatico per parlare di Dio è fondato su un movimento metaforico che applica categorie finite all'infinita realtà del Principio (così come viene messo in chiaro dal *Periphyseon*) il risultato di tale discorso *per metaphoram* deve essere sottoposto a una lettura antifrastica per cogliere a pieno la completa

[21] Cfr. *ibid.*, 9, 6, ed. Madec, p. 61,139-142; ed. Mainoldi, pp. 96,28 - 98,3.

[22] L'antifrasi, pertanto, non deve essere pensata, una volta che essa divenga dispositivo per parlare del divino, come affermazione del contrario di quanto è ironicamente detto (la negazione 'ironica' di A non deve terminare nella semplice affermazione di non-A); in questo modo, infatti, l'antifrasi permetterebbe l'attribuzione di una determinazione finita a Dio tradendo la Sua ineffabilità. L'antifrasi del discorso su Dio deve, invece, terminare nel silenzio di fronte all'indecidibile e al numinoso; Dio non essendo essere non è, infatti, non-essere ma è al di sopra dell'essere e del non-essere e, ugualmente, non essendo verità non è menzogna ma causa ineffabile al di là della verità.

incommensurabilità tra linguaggio creaturale e natura divina (secondo la lezione del *De praedestinatione*).

2. *La natura del simbolo*

L'aporetico tentativo creaturale per giungere a una conoscenza veritiera dell'ineffabile realtà divina può avvalersi, tuttavia, dell'ausilio offerto da un importante strumento semiotico-teologico: il simbolo[23].

Eriugena identifica il *symbolum*, sulla scorta delle riflessioni dionisiane, con ogni *res* finita. Simboli sono così non solo tutte le creature, le cause primordiali quali somme teofanie del divino e «omnes species visibilis et invisibilis creaturae»[24], ma anche le diverse immagini contenute nelle Scritture, a partire dalle antiche visioni profetiche sino ad arrivare alle pratiche liturgiche e ai sacramenti di cui i due Testamenti recano memoria (*symbola legalia* quali l'arca dell'Alleanza o la pratica battesimale)[25]. Natura e Scrittura, infatti, sono per

[23] Fra gli studi dedicati alla dottrina del simbolo in Eriugena si possono qui ricordare: P. DRONKE, *Les Conceptions de l'Allégorie chez J. S. Érigène et Hildegarde de Bingen*, in *Allégorie des poètes, Allégorie des philosophes. Études sur la poétique et l'herméneutique de l'allégorie de l'Antiquité à la Riforme: table ronde internationale de l'Institut des traditions textuelles*, éd. par G. Dahan – R. Goulet, Paris 2005, pp. 219-230; S. GERSH, *Eriugena's Ars Rhetorica. Theory and Practice*, in *Iohannes Scottus Eriugena. The Bible and Hermeneutics*, Proceedings of the ninth International Colloquium of the Society for the promotion of Eriugenian studies (Leuven, Louvain-La-Neuve, 7-10 June 1995), ed. by G. van Riel – C. Steel – J. McEvoy, Leuven 1990, pp. 261-278; ID., *Concord in Discourse: Harmonics and Semiotics in Late Classical and Early Medieval Platonism*, Berlin – New York 1996 (Approches to semiotics, 125); É. JEAUNEAU, *Les quatre éléments du monde et les quatre sens de l'Écriture*, in ed. di IOANNES SCOTUS ERIUGENA, *Omelia super prologum Iohannis*, Paris 1969 (SC, 151), pp. 327-328; ID., *Allegoria, mysterium, sacramentum, symbolum*, in ed. di IOANNES SCOTUS ERIUGENA, *Commentarius in evangelium Iohannis* cit. (alla nota 10), pp. 397-402; J. PÉPIN, *Mysteria' et 'symbola' dans le commentaire de Jean Scot sur l'évangile de Jean*, in *The Mind of Eriugena*, Papers of a colloquium (Dublin, 14-18 July 1970), ed. by J. J. O'Meara – L. Bieler, Dublin 1973, pp. 16-30; ID., *Aspects théoriques du symbolisme dans la tradition dionysienne*, in *Simboli e simbologia nell'alto Medioevo*, XXIII Settimana di Studi sull'Alto Medioevo (Spoleto, 3-9 Aprile 1975), 2 voll., Spoleto 1976 (Settimane di Studio della Fondazione C.I.S.A.M., 23), II, [pp. 765-814], pp. 33-66; A. M. RIGONI, *La lettera e la tomba. Nota su 'allegoria' e 'simbolo' nel pensiero di Giovanni Scoto Eriugena*, in «Conoscenza religiosa», 3 (1978), pp. 267-285; F. ZAMBON, *Romanzo e allegoria nel Medioevo*, Trento 2000, pp. 1-21.

[24] Cfr. IOHANNES SCOTUS ERIUGENA, *Expositiones super Hierarchiam caelestem sancti Dionysii*, 1, PL 122, 136C, ed. Barbet cit. (alla nota 15), p. 12,420.

[25] Cfr. *ibid.*, 1, 135C-136C, pp. 11,385 - 12, 416.

Eriugena due luoghi complementari della Rivelazione divina, in quanto diversi momenti di un unico atto creatore[26].

Eriugena attribuisce tale natura 'concreta' al simbolo, facendo così dell'intera realtà un unico atto di parola[27], anche nel terzo libro del *Periphyseon*[28]. Trattando della relazione tra Creatore e creatura, il maestro palatino si sofferma ad analizzare il termine *vestigium* con il quale le Scritture definiscono in alcuni casi le realtà mondane[29]. Eriugena osserva a questo proposito come le *res* create agiscano realmente quali tracce o indizi del proprio trascendente Principio. La natura divina può essere conosciuta attraverso la dimensione fisica da menti speculative come Mosè (nella rivelazione del roveto ardente) o Abramo (che intuì la natura di Dio osservando il moto delle stelle). I singoli enti, quindi, sono manifestazioni della natura divina, *symbola* dell'essenza trinitaria

[26] Su questa dottrina cfr. Id., *Omelia super prologum Iohannis*, 14, PL 122, 291B, ed. Jeauneau cit. (alla nota 23), p. 270,5-7 (e nuova ed. É. Jeauneau, Turnhout 2008 [CCCM, 166], p. 27,5-7) per il parallelo tra gerarchia degli elementi nel mondo fisico e gerarchia dei sensi reconditi nell'universo scritturale. Una simile idea compare anche in Id., *Periphyseon*, V, 1008A, ed. Jeauneau cit. (alla nota 1), V, p. 207,6710 seqq., dove si parla dell'*incrassari* come «prendere corpo» del Verbo; e cfr. anche Id., *Commentarius in evangelium Iohannis* cit. (alla nota 10), I, 29, PL 122, 307A, ed. Jeauneau cit. (alla nota 10), p. 154,50-54 (e nuova ed. É. Jeauneau, Turnhout 2008 [CCCM, 166], p. 65,48-52).

[27] Questo atteggiamento è quello che già Jacques Le Goff definiva come attitudine simbolica della cultura medievale; cfr. J. Le Goff, *L'uomo medievale* in *L'uomo medievale*, a c. di J. Le Goff – F. Cardini, Roma – Bari 1990, [pp. 11-38], pp. 34-35. Umberto Eco parla a questo proposito di pansimbolismo e di allegorismo universale; cfr. U. Eco, *Sugli specchi e altri saggi*, Milano 1985, pp. 225-229. Conclusioni analoghe, sebbene con toni differenti, sono quelle di Costantino Marmo il quale parla di «pansematicismo» e «pansemiosi»; cfr. C. Marmo, *The Decline of Symbols in XIIth Century Theology*, in *The Word in Medieval Logic, Theology and Psychology*, Act of the 12th international colloquium of the S.I.E.P.M. (Kyoto, 27 September – 1 October 2005), ed. by T. Shimizu – C. Burnett, Turnhout, 2009 (Rencontres de philosophie médiévales, 14). Sul tema della mentalità simbolica medievale testi di riferimento rimangono: É. De Bruyne, *Études d'esthetique medievale*, Paris 1946; H. de Lubac, *Exégèse médiévale: les quatre sens de l'Écriture*, 4 voll., Paris 1959-1964; P. Dronke, *Fabula. Explorations into the Uses of Myth in Medieval Platonism*, Leiden – Köln 1974 (Mittellateinische Studien und Texte, 9); Id., *Imagination in the Late Pagan and Early Christian World. The First Nine Centuries A. D.*, Firenze 2003 (Millennio medievale. Strumenti e studi, 4); J. Huizinga, *Herfsttij der Middeleeuwen*, Haarlem 1919; J. Whitman, *Allegory. The Dynamics of an Ancient and Medieval Technique*, Oxford 1987.

[28] Cfr. Iohannes Scotus Eriugena, *Periphyseon*, III, 689C, ed. Jeauneau cit. (alla nota 1), III, pp. 100,2913 seqq.

[29] *Ibid.*, 689C, p. 100,2917.

che devono essere correttamente interpretati per condurre alla conoscenza del Principio[30].

I meccanismi mediante i quali il simbolo rende possibile questo disvelamento del divino sono, tuttavia, differenti a seconda della natura del *symbolum* stesso. Eriugena, infatti, distingue due tipologie di dispositivi simbolici: i simboli intelligibili e quelli sensibili. Il simbolo sensibile è costituito da una *res* creata che appartiene al mondo sensibile e materiale (quali, ad esempio, le creature o gli oggetti che sono al centro delle visioni veterotestamentarie[31]). Il meccanismo che rende possibile la manifestazione della natura divina nei simboli sensibili può essere individuato nella presenza, sia nella *res* dotata di *virtus* simbolica sia nella stessa sostanza trascendente, di una identica qualità o proprietà. Tale meccanismo semiotico è chiaramente individuabile analizzando la decifrazione di alcune immagini simboliche che lo stesso Eriugena propone nelle *Expositiones in hierarchiam coelestem*, il commento sistematico all'opera dionisiana composto da Eriugena tra l'865 e l'870[32]. Soffermandosi sull'*imago* del sole quale *symbolum* del Cristo, il maestro palatino, infatti, osserva che l'astro può rimandare alla persona del Figlio in quanto entrambi possiedono la medesima proprietà di vivificare e illuminare: il sole rischiara le tenebre mentre il Cristo dissolve l'oscurità del peccato[33]. In modo analogo Eriugena fornisce una propria interpretazione dell'immagine del verme che Dionigi indica, rifacendosi ad alcuni passi scritturali, come simbolo del Cristo. Sia del verme che del Cristo, infatti, si può dire che dimorano nella profondità della natura: il verme vive nel sottosuolo e, quindi, all'interno della terra mentre Cristo, Sapienza del Padre, conosce «secreta... totius naturae»[34] e così è al centro della Natura creata («in intimis naturae conditae sinibus subsistit»)[35]. Il simbolo sensibile, pertanto, opera

[30] Cfr. *ibid.*, 689D, p. 100,2930.

[31] Cfr. ID., *Expositiones super Hierarchiam coelestem*, 1, 136AB, ed. Barbet cit. (alla nota 15), p. 11,396-402.

[32] Cfr. R. ROQUES, s.v. *Jean Scot (Érigéne)*, in *Dictionnaire de spiritualite*, VIII, Paris, 1974, [coll. 735-761], col. 736.

[33] Cfr. IOHANNES SCOTUS ERIUGENA, *Expositiones super Hierarchiam coelestem*, 2, 165CD, ed. Barbet cit., p. 45,946-954.

[34] *Ibid.*, 168D, p. 49,1077.

[35] *Ibid.*, 169A, p. 49,1082-1083.

attraverso *imagines* e *similitudines* nelle quali si costruisce una relazione analogica tra le qualità delle nature create e le proprietà della natura divina[36]. Tali simboli richiedono, quindi, una adeguata decifrazione. Le «divinorum eloquiorum illuminationes», infatti, non possono essere considerate «per se ipsas», ma devono essere interpretate secondo la logica del senso traslato[37].

Il simbolo intelligibile (*intellectualia* o *intelligibilia symbola, invisibiles significationes*[38]), invece, può essere fatto coincidere con le somme teofanie create. Trattando della teofania nel quarto capitolo delle *Expositiones*[39], Eriugena sottolinea che il disvelamento

[36] Il problema dell'analogia e del suo ruolo nel sapere simbolico eriugeniano rappresenta una complessa questione. Sull'importanza dell'analogia per la dottrina del dire traslato e del simbolo nella tradizione neoplatonica pagana cfr.: J. DILLON, *Image, Symbol and Analogy: Three Basic Concepts of Neoplatonic Allegorical Exegesis*, in *The Significance of Neoplatonism*, ed. by B. Harris, Norfolk 1976 (Studies in Neoplatonism, 5/1), [pp. 247-262], p. 257; A. D. R. SHEPPARD, *Studies on the 5th and 6th Essays of Proclus' Commentary on the Republic*, Göttingen 1980, (Hypomnemata, 61), pp. 197 seqq.; W. BEIERWALTES, *Proklos: Grundzüge seiner Metaphysik*, Frankfurt a.M. 1965, pp. 334 seqq. (tr. it., Milano 1990, pp. 362 seqq.); R. CHIARADONNA, *Sostanza, Movimento, Analogia. Plotino critico di Aristotele*, Napoli 2002 (Elenchos, 37); A. CHARLES, *Analogie et pensée sérielle chez Proclus*, in «Revue Internationale de Philosophie», 23 (1969), pp. 69-88. Eriugena impiega più volte la categoria di analogia nei suoi scritti per indicare sia la quantità di luce divina alla quale ciascuna realtà può attingere sia la legge che governa la processione della *dynamis* divina; cfr., ad esempio, IOHANNES SCOTUS ERIUGENA, *ibid.*, IX, p. 137,145; IV, p. 68,92; IV, p. 72,278; e cfr. ID., *Periphyseon*, V, 902B, ed. Jeauneau cit. (alla nota 1), p. 60,1936; *ibid.*, III, 644A, p. 38,1053.

[37] Cfr., ad esempio, IOHANNES SCOTUS ERIUGENA, *Expositiones super Hierarchiam coelestem*, 1, 132D, ed. Barbet cit., p. 8,259-260. Questo centrale accorgimento per il corretto utilizzo delle immagini simboliche è efficacemente riassunto dal parallelo istituito nel secondo capitolo delle *Expositiones* tra i simboli stessi e l'arte poetica; cfr. *ibid.*, 2, 146BC, p. 24,142-151: «Quemadmodum ars poetica, per fictas fabulas allegoricasque similitudines, moralem doctrinam seu physicam componunt ad humanorum animorum exercitationem – hoc enim proprium est heroicorum poetarum, qui virorum fortium facta et mores figurare laudant – ita theologia, veluti quaedam poetria, sanctam scripturam fictis imaginationibus ad consultum nostri animi et reductionem a corporalibus sensibus exterioribus, veluti ex quadam imperfecta pueritia, in rerum intelligibilium perfectam cognitionem, tanquam in quamdam interioris hominis grandaevitatem conformat». Come la poesia attraverso le «fictas fabulas» propone all'uomo verità di carattere morale e fisico così la *theologia* mediante i simboli permette di accedere alla conoscenza delle realtà trascendenti; come, tuttavia, l'allegoria poetica deve essere correttamente decifrata per rivelare il proprio contenuto nascosto così il simbolo deve essere interpretato per permettere il ritorno «in rerum intelligibilium perfectam cognitionem».

[38] *Ibid.*, 7, 182C, p. 103,476; p. 103,473; 1, 141B, p. 17,600.

[39] Cfr. *ibid.*, 4, p. 77,480-482.

della natura divina da essa reso possibile non avviene attraverso alcuna immagine («ultra omnem imaginationem»[40]) ma mediante un sapere puro, di natura intellettuale. In modo analogo nell'ottavo capitolo il maestro palatino contrappone alla manifestazione del divino che le realtà materiali rendono possibile mediante simboli sensibili e figure («in figuris et symbolis sensibilibus») una conoscenza per *principalia exempla*, ovvero 'modelli originari', che possono essere identificati con le cause primordiali e che rappresentano i paradigmi eterni del cosmo finito[41].

I simboli intelligibili, quindi, possono operare come *signa* della sostanza trinitaria unicamente in ragione di un meccanismo di tipo metafisico. Tali realtà finite rimandano all'essenza divina attraverso il legame ontologico che le congiunge con lo stesso Principio del Tutto. Ogni *res* creata mantiene, infatti, un rapporto con l'essenza divina dalla quale è scaturita, in quanto ciascun effetto è precontenuto nella propria causa superiore: poiché tutto ciò che esiste procede da Dio e tale processione è, secondo la prospettiva neoplatonica, il fluire della stessa *dynamis* del Principio primo, si può affermare che la stessa natura divina possiederà in qualche modo i medesimi tratti della sua creatura[42]. Le caratteristiche che sono presenti nella realtà creata devono essere già presenti, in un superiore status henologico, anche nel Principio

[40] Cfr. *ibid.*, p. 77,465.

[41] Cfr. *ibid.*, 8, p. 133,543-565.

[42] Una accurata descrizione di tale meccanismo semiotico-metafisico è quella fornita da Umberto Eco con la categoria di 'pansemiosi metafisica'. Per Eco il meccanismo che rende possibile tale forma di pansemiosi non si fonda sull'utilizzo di una similitudine morfologica o allegorica, espressa mediante un apparato di immagini, tra i termini del processo traslativo ma su un 'calcolo' metafisico: partendo dal *prius* delle qualità del mondo creato si deducono *per posterius* le proprietà di Dio quale principio causale. Eco ricorda in questo caso la distinzione tomista tra la rappresentazione della causa mediante l'effetto *quantum ad similitudinem formae*, come nel caso di una statua, e per *causalitas causae*. Quest'ultima soluzione si può identificare con la *representatio per vestigium*, ovvero con la relazione che sussiste tra un effetto e la causa che lo produce (come il caso considerato da Tommaso dell'orma che rimanda al piede e all'uomo che l'hanno prodotta; cfr. U. Eco, *La metafora nel Medioevo latino*, in *Metafora e conoscenza*, a c. di A. M. Lorusso, Milano 2005 (Pubblicazioni DASES, 131), [pp. 149-203], p. 191; e Id., *Arte e bellezza nell'estetica medievale*, Milano 1987, pp. 75-77 e pp. 88-89; il medesimo materiale è presente, organizzato in maniera diversa e con alcune differenze contenutistiche, in Id., *Sugli specchi e altri saggi*, Milano 1985 (Tascabili Bompiani, 452), pp. 219-221.

creatore. Tale legame risulta particolarmente intenso nel caso delle cause prime, le più perfette fra le creature e le più prossime alla natura divina[43]: tali realtà create potranno, quindi, rimandare in modo più efficace e pieno alla stessa essenza di Dio.

3. *I limiti della conoscenza simbolica*

L'analisi eriugeniana intorno alla natura del *symbolum* e ai meccanismi che rendono possibile il disvelamento simbolico della natura divina permette di individuare chiaramente i limiti del sapere fondato sui dispositivi simbolici stessi.

Per mettere in luce tali limiti è necessario sottolineare, innanzitutto, come la ricostruzione eriugeniana del funzionamento dei simboli sensibili e di quelli intelligibili conduca a scoprire una sorta di convergenza tra i meccanismi di queste due tipologie di *symbolum*. Se il simbolo sensibile rimanda alla natura divina in ragione della presenza sia nella *res* simbolica sia nella sostanza trascendente di medesime proprietà (il dissolvere le tenebre oppure l'abitare nelle profondità della Natura) risulta chiaro che la significazione traslata prodotta dal *symbolum* sensibile stesso deve fondarsi su una precedente attribuzione di alcune proprietà alla natura divina. L'individuazione nella sostanza divina di determinati predicati è possibile, tuttavia, mediante un'operazione di natura metafisica che, partendo dalla realtà creata, attribuisce all'essenza divina, in ragione del vincolo ontologico tra creatura e Creatore, alcune qualità presenti nel mondo finito; ogni tentativo di parlare di Dio, infatti, consiste nel trasferire alcune proprietà finite dalla dimensione creaturale all'infinita natura divina. Una simile operazione, tuttavia, appare del tutto analoga a quella che si produce nel simbolo intelligibile: la relazione causale tra principio ed effetto spinge la ragione creaturale a trasferire induttivamente gli

[43] Eriugena, infatti, individua la ragione della superiore conoscenza del divino che le gerarchie angeliche possiedono, in una conoscenza che viene definita «vere, absque ullo figmento» con «nulla (...) imaginatio», «nullum sacramentum», nella particolare condizione ipostatica degli angeli stessi; questi appartengono ad un livello henologico che il maestro palatino descrive come «subiectissimus», ovvero «proximus subiectus sibi», vicinissimo alla sostanza divina; cfr. IOHANNES SCOTUS ERIUGENA, *ibid.*, 7, 184A, pp. 105,546 - 106,550.

attributi delle *res* finite alla loro causa trascendente facendo delle prime simboli per la seconda.

Simboli sensibili e simboli intelligibili, quindi, operano a partire da un 'calcolo metafisico' in base al quale le qualità delle realtà create devono essere in una qualche misura presenti nell'essenza che le ha portate all'essere. Così ricostruito il meccanismo del dire simbolico appare del tutto analogo a quello della *metaphora* che si produce in ogni sforzo catafatico di approcciarsi al divino. La sapienza simbolica appare, quindi, come un tentativo di conoscere la sostanza trinitaria mediante predicati finiti. Tale tentativo non può che produrre una descrizione sempre inadeguata del proprio oggetto: la natura divina è, infatti, infinita, sottratta alla relazione opposizionale e come tale incommensurabile rispetto a ogni proprietà determinata.

Lo stesso Eriugena, d'altronde, denuncia chiaramente i limiti della sapienza simbolica. Nelle *Expositiones*, infatti, afferma che il sapere fornito dai *symbola* consiste in una comprensione delle realtà celesti non piena e autentica ma solamente mediata e parziale[44]. Il filosofo irlandese ribadisce il carattere ineffabile della natura divina e la conseguente impossibilità per ogni strumento linguistico-concettuale determinato, compresi i *symbola* stessi, a darne una descrizione che non sia perifrastica («periphrasin»), indiretta («per ambitum»), fondata sull'analogia («secundum analogiam»)[45].

Diviene così chiaramente comprensibile la scelta eriugeniana di intendere i *symbola* come «sacra velamina» che «circumvelant» l'autentica natura di Dio. I simboli sono veli che avvolgono la sostanza divina; in questo modo ciascuna immagine simbolica mostra ma al tempo stesso cela e nasconde l'oggetto del proprio sapere, il *radium* e la *claritas* che promanano dal Principio divino[46]. Scopo del simbolo è, quindi, non fornire una conoscenza esaustiva di Dio ma innescare un movimento anagogico che permetta all'uomo di sollevarsi al di sopra della propria dimensione, materiale ed immanente, e di avvicinarsi il più possibile all'essenza tearchica[47].

[44] Cfr. *ibid.*, 13, 243C-244C, pp. 177,392 - 178,442.

[45] *Ibidem.*

[46] Cfr. *ibid.*, 1, 135AC, pp. 10,355 - 11,368, e 11,373-379.

[47] Eriugena afferma, infatti, che il simbolo è fondato «iuxta rationes anagoge»; cfr. *ibid.*, p. 11, 376.

4. *L'utilità della conoscenza simbolica*

La sfida per la ragione creaturale rappresentata dall'idea dell'ineffabilità della natura divina non può essere pienamente vinta, quindi, neppure dal pensiero simbolico. Il simbolo nella dottrina eriugeniana opera, infatti, sempre mediante determinazioni e concetti finiti: proprietà creaturali vengono attribuite, attraverso forme di discorso traslato, al Creatore (simbolo sensibile) oppure la natura dell'effetto diviene immagine della propria Causa trascendente (simbolo intelligibile). Nessuna proprietà determinata, tuttavia, può descrivere adeguatamente il divino in quanto l'eterna sostanza trinitaria è infinita.

Al tempo stesso, tuttavia, Eriugena riconosce alla sapienza simbolica una peculiare importanza. Egli, innanzitutto, individua nella conoscenza mediante *symbola* una importante occasione, per quanto finita e sempre «metaphorica», di disvelamento dell'essenza trinitaria: nelle opere eriugeniane il sapere *per symbolum* è inteso come disvelamento mediante predicati determinati della natura e della verità divine.

Una delle testimonianze testuali più significative in questo senso è offerta dalla parte finale del Commento al vangelo di Giovanni, opera eriugeniana tarda interrotta forse dalla morte dell'autore. Eriugena, trattando della Rivelazione della verità divina e degli espedienti allegorico-traslati attraverso i quali essa si compie nelle Scritture, osserva che i *symbola* rappresentano lo strumento in grado di garantire l'accesso a una conoscenza teologica. Tale tipologia di sapere costituisce, secondo lo schema proposto dal maestro palatino nella sua *Omelia* al prologo dello stesso vangelo di Giovanni, il quarto e più perfetto grado di verità presente nel testo sacro dopo la storia, il senso morale e quello fisico (ciascuno di questi momenti è associato a un diverso elemento, ovvero terra, acqua, fuoco ed etere, secondo una gerarchia di crescente perfezione)[48]. Quale esempio di tale rivelazione sim-

[48] Alcuni critici hanno, d'altronde, messo in luce come l'essere *solummodo dictum* del simbolo nel commento eriugeniano al vangelo di Giovanni sottolinei la capacità dei *symbola* stessi di veicolare le più alte verità teologiche; il simbolo in questo modo è, infatti, descritto come una sorta di dottrina, secondo la definizione eriugeniana, e quindi orientato alla manifestazione di un sapere superiore. Cfr. RIGONI, *La lettera e la tomba* cit. (alla nota 23), pp. 282-284.

bolica il filosofo palatino propone, nell'incipit del vangelo di Giovanni[49], l'immagine dell' 'uccello spirituale' («spirituale petasum») che si solleva al di sopra della pianura della storia per guardare direttamente, quasi superando i limiti della ragione creaturale, il volto di Dio[50]. Il simbolo appare così associato alla più alta forma di sapere che l'uomo può attingere.

A una particolare tipologia di simbolo, il simbolo dissimile, inoltre, Eriugena attribuisce una peculiare importanza e una grande utilità nell'economia del proprio progetto teologico. I simboli *dissimilia et confusa* sono rappresentati da quelle immagini palesemente difformi rispetto alla dignità della realtà divina alla quale rimandano[51]. La Scrittura, infatti, a volte parla dell'essenza trinitaria attraverso *signa* bassi e persino mostruosi quali l'immagine di chimere[52] o di uomini dotati di ali[53], di animali vili come il verme o di sentimenti disdicevoli come l'ira[54]. L'evidente inadeguatezza di tali simboli a descrivere in modo autentico le nature angeliche e Dio rende tali immagini dissimili preziosi strumenti 'pedagogici'. Poiché ogni simbolo non può che risultare un disvelamento parziale dell'infinita sostanza divina[55], le immagini simboliche che denunciano chiaramente la loro difformità rispetto al referente al quale rimandano permettono al fedele di ricordare la trascendenza della stessa natura tearchica evitando pericolose identificazioni tra creature e Creatore. Il simbolo dissimile appare chiaramente altro dalla natura divina e non induce

[49] Cfr. IOHANNES SCOTUS ERIUGENA, *Commentarius in evangelium Iohannis*, VI, 6, 248AB, ed. Jeauneau cit. (alla nota 26), p. 366,97-99 (e nuova ed. Jeauneau cit. *ibid.*, p. 137,90-92): «Symboli exemplum fiat: 'In principio erat Verbum, et Verbum erat apud Deum, et Deus erat Verbum' (*Jo* 1, 1). Hoc solummodo dictum, in hoc nulla res gesta cognoscitur».

[50] ID., *Omelia super prologum Iohannis*, 4, 285B, ed. Jeauneau cit. (alla nota 26), p. 218,1 (e nuova ed. Jeauneau cit. *ibid.*, p. 8,1).

[51] Cfr. ID., *Expositiones super Hierarchiam coelestem*, 1, 132D, p. 8,262.

[52] Cfr. *ibid.*, 2, 153B, p. 31,422-426.

[53] Cfr. *ibid.*, 156AB, p. 34,546-551.

[54] Cfr. *ibid.*, 153B, p. 31,418-422.

[55] Eriugena ribadisce con forza questa dottrina nelle *Expositiones* parlando di una significazione «vere» e una «non autem vere». La prima è l'unica veramente adeguata alla natura divina e nega di Dio ogni positività; la seconda, invece, cerca di attribuire al Creatore alcune qualità e per questo risulta sempre parziale: cfr. *ibid.*, 156B, p. 34,517. Solo la negazione può essere considerata teologicamente vera in se stessa mentre l'affermazione ha unicamente una valenza «metaphorica»: cfr. *ibid.*, 156B, p. 34,527.

a ritenere che il dispositivo simbolico sia in grado di restituire un autentico aspetto dell'essenza trascendente.

I simboli dissimili, inoltre, agiscono quali veli che proteggono il mistero divino. La conoscenza teologica che è contenuta in tali immagini difformi, infatti, non risulta immediatamente accessibile. L'interprete dei *symbola* dissimili deve essere in grado di comprendere il gioco allegorico-traslativo presente nell'immagine mostruosa per ricostruire le qualità determinate che attraverso di essa sono attribuite a Dio: il verme rimanda alla Sapienza propria del Cristo, mentre l'ira sta a significare la vittoriosa lotta del Figlio di Dio contro il peccato. Il sapere, sempre parziale e insufficiente, intorno alla natura di Dio che i simboli dissimili veicolano risulta, quindi, protetto dalla complessa «figura» difforme e può essere così colto solamente da quanti siano adeguatamente purificati e già progrediti nei sacri misteri[56].

5. *Excursus*

Il simbolo e la peculiare tipologia di conoscenza che esso offre all'uomo costituiscono una questione discussa e analizzata anche nelle opere di Roberto Grossatesta. L'interesse del maestro francescano per tale problematica suggerisce una linea di ricerca (la relazione tra l'indagine sul simbolismo in Dionigi, Eriugena e Grossatesta; il perdurare nel pensiero medievale del tema neoplatonico della conoscenza teologica *per symbola*) che, benché qui

[56] Tra gli autori antichi presso i quali Eriugena poteva trovare una simile dottrina Macrobio appare come una fonte di particolare importanza per la riflessione del maestro irlandese. Già Jean Pépin ipotizzò che l'impiego da parte di Eriugena del concetto di *velamen* nel contesto metafisico-misterico della trattazione sul linguaggio simbolico (il simbolo come velo della natura divina di cui si parla nel *Periphyseon* e nelle *Expositiones*) potesse essere spiegato attraverso la mediazione di alcune nozioni neoplatoniche da parte dei *Commentarii* macrobiani al *Somnium Scipionis*: cfr. J. Pépin, *Aspects théoriques du symbolisme* cit. (alla nota 23), pp. 45 seqq. Dopo aver rifiutato ogni elemento osceno come indegno dei miti 'filosofici', Macrobio, infatti, introduce un riferimento ad un «pium figmentorum velamen», al velo costituito da finzioni non sconvenienti. La necessità di una maschera che nasconda i contenuti speculativi più alti dei testi dove viene rivelata una verità superiore è giustificata dal rischio che persone non degne e non preparate possano cogliere direttamente i misteri trascendenti; Macrobio a questo proposito distingue i «reliqui», ovvero la massa dei non iniziati, da coloro che possono penetrare il segreto delle figure allegoriche; cfr. *ibid.*, pp. 57-58.

possa essere solamente accennata, meriterebbe di certo ulteriori approfondimenti.

Grossatesta, agostiniano per formazione, influenzato dalla tradizione neoplatonica e traduttore del *corpus areopagiticum*, è uno dei primi pensatori a misurarsi all'inizio del secolo XIII, avvalendosi della parafrasi di Filopono e del commento di Temistio, con gli *Analitici secondi* di Aristotele, testo difficile e lontano dall'epistemologia di Agostino. Proprio nel commento agli *Analitici secondi*, Grossatesta indica quale forma di conoscenza autenticamente certa ed epistemica lo *scire maxime proprie*, ovvero il sapere della causa (distinto dallo *scire communiter*, dallo *scire proprie* e dallo *scire magis proprie*). Egli indica nel procedimento sillogistico *propter quid* il metodo per la creazione di tale tipo di sapere; questa tipologia di sillogismo permette di giungere alla *scientia propter quid*, ovvero alla conoscenza scientifica della causa prossima, che Grossatesta distingue dalla semplice *scientia quia*, la quale muove dall'effetto per cercare di ricostruire la causa che lo ha prodotto. Dopo aver indicato 1) nell'universalità (per l'oggetto e per il tempo), 2) nel fatto che le determinazioni si predichino *per se* e 3) che si riferiscano all'oggetto primo[57], i caratteri che le premesse devono possedere per garantire la necessità del risultato finale nel processo deduttivo, Grossatesta seguendo Aristotele tratta solo degli universali quali principi della dimostrazione e individua nell'*intellectus* (l'aristotelico νοῦς) la facoltà deputata a cogliere tali principi[58].

Grossatesta distingue, tuttavia, cinque modi di essere degli universali[59]. Gli universali esistono, innanzitutto, nella mente di Dio come idee, nell'accezione, nota Grossatesta, che a questo termine aveva dato Platone; la mente umana, però, costretta nella condizione di peccato, non può attingere a questa forma dell'universale. Un secondo modo di essere degli universali è l'essere nelle intelligenze create, ovvero nelle sostanze separate; quando l'intelletto coglie questa tipologia di universali riceve una illuminazione da una superiore luce creata e vede le forme o *descriptiones* delle cose.

[57] Cfr. Robertus Grosseteste, *Commentarius in Posteriorum analyticorum libros*, lib. I, c. 2,1 - c. 4,30, ed. P. Rossi, Firenze 1981 (Corpus Philosophorum Medii Aevi. Testi e studi, 2), pp. 99-110.

[58] Cfr. *ibid.*, c. 19, 22-84 (pp. 279-281).

[59] Cfr. *ibid.*, c. 7, 88 seqq. (p. 139).

La terza forma degli universali è quella di *virtutes causales* contenute nei corpi celesti. Viene poi la conoscenza delle cose terrestri nelle loro cause formali (*causa formalis*) espressa dal concetto universale e, quindi, l'universale di cui parla Aristotele nella sua teoria dell'astrazione e nella sua trattazione dei generi e delle specie. Infine c'è la conoscenza degli accidenti uniti alle essenze, grazie ai quali le cose possono essere conosciute.

Lo stesso Grossatesta afferma, però, che la conoscenza raggiungibile dall'uomo nella dimensione empirica è solo quella degli universali nelle cose (*in subiectum*), conoscenza sempre minacciata dalle distorsioni e aberrazioni prodotte dalla stessa realtà sensibile. Grossatesta, infatti, sottolinea come ogni operazione di astrazione cognitiva porti con sé quale residuo materiale un *phantasma*, ovvero un'immagine fisica che rappresenta il prodotto della conoscenza sensibile (basata sull'uso dei cinque sensi)[60]. Grossatesta ritiene che l'interferenza di questo residuo cognitivo materiale possa essere responsabile di errori dottrinali anche gravi; il pensatore francescano, infatti, attribuisce proprio all'azione di tale fattore perturbante le inesattezze che egli ritiene di ravvisare in Aristotele quale l'errata concezione dell'eternità divina.

Di contro al sapere contingente e astrattivo, sempre condizionato da una impostazione spazio-temporale, Grossatesta riprende il lessico e la dottrina dionisiana non sviluppando una riflessione sulle differenti facoltà della mente ma sulle diverse condizioni, in via e nella futura gloria divina, dell'anima umana[61]. Il simbolo appare così occasione di una conoscenza superiore che permette all'uomo di affrancarsi, almeno in parte, dalla condizione di ignoranza post-lapsaria; grazie al *lumen proprium*[62] la mente umana è risvegliata e spinta all'ascesi dal contatto con il mondo sensibile quale *vestigium*, riflesso del mondo superiore.

L'incontro con Dionigi, sulla cui *Gerarchia celeste* Grossatesta lavorerà nell'ultimo periodo della sua speculazione (tra il 1239 e il 1243), fa sì che il maestro francescano, partendo dalla dottrina aristotelica del sapere umano come astrazione dal sensibile, affidi

[60] Cfr. J. McEvoy, *The Philosophy of Robert Grosseteste*, Oxford 1986, p. 355.
[61] Cfr. *ibid.*, pp. 357-358.
[62] Cfr. Robertus Grosseteste, *ibid.*, c. 14, 195-291 (pp. 212-216).

la conoscenza del divino all'oscura intuizione mediante i simboli materiali, ribadendo che per l'individuo dopo la caduta il mondo trascendente non può essere conosciuto direttamente nemmeno attraverso una corretta metodologia scientifica. Questo è, infatti, il compito del simbolo.

ERNESTO SERGIO MAINOLDI

IL PROBLEMA DEI MODELLI STORIOGRAFICI APPLICATI ALLO STUDIO DELLA TRADIZIONE ERIUGENIANA

Giovanni Scoto è un autore che ha attirato costantemente e in modo singolare – in ragione delle peculiarità del suo pensiero – l'interesse degli storici della filosofia medievale, suscitando tuttavia posizioni divergenti in merito alla collocazione storiografica della sua opera. Indubbiamente l'inquadramento del pensiero e dell'opera di Giovanni Scoto è reso complesso da un lato dalla ricchezza delle fonti da cui il pensatore irlandese ebbe possibilità di attingere, dall'altro in ragione della mancanza di linearità constatabile nella ricezione medievale del suo insegnamento. Nell'ottica di questa analisi ci sembra importante richiamare come la comprensione di un autore non possa prescindere dalla ricostruzione della ricezione della sua opera, né dall'identificazione delle sue fonti e del modo in cui questi si sia rapportato a esse:

> Il testo e la sua trasmissione costituiscono due elementi fra loro non dissociabili, se non a pena di gravi fraintendimenti o mistificazioni. Senza un'indagine su come il testo si è trasmesso nel corso del tempo, l'opera originaria rimane sostanzialmente inconoscibile, vuoi perché in genere non è possibile ricostruirla, vuoi perché quand'anche essa sia correttamente ricostruita non se ne può comprendere la vitalità; e d'altra parte la piena comprensione dell'efficacia storica dell'opera attraverso il tempo – nelle sue successive copiature, nelle sue letture, nelle sue modifiche, in una parola nella sua fruizione – non si può comprendere se non presupponendo il testo originario e apprezzandone le successive trasformazioni[1].

[1] P. CHIESA, introduzione a *La trasmissione dei testi latini del medioevo. Mediaeval Latin Texts and their Transmission (Te. Tra. 2)*, a c. di P. Chiesa – L. Castaldi, Firenze 2005, p. XIII.

10.1484/M.NUTRIX-EB.1.101242

L'interpretazione storiografica del pensiero e dell'opera di Giovanni Scoto nella storia della filosofia e della teologia altomedievali non ha finora raggiunto risultati unanimi o approdi di sintesi generale, ma l'orientamento di ricerca prevalso dagli inizi del secolo scorso a tutt'oggi sembra essere volto a ricercare i motivi centrali della speculazione del maestro irlandese al di fuori dei confini del medioevo latino, prediligendosi il leggere l'opera e il pensiero eriugeniani alla luce della categoria storiografica del neoplatonismo. In base a questa lettura il pensiero e l'opera di Giovani Scoto hanno trovato una collocazione ideale nella storia del *Fortleben* del neoplatonismo tardo antico, collocazione che viene sovente giustificata in base alla constatazione per cui Giovanni Scoto sarebbe stato un 'gigante isolato' nell'epoca in cui visse e che avrebbe saputo riesumare il più puro pensiero neoplatonico dalle sue principali fonti, 'distillando' da Agostino il neoplatonismo di Plotino e dallo pseudo-Dionigi il neoplatonismo di Proclo.

Non è nostro intento porre qui in discussione la possibilità applicativa della categoria storiografica del neoplatonismo all'interpretazione di Giovanni Scoto, quanto di valutarne gli esiti ai fini della comprensione della genesi e degli intenti della sua speculazione, chiedendoci se le analogie strutturali tra il pensiero eriugeniano e il pensiero platonico e/o neoplatonico riescano a individuarne e a esaurirne i motivi ispiratori e gli scopi, e soprattutto – ed è questo il caso che qui ci interessa in particolare – se possano essere addotti a paradigma esplicativo della anomala ricezione medievale del suo lascito letterario e dottrinale. In altre parole è nostro interesse verificare la potenza del modello prevalente nella storiografia eriugeniana dell'ultimo secolo alla luce dei motivi che hanno determinato la trasmissione dei testi di Giovanni Scoto e la ricezione del suo pensiero, ovvero il suo *Fortleben*, in relazione ai testi, ai concetti e ai problemi che sono stati ripresi da Giovanni Scoto vuoi dalla tradizione filosofica e letteraria antiche vuoi dalla tradizione patristica greco-latina e da lui trasmessi in un'originale sintesi al medioevo latino.

Le ricerche intorno al *Fortleben* costituiscono un ramo degli studi eriugeniani che si distingue a tutt'oggi per la mancanza di una sintesi capace di mettere a confronto i risultati delle ricerche e delle scoperte susseguitesi negli ultimi decenni, e di formulare un'ipotesi interpretativa in grado di rendere conto dei dati acquisiti e conseguentemente di mettere in moto il lavoro critico degli studiosi, chiamandoli a intraprendere nuove ricerche che possano confermare o falsificare le nuove ipotesi interpretative. Sembra invece che le ricerche sul *Fortleben* eriugeniano abbiano incontrato una durevole fase di stallo, nonostante le ottime premesse segnate dai colloqui dedicati a questo tema, tenutisi a Laon nel 1975 e a Bad-Homburg nel 1985[2]. Ci chiediamo allora, a modo di formulazione di un'ipotesi da verificare, se il motivo di questa perdita di interesse possa risiedere nella oggettiva difficoltà di applicare la lettura neoplatonizzante alla storia della ricezione eriugeniana.

Di fronte all'enigmaticità del *Fortleben* eriugeniano, costellato di critiche, accuse di eresia, lunghi periodi di silenzio, ma anche periodiche riapparizioni, entusiastiche riprese e rinascite inaspettate, sarebbe dunque più opportuno optare per una sospensione fenomenologica volta a riconsiderare i dati al di fuori delle interpretazioni prevalse. Ricordiamo qui in sintesi i contorni del problema storiografico[3]: sin dalla sua apparizione ufficiale nella disputa sulla predestinazione (850/851) Giovanni Scoto destò lo sconcerto dei suoi contemporanei vuoi per la novità della sua metodologia vuoi per l'eccentricità delle sue proposte teologiche ed esegetiche. Successivamente, tra la fine del secolo IX e la fine del X, l'influenza di Giovanni Scoto sembra essersi affermata nelle scuole tardo-carolingie e ottoniane, dove non solo al suo insegnamento sulle arti liberali venne attribuita una sorta di canonicità, ma anche alcune sue proposte teologiche mostrano di aver ottenuto un certo credito. Nel secolo XI l'opera e il pensiero di Giovanni Scoto trovarono scarsa considerazione all'interno delle principali discussioni teologiche e filosofiche, quali la disputa sugli universali o le riflessioni sul ruolo della *ratio* in teologia, che avrebbe dato vita alla grande sistemazione di Anselmo di Aosta. Anche l'esemplatura

[2] Gli atti di questi due convegni sono rispettivamente raccolti nei volumi *Jean Scot Érigène et l'histoire de la philosophie* (Laon, 7-12 Juillet 1975), a c. di R. Roques, Paris 1977 (Colloques Internationaux du CNRS, 561), e *Eriugena redivivus. Zur Wirkungsgeschichte seines Denkens im Mittelalter und im Übergang zur Neuzeit*, Vorträge des V. Internationalen Eriugena-Colloquiums (Werner-Reimers-Stiftung, Bad Homburg, 26-30 August 1985), hrsg. von W. Beierwaltes, Heidelberg 1987.

[3] Per la seguente ricostruzione ci basiamo sui seguenti contributi: P. Lucentini, *Platonismo medievale. Contributi per la storia dell'eriugenismo*, Firenze 1979; J. J. O'Meara, *Eriugena's Immediate Influence*, in *Eriugena redivivus* cit., pp. 13-25; E. Jeauneau, *Le renouveau érigénien du XIIe siècle*, *ibid.*, pp. 26-46.

di codici in questo periodo lascia trapelare la marginalità di Giovanni Scoto rispetto agli interessi prevalenti. Il nome di Eriugena appare tuttavia in questa epoca nella disputa eucaristica che ha visto opporsi Berengario di Tours e Lanfranco di Pavia: a Giovanni Scoto venne infatti erroneamente attribuito un trattato contro la realtà del sacramento, che oggi sappiamo essere il *De corpore et sanguine Domini* di Ratramno di Corbie; il maestro irlandese si trovò così associato alla condanna di Berengario al Concilio di Vercelli del 1050. L'andamento declinante del *Fortleben* eriugeniano era tuttavia destinato a incontrare una svolta con il secolo XII, quando la lettura delle sue opere lasciò evidenti tracce negli scritti dei maggiori autori del tempo: da Guglielmo di Saint-Thierry ad Alano di Lilla, da Ugo di San Vittore a Onorio di Ratisbona. Non troviamo però significative tracce di eriugenismo in autori come Pietro Abelardo e in ambienti come la scuola di Chartres, per i quali l'interesse per la filosofia, e in particolare la propensione platonizzante, ha guidato la riflessione teologica in direzione di una filosofia della natura volta a identificare le ragioni cosmiche della Rivelazione. Tra la fine del secolo XII e gli inizi del XIII, si registra l'incontro tra la filosofia di Giovanni Scoto e l'avicennismo, nelle fitte pagine del trattato *De causis primis et secundis et de fluxu qui consequitur eas*. A chiudere questo periodo di rimarchevole fortuna – e verosimilmente in reazione a essa – arrivò la condanna pontificia del 1225 all'indirizzo del *Periphyseon*, definito nella bolla papale «liber totus scatens vermibus haeretice pravitatis». Ciò nonostante le opere eriugeniane continuarono a circolare durante il secolo XIII, come dimostra la presenza delle *Expositiones in ierarchiam caelestem* e degli ampi *excerpta* dal *Periphyseon* nel *Corpus dionysiacum* dell'Università di Parigi. Tuttavia i punti cardinali del pensiero teologico eriugeniano sembrano essere rimasti esclusi da questa sopravvivenza. Alla fine del secolo XIII, con Enrico di Susa e Martino il Polacco si affermerà l'associazione tra Giovanni Scoto e gli eretici amalriciani (condannati a Parigi nel 1210), che resterà canonica nella storia del pensiero medievale, alimentando in seguito la vulgata del 'panteismo' eriugeniano. L'associazione tra Eriugena e la condanna degli amalriciani sarà confutata solo negli anni '70 del secolo scorso dalle ricerche di Paolo Lucentini[4]. La marginalità

[4] Cfr. P. LUCENTINI, *L'eresia di Amalrico*, in *Eriugena redivivus* cit., pp. 174-191

della teologia eriugeniana rispetto all'asse portante della teologia scolastica, non impedì tuttavia che il nome del maestro palatino facesse capolino nell'opera di Alberto Magno e di Tommaso d'Aquino, nei testi degli autori renani e infine, in modo notevole, nell'ultimo grande autore medievale, Nicolò Cusano.

Questo stato di cose ci pone due quesiti: il primo ci chiede il motivo per cui un teologo dello spessore di Giovanni Scoto – che Ugo di San Vittore definì, nel *Didascalicon*, «theologus nostri temporis»[5] – non abbia trovato una collocazione stabile nella tradizione teologico-filosofica della cristianità latina, a differenza di un filosofo come Boezio, cristiano ma affatto lontano da quel metodo esegetico-apologetico di ascendenza patristica che costituirà un modello di cui la speculazione medievale non potrà mai fare del tutto a meno, o di un teologo preoccupato in primo luogo del ruolo della *ratio* come Anselmo d'Aosta, casi in cui l'influenza letteraria e dottrinale ha avuto ben altri contorni rispetto a quella del pensatore irlandese. E perché nella stagione della Scolastica, quando la lettura dei filosofi antichi e arabi si trovò al centro degli interessi speculativi e dei dibattiti universitari, costituendo un imprescindibile elemento di confronto, il nome di Giovanni Scoto rimase comunque marginale? Il secondo quesito ci chiede – sul versante opposto – il motivo per cui Giovanni Scoto non venne mai dimenticato del tutto, nonostante le condanne, i sospetti e la tradizione intermittente della sua opera, ma si trovò periodicamente riscoperto e ripreso con entusiasmo da taluni dei suoi lettori. Questi due questi si possono riassumere nella domanda: cosa ha rappresentato Giovanni Scoto Eriugena per il Medioevo latino?

A latere di questa sommaria ricapitolazione va rilevato che l'analisi delle non poche annotazioni marginali ai testi eriugeniani e degli espliciti appunti critici a questi mossi dai lettori fa emergere come a essere percepito come problematico non fu tanto l'essere filosofo di Giovanni Scoto, quanto il suo essere teologo: nessun critico medievale del maestro irlandese ha percepito un suo platonizzare, nessuno lo ha accusato di aver seguito i filosofi pagani,

(oggi anche in Id., *Platonismo, ermetismo, eresia nel Medioevo*, Louvain-la-Neuve 2007 [Textes et Études du Moyen Âge, 41], pp. 363-385).

[5] Hugo de Sancto Victore, *Didascalicon de studio legendi*, III, 2, PL 176, 765C, ed. C. H. Buttimer, Washington 1939 (Studies in Medieval and Renaissance Latin, 10), p. 49,3-4.

mentre più frequenti risultano le critiche all'indirizzo del suo favore verso la teologia orientale[6]. Al pari dunque della vulgata del presunto 'panteismo' eriugeniano, escogitata dalla storiografica post-medievale per spiegare – banalizzando – le peculiarità del pensiero dell'Irlandese e giustificare la condanna del 1225, la lettura neoplatonizzante, al di là di cogliere talune macroaffinità strutturali interne ed esterne alla sua opera, non riesce a penetrare il problema storiografico dettato dalla sua frastagliata ricezione.

Riferendoci ad alcuni episodi di *Fortleben*, attraverso i quali riflettere sui motivi profondi e sugli elementi genetici dell'opera eriugeniana, cercheremo qui di porre la 'ragion neoplatonica' in una luce maggiormente critica in relazione al caso di Giovanni Scoto. Prima di affrontare l'analisi che ci siamo proposti, vogliamo anche sottolineare che nel caso del pensatore irlandese lo studio del *Fortleben* risulta affatto centrale non solo ai fini della comprensione della sua opera e della sua fortuna, ma si dimostra addirittura decisivo nelle problematiche ecdotiche relative all'edizione dei suoi testi, tra cui *in primis* il *Periphyseon*, dal momento che l'ultimo, in ordine cronologico, di una già nutrita schiera di editori del capolavoro eriugeniano, Édouard Jeauneau, ne ha stabilito il testo in base a criteri ecdotici conseguenti all'ipotesi che la cesura tra autore e *Fortleben* si sia già prodotta nella fase redazionale dell'opera, attestata dai manoscritti d'autore[7]. Secondo Jeauneau infatti il copista irlandese, la cui grafia, indicata convenzionalmente con la sigla i^2, compare nei due testimoni stemmaticamente più alti della tradizione dell'opera, non si sarebbe limitato alla funzione di mero copista, ma avrebbe svolto la funzione di revisore del testo autonomamente rispetto alle intenzioni dell'autore[8]. Non è qui il tempo e il luogo per analizzare nel dettaglio le problematiche filologiche e dottrinali derivanti da questa ipotesi, tuttavia proprio un

[6] Cfr. E. S. MAINOLDI, *L'influenza eriugeniana sulla dottrina della beatitudo nel XII secolo*, in *De vita beata. La felicità nel Medioevo*, Atti del XIII Convegno della Società Italiana per lo Studio del Pensiero Medievale (Milano, 12-13 settembre 2003), a c. di M. Bettetini – F. D. Paparella, Leuven 2005, [pp. 123-201], p. 187, nota 139, e pp. 199-200.

[7] IOHANNES SCOTUS ERIUGENA, *Periphyseon*, ed. É. Jeauneau, 5 voll., Turnhout 1996-2003 (CCCM, 161-165).

[8] Cfr. É. JEAUNEAU, Nisifortinus*: le disciple qui corrige le maître*, in *Poetry and Philosophy in the Middle Ages. A Festschrift for Peter Dronke*, ed. by J. Marenbon, Leiden 2001, pp. 113-129.

frammento testuale nella grafia di i^2, risalente all'ultimo quarto del secolo IX ed esterno alla tradizione manoscritta del *Periphyseon*, in cui si riflette l'insegnamento di scuola di Giovanni Scoto, ci sembra utile per intraprendere la verifica dei modelli storiografici applicati allo studio della tradizione eriugeniana.

L'esempio, che vogliamo qui sottoporre ad attenzione e dalla cui analisi speriamo di portare elementi convincenti alla nostra tesi, è tratto da un breve testo tràdito, insieme ad altri materiali, da un folio volante rilegato in testa al ms. 55 della Bibliothèque municipale di Laon: in questo testo (da qui in avanti *L*) sono contenute alcune annotazioni esegetiche relative a passi della Sacra Scrittura; esso è stato scoperto da Bernhard Bischoff e presentato in uno studio congiunto con Édouard Jeauneau al convegno eriugeniano di Laon del 1975[9] (i corsivi sono miei):

L	IOHANNES SCOTUS
Increatus ingenitus Pater; increatus genitus Filius; creatum et genitum omnis creatura, quae in primis causis creata et genita in generatione et nascendo; creatum et non genitum omnis creatura, quae in primis causis creata et non adhuc *genita*, sed restat, ut nascatur[10].	Pater siquidem ingenitus est, Filius vero genitus, spiritus neque ingenitus neque genitus. *Et innumerabilia exempla huiusmodi sunt*[11]. Per non factum, sed genitum, *omnia facta, sed non genita*[12]. (...) In seipsum omnia recapitulans, per quem et esse, et permanere, et *ex quo*, quae genita sunt, et *ad quem* genita sunt, et manentia et mota participant Deum[13].

[9] B. BISCHOFF – É. JEAUNEAU, *Ein neuer Text aus der Gedankenwelt des Johannes Scottus*, in *Jean Scot Érigène et l'histoire de la philosophie* cit., pp. 109-116 (i corsivi sono miei).

[10] Ms. Laon, Bibliothèque Municipale 55, ff. 1$^{+ \text{r-v}}$, grafia di i^2.

[11] IOHANNES SCOTUS ERIUGENA, *Periphyseon*, IV, PL 122, 756C, ed. Jeauneau, IV, p. 23,604-605.

[12] ID., *Omelia «Vox spiritualis aquilae»*, 7, PL 122, 287A, ed. É. Jeauneau, Paris 1969 (SC, 151), p. 232,10.

[13] MAXIMUS CONFESSOR, *Ambigua ad Iohannem*, 3, *latina interpretatio* IOHANNIS SCOTI ERIUGENAE, ed. É. Jeauneau, Turnhout 1988 (CCSG, 18), p. 28,209-212.

Il quadrato logico descritto da *L* combina le possibilità affermative e negative dei participi *creatus* e *genitus*, da cui discendono le definizioni del Padre, del Figlio, delle creature in potenza nelle cause primordiali e delle creature in atto generate dalle cause primordiali[14]. Esso costituisce un esempio del metodo dialettico della divisione, dal quale deriva nondimeno la principale divisione su cui si edifica il *Periphyseon*, scaturita dalla combinazione dell'affermazione e della negazione del verbo *creare* nella sua forma attiva e passiva predicato del sostantivo *natura*:

> N. Videtur mihi divisio naturae per quattuor differentias quattuor species recipere, quarum prima est in eam quae creat et non creatur, secunda in eam quae creatur et creat, tertia in eam quae creatur et non creat, quarta quae nec creat nec creatur[15].

Tornando alla divisione proposta da *L* dobbiamo notare come il suo sotteso dottrinale sia riconducibile alla teologia trinitaria, ciò che si deduce dall'utilizzo dei termini *creatio* e *generatio* (oltre ai prosoponimici *Pater* e *Filius*); sul versante della *generatio* troviamo la seguente *similitudo*: come il Figlio è generato dal Padre così le realtà corporee sono generate dalle cause primordiali; sul versante della *creatio* registriamo invece la seguente *differentia*: mentre il Figlio non è creato nel Padre, le realtà corporee sono create nelle cause primordiali. Questa divisione costituisce un esempio tipicamente eriugeniano di applicazione delle regole della dialettica agli assiomi della teologia: nel passo del *Periphyseon* portato sopra a raffronto[16] Eriugena sottolinea che analoghe divisioni dialettiche potrebbero dare vita a «innumerabilia exempla»: uno di questi esempi è costituito proprio dalla *divisio* descritta in *L*.

Dal punto di vista della costruzione letteraria *L* si presenta come una serie di definizioni giustapposte, cosa che ci suggerirebbe di interpretare queste righe come un appunto in cui vengono

[14] Possiamo riassumere queste relazioni nel seguente schema:

	increatus	creatus
ingenitus	*Pater*	*omnis creatura in causis primis*
genitus	*Filius*	*omnis creatura genita a causis primis*

[15] IOHANNES SCOTUS ERIUGENA, *Periphyseon*, I, 441B, ed. Jeauneau cit., I, pp. 3,19 - 4,21.

[16] Cfr. il testo corrispondente alla nota 11.

sinteticamente registrati sulla pergamena i passaggi fondamentali di un'argomentazione, forse la trascrizione di un insegnamento orale; difficilmente la genesi di questo frammento potrebbe essere quella di un testo scritto: se lo fosse dovremmo rilevare la distanza per qualità stilistica e per capacità di organizzare gli argomenti rispetto alle glosse aggiunte ai manoscritti del *Periphyseon* per mano dello stesso i^2. La nostra ipotesi è dunque che in questo frammento si abbia la trascrizione dell'insegnamento orale di Giovanni Scoto.

Tornando all'analisi dei contenuti di *L* possiamo notare che la definizione delle realtà create nelle cause primordiali come *genita* o *non genita*, pur essendo poco frequente nell'opera di Eriugena, trovi una ricorrenza letterale nei passi dell'*Omelia* e della *Versio Ambiguorum*, ovvero della traduzione eriugeniana degli *Ambigua* di Massimo il Confessore, che abbiamo portato sopra a raffronto[17]. Il riferimento agli *Ambigua* non è peregrino, dal momento che – come emerge anche dall'analisi proposta da Jeauneau[18] – l'intero frammento presenta più di un punto di contatto con l'opera del Confessore, al punto che potremmo supporre per esso una dipendenza testuale specificamente massimiana.

Un ulteriore parallelo tra un successivo passo di *L*, la *Versio Ambiguorum* e il *Periphyseon* presenta una chiara concordanza tra il *reditus* escatologico eriugeniano e la teologia neotestamentaria della resurrezione del corpo, attestando la mediazione esegetica di Massimo:

L	IOHANNES SCOTUS
«Deliges proximum tuum tanquam te ipsum» (*Mt* 22, 39; *Mr* 12, 31). Proximum vocat corpus. Deligitur ergo corpus, quando convertitur per puritatem in modum animae idest, ut spirituale ‹corpus in› anima‹m› inef-	(...) Ex anima et corpore per bonitatem a Deo factus est homo (...) et *de diligendo proximo sicut seipsam* iubens mandatum, prudenter corpus recipit, per virtutes etiam illud famulari Deo efficit ut conservum, et per suam

[17] Cfr. i testi corrispondenti alle note 12-13.

[18] Cfr. BISCHOFF – JEAUNEAU, *Ein neuer Text* cit., pp. 111-116.

L	IOHANNES SCOTUS
fabili quodam modo et mira puritate convertitur et sic omnia id est corpus et anima ad suum principium revertuntur[19].	medietatem factorem faciet possessurum, et data immortalitate insolubili vinculo illud sibi coniuncturum, *ut quod Deus animae, hoc anima corpori fiat*, et unus ostendatur omnium creator (...)[20]. Prima igitur humanae naturae reversio est quando corpus solvitur (...). Secunda in resurrectione implebitur (...). Tertia, quando corpus in spiritum mutabitur. Quarta, quando spiritus, et, ut apertius dicam, tota hominis natura in primordiales causas revertetur, quae sunt semper et incommutabiliter in Deo. Quinta, quando ipsa natura cum suis causis movebitur in Deum[21].

La chiusa del passo costituisce un palese riferimento alla teoria massimiana del ritorno del corpo risorto e spiritualizzato all'anima e da qui, insieme ad essa, a Dio. Questa teoria spiega meglio le ragioni dell'interpretazione che vede sotto il termine evangelico *proximus* un riferimento anagogico al *corpus*, con riferimento alla teologia della *deificatio*. L'ispirazione del brano si svela dunque nella teologia della *théosis* di Massimo il Confessore, il cui fondamento è cristologico, ruotando intorno al problema dell'*inhumanatio* della natura divina in Cristo al fine della *deificatio* della natura umana nello stesso Cristo. Possiamo così constatare come l'ispirazione trinitaria della divisione da cui abbiamo preso le mosse proceda, nello svolgimento di *L*, verso il teologumeno del-

[19] Ms. Laon, Bibliothèque Municipale 55, *ibidem*. La lezione «ut spirituale ‹corpus in› anima‹m›» è una mia ricostruzione congetturale di lacune nel codice.

[20] MAXIMUS CONFESSOR, *Ambigua ad Iohannem*, 3, *latina interpretatio* IOHANNIS SCOTI ERIUGENAE, ed. Jeauneau, p. 35,441-442 e 446-452.

[21] IOHANNES SCOTUS ERIUGENA, *Periphyseon*, V, 876AB, ed. Jeauneau, V, p. 24,685-694.

la *deificatio* dell'uomo come unità di anima e corpo risorto, analogamente alla trattazione del tema filosofico della quadripartizione delle nature nel *Periphyseon*, che procede dal problema iniziale della divisione dell'intera realtà delle cose che sono e delle cose che non sono, le cui specie sono riconducibili ad unità sotto il vocabolo ΦΥCIC-*natura* quale genere che le comprende nel linguaggio e nella realtà, e approda (nel V libro) all'indagine di come questa unità si configuri come *deificatio* cristologica nel *reditus*.

Il problema del *Periphyseon*, seguendo lo svolgimento dell'opera, è in ultima istanza riconducibile alla teologia della creazione universale della realtà nel Verbo, alla teologia dell'*adunatio* della natura increata con la natura creata in virtù dell'incarnazione del Verbo e al ritorno di tutte le cose al Verbo come *deificatio* nel Verbo. Nell'impalcatura dialettica del pensiero eriugeniano non ci sembra dunque agire una preoccupazione cosmologica o metafisica platonizzante, quanto piuttosto una risposta al problema posto al pensiero umano dall'*incarnatio-resurrectio* del Verbo. Il movimento di *processio* e *reditus* che esso sottende, come del resto le *divisiones* incontrate, non sarebbero infatti correttamente compresi in mancanza di un riferimento al problema cristologico. L'orizzonte storico da cui parte e a cui guarda la speculazione eriugeniana è costituito non tanto dai problemi storici e teoretici del platonismo antico o del neoplatonismo tardo-antico, quanto dalla dottrina trinitaria e cristologica, dal momento che la terminologia stessa con cui Eriugena conduce la sua indagine speculativa (*creatio*, *generatio*, *natura*, *adunatio naturarum* ecc.) non è comprensibile se non alla luce della tradizione teologica risalente alle formule dei concili di Nicea I (325) e di Calcedonia (451). Analogamente, lo sfondo ipotestuale che si mostra con maggiore incisività dietro il progetto del *Periphyseon* – e che vediamo riecheggiato in questo appunto registrato su pergamena da i^2 – è costituito dall'insegnamento del grande difensore della dottrina calcedonese, Massimo il Confessore. I problemi a cui guarda Eriugena sono la dottrina della creazione di ogni realtà per mezzo del Verbo e nel Verbo, l'escatologia della resurrezione, la spiritualizzazione del corpo e la redenzione universale nel Verbo, problemi esulanti o apologeticamente rifiutati dalla filosofia neoplatonica. Equiparare la *processio* e il *reditus* eriugeniani al *próodos* e all'*epistrophé* neoplatonici significherebbe – a nostro avviso – tralasciare i motivi cristologici ispiratori di questa costruzione filosofica per andare alla ricerca di analogie strutturali con autori che non rientrano nel panorama autoriale di Giovanni Scoto.

Per contro la lettura neoplatonizzante, che ha impregnato gli studi eriugeniani lungo tutto l'arco del '900, ha insistito su tali analogie strutturali, che non avrebbero potuto essere argomentate sino in fondo se non alla luce di una lettura parziale e decontestualizzante dell'opera eriugeniana, tanto da portare in certi casi a veri e propri travisamenti, come ad esempio il riconoscimento infondato di citazioni di Plotino nel *Periphyseon* in un contributo del 1927 di Margit Techert[22].

È interessante tuttavia osservare come in alcuni dei maggiori contributi alla conoscenza dell'opera e del pensiero di Giovanni Scoto sia gradualmente emersa, a fianco della lettura neoplatonizzante, la necessità di contestualizzare meglio la comprensione del pensatore irlandese. Maïeul Cappuyns, per esempio, nelle conclusioni della sua fondamentale monografia eriugeniana del 1933[23], pur pagando il fio all'egemonia del 'paradigma' neoplatonizzante (afferma infatti che Giovanni Scoto «n'est que la forme chrétienne du monisme néo-platonicienne»[24]), avanza non marginali osservazioni critiche volte a limitare le letture puramente teoretiche: «N'étant ni proprement philosophe, ni rationaliste, ni panthéiste, Érigène perd une bonne part de l'originalité qu'on se plaît à lui reconnaître. (...) Ramené à des formes de pensé moins extraordinaires, moins modernes, le système érigénien s'explique»[25]. Cappuyns pone dunque per primo il problema dell'appropriatezza dei paradigmi di lettura al caso di Giovanni Scoto, pena l'approdo ai risultati più disparati e improbabili.

Un'analoga evoluzione può essere osservata nell'interpretazione del pensiero di Giovanni Scoto proposta da Tullio Gregory:

[22] Cfr. M. TECHERT, *Le plotinisme de Jean Scot Érigène*, in «Revue néo-scholastique de philosophie», 28 (1927), pp. 28-68. M. CAPPUYNS, *Jean Scot Érigène, sa vie, son œuvre, sa pensée*, Louvain – Paris 1933, p. 216, nota 2, così commentava questo falso riconoscimento: «Il y a quelques années, on a cru découvrir un lien direct entre Jean Scot et l'œuvre de Plotin (...). Mais c'est là une illusion».

[23] Cit. alla nota precedente.

[24] *Ibid.*, p. 385.

[25] *Ibid.*, p. 386.

nei suoi *Tre studi* eriugeniani, comparsi nel 1963[26], si coglie la forza del modello storiografico egemone già dall'*incipit*, dove il motivo del neoplatonismo compare ancor prima del nome del maestro irlandese: «Elaborato secondo motivi schiettamente neoplatonici il pensiero di Giovanni Scoto Eriugena si svolge attorno ad un problema centrale: quello della derivazione del molteplice dall'uno attraverso momenti successivi che scandiscono il ritmo di una dialettica ontologica, cioè oggettiva ed autonoma rispetto all'attività del soggetto pensante»[27]. E i nomi di Platone, Plotino e Proclo (gli ultimi due sconosciuti a Eriugena) vi compaiono ancora prima degli autori, latini e greci, di cui il maestro palatino riporta intere pagine nelle sue opere: Agostino, Gregorio Nisseno, lo pseudo-Dionigi e Massimo il Confessore[28].

L'applicazione del 'paradigma' neoplatonizzante allo studio del *Fortleben* eriugeniano aveva peraltro già portato Gregory[29], muovendosi su un terreno già dissodato da uno studio di Jacquin del 1910[30], a indicare in Giovanni Scoto una delle figure ispiratrici del platonismo della scuola di Chartres. Nell'indice dei nomi Giovanni Scoto compare ben 18 volte, ma i parallelismi indicati riguardano al più degli accostamenti dottrinali e in nessun caso delle concordanze testuali. La proposta esegetica di Gregory, per quanto non confermata dalle analisi testuali, serviva tuttavia a porre a confronto il 'paradigma' neoplatonizzante con il problema del *Fortleben* eriugeniano sulla base di precisi temi di verifica. Ritornando sull'argomento anni dopo, in uno studio sulla ricezione di Giovanni Scoto nel secolo XII, Édouard Jeauneau, grande conoscitore nonché editore dei testi eriugeniani, ma anche degli autori della scuola di Chartres, concludeva che «à Chartres Jean Scot y brille par son absence»[31].

La posizione storiografica di Gregory su Giovanni Scoto era però destinata a trovare un'ulteriore evoluzione. Nel 1972 infat-

[26] Cfr. T. GREGORY, *Giovanni Scoto Eriugena. Tre studi*, Firenze 1963.

[27] *Ibid.*, p. 1.

[28] Cfr. *ibid.*, pp. 2-3.

[29] Cfr. ID., *Anima mundi. La filosofia di Guglielmo di Conches e la scuola di Chartres*, Firenze 1955.

[30] Cfr. M. JACQUIN, *L'influence doctrinale de Jean Scot au début du XIIIe siècle*, in «Revue des sciences philosophiques et théologiques», 4 (1910), pp. 104-110.

[31] JEAUNEAU, *Le renouveau érigénien* cit. (alla nota 3), p. 44.

ti, al V Congreso Internacional de Filosofia Medieval, tenutosi a Madrid, rispondendo alle pretese di una neutralità religiosa della filosofia medievale avanzate nello stesso convegno da Ferdinand Van Steenberghen, Gregory affermava, prendendo ad esempio proprio il caso di Giovanni Scoto, che:

> Il me semble du rest difficile de nier que c'est seulement dans l'horizon de l'expérience chrétienne que les grands problèmes de la philosophie médiévale assument leur pleine signification: le rapport dialectique entre les *naturae* de Jean Scot Érigène trouve sont point central dans la doctrine du Verbe incarné[32].

Sulla base di questa conclusione, e riferendoci agli esempi sopra analizzati, ci chiediamo in definitiva se è plausibile ritenere che Giovanni Scoto concepisse il procedere del mondo dall'Uno secondo un modello di processione che risponde alla concezione pagana della cosmogonia, quando la teologia del Verbo occupa una posizione centrale nella riflessione eriugeniana intorno all'origine causale di ogni realtà. Avendo qui sopra constatato come dietro agli argomenti eriugeniani dal carattere maggiormente tecnico-dialettico si possa ritrovare un'ispirazione essenzialmente teologica, siamo portati a concludere che la struttura concettuale sottostante ai termini *processio* e *reditus*, non sia che uno strumento per interpretare ciò che il credo cristiano confessa, ovvero l'incarnazione del Verbo e la deificazione della natura umana nel Verbo, e non per dissertare astrattamente di temi filosofici quali il rapporto uno-molti, essere-divenire o per risolvere i problemi speculativi posti dai filosofi neoplatonici tardo-antichi: Eriugena indaga sui rapporti tra le divisioni della natura non perché è neoplatonico, ma perché è un teologo cristiano che muove la sua riflessione dal punto di vista dell'economia del Verbo. Pur essendo assodato il ruolo strumentale della filosofia, al pari dell'utilizzo retorico e letterario dei miti dell'antichità, crediamo che, prima di appellarsi alla categoria del platonismo cristiano, nel caso di Giovanni Scoto sia necessario valutare l'apporto delle fonti antiche, la loro consi-

[32] T. GREGORY, *La conception de la philosophie au Moyen Âge*, in *Actas del V Congreso Internacional de Filosofia Medieval*, Madrid 1979, [pp. 49-57], p. 52.

derazione da parte dell'autore e valutare se e come i capisaldi di un sistema filosofico siano stati rispettati o meno.

Nell'opera di Giovanni Scoto bisogna distinguere tra la strumentazione logica, che ha una base linguistica nella dialettica antica e tardo-antica, e che possiamo dire tanto aristotelica quanto neoplatonica, dalle sue reali intenzioni, che sono quelle di un autore cristiano alto-medievale. Dal momento che la filosofia platonica, aristotelica o neoplatonica nel loro complesso sono funzionali alla visione del mondo pagana, gli strumenti della razionalità filosofica da esse sviluppati potranno essere utilizzati ai fini dell'illustrazione della *visio mundi* cristiana solo a patto di essere distinti dalle implicazioni del 'paradigma' pagano.

Bisogna dunque guardarsi dalla supposizione che alla coincidenza o affinità terminologica corrisponda una coincidenza o affinità di concetti e problemi. Il motivo per cui Giovanni Scoto sceglie il termine *natura* come vocabolo universale per designare la totalità delle cose *quae sunt* e delle cose *quae non sunt* è riconducibile all'importanza che questo termine ha assunto nella tradizione teologica cristiana, che di esso si è avvalso per definire il dogma del farsi uomo di Dio e del farsi dio dell'uomo sancito dalla dottrina calcedoniana sulle nature di Cristo. L'analogia strutturale di questo duplice movimento, da Dio all'uomo e dall'uomo a Dio, con i concetti neoplatonici di *próodos-epistrophé* è altrettanto distante da quanto lo è rispetto ai concetti vedici di *srishti* e *moksha*[33]. Potremmo, volendo, trovare in ogni filosofia e in ogni religione strutture concettuali fondate sul binomio di allontanamento-avvicinamento, andata-ritorno, progresso-regresso: avremmo forse individuato un archetipo del pensiero umano, non un fatto storiograficamente discriminante.

Venendo dunque ai fattori discriminanti dobbiamo chiederci se può essere considerato neoplatonico il persistere dell'individualità pur nello stato di apocatastasi escatologica, che Giovanni Scoto descrive con argomenti dialettici nei quali si vede una contraddizione fondamentale agli assiomi su cui si basa l'idea del *próodos* e dell'*epistrophé* neoplatonici, ovvero della distinzione tra

[33] Sulle analogie dottrinali tra neoplatonismo e pensiero indiano si veda la miscellanea *Neoplatonism and Indian Thought*, ed. by R. Baine Harris, Norfolg (Virginia) 1982.

l'essenza permanente e gli attributi impermanenti; per Giovanni Scoto gli attributi sussisteranno in un modo ineffabile, noto solo al Creatore:

> Nec sic tamen praedictas substantiarum qualitates suas substantias, circa quas volvuntur, omnino deserere et in materiem sensibilis mundi convenire arbitramur. *Sed mirabili et ineffabili modo, soli fabricatori illius cognito, et circa suas substantias, quibus inseparabiliter adhaerent, semper permanent* et hunc mundum modo quodam intelligibili compositionibus suis perficiunt atque componunt[34].

Lo schema *próodos-moné-epistrophé* è del resto strettamente funzionale a una concezione che ammette l'eternità del mondo, tema su cui possiamo ascoltare lo stesso Eriugena, che nel *Periphyseon* prende le distanze nettamente da tale concezione:

> ALUMNUS. (...) Veruntamen neque talibus opinionibus, quas vera deridet ratio, te assentire aestimarim, neque *talem* [*mundi*] *aeternitatem*, vel ut verius dicam, semiaeternitatem praedictis tuis rationibus suasisse, neque sic et facta simul et aeterna docuisse; sed altiori naturarum contuitu ultra humanas opiniones modo quodam adhuc nobis incognito divinorum arcanorum adyta penetrare te sentio, vestigia patrum, qui talia scrutati sunt, altius sequendo. Aiunt enim naturam huius mundi semper mansuram (...). NUTRITOR. *Falsis ratiocinationibus humanarum opinionum longe a veritate distantium quondam me deceptum esse negare non possum, quia deceptus sum.* His enim omnibus, aut pene omnibus rudis iam assensum praebui, quadam similitudine veri carnalibusque sensibus, ut multis evenit, seductus. Nunc vero sanctorum patrum vestigia sequens, divini luminis radio ab erroribus meis et aliorum me revocante inque viam rectam ducente, paululum pedem retraho. (...) Nulla enim peior mors est quam veritatis ignorantia, nulla vorago profundior quam falsa pro veris approbare, quod proprium est erroris. Ex his enim turpissima et *abominabilia monstra in humanis cogitationibus* solent fingi. Quae dum carnalis anima veluti vera et amat et sequitur, dorsum convertens vero lumini umbrasque fugaces comprehendere volens et non valens, in barathrum miseriae consuevit ruere. Hinc assi-

[34] IOHANNES SCOTUS ERIUGENA, *Periphyseon*, V, 886CD, ed. Jeauneau, V, p. 39,1199-1205.

> due debemus orare ac dicere: Deus, nostra salus atque redemptio, qui dedisti naturam, largire et gratiam. Praetende lumen tuum in umbris ignorantiae palpitantibus quaerentibusque te. *Revoca nos ab erroribus*[35].

Per Eriugena la prospettiva dell'eternità del mondo è un errore filosofico che si scontra con la dottrina rivelata, dal momento che in questa concezione dell'economia cosmica si distingue uno degli elementi fondamentali che segnano la distanza tra il filosofare pagano e il filosofare cristiano. La concezione dell'eternità del mondo è infatti antitetica al progetto escatologico cristiano, per cui si avrà la resurrezione dei morti e la vita in un mondo ipercosmico, in una condizione di deificazione individuale. Data l'eternità del mondo non può essere il corpo a tornare all'anima, dopo la risurrezione – come affermano i cristiani –, ma deve essere l'anima a tornare al corpo, per metempsicosi – come affermano la filosofia e la religione espressa dalla civiltà greco-romana.

Anche nella concezione della materia Eriugena si distingue in modo radicale dai platonici e dai neoplatonici: né la materia eterna del *Timeo* platonico, oggetto degli esercizi plastici del Demiurgo, né il male secondo Plotino, bensì causa primordiale creata da Dio eterna nel non essere ma non coeterna a lui. La materia, per Giovanni Scoto, sta infatti tra *ea quae non sunt*. Da qui vediamo come la concezione del male non possa essere intesa filosoficamente soltanto alla stregua di mera assenza di bene, né come un moto involontario che nasce dall'ignoranza del bene, come vuole una lunga tradizione filosofica che si dipana da Socrate a Proclo: il male eriugeniano si riconduce in ultima istanza alla trasgressione superba della volontà creaturale, di angeli e uomini, dunque al tema biblico della caduta, come egli sottolinea nell'*Omelia «Vox spiritualis aquilae»*, commentando il prologo del quarto vangelo: «Iam dividitur non humanitas rationalis mundi, sed voluntas», parole che Marta Cristiani traduce: «Ecco introdursi una divisione all'interno dell'universo razionale, che non concerne la natura dell'uomo, bensì la volontà»[36].

[35] *Ibid.*, III, 649C-650B, ed. Jeauneau, III, pp. 45,1278 - 46,1312.

[36] Id., *Omelia «Vox spiritualis aquilae»*, 20, 294CD, ed. Jeauneau cit. (alla nota 12), p. 298,6-7; tr. it. a c. di M. Cristiani, Milano 1987, p. 58,6-7.

Possiamo infine citare il caso della gnoseologia, dove i punti di contatto tra Giovanni Scoto e il modello platonico di tripartizione della conoscenza sono maggiormente evidenti, ma nonostante ciò il maestro irlandese, guidato dalla sua riflessione sulla *théosis*, è chiamato a stabilire un limite tra la gnoseologia tripartita e la iper-gnoseologia pertinente allo stato di deificazione, dal momento che l'*adunatio* della natura umana creata con la natura divina increata può essere concepita come *théosis* solo spingendosi al di là del concetto stesso di *natura*, fondamento e limite di ogni conoscenza umana. Scrive a proposito Giulio d'Onofrio in un suo saggio sull'*Omelia «Vox spiritualis aquilae»*:

> Il volo dell'aquila [ovvero dell'evangelista Giovanni] «ultra omnia quae sunt et quae non sunt» ha proprio il senso di un trascendimento assoluto delle capacità create di contemplazione. Al di sopra della tripartizione platonica della conoscenza, Giovanni Scoto sembra dunque voler introdurre nell'*Omelia* un ulteriore livello, superiore ad ogni creaturalità[37].

Senza volerci spingere oltre nell'elenco delle distanze dottrinali, quello che ci preme sottolineare è la paradigmaticità delle differenze riscontrate, essendo queste conseguenti al mutamento di *paradigma*, ovvero di visione del mondo, comportato dal passaggio dal paganesimo al cristianesimo. La filosofia e la teologia pagane si misurano in ragione del cosmo e di conseguenza l'orizzonte della trascendenza nel neoplatonismo resta la trascendenza dell'Uno rispetto al cosmo. Per il pensiero cristiano il problema è inverso: la trascendenza super-creazionale di Dio è un principio assodato, l'orizzonte e il fondamento sono invece definiti dalla relazione tra la natura divina increata e la natura umana creata, la quale assomma in sé il cosmo, trovando il suo nodo centrale nell'entrata di Dio nella creazione, con l'incarnazione, finalizzata a che l'uomo trascenda la creazione in Dio deificandosi.

Tornando al problema storiografico eriugeniano, vogliamo richiamare in ultima battuta la lettura di Claudio Leonardi, che in modo piuttosto singolare si discosta dall'egemonia neoplatonizzante, anzi ne è antitetica, ma che – a nostro avviso – ha il pregio

[37] G. D'ONOFRIO, *Oltre la teologia. Per una lettura dell'«Omelia» di Giovanni Scoto Eriugena sul Prologo del Quarto Vangelo*, in «Studi medievali», 31 (1990), [pp. 285-356], p. 300.

di offrire una chiave di lettura di cui dovrà tenere conto ogni futuro tentativo di riconsiderare il caso di Giovanni Scoto in funzione della sua peculiarità dottrinale e del suo *Fortleben*: Leonardi scrive a premessa degli atti del convegno *Gli umanesimi medievali*, il cui interesse critico verteva sull'indagine del rapporto tra autori medievali e retaggio dell'antichità:

> Sarebbe grave errore credere che la tradizione medievale si presenti come un blocco intellettuale e spirituale unico. Si è formata una tradizione egemone, di derivazione origeniana, e dunque medio- e neoplatonica; e una tradizione minoritaria, di più diretta derivazione neotestamentaria, che potremmo far risalire a Ireneo di Lione (secolo III), e che è espressa più tardi da Massimo il Confessore a Bisanzio (secolo VI-VII) e da Giovanni Scoto Eriugena (secolo IX) in Occidente. Questa tradizione sembra rispondere ad una domanda del salmo 8: «Quid est homo, quod memor es eius?». (...) In questa visione si realizza il primato di Dio nell'uomo ma anche il primato dell'uomo sulla natura; se è vero che la natura rivela Dio, tanto più lo rivela l'uomo[38].

Se il compito dello storico del pensiero è la comprensione di un autore e della sua opera nell'orizzonte del tempo e della cultura in cui questi è vissuto, le somiglianze strutturali dovranno essere tenute ben distinte dall'individuazione dei motivi propulsori e traenti del suo pensiero, quali emergono dalla sua opera, analizzata nel rispetto delle sue fonti e del suo *Fortleben*, pena il fraintendimento di opera, fonti, pensiero e *Fortleben*.

[38] C. LEONARDI, *Premessa*, in *Gli umanesimi medievali*, Atti del II Congresso dell'«Internationales Mittellateinerkomitee» (Firenze, Certosa del Galluzzo, 11-15 settembre 1993), a c. di C. Leonardi, Firenze 1998, pp. VII-VIII.

CHRISTOPHE ERISMANN

UN PÉCHÉ DE NATURE

PÉCHÉ ORIGINEL ET RÉALISME DES UNIVERSAUX SELON ODON DE CAMBRAI

Pour qui s'interroge sur la particularité de la philosophie médiévale, l'une des réponses les plus évidentes est probablement, outre la pluralité des traditions et des cultures – grecque, arabe, latine, chrétienne, musulmane, juive – qui la composent, le rapport étroit entretenu avec la théologie. La plupart des philosophes médiévaux étaient également des théologiens, et cela de Boèce à Guillaume d'Ockham. Ainsi, la philosophie médiévale a été élaborée, en partie du moins, sur la base de discussions de problèmes qui dépassent ce que nous pourrions considérer comme son seul champ. Fruit du dialogue et de la controverse, elle n'a jamais été cantonnée à une délimitation rigide de son domaine de compétence. La proximité des deux disciplines et la constance du dialogue ont été la cause d'une stimulation et d'un enrichissement mutuels considérables. Il est fréquent que des théories ou des élaborations conceptuelles que l'historien considère être parmi les meilleures pages de la philosophie médiévale aient comme point de départ ou d'ancrage une question ou un débat théologique.

Les exemples de tels phénomènes ne manquent pas: il suffit de penser aux réflexions que le débat eucharistique a suscitées sur le statut de l'accident. La nécessité de comprendre et d'expliquer rationnellement le dogme chrétien a donné lieu à des constructions théoriques imbriquant théologie et philosophie. La résolution de points délicats du dogme a nécessité à de multiples reprises le recours à des thèses et des théories philosophiques. Les théories philosophiques mises en jeu proviennent souvent du domaine de l'ontologie, plus précisément encore du débat sur le

10.1484/M.NUTRIX-EB.1.101243

problème des universaux. Ainsi la question de la Trinité a été l'un des lieux de débats les plus vifs à propos des universaux, et ce dès l'époque patristique. Une solution souvent envisagée pour penser l'unité des trois personnes dans la divinité se base sur une forme de réalisme et propose de concevoir l'essence divine comme un universel partagé par les trois personnes de la Trinité. Cette solution, que Richard Cross a nommée la *generic view of Trinity*[1], la conception générique de la Trinité, défendue à l'origine notamment par Grégoire de Nysse, a fortement contribué à lier la problématique philosophique des universaux à celle, théologique, de la Trinité. Cet universel doit être immanent, faute de quoi il faudrait ajouter une quatrième entité aux trois personnes. Il doit de même être présent intégralement dans chacune des personnes pour éviter tout subordinationisme. Le choix d'une formule trinitaire entre *una essentia, tres substantiae*, ou *una substantia, tres personae*, reflète souvent une orientation ontologique: la préférence accordée à la formulation *tres substantiae* témoigne fréquemment d'une sympathie à l'égard du nominalisme ou du conceptualisme[2].

Dans le même ordre d'idées, rappelons que très souvent durant le Moyen Âge, une solution au problème des universaux n'est pas jugée ou critiquée pour elle-même, mais bien pour ses possibles conséquences théologiques, preuve d'une conscience aiguë du lien unissant les deux questions. Ainsi Anselme accusera Roscelin de ne pas pouvoir comprendre la Trinité, s'il ne peut comprendre comment les hommes sont un dans l'espèce[3]. Le

[1] Richard Cross décrit en ces termes la «generic view of God's trinitarian substance» défendue par un courant de la pensée patristique grecque; cfr. R. Cross, *On Generic and Derivation Views of God's Trinitarian Substance*, in «Scottish Journal of Theology», 56 (2003), [pp. 464-480] p. 471: «The generic view does, and the Western view does not, sanction the theory that the divine essence is correctly classified as a universal». Cfr. aussi Id., *Two Models of Trinity*, in «The Heythrop Journal», 43 (2002), pp. 275-294.

[2] Pour une illustration du résultat doctrinal de l'application d'une théorie conceptualiste ou nominaliste des universaux au cas de la Trinité, cfr. C. Erismann, *The Trinity, Universals, and Particular Substances: Philoponus and Roscelin*, in «Traditio», 53 (2008), pp. 277-305.

[3] Cfr. Anselmus Cantuariensis, *Epistola de incarnatione Verbi*, 1, PL 158, 265B, ed. F. S. Schmitt, Anselmi *Opera Omnia*, 6 voll., Rome – Edinburgh 1946-1961, II, p. 10,4-7: «Qui enim nondum intelligit quomodo plures homines in specie sint unus homo: qualiter in illa secretissima et altissima natura comprehen-

problème philosophique des universaux est aussi essentiel en christologie. La question de la réalisation complète de l'universel dans chaque individu est théologiquement importante, car elle permet de montrer que le Christ, dans l'Incarnation, a assumé l'entièreté de la nature humaine. En effet Jésus n'a pas assumé l'être d'un seul individu, mais l'être de l'espèce, de l'humanité.

Cet usage de théories philosophiques en théologie n'implique pas pour autant une indistinction des domaines. La réflexion sur les domaines de validité respectifs des thèses et des concepts a été constante. L'exemple le plus éclairant est le débat, central durant le haut Moyen Âge, de Jean Scot Érigène jusqu'au XIIe siècle, à propos de la possible application de la doctrine philosophique des catégories aristotéliciennes à Dieu, la question de la *praedicatio in divinis*. Nous sommes ici confrontés à une interrogation sur le statut et la possibilité de la théologie, mais également sur la validité et la pertinence du transfert de certains concepts de la philosophie à la théologie. Cette question témoigne surtout d'une claire prise de conscience de deux plans du savoir distincts, l'un qui concerne l'homme et le monde sensible, l'autre qui concerne Dieu. Autant les dix catégories s'avèrent un outil fondamental pour la compréhension du monde sensible, autant leur validité est sujette à caution lorsqu'il s'agit de l'entité divine. Et donc si *vera philosophia est vera religio* comme le dit un adage répandu, les instruments conceptuels de l'une et de l'autre ne sont pas identiques. On peut reconnaître la validité des catégories pour un champ d'enquête – le monde sensible – et en récuser la pertinence pour un autre – le discours théologique. À titre d'exemple d'une formulation claire de cette opinion, on peut invoquer Jean Scot Érigène qui écrit notamment: «Mais comme saint Augustin l'indique dans son livre intitulé la *Trinité*, la validité des catégories devient entièrement caduque lorsqu'on en arrive à la théologie, c'est-à-dire à l'étude de l'essence divine»[4]. La doctrine catégo-

det quomodo plures personae, quarum singula quaeque perfectus est deus, sint unus deus?».

[4] IOHANNES SCOTUS ERIUGENA, *Periphyseon*, I, PL 122, 463B, ed. É. Jeauneau, 5 voll., Turnhout 1996-2003 (CCCM, 161-165), I, p. 33,903-905: «Sed, ut ait sanctus pater Augustinus in libris de trinitate, dum ad theologiam (hoc est ad divinae essentiae investigationem) pervenitur, kategoriarum virtus omnino extinguitur».

riale n'en sera pas moins l'outil privilégié par Jean Scot pour élaborer son ontologie du monde sensible[5].

L'une des questions théologiques qui a servi d'expérience de pensée, de laboratoire conceptuel à des thèses philosophiques est celle du péché originel, plus exactement de sa transmission. Savoir comment le péché commis par Adam et Ève peut être transmis à l'ensemble des hommes est une question qui, durant le haut Moyen Âge latin, a été particulièrement discutée. Elle a été parfois résolue à l'aide d'une doctrine philosophique, le réalisme ontologique en matière d'universaux. La meilleure formulation d'une réponse à la question de la transmission du péché se fondant sur le réalisme se trouve dans un traité d'Odon de Cambrai ou de Tournai (Odo Cameracensis ou Tornacensis, 1060-1113). Celui qui fut le refondateur de l'Abbaye de Saint Martin de Tournai a consacré un court traité au péché originel, dont la solution a été préparée par le *De conceptu virginali et de originali peccato* d'Anselme de Canterbury[6]. La version de cette solution proposée par Odon est cependant plus explicite et repose sur une théorie des universaux plus expressément exprimée que celle d'Anselme, même si les deux sont doctrinalement très proches[7]. Les formules

[5] Cfr. C. ERISMANN, *The Logic of Being. Eriugena's Dialectical Ontology*, in «Vivarium», 45 (2007), pp. 203-218.

[6] Ces deux théories ont été analysées dans: O. LOTTIN, *Psychologie et morale aux XIIe et XIIIe siècles*, 6 voll., Abbaye du Mont César, Louvain 1954, IV, pp. 13-23; H. RONDET, *Le péché originel dans la tradition patristique et théologique*, Fayard, Paris 1967, pp. 174-189 ('Saint Anselme et ses disciples'); J. GROSS, *Entwicklungsgeschichte des Erbsündendogmas im Zeitalter der Scholastik (12.-15. Jahrhundert)*, München – Basel 1960, pp. 14-45 ('Anselm von Canterbury und sein Kreis'); J. N. ESPENBERGER, *Die Elemente der Erbsünde nach Augustin und der Frühscholastik*, Mainz, 1905, pp. 59-85 ('Die anselmische Gruppe'); R. MARTIN, *La question du péché originel dans s. Anselme*, in «Revue des sciences philosophiques et théologiques», 5 (1911), pp. 735-749; F. BLACHÈRE, *Le péché originel d'après Saint Anselme*, in «Revue augustinienne», 6 (1905), pp. 241-255. Plus particulièrement consacrés à Odon: T. GREGORY, *La dottrina del peccato originale e il realismo platonico: Oddone di Tournai*, in «Studi Storici (Istituto Storico Italiano per il Medio Evo)», 26-27 (1958), pp. 31-51; I. M. RESNICK, *Odo of Tournai's* De peccato originali *and the Problem of Original Sin*, in «Medieval Philosophy and Theology», 1 (1991), pp. 18-38; P. KING, *Damaged Goods: Human Nature and Original Sin*, in «Faith and Philosophy», 24 (2007), pp. 247-267.

[7] Nous avons proposé une reconstruction de cette théorie des universaux dans C. ERISMANN, *Immanent Realism. A Reconstruction of an Early Medieval Solution to the Problem of Universals*, in «Documenti e studi sulla tradizione filosofica medievale», 18 (2007), pp. 211-229; pour une analyse détaillée des deux théories, voir les chapitres que nous consacrons à Anselme et Odon dans *L'homme commun*.

d'Odon sont plus tranchées, plus assumées aussi. Sa théorie des universaux étant plus explicite, il est plus aisé chez Odon de voir en quoi elle sous-tend sa solution au problème de la transmission du péché originel.

1. *Le cas du péché originel et la solution d'Odon de Cambrai*

La question du péché originel fournit une expérience de pensée intéressante pour un auteur réfléchissant sur le rapport entre espèce et individus et sur le statut ontologique de l'espèce. Le cas du péché originel permet en effet de raisonner sur l'espèce humaine en ne prenant en compte qu'un ou deux individus, à savoir Adam et Ève, et non une multitude innombrable. Le donné même du problème postule le cas où, comme hommes, n'existaient qu'Adam et Ève. Ne considérant qu'Adam, on peut réfléchir sur l'universel homme comme s'il s'agissait d'une espèce monadique, c'est-à-dire d'une espèce à un seul individu (le phénix est l'exemple canonique de ce type d'espèce). Au travers de la question de la relation de deux individus à leur espèce, c'est tout le problème des universaux qui émerge et qui, dans le cas d'Odon, affleure régulièrement à la surface du texte. Cependant, le point de départ de la discussion et les termes du problème sont théologiques.

Le problème théologique. Le problème traditionnel du péché est de savoir comment tous les hommes ont pu pécher en Adam, ou, pour le formuler autrement, comment les générations ultérieures

La genèse du réalisme ontologique durant le haut Moyen Âge latin, Paris 2011. Cfr. aussi: E. BERTOLA, *Odone di Tournai (o di Cambrai) ed il problema degli universali*, in «Rivista di filosofia neo-scolastica», 69 (1977), pp. 20-35; A. THOMPSON, *The Debate on Universals before Peter Abelard*, in «Journal of the History of Philosophy», 33 (1995), pp. 409-430; E.-H. KLUGE, *Roscelin and the Medieval Problem of Universals*, in «Journal of the History of Philosophy», 14 (1976), pp. 405-414; I. M. RESNICK, *Odo of Tournai, the Phoenix, and the Problem of Universals*, in «Journal of the History of Philosophy», 35 (1997), pp. 355-374; Y. IWAKUMA, *The Realism of Anselm and his Contemporaries*, in *Anselm. Aosta, Bec and Canterbury*, edd. D. E. Luscombe – G. R. Evans, Sheffield 1996, pp. 120-135; G. D'ONOFRIO, *L'«età boeziana» della teologia*, in *Storia della teologia*, ed. G. d'Onofrio, 3 voll., Casale Monferrato 1996, II, [pp. 283-391], pp. 295-299 ('Realismo e teologia platonica: da Oddone di Tournai a Guglielmo di Champeaux'). Il convient d'ajouter les pages consacrées à Odon, curieusement appelé Odon de Tours, par P. KING, dans *Peter Abailard and the Problem of Universals*, Unpublished doctoral thesis, Princeton University 1981, pp. 124-128.

sont elles aussi pécheresses; au centre de la discussion se trouve le passage biblique de *Rm* 5, 12, qui stipule que tous les hommes ont péché en Adam («in quo omnes peccaverunt»). Le problème est donc pour les théologiens d'expliquer comme le péché d'Adam a pu se transmettre aux générations suivantes et comment il se fait qu'un être humain soit pécheur dès le premier instant de son existence.

Une réponse 'philosophique'. Pour répondre à une question théologique, Odon invoque une doctrine logico-ontologique[8]. Sa solution, proche de celle d'Anselme, repose sur l'affirmation de l'existence des universaux dans les individus et sur une conception de l'âme comme *species*, impliquant qu'existe réellement l'espèce universelle âme humaine, dont l'âme de Pierre et celle de Paul sont des individus. Il convient de présenter l'argument de la solution odonienne, puis d'en souligner les présupposés ontologiques, pour ensuite déterminer précisément quel est l'outil philosophique dont se sert Odon.

L'on peut présenter la solution avancée par Odon de la façon suivante. Au moment où le péché originel a été commis, l'espèce homme ne comptait que deux individus, Adam et Ève. Ces deux personnes coïncidaient avec l'essence commune «homme»; en effet, l'espèce n'existe que réalisée dans ses individus. Adam et Ève – les deux seules instances de l'universel – ayant péché, et puisque toute la nature commune homme était réalisée en eux, Odon peut conclure que la nature commune – en tant qu'universel – est concernée par ce péché, car nulle part (i.e. en aucun individu) la nature humaine n'est restée sauve. Ce péché, qui était à l'origine un péché personnel, devient un péché lié à la nature commune (puisque cette dernière n'existait pas en dehors de ces deux personnes): comme la nature commune, qui détermine tous les individus futurs, est atteinte, tous les hommes à venir sont impliqués dans le péché.

[8] Comme le note bien E. BERTOLA, *Odone di Tournai (o di Cambrai)* cit. (à la note préc.), p. 25, qui parle également d'une «applicazione del 'realismo' alla dottrina del peccato originale» et d'un «esempio di estensione in campo teologico di questo tema logico-metafisico: (...) in realtà egli tenta una spiegazione razionale o speculativa o 'logica' del peccato originale, applicando, si può dire fino in fondo, la soluzione 'realista' da lui data al problema degli universali».

La solution qu'Odon propose, à la suite d'Anselme, est ontologique[9]. Il n'est pas tant question de volonté ou de concupiscence que de nature, d'espèce, d'universel. La solution repose sur une équation nécessaire entre Adam et l'espèce humaine. Et cette équation n'est possible que grâce à une certaine conception du rapport individu/espèce, une certaine conception de l'universel. Le principe de la solution peut se résumer à l'affirmation suivante: quand Adam a péché, l'homme (*i. e.* l'universel) a péché («cum Adam peccavit, homo peccavit»). Ainsi un péché à l'origine personnel devient un péché de nature. La nature est atteinte par le péché d'Adam; la nature viciée par le péché est transmise telle quelle aux générations futures. Selon l'ontologie d'Odon, un individu est composé de son essence, c'est-à-dire l'être substantiel de son espèce (commun à tous les membres de l'espèce), et d'une collection d'accidents qui lui est propre et qui permet de distinguer Paul de Pierre. L'individu – Odon insiste souvent sur ce point – n'a d'autre être substantiel que son espèce[10]. Substantiellement, Pierre n'est rien d'autre qu'homme. Odon rejoint sur ce point un adage boécien: «homo vero Socratis atque Ciceronis

[9] Sur ce point comme sur la théorie des universaux – ce qui n'est guère étonnant vu le lien existant entre les deux problématiques durant le haut Moyen Âge – il est possible de lire chez Jean Scot Érigène une esquisse des théories odonienne et anselmienne. Jean Scot insiste en effet sur la création de la nature universelle de tous les hommes en Adam («omnium hominum uniuersam naturam in primo homine deus condiderit») et sur l'existence d'une unique nature commune pour tous les hommes qui était présente intégralement en Adam. Cfr. IOHANNES SCOTUS ERIUGENA, *De praedestinatione*, 16, 3, PL 122, 419B, ed. G. Madec, Turnhout 1978 (CCCM, 50), pp. 95,68 - 96,80; ed. E. Mainoldi, Firenze 2003, p. 162,6-16: «Cum itaque omnium hominum universam naturam in primo homine Deus condiderit – adhuc enim, ut ait Augustinus, ille unus omnes fuit –, quod in ipso naturaliter creatum est nullo modo potuit naturalem legem creatoris transire. Non igitur in illo peccavit quod in illo Deus creavit; 'in quo tamen omnes peccaverunt' (*Rm* 5, 12), ac per hoc in ipso omnes moriuntur, et consequenter omnes puniuntur. Proinde rectissime creditur, quemadmodum in illo Deus generalem humani generis creare voluit substantiam, ita et omnium hominum propriam substituit voluntatem. Si enim in uno communis omnium et corporalis et spiritualis naturae humanae plenitudo sit constituta, necessario ei inerat singulorum voluntas propria». La référence augustinienne est: AUGUSTINUS HIPPONENSIS, *De civitate Dei*, XIII, 14, PL 41, 386, éd. B. Dombart – A. Kalb, 2 voll., Turnhout 1955 (CCSL, 47-48), II, p. 395,3-4: «Omnes enim fuimus in illo uno, quando omnes fuimus ille unus».

[10] Cfr. ODO CAMERACENSIS (ODO SANCTI MARTINI TORNACENSIS), *De peccato originali*, PL 160, [1071-1102], II, 1078D-1079B; en partic. cfr. 1079A: «Individua vero nihil habent substantialiter plus quam species, nec aliud sunt substantialiter quam species».

tota substantia est»[11]. Un individu est donc substantiellement constitué par la commune nature humaine. Or cette dernière a été corrompue par le péché d'Adam. Un individu reçoit donc comme nature une nature viciée et hérite ainsi du péché. Le point délicat de la théorie est évidemment d'expliquer comment l'acte d'un individu peut entraîner une modification de la nature. C'est là que la théorie des universaux adoptée par Odon entre en ligne de compte. Odon soutient que l'homme, c'est-à-dire l'universel spécifique homme, a péché quand Adam a péché. Cette assertion est rendue métaphysiquement vraisemblable par l'adoption d'un réalisme de l'immanence. L'universel homme n'existe que dans ses individus. Or, au moment du péché, seuls existaient Adam et Ève; l'universel spécifique était donc intégralement réalisé en Adam et en Ève, c'est-à-dire qu'il n'était instancié que deux fois; et comme il n'y avait aucun autre individu et puisque les universaux n'ont par définition aucune existence séparée, l'universel spécifique homme n'existait nulle part ailleurs qu'en Adam et en Ève. Comme les deux seuls individus existant ont péché, Odon croit pouvoir défendre la thèse selon laquelle l'universel a péché, puisqu'il n'existait que dans ces deux entités pécheresses. Or l'universel est entièrement réalisé dans chaque individu dépendant de lui et, en vertu de l'immanentisme strict adopté par Odon, il n'existe nullement en dehors des individus. N'ayant pas d'existence séparée et ne subsistant que dans des individus pécheurs, l'universel – si l'on accepte cette formulation métaphorique – s'est retrouvé dépourvu d'un lieu de subsistance exempt du péché. N'étant intacte nulle part, la nature commune a été atteinte par le péché. Et ainsi, la nature transmise par les voies de la filiation transmettra le péché, génération après génération. Chaque nouvel individu homme qui vient au monde n'existe que par la nature homme qui lui donne sa substance; cette nature ne lui est en rien propre, c'est la même pour tous les hommes; elle lui transmet les caractéristiques de l'être spécifique, telle la rationalité, mais aussi le péché. Car Odon insiste bien sur le fait que la naissance d'un nouvel individu n'implique pas l'apparition d'une

[11] Cfr. ANICIUS MANLIUS SEVERINUS BOETHIUS, *In Isagogen Porphyrii, ed. secunda*, III, PL 64, 106B, ed. S. Brandt, Wien – Leipzig 1906 (CSEL, 48), p. 21,516-518.

nouvelle substance, mais seulement d'un nouvel ensemble de propriétés non-essentielles, puisque la substance est une et commune à tous les individus[12].

L'on voit bien les présupposés ontologiques de cette solution: le premier est qu'une entité telle que la nature humaine – *i. e.* un universel spécifique – existe réellement et est commune à plusieurs individus spatio-temporellement distincts. L'idée même d'un péché de nature (opposé au péché personnel) revient à attribuer une réalité ontologique à la nature commune, tant elle repose sur la distinction prisée par les réalistes entre ce qui est commun (l'essence) et ce qui est propre à chaque individu. C'est d'ailleurs cette distinction entre la nature commune et la personne qui permettra de fonder la distinction entre péché de nature et péché de personne. L'on peut étayer le dossier du lien entre l'acceptation des entités universelles et le choix d'une solution reposant sur le péché de nature par un contre-exemple. Pierre Abélard, qui est un opposant farouche à l'existence réelle des universaux, sera cohérent sur ce point. Opposé aux universaux et partisan du particularisme ontologique, il rejettera l'idée d'un péché de nature pour affirmer que le péché ne peut être que personnel (c'est-à-dire propre à chaque individu).

Le deuxième présupposé ontologique est la réalisation complète de la nature spécifique en chaque individu. L'universel n'a pas d'existence séparée, mais existe intégralement réalisé ou instancié dans chaque individu. C'est ce type d'existence immanente de l'universel qui rend possible la solution odonienne. C'est parce que la nature humaine était intégralement présente en Adam et Ève et nulle part ailleurs qu'elle pu être affectée par leur péché. Si Odon avait été partisan d'une théorie que l'on qualifie de platonicienne, postulant des universaux séparés, les actions des individus n'auraient en rien pu atteindre la perfection de l'universel. Les individus n'auraient pu qu'«aggraver leur cas» en augmentant leur imperfection et en s'éloignant du modèle que constitue l'universel.

Ces deux présupposés – l'existence réelle des universaux et leur stricte immanence dans les particuliers – permettent d'iden-

[12] Cfr. ODO CAMERACENSIS, *ibid.*, III, 1091CD.

tifier l'outil philosophique dont se sert Odon pour répondre au problème théologique de la transmission du péché originel.

L'outil philosophique. La doctrine philosophique sur laquelle se fonde l'explication odonienne de la transmission du péché originel est une forme particulière de réalisme des universaux que nous pouvons appeler réalisme de l'immanence. Il convient de définir ces trois notions de réalisme, d'immanence et d'universaux.

Par 'réalisme', nous entendons une doctrine universaliste et essentialiste, c'est-à-dire une position postulant des entités universelles réelles et non les seuls individus, comme le prône le particularisme ontologique. Cette doctrine a été conçue dans le cadre défini par Aristote dans les *Catégories* et par Porphyre dans l'*Isagoge,* selon lequel chaque individu appartient de façon non-problématique à une espèce et à des genres identifiables. Un individu est nécessairement un individu d'une espèce donnée. L'universel est pensé comme existant réellement dans les individus qui l'instancient; il n'a pas d'existence séparée, il est en ce sens immanent. Son existence n'en est pas moins réelle que celle des individus qui l'instancient. La notion d'immanence exprime donc le mode d'être des universaux. Fidèle à l'optique aristotélicienne des *Catégories*, et donc en opposition à la thèse platonicienne de la séparation, Odon défend l'existence réelle des universaux dans les individus. Un universel n'existe que dans les individus qui l'instancient. Ce point est capital pour l'argumentation odonienne.

L'universel est envisagé selon sa caractéristique de la réalisabilité multiple. Un universel est une entité qui existe de façon identique dans plusieurs particuliers. Dans la compréhension qu'Odon a du problème – il est en cela fidèle à Anselme[13] –,

[13] C'est le sens de la définition d'une page célèbre du *Monologion*; cfr. ANSELMUS CANTUARIENSIS, *Monologion*, 27, PL 158, 180BC, ed. Schmitt cit. (à la note 3), I, p. 45,6-12: «Nempe cum omnis substantia tractetur aut esse universalis, *quae pluribus substantiis essentialiter communis est, ut hominem esse commune est singulis hominibus*; aut esse individua, *quae universalem essentiam communem habet cum aliis, quemadmodum singuli homines commune habent cum singulis, ut homines sint*: quomodo aliquis summam naturam in aliarum substantiarum tractatu contineri intelligit, quae nec in plures substantias se dividit, nec cum alia aliqua per essentialem communionem se colligit?» [(notre traduction): «Toute substance, on le sait, est traitée comme universelle, *commune essentiellement à plusieurs substances – être homme*

l'universel est envisagé d'un point de vue métaphysique bien plus que logique. Il est pensé comme une entité qui est multiplement réalisable. On définit l'universel comme une entité qui peut être multiplement instanciée, *esse in multis*, et non sous l'aspect de sa prédicabilité, *dici de multis*. Axer le problème sur celui de la réalisabilité multiple de l'universel revient à l'envisager comme un *koinón* et non comme un *kathólou*.

L'universel est réalisé intégralement et simultanément dans chacune de ses subdivisions et non selon une variation de degrés. La différence entre deux individus d'une même espèce résulte non d'une différence essentielle – car l'essence est commune –, mais du fait que chaque individu possède un faisceau d'accidents qui est unique. Dans ce système, l'individu n'a pas d'autre être substantiel que celui communiqué par son espèce. L'espèce exprime tout l'être de son individu; la part strictement individuelle de l'individu provient des accidents, en dernier lieu des accidents spatio-temporels.

2. *Un concept fondamental: le péché de nature*

La solution s'articule sur la distinction entre péché personnel et péché de nature. Adam a commis un péché personnel, mais c'est un péché de nature qui atteint les générations suivantes, car le péché personnel d'Adam et Ève a entraîné une modification de la nature humaine; et le péché personnel, puisqu'il a été commis par tous les individus de l'espèce homme existants, est devenu un péché de nature. La distinction entre péché de nature et péché de personne repose évidemment sur la distinction entre nature et personne. Cette distinction est l'héritière de celle établie par les Pères Cappadociens, Grégoire de Nysse avant tout, entre l'*ousia*

est commun à tous les hommes pris individuellement – ou comme individuelle, *ayant en commun avec d'autres une essence universelle* – tous les hommes pris individuellement ont *en commun d'être hommes*. Comment reconnaître alors que la nature suréminente soit contenue dans le traité des autres substances, elle qui ne se divise pas en plusieurs substances, ni ne se rassemble avec d'autres par une *communion essentielle*?»]. Pour une analyse de la portée de ce texte, cfr. C. ERISMANN, *Un autre aristotélisme? La problématique métaphysique durant le haut Moyen Âge latin. À propos d'Anselme*, Monologion *27*, in «Quaestio. Annuario di storia della metafisica», 5 (2005), pp. 143-160.

(comprise comme la nature ou essence commune) et l'hypostase (c'est-à-dire l'individu). La distinction entre nature et personne est cependant moins générale dans la mesure où «personne» ne désigne que les entités rationnelles, alors qu'«hypostase» peut s'appliquer aux individus de n'importe quelle espèce. Grégoire de Nysse peut ainsi nommer «hypostase» ce cheval-ci. Dans le cas d'*ousia*-hypostase, comme dans celui de nature-personne, ces distinctions recouvrent celle entre une entité commune à plusieurs individus (l'*ousia* ou la nature) et une réalité individuelle non-communicable et non-prédicable (l'hypostase ou la personne).

L'idée même de péché de nature implique, nous l'avons souligné, l'octroi d'une certaine réalité ontologique à ces entités universelles que sont les natures communes. Odon, dans un paragraphe qui expose l'argument central de sa solution, témoigne d'une conception forte des natures communes:

> *Ce en quoi le péché naturel diffère du péché personnel.* On distingue en effet deux sortes de péché, [le péché] personnel et [le péché] naturel. Le péché naturel est celui avec lequel nous naissons et que nous traînons depuis Adam, en qui nous avons tous péché. Mon âme était en effet en lui, non selon la personne, mais selon l'espèce (*specie, non persona*), non par nature individuelle, mais par nature commune (*non individua, sed communi natura*); et la nature commune de toute âme humaine était en Adam souillée par le péché. C'est pourquoi toute âme humaine est coupable par sa nature, bien qu'elle ne le soit pas selon sa personne. Ainsi, le péché par lequel nous avons péché en Adam m'est naturel, alors qu'il est personnel pour Adam. Il est plus grave en Adam, plus léger en moi. J'ai péché en lui non pas moi qui suis, mais ce que je suis (*in eo non qui sum, sed quod sum*). J'ai péché en lui, non pas moi, mais ce que je suis (*non ego, sed hoc quod sum ego*). J'ai péché en tant qu'homme, pas en tant qu'Odon. J'ai péché par ma substance, non par ma personne; et parce que la substance n'existe que dans la personne, le péché de la substance est aussi un péché de la personne, mais ce n'est pas un péché personnel. Car un péché personnel est [un péché commis par] moi qui suis, non pas [par] ce que je suis, [un péché] par lequel je pèche, moi Odon, non pas en tant qu'homme, [un péché] par lequel je pèche comme personne, non comme nature. Mais puisque la personne ne peut exister sans la na-

ture, le péché de la personne est aussi un péché de la nature, mais pas un péché naturel[14].

Élaborant la distinction, également présente chez Anselme, entre péché personnel et péché naturel, Odon invoque les deux entités fondamentales de son ontologie: les individus (ou personnes dans le cas de l'espèce humaine, dont la rationalité est une différence constituante) et les natures communes (*i. e.* des universaux). Tout le texte est sous-tendu par l'opposition entre l'individu («Odo», «ego», «qui sum», «persona») et l'universel («homo», «natura communis», «quod sum», «species»). Nous avons là une occurrence nette du postulat de base du réalisme ontologique altomédiéval: la présence dans chaque individu d'une part commune (l'universel spécifique) et d'une part propre non-substantielle. Odon distingue, dans le même individu, ce qu'il est en tant que personne de ce qu'il est en tant que membre d'une espèce, en tant qu'instanciation d'un universel spécifique. Dans d'autres passages, Odon exprime cette dualité – le pivot doctrinal de toute formulation du réalisme ontologique altomédiéval – par le couple d'expressions: *quod est* (ce que les individus d'une même espèce ont en commun: l'unique substance spécifique) et *quod habet* (ce par quoi un individu diffère des autres, à savoir le faisceau d'accidents qui lui est propre). Ainsi, il peut dire des différents individus d'une même espèce: «per hoc quod habent diversa sunt, per hoc quod sunt, unum sunt»[15]. Si l'existence des individus est évidente, le poids ontologique qu'Odon confère à la nature commune est

[14] ODO CAMERACENSIS, *ibid.*, II, 1085AC (notre traduction): «*Quid distat naturale peccatum et personale.* Dicitur enim duobus modis peccatum, personale et naturale. Et naturale est cum quo nascimur, et quod ab Adam trahimus in quo omnes peccavimus, In ipso enim erat anima mea, specie, non persona, non individua, sed communi natura. Nam omnis humanae animae natura communis erat in Adam obnoxia peccato. Et ideo omnis humana anima culpabilis est secundum suam naturam, etsi non secundum suam personam. Ita peccatum quo peccavimus in Adam, mihi quidem naturale est, in Adam vero personale. In Adam gravius, levius in me; nam peccavi in eo non qui sum, sed quod sum. Peccavi in eo non ego, sed hoc quod sum ego. Peccavi homo, sed non Odo. Peccavi substantia, non persona; et quia substantia non est nisi in persona, peccatum substantiae est etiam personae, sed non personale. Peccatum vero personale est quod facio ego qui sum, non hoc quod sum, quo pecco Odo, non homo, quo pecco persona, non natura; sed quia *persona non est sine natura*, peccatum personae est etiam naturae, sed non naturale».

[15] *Ibid.*, 1083A.

élevé. D'une part, Odon affirme une thèse réaliste forte: «persona non est sine natura»; présente également chez Anselme[16], elle témoigne de la dépendance ontologique de l'individu face à son universel spécifique. Pour être plus précis, il conviendrait de parler d'interdépendance ontologique, car si l'individu n'est rien sans son universel, comme Odon est immanentiste, l'universel a besoin d'être instancié par ses individus pour exister[17].

Un argument théologique est aussi à avancer: si la nature permet de transmettre le péché de façon suffisamment efficace pour que l'on puisse dire qu'Odon a péché, sa réalité est certaine. Ce texte permet surtout de souligner l'intrication des problématiques du péché et des universaux. Car, comme le constate fort justement Tullio Gregory: «La trasmissione del peccato originale trova così il suo fondamento nella realtà oggettiva degli universali»[18]. Le réalisme ontologique permet à Odon d'impliquer la nature dans le péché personnel: «Si peccavit Adam, peccavit homo et in peccato personae culpabilis factus est homo communis natura, et qualem Adam fecit naturam humanam in se, talem posteris enim tradidit post se»[19]. La faute de la personne – *i. e.* la faute commise par tous les individus existant à un moment donné – entraîne la faute de la nature:

> *Que la culpabilité de la personne implique celle de la nature.* Voici que chacune des deux personnes a péché à la suggestion du serpent; je dis chacune des deux, leur substance n'étant pas encore ailleurs qu'en elles-mêmes, celle-ci n'étant pas encore ailleurs que là [en elles]. Si chaque personne a vraiment péché, elle n'a pas péché sans sa substance. La substance des personnes est donc souillée par le péché, et le péché infecte la substance parce qu'elle n'est nulle part hors des personnes pécheresses. Or la substance des deux personnes est une et la même, elle est leur substance commune et spécifique. C'est donc dans les personnes pécheresses que la nature spécifique,

[16] Cfr. ANSELMUS CANTUARIENSIS, *De conceptu virginali et de originali peccato*, 23, PL 158, 457A, ed. Schmitt cit. (à la note 3), II, p. 165,20.

[17] Sur la question de l'importance de l'interdépendance ontologique dans la version du réalisme défendue par Odon, cfr. C. ERISMANN, *Immanent Realism. A Reconstruction of an Early Medieval Solution to the Problem of Universals*, in «Documenti e studi sulla tradizione filosofica medievale», 18 (2007), pp. 211-229.

[18] GREGORY, *La dottrina del peccato originale* cit. (à la note 6), p. 47.

[19] ODO CAMERACENSIS, *ibid.*, III, 1088CD (cfr. aussi *infra*, à la note 24).

> qui ne se trouve nulle part en dehors d'elles, est infectée par le péché. Dans l'âme d'Adam et dans l'âme d'Eve, lesquelles ont péché personnellement, toute la nature de l'âme humaine a été infectée, elle qui est la substance commune et spécifique de toutes les deux. En effet, celle-ci n'existait pas en dehors d'elles. Car si elle avait déjà été distribuée en d'autres personnes, elle n'aurait pas été infectée toute entière à cause d'elles seules. Et si celles-ci avaient péché, peut-être le péché n'aurait-il pas été commis par d'autres [âmes], dans lesquelles la nature de l'âme humaine serait restée intacte. Mais à présent, où l'âme humaine pourrait-elle être pure, elle qui est pécheresse partout?[20]

Un premier constat lexicographique s'impose d'emblée. Ce passage confirme que *substantia* a chez Odon de Cambrai le sens de substance seconde, d'essence spécifique. C'est ainsi qu'elle peut être dite ici à deux reprises *communis* et *specialis*. Odon n'utilise jamais *substantia* pour désigner le *hoc aliquid*, l'individu; il lui préfère toujours *individuum* ou *persona*. Ce texte, comme l'ensemble de la solution odonienne, repose sur un immanentisme strict. L'universel – la nature commune –, n'existe pas en dehors de ses instanciations: quand bien même il n'y a que deux personnes, l'universel n'existe pas en dehors de ces deux instanciations. Odon n'admet aucune séparation de l'universel. L'unicité de la substance pour les différents individus d'une même espèce apparaît nettement. La substance dans le sens odonien d'essence est une et une seule pour tous les individus de l'espèce. Dans le cas qui nous intéresse ici, il y a deux individus, la substance est une: «una et eadem est utriusque personae».

[20] *Ibid.*, II, 1081D-1082A (notre traduction): «*Quod in culpa personae est culpa naturae.* Ecce peccavit utraque persona suggestione serpentis, peccavit, inquam, utraque necdum substantiam suam habentibus alibi quam in se, quae nondum erat alibi quam ibi. Si vero persona peccavit, sine sua substantia non peccavit. Est ergo personae substantia peccato vitiata, et inficit peccatum substantiam, quae nusquam est extra peccatricem personam. Substantia vero *una et eadem est utriusque personae* communis ipsis et specialis. In peccatricibus ergo personis est infecta peccato natura specialis, quae non est alibi quam in ipsis. In anima Adam ergo et in anima Evae, quae personaliter peccaverunt, infecta est peccato tota natura humanae animae; quae communis substantia est, est specialis utriusque. Extra has enim nondum est eam esse. Si enim fuisset in aliis divisa, pro ipsis solis non inficeretur tota. Quia si peccassent istae, forsitan non peccassent aliae, in quibus esset salva humanae animae natura. Nunc autem ubi poterat anima humana munda esse quae peccatrix erat ubique?».

Odon doit alors préciser que l'espèce n'a pas péché par elle-même mais par la personne («humana natura per se non peccat, sed per personam»)[21]. En effet, stipule Odon, il ne faut pas attribuer à l'universel ce qui ne convient qu'aux seules personnes. Les universaux sont immuables, et la mutabilité des individus n'atteint pas le degré de l'universel. L'immanentisme odonien lui permet de soutenir que l'espèce n'a pas péché par soi, mais par les individus seuls: «Sed nec nos dicimus ipsam speciem per se, sed in solis personis peccasse». Mais pour que sa solution puisse s'articuler, Odon est obligé de nuancer l'immutabilité des universaux et d'admettre qu'une propriété des individus peut concerner en second lieu un universel si l'ensemble des individus instanciant cet universel commettent la même action ou subissent la même atteinte[22]. C'est le prix doctrinal à payer pour que la nature humaine ait pu être corrompue par le péché de ses deux uniques individus de l'époque. Ainsi, et ainsi seulement, le péché d'Adam, à l'origine un péché de personne, peut, étant donné le statut monadique de l'espèce humaine à l'époque d'Adam qui implique que l'ensemble de la nature était en lui, entraîner la nature. Odon peut ainsi défendre un passage du péché de cet individu donné,

[21] Cfr. *ibid.*, 1082AC: «*Quomodo humana natura per se non peccat, sed per personam.* Sed forte dicet aliquis: Si natura communis, humana scilicet anima peccavit in personis, quis potest negare speciem peccasse? Sed absurdum est hoc dicere de ipsa specie, et ipsis universalibus ascribere quod solis convenit personis. Praeterea universalia semper sunt quod sunt, et, utcunque varientur individua, consistunt immutabiliter universalia, et quamvis de ipsis vere dicatur mutabilitas individuorum, non est tamen in ipsis. *Sed nec nos dicimus ipsam speciem per se, sed in solis personis peccasse.* Et quamvis de universalibus dicantur individuorum accidentia, non tamen sunt in universalibus ipsis, hoc quod sunt, sed loco ab individuis secundo; nam sicut diversae sunt ab individuis species, similiter et eorum proprietates, ut hominis ea proprietas quod species est, quod universale, quod commune, quod essentia incommutabilis in se quod de pluribus dicitur, et caetera quibus universalia discernuntur ab individuis, non convenit ipsis individuis. Similiter quod Petrus individuum est, persona, quod de nullo dicitur, quod mutabilis est, et caetera quibus individua disjunguntur ab universalibus, ipsis non [le *non* du ms. Douai est préféré au *tamen* de Migne] conveniunt universalibus».

[22] Le problème philosophique ne réside pas tant dans le passage des individus à l'espèce en disant que l'espèce a été infectée par le péché, ce qui est vrai quand cela est dit des deux premiers hommes, mais dans le mouvement de retour de l'espèce aux individus sous la forme de l'affirmation «chaque homme est désormais atteint par le péché». Odon serait-il prêt à défendre que si Adam et Eve avaient été musiciens, alors homme aurait été musicien, donc tous les hommes seraient musiciens?

Adam, à l'universel, envisagé, avec une forte réminiscence de Porphyre[23], sous les traits de l'*homo specialis* ou de l'*homo communis*:

> Et si Adam a péché, l'homme a péché, parce que si cet homme lui-même a péché, la nature humaine qui est homme a péché. En effet, la nature humaine était alors entièrement en lui, et l'homme spécifique n'était nulle part ailleurs (*nec usquam erat alibi specialis homo*). Puisque en effet une personne a péché, à savoir cet homme-ci, toute la nature a péché, à savoir l'homme commun (*peccavit tota natura, scilicet communis homo*). Et dans le péché de la personne, l'homme de la nature commune a été rendu coupable (*culpabilis factus est homo communis naturae*). Et telle Adam a fait la nature en lui-même, telle il l'a transmise à ceux qui viennent après lui[24].

La solution odonienne au problème du péché originel et de sa transmission s'articule sur le passage du particulier à l'universel, de l'individu à l'espèce, d'un homme particulier à l'homme général. Ainsi le péché qui a été commis par un individu («Adam», «ipse homo», «persona») implique l'universel spécifique («homo», «humana natura», «specialis homo», «tota natura», «communis homo», «homo communis naturae»), car Odon semble mettre sur le même plan ontologique l'individu donné dont il est question ici et l'universel homme que des expressions telles que «l'homme commun» ou «l'homme spécifique» tendent à réifier. Le processus naturel de la génération transmettra ensuite cette nature humaine corrompue qui formera l'être substantiel de tous les hommes à venir, qui de ce fait seront atteints par le péché dès la première seconde de leur existence.

[23] Cfr. PORPHYRIUS TYRIUS, *Isagoge*, éd. A. Busse, Berlin 1887 (CAG IV, 1), p. 6,16-23.

[24] ODO CAMERACENSIS, *ibid.*, III, 1088CD (notre traduction): «Et si peccavit Adam, peccavit homo; quia si peccavit ipse homo, peccavit humana natura, quae est homo. Sed humana natura tota tunc erat in ipso, nec usquam erat alibi specialis homo. Cum ergo peccavit persona, scilicet ipse homo, peccavit tota natura, scilicet communis homo. Et in peccato personae, culpabilis factus est homo communis naturae. Et qualem Adam fecit humanam naturam in se, talem posteris eam tradidit post se».

3. *Conclusion*

Il est possible de récapituler l'argumentation d'Odon en soulignant les thèses ontologiques sous-jacentes à son raisonnement théologique.

Réponse au problème du péché originel	*Thèses ontologiques sous-jacentes*
1. Au moment du péché originel, toute la nature humaine était en Adam et en Ève.	a) Universalisme. Existence réelle des universaux génériques et spécifiques, dans ce cas, existence réelle de l'universel spécifique homme. b) Immanentisme strict. L'universel n'existe que dans les individus qui l'instancient (Adam et Ève dans ce cas précis).
2. Adam et Ève ont péché, donc tous les individus existants ont péché.	[*donné théologique*]
3. Si tous les individus ont péché, alors la nature a péché.	[*Il est difficile à Odon de fonder philosophiquement cet argument problématique. Il s'appuie cependant sur:*] a) Immanentisme (l'universel n'existe que dans les individus qui l'instancient). b) Réalisation complète de l'universel dans chacune de ses instances (l'universel homme est intégralement réalisé en chaque individu de l'espèce, ici il est intégralement réalisé en Adam et l'est aussi en Ève).
4. Le péché de nature entraîne une modification de la na-	a) Existence réelle des universaux spécifiques qui sont

ture, à savoir la perte d'une de ses caractéristiques, la justice originaire.	composés du genre et des différences spécifiques (analogiquement la perte de la justice originaire s'apparente à la perte d'une différence spécifique).
5. Si la nature est viciée, quiconque existera par cette nature (i.e. n'importe quel homme) héritera du péché.	a) Essentialisme. Un individu n'a d'autre essence que celle donnée par son universel spécifique (Pierre n'est rien de plus qu'homme). b) Dépendance ontologique. Un individu n'existe que s'il réalise son universel spécifique (*persona non est sine natura*).

Odon offre un bel exemple d'application d'une doctrine philosophique à un problème strictement théologique. Je rejoins pleinement le constat d'Ermenegildo Bertola qui écrit à propos d'Odon: «Siamo dunque di fronte ad una soluzione di un problema della logica che viene usata come strumento per la spiegazione ed il chiarimento, perciò per la interpretazione di una verità di fede»[25]. Mais la relation n'est pas à sens unique. Cette démarche a permis à Odon d'avancer une réponse cohérente à la question du péché originel, mais lui a également fourni le cadre pour affiner et préciser sa version du réalisme ontologique. La doctrine philosophique, plus qu'un simple outil, a bénéficié de son utilisation dans un contexte ontologique précis, celui d'une espèce ne comportant que deux individus. Odon, avec son traité sur le péché originel, délivre ce qui est l'une des formulations les plus abouties et thématisées du réalisme ontologique dans sa version altomédiévale. Anselme est en effet moins explicite quant à son engagement réaliste, et la doctrine de Guillaume de Champeaux appelée 'réalisme' de l'essence matérielle ne peut se lire dans les mots propres de son auteur, mais est uniquement transmise par les témoignages plus ou moins bienveillants de ses adversaires.

[25] BERTOLA, *Odone di Tournai* cit. (à la note 7), p. 25.

CONSTANT J. MEWS

PHILOSOPHY, COMMUNITIES OF LEARNING AND THEOLOGICAL DISSENT IN THE TWELFTH CENTURY

The second decade of the twelfth century witnessed the emergence of three communities of great significance for medieval intellectual and religious life: the cathedral school of Notre-Dame, the abbey of Saint-Victor, and the abbey of Clairvaux. At Easter 1111 (as I will argue) William of Champeaux resigned his position at Notre-Dame to establish a community of Augustinian canons at the disused chapel of Saint-Victor, just outside the Ile-de-la-cité. Peter Abelard, who returned to Paris in that year after a period of absence from France, challenged William's understanding of universals during the course of lectures on rhetoric. Abelard considered that the only reason William had become a canon regular was to help him become a bishop, as indeed happened in late July 1113, when he become bishop of Châlons-sur-Marne. By 1115 William had completely turned away from the academic community in Paris through befriending and ordaining a twenty-five year old monk, named Bernard, as abbot of Clairvaux. At Clairvaux, monks wanted to learn about love, not dialectic. Even though he had helped found Saint-Victor, William eventually became a monk at Clairvaux, eight days before his death on 18 January 1121[1]. Two other important events occurred

[1] Cfr. Rupertus Tuitiensis, *De vita apostolica dialogorum libri quinque*, V, 16, PL 170, 659C-660C; Simeon Dunelmensis, *Historia regum*, in Id., *Opera omnia*, ed. T. Arnold, 2 voll., London 1882-1885 (Rolls Series 75), II, pp. 259-260: «Gwillelmus de Campellis, Catalaunensis episcopus, viii. diebus ante exitum, suscepto habitu monachico, vita decedit xv. Kal. Februarii». There has been confusion about the year of William's death, because it was given as 1121 *vetus stylus*

10.1484/M.NUTRIX-EB.1.101244

in 1115. A young scholar from Saxony, by the name of Hugh, arrived at Saint-Victor and would quickly replace William as its leading teacher. Abelard, now ensconced at Notre-Dame, became involved in a more intimate form of intellectual community through his instruction of a niece of a cathedral canon, by the name of Heloise.

These events and their consequences are well known through the testimony of Abelard in the *Historia calamitatum*[2]. They are often interpreted in terms of a clash between individuals, culminating in the encounter between Abelard and Bernard at the Council of Sens in 1141. Alternatively, their confrontation is interpreted as between two great theological traditions, one monastic, the other scholastic[3]. We must be careful, however, about such rhetorical classifications. Riccardo Quinto has reminded us that the notion of *scolastica* could easily be used by some writers in a pejorative sense to describe teachers presumed to be unspiritual[4]. Rather than classify medieval thought as either scholastic or monastic, I want to suggest that in the decade 1110-1120 we see a multipli-

by chroniclers. On this and other issues relating to William, see my study, Logica *in the Service of Philosophy: William of Champeaux and his Influence*, in *Schrift, Schreiber, Schenker. Studien zur Abtei Sankt Viktor zu Paris und zu den Viktorinern*, ed. R. Berndt, Berlin 2005 (Corpus Victorinum. Instrumenta, 1) [pp. 77-117], p. 111; and *William of Champeaux, the Foundation of St-Victor (Easter, 1111) and the Evolution of Abelard's Early Career*, in *Arts du langage et théologie aux confins des* XI*e et* XII*e siècle*, éd. par I. Rosier-Catach, Turnhout 2011, pp. 83-104.

[2] The text of the *Historia calamitatum*, ed. J. Monfrin, Paris 1957, is substantially unaltered in an edition that accompanies the translation of JEAN DE MEUN, *La vie et les epistres Pierres Abaelart et Heloys sa fame*, ed. E. Hicks, Paris 1991, and in a richly annotated volume, with accompanying Italian translation, *Epistolario di Abelardo ed Eloise*, ed. I. Pagani, with reflections on the transmission of its text by G. Orlandi, Torino 2004 (Classici Latini. Autori della tarda antichità, del Medioevo e dell'Umanesimo).

[3] J. LECLERCQ first introduced the notion of monastic theology in relation to St. Bernard in *Saint Bernard et la théologie monastique au* XII*e siècle*, in *Saint Bernard théologien. Actes du Congrès de Dijion (15-19 septembre 1953)*, «Analecta Sacri Ordinis Cisterciensis», 9 (1953), pp. 7-23, but diffused it more widely in relation to monastic culture as a whole in *L'Amour des lettres et le désir de Dieu*, Paris 1957 [1990] (Engl. tr. by C. Misrahi: *The Love of Learning and the Desire for God: A Study of Monastic Culture*, New York 1961 [1982]). For an incisive review of the history of the concept, see F. GASTALDELLI, *Teologia monastica, Teologia scolastica e lectio divina*, in «Analecta Cisterciensia», 46 (1990), pp. 25-63.

[4] R. QUINTO, *Scholastica. Storia di un concetto*, Padova 2001 (Studia Mediaevalia Patavina), reprinting studies that originally appeared in «Medioevo», in 1991, 1993, and 1996.

cation of what I call 'communities of learning', some structured around a school, others around a religious community. Rather than speak about a centre of learning, I prefer to speak of an evolving cluster of communities of learning, bound together by ideals of *amicitia*, each with its own preferred authors and each with its own interpretation of *philosophia*. The historian of scholasticism needs to be aware of the political pressures, as much as of the intellectual influences, that shape a system of thought within a society shaped by a religious ethos. In *The Implications of Literacy*, Brian Stock developed the notion of a textual community, as a community held together by its interpretation of a particular text, whether it be the writings of Ovid or the Bible[5]. I would extend this notion by considering the particular cluster of texts that provided an interpretative framework for a range of different communities of learning, competing with each other in their interpretation of both philosophy and theology.

1. *William of Champeaux (d. 1122) and Peter Abelard (1079-1142)*

1.1. In recent years there has been a renewal of interest in William of Champeaux. His *Introductiones dialecticae* have been edited by Yukio Iwakuma[6]. Karin Margareta Fredborg has argued for his authorship of important commentaries on Cicero's *De inventione* and the *Rhetorica ad Herennium*, now being edited by John O. Ward and Juanita Ruys[7]. Irène Rosier-Catach identified Wil-

[5] B. STOCK, *The Implications of Literacy: Written Language and Models of Interpretation in the Eleventh and Twelfth Centuries*, Princeton 1983.

[6] Y. IWAKUMA, Introductiones dialecticae *secundum Wilgelmum and secundum G. Paganellum*, in «Cahiers de l'Institut du Moyen Âge Grec et Latin», 63 (1993), pp. 45-114; see also his studies: *Pierre Abélard et Guillaume de Champeaux dans les premières années du XIIe siècle: une étude preliminaire*, in *Langage, sciences, philosophie au XIIe siècle*, ed. J. Biard, Paris 1999, pp. 93-123; *William of Champeaux and the* Introductiones, in *Aristotle's* Perihermeneias *in the Latin Middle Ages: Essays on the Commentary Tradition*, ed. H. A. G. Braakhuis – C. H. Kneepkens, Groningen – Haren 2003, pp. 1-30; *William of Champeaux on Aristotle's Categories*, in *La tradition médiévale des Categories (XIIe-XIVe siècles): Actes du XIIIe symposium européen de logique et de semantique médiévales (Avignon, 6-10 Juin 2000)*, éd. par J. Biard – I. Rosier, Louvain 2004, pp. 313-328.

[7] K. M. FREDBORG, *The Commentaries on Cicero's* De Inventione *and* Rhetorica Ad Herennium *by William of Champeaux*, in «Cahiers de l'Institut du Moyen Âge Grec et Latin», 17 (1976), pp. 1-39.

liam as the *magister G.*, whose opinions on speculative grammar are recorded in the *Notulae Dunelmenses*, and respond in very particular ways to the *Glosulae* on Priscian's *Institutiones grammaticae* Books I-XVI. This commentary first circulates in northern France in the 1080s (perhaps initially in Rheims), but then is expanded upon, perhaps by William, by the early twelfth century[8]. While the *Glosulae*'s analysis of the meaning of words and the things they signified may have influenced vocalist dialecticians like Roscelin of Compiègne, it may have had more influence on realist dialecticians, like William of Champeaux[9]. As Rosier-Catach argues, William's teaching, criticized by Abelard in his *Dialectica* for relying too much on grammatical authority, drew on arguments of Priscian to support his claims[10]. As I have argued elsewhere, Abelard's account of how he interrupted William's lecturing on rhetoric by disputing his account of universals can easily give us a misleading image of his contribution to the study of philosophy, which was to present grammar, dialectic, and rhetoric as related to the goal of *logica* within a vision of philosophy, shaped by that of Boethius[11].

The issue of universals is not a particularly significant issue in William's *Introductiones dialecticae*, designed for beginners in the

[8] I. Rosier-Catach, *Abélard et les grammairiens: sur le verbe substantif et la prédication*, in «Vivarium», 41 (2003), pp. 175-248. On the *Glosulae* on Priscian, see M. T. Gibson, *The Early Scholastic 'Glosule' to Priscian, 'Institutiones Grammaticae': The Text and Its Influence*, in «Studi Medievali», 3ª ser., 20 (1979), pp. 235-254.

[9] I suggest that the discussion of *voces* and *res* in the *Glosulae* may have influenced the arguments of Roscelin, that the three persons of the Trinity each signify a distinct *res* in *Nominalism and Theology before Abaelard: New Light on Roscelin of Compiègne*, in «Vivarium», 30 (1992), pp. 4-33. I. Rosier-Catach emphasizes its influence on William of Champeaux in *Priscian on Divine Ideas and Mental Conceptions: The Discussions in the Glosulae in Priscianum, the Notae Dunelmenses, William of Champeaux and Abelard*, in «Vivarium», 45 (2007), pp. 219-237.

[10] Cfr. Petrus Abaelardus, *Dialectica*, ed. L. M. de Rijk, Assen 1970, p. 113: «Hi vero qui omnem vocum impositionem in significationem deducunt, auctoritatem pretendunt ut ea quoque significari dicant a voce quibuscumque ipsa est imposita, ut ipsum quoque hominem ab *animali* vel Socratem ab *homine* vel subiectum corpus ab *albo* vel *colorato*; nec solum ex arte verum etiam ex auctoritate gramatice id conantur ostendere. Cum enim tradat gramatica omne nomen substantiam cum qualitate significare, *album* quoque, quod subiectam nominat substantiam et qualitatem determinat circa eam, utrumque dicitur significare; sed qualitatem quidem principaliter, causa cuius impositum est, subiectum vero secundario».

[11] Cfr. Id., *Historia calamitatum*, ed. Hicks cit. (above, note 2), p. 5; see Mews, Logica *in the service of philosophy* cit. (above, note 1).

discipline. William opens with the same claim about dialectic as Abelard makes, that it was discovered to distinguish truth from falsehood and that it is studied through *voces*. Unlike Abelard, William relates dialectic to both grammar and rhetoric[12]. He acknowledges that a *vox* is said to be a universal because it signifies a universal thing, a sensible, animated substance diffused in all living things, without any awareness of debate on the issue. William's interest in dialectic is based more on identifying the different *media* or principles on which all argument is based. The first philosophers were often deceived in their arguments by using mistaken arguments, putting together contraries through a lack of skill in argument. For this reason, they developed the discipline of dialectic, to consider the nature of argument[13].

In a subsequent version of these *Introductiones*, William relates dialectic not just to *logica*, but to philosophy as a whole. He divides philosophy into *speculativa* (namely the quadrivium), *activa* (namely ethics) and *dissertiva* (to do with speech), terminology from Boethius's commentaries on Porphyry and on Cicero's *Topica*[14]. The *Glosulae* on Priscian had distinguished *logica* as *sermocinalis* (to do with words) and *dissertiva* (to do with the finding and judgment of arguments)[15]. We find precisely the same effort to link dialectic and rhetoric to *logica*, in William's commentary on Cicero's *De inventione*[16]. In the *Note Dunelmenses*, we find a de-

[12] Cfr. GUILLELMUS DE CAMPELLIS, *Introductiones dialecticae*, ed. Iwakuma cit. (above, note 6), p. 57.

[13] Cfr. *ibid.*, p. 74.

[14] Cfr. *ibid.*, p. 110: «Sed in his cum ita sint, logicae peritia est necessariam, quae tertia pars est philosophiae. Dividitur enim in tribus partibus philosophia, scilicet in speculativa, in activa, in dissertiva. Speculativa est naturalis quae rerum omnium naturas inquirit, quae in quattuor partibus est divisa, scilicet astronomia, geometria, arithmetica, musica. Activa vero est moralis scientia, quae morem recte vivendi atque ordinatum demonstrat; haec autctorum ac historiarum exercitium complectitur. Siquidem dissertiva, quam dialecticen vocant, est rationalis scientia».

[15] See the discussion of Y. IWAKUMA, *The Division of Philosophy and the Place of the Trivium From the 9th to the mid-12th Centuries*, in *Medieval Analyses in Language and Cognition*, ed. S. Ebbesen – R. L. Friedman, Copenhagen 1999 (Historisk-filosofiske Meddelelser of Danish Academy of Sciences and Letters, 77), pp. 165-189.

[16] Cfr. GUILLELMUS DE CAMPELLIS, *Commentarius in Ciceronis De inventione*, ms. York, Minster Library, XVI.M.7, ff. 1vb-2ra: «Gramaticus et dialeticus et rethor in materia eadem versantur, scilicet in oratione, sed in modo tractandi differunt. Gramaticus enim quaerit seriem recte constructionis formare, non veritatem vel

tailed report of the opinions of many masters on both grammar and rhetoric, but overwhelmingly it is the views of master G., which are most represented[17]. Students in William's school had to focus as much on Priscian, Boethius, and Cicero, as on Aristotle.

1.2. Abelard's critique of William of Champeaux was not based solely on his teaching about universals. At issue was a conception of language and the primacy Abelard accorded to Aristotelian dialectic. In the first two treatises of the *Dialectica*, Abelard is particularly critical of William's reliance on the authority of Priscian in his analysis of the meaning of a word, which William claimed signified any object on which it was imposed, on the strength of Priscian's definition that a noun signified a substance with quality. Abelard understood that this argument was based on the explanation of the *Glosulae* on Priscian that a noun named a subject substance and determined its quality, but insisted that it principally signified the quality for which it received that name, not the subject itself. He commented that *auctoritas* frequently extended

falsitatem discernere, neque ornatum verborum docere. Dialeticus vero solam veritatem et falsitatem in orationibus investigat. Rethor vero docet quomodo aliquis mentes audientium in oratione sua pulchris ornatibus verborum et senten-ciarum possit captare et allicere. Ecce quomodo de oratione agit, intendit autem, ut superius dictum est, oratorem in publicis et privatis causis eloquentem reddere. Nota idem esse intencionem et finalem causam. Hec autem scientia supponitur logice. Logica alia sermocinalis ut gramatica, alia disertiva ut dialetica et rethorica. Rethorica vero dividitur in V partes, id est, scientias: inventionem, que hic large accepta continet et iudicium, et in dispositionem et in pronunciationem et memoriam et elocutionem [cfr. *De inventione*, I, 7, 9]. Sed queritur, cum rethorica dicatur habere V partes, quare Tullius in Topicis inquit: 'Omnis diligens ratio disserendi distribuitur in II partes: in scientiam inueniendi et scientiam iudicandi' [*Topica*, II, 6]. Que sic solvitur: logica strictim aliquando accipitur, aliquando large. Quando strictim, habet hanc diffinitionem: 'diligens ratio disserendi', et tunc continet dialeticam et rethorice partem illam que vocatur inventio, large accep[t]a, scilicet ut et iudicium contineat. Strictim vero accepta, dividitur tamen in II partes, id est inventionem et iudicium. In hoc quod dicitur 'ratio disserendi', continet inventionem; in hoc quod 'diligens', iudicium. Large vero accepta, continet gramaticam, dialeticam et totam rethoricam que dividitur in V partes».

[17] Extracts from the *Note Dunelmenses* are provided by R.W. HUNT, *Studies on Priscian in the Eleventh and Twelfth Centuries*, in «Mediaeval and Renaissance Studies», 1 (1941-1943), pp. 194-231, reprinted in ID., *The History of Grammar in the Middle Ages: Collected Papers*, ed. G. L. Bursill-Hall, Amsterdam 1980, pp. 1-38; and by M. DICKEY, *Some Commentaries on the* De Inventione *and* Ad Herennium *of the Eleventh and Early Twelfth Centuries*, in «Mediaeval and Renaissance Studies», 6 (1968), pp. 1-41.

the notion of 'signification' too widely, rather than to what was in the will of person imposing the word[18]. In his *Dialectica*, Abelard never alludes to Cicero's *De inventione*, a text that he cites several times in the *Logica 'Ingredientibus'*. He is convinced that dialectic is the *dux universae doctrinae* and holds authority over all philosophy[19]. Abelard's decision to challenge William's ideas about universals during a course of lectures on rhetoric highlights the contrast between the two teachers. William of Champeaux laid the foundations for a vision of philosophy that was based as much on Priscian, Cicero and Boethius as on Aristotle.

1.3. The theological *sententiae* attributed to William in the *Liber pancrisis* show that he was also interested in transferring his skills in studying words to questions of divinity, in a more abstract fashion than Anselm of Laon, such as about how God could be said to be a Trinity of persons, about free will and providence[20]. Although Abelard never recalls that he studied theology under William, his arguments in the *Theologia 'Summi boni'* clearly respond to William's discussion of the meaning of words like *pater* and *filius* predicated of God. At the outset of the *Liber pancrisis*, William had endeavoured to explain that when words were applied to God, they inevitably changed their meaning from their conventional sense, and thus could not be used to imply division in God. While not presenting anything like as sophisticated an argument as Abelard in the *Theologia 'Summi boni'* William does seek to explain the doctrine of the Trinity through examining the meaning of key *voces*: in this case, he holds that the words *pater*, *filius* and *spiritus sanctus* signify different attributes of God, that

[18] Cfr. PETRUS ABAELARDUS, *Dialectica*, ed. de Rijk cit. (above, note 10), p. 114: «Laxe tamen nimium saepe auctoritas ad omnem impositionem *significationis* nomen extendit».

[19] Cfr. *ibid.*, p. 470: «Haec autem est dialectica, cui quidem omnis veritatis seu falsitatis discretio ita subiecta est, ut omnis philosophiae principatum dux universae doctrinae atque regimen possideat».

[20] GUILLELMUS DE CAMPELLIS, *Sententiae*, ed. in O. LOTTIN, *Psychologie et Morale aux XIIe et XIIIe siècles*, V. *Problèmes d'histoire littéraire. L'école d'Anselme de Laon et de Guillaume de Champeaux*, Gembloux 1959, pp. 189-227. I sketch out the distinction between the schools of Anselm of Laon and William of Champeaux in *St. Anselm and the Development of Philosophical Theology in Twelfth-Century Paris*, in *From St. Anselm to Abelard*, ed. G. E. M. Gasper and H. Kohlenberger, Toronto 2006, pp. 196-222.

from which all things come, the wisdom through which all things are made and the charity extended to God by all creation[21].

Abelard's polemical attitude towards William, so clearly articulated in the *Historia calamitatum*, should not prevent us from grasping the full extent of his debt to the teacher, whose position at Notre-Dame he so much wanted to obtain. If we compare the *sententiae* attributed to William in the *Liber pancrisis*, to those assigned to Anselm of Laon, it is clear that William was much more the speculative thinker. It is quite misleading, I would argue to speak, as Weisweiler and Lottin did, of 'the school of Anselm of Laon and William of Champeaux' as if they constituted a single school. Although William studied under Anselm (and perhaps other masters), his primary reputation in Paris was in the arts of language rather than as an authority on Scripture. When Abelard went to study under Anselm in 1113, because William had left Saint-Victor to become bishop of Châlons-sur-Marne, he may already have become familiar with the more speculative type of theological questions attributed to William in the *Liber pancrisis.* Inevitably, Abelard was disappointed by what he considered to be the lack of substance and originality in the school of Anselm, based perhaps more exclusively on Scripture and the writings of the Fathers. Abelard's practice of combining teaching in philosophy with *lectio sacra* in those early years at Notre-Dame after 1113, when he also became a tutor to Heloise may owe more to William of Champeaux than he cares to acknowledge.

2. *William at Saint-Victor (1111-1113)*

2.1. While in my book, *Abelard and Heloise* (2005), I accepted the traditional dating of William's departure from Notre-Dame to 1108, I have since discovered evidence that he did not do so until Easter 1111, and that Abelard returned to Paris to challenge him in debate at Saint-Victor only in this year[22]. We gain valuable

[21] Cfr. GUILLELMUS DE CAMPELLIS, *ibid.*, n. 236, p. 192: «Ipse enim suo, ut dictum est, spatio manendi ante omnia solus exsistens, felix, nullo indigens, omnia de nihilo, non de praeiacente materia vel forma, sua sapientia creavit et sua caritate dilexit. Quae quidem sapientia Filius Patris, caritas vero Spiritus utriusque sanctus nominatur».

[22] Cfr. PETRUS ABAELARDUS, *Historia calamitatum*, PL 178, 118A-119A, ed.

insight into the character of William's school in the first year of its existence, from a letter, not known to Robert Henri Bautier in his account of the early years of Saint-Victor, by a German student, preserved in the *Codex Udalrici*:

> I am in Paris in the schools of master William, the greatest man of all of this time, whom I have got to know in every kind of teaching. When we hear his voice, we think it is not a man speaking, from an angel from heaven; for the sweetness of his words and the depth of his teachings transcend any human manner. Having been archdeacon and almost number one to the king, he gave up everything which he possessed, and last Easter retired to a certain very poor chapel, to serve God alone, and there he demonstrated his devotion and kindness to all who came to him, freely and for the sake of God alone, in the matter of master Manegold of blessed memory. And there he rules the studium in divine and human sciences in a way that I have neither seen nor heard has happened anywhere in our time[23].

This German student gives a much more favourable account of William's conversion than Abelard. He also conveys a sense of the special atmosphere generated by William at Saint-Victor by not charging money of students like a secular master for classes in both secular and religious subjects. The comment about William

Hicks cit. (above, note 2), p. 5: «Elapsis autem paucis annis, cum ex infirmitate jam dudum convaluissem, praeceptor meus ille Guillhemus Parisiacensis archidiaconus, habitu pristino commutato, ad regularium clericorum ordinem se convertit, ea ut referebant intentione ut quo religiosor crederetur ad majoris praelationis gradum promoveretur, sicut in proximo contigit, eo Catalaunensi episcopo facto». I had followed the traditional date in C. MEWS, *Abelard and Heloise*, New York 2005, pp. 30-31.

[23] *Udalrici codex*, ed. Ph. Jaffé, Berlin 1869 (*Bibliotheca rerum germanicarum*, 5), no. 160, p. 286: «Parisius sum modo, in scolis magistri Gwillelmi, summi viri omnium huius temporis, quos ego noverim in omni genere doctrinae. Cuius vocem cum audimus, non hominem sed quasi angelum de caelo loqui putamus; nam et dulcedo verborum eius et profunditas sententiarum quasi humanum modum transcendit. Qui cum esset archidiaconus fereque apud regem primus, omnibus quae possidebat dimissis, in praeterito pascha ad quandam pauperrimam ecclesiolam, soli Deo serviturus, se contulit; ibique postea omnibus undique ad eum venientibus gratis et causa Dei solummodo, more magistri Manegaldi beatae memoriae, devotum ac benignum se praebuit. Iamque tantum studium regit tam in divinis quam in humanis scientiis, quantum nec vidi nec meo tempore usquam terrarum esse audivi». The student's letter is translated and annoted in MANEGOLD, *Liber contra Wolfelmum*, Eng. tr. by R. Ziomkowski, Leuven 2002, pp. 121-122.

following the example of Manegold shows how he was himself seen as following an established tradition, also pursued by Odo at Tournai[24]. By adopting a religious habit, William acquired a charismatic authority in the eyes of his disciples. The legacy of Abelard's public disputation with William about universals was an enduring suspicion not just between William and Abelard, but between the community that attached itself to William and the circle of Abelard's followers.

2.2. The reference to William leaving the cathedral 'last Easter' needs to be combined with the evidence of an unnoticed charter that indicates that William was still an archdeacon after Easter 1110. It implies that William must have resigned his position at Easter 1111 (2 April), when he was replaced as archdeacon by Girbert, a future bishop of Paris[25]. Robert of Torigny twice dates William's departure from the cathedral to 1112, probably wrong by just one year, as this would leave too little time for the events described in the *Historia calamitatum*[26]. Dating William's departure

[24] See above, the essay of Christophe Erismann.

[25] *Guillermus archidiaconus* signs a charter, drawn up by Stephen as royal chancellor, conferring royal protection to the canons of Saint-Etienne de Dreux, against monks of Coulombes, delivered at Paris and dated to 1110 (i.e. after Easter, but before 3 August); cfr. *Recueil des actes de Louis VI roi de France (1108-1137)*, ed. J. Dufour, 4 voll., Paris 1992-1994, nn. 43, 1, 81; and A. LUCHAIRE, *Louis VIe le Gros. Annales de sa vie et de son règne*, Paris 1890, n. 99, p. 54. Other signatories are Bernier, dean of Notre-Dame, Reinaldus de Cala (presumably Renaud, the other archdeacon of Paris), precentor Adam (subsequently a canon of Saint-Victor) and an unknown figure, Raherius de Dongione. The charter seems to have been missed by Bautier because it refers to Dreux and thus was not included in *Cartulaire général de Paris*, I, ed. R. de Lasteyrie, Paris 1887. Girbert is first mentioned as archdeacon in 1112 (*Cartulaire*, n. 160, p. 185; LUCHAIRE, *Annales* cit., n. 142, p. 75; Dufour, *Actes*, n. 73, p. 165), but was replaced by Henricus in 1117 (*Cartulaire*, no. 174, p. 198).

[26] Cfr. ROBERTUS DE TORIGNIACO (DE TORINNEIO), *De immutatione ordinis monachorum*, PL 203, 1313AB, subsequently added, with minor changes, as an annotation to the Avranches (Mont Saint-Michel) copy of the *Chronicon*, MGH, *Scriptores*, 6, Hannover 1844, p. 484 (ed. L. Delisle, *Chronique de Robert de Torigny*, 2 voll., Rouen 1872-1873, II, p. 190, signalled as *C*): «Eodem [*C* Hoc] tempore magister Willelmus de Campellis, qui fuerat archidiaconus Parisiensis, vir admodum litteratus et religiosus [*C om.* et religiosus], habitum canonici regularis assumens cum aliquibus discipulis suis, extra urbem Parisiensem [*C* Parisius] in loco, ubi erat quaedam capella Sancti Victoris martyris, coepit monasterium aedificare clericorum. Assumpto autem illo ad episcopatum Cathalaunensium, venerabilis Geldoinus [*C* Gelduvinus] discipulus ejus primus abbas ibi factus est.

to 1111 would make sense, however, of a number of details in this account. Abelard reports that he was initially offered a position at Notre-Dame by the teacher who first replaced William, but was forced to leave Paris after William turned against his substitute and engineered a second replacement[27]. After William took his small community away from Saint-Victor, Abelard took up a position at Mont Sainte-Geneviève (presumably offered by Stephen of Garlande). This prompted William to return to Saint-Victor, re-establishing his community, and to re-open a public school, to give support to his new replacement at Notre-Dame, whom Abelard reports had a certain reputation in grammar, but despairing of worldly glory decided to become a monk. Abelard implies that William now returned to the city to teach, presumably at Notre-Dame, while living at Saint-Victor[28]. The years between 1111 and 1113 were ones of acute rivalry between the rival schools at Sainte-Geneviève, Notre-Dame, and Saint-Victor. Abelard may have started to compose the *Dialectica*, composed for the education of his nephews, in the years before 1111, when he had returned to Brittany to recover from overwork, and wished

Sub cujus regimine multi clerici nobiles saecularibus et divinis litteris instructi, ad illum locum habitaturi convenerunt; inter quos magister Hugo Lothariensis, et scientia litterarum et humili religione maxime effloruit. Hic multos libros edidit, quos, quia vulgo habentur, non oportet enumerare [*C om.* quos... enumerare; *add.* Hoc anno etiam exordium Savigneii fuit.]»

[27] Cfr. Petrus Abaelardus, *Historia calamitatum*, 119C-120A, ed. Hicks cit., pp. 5-6: «Hinc tantum roboris et auctoritatis nostra suscepit disciplina, ut hii qui antea vehementius magistro illi nostro adhaerebant et maxime nostram infestabant doctrinam, ad nostras convolarent scholas, et ipse qui in scholis Parisiacae sedis magistro successerat nostro locum mihi suum offerret, ut ibidem cum ceteris nostro se traderet magisterio ubi antea suus ille et noster magister floruerat. Paucis itaque diebus ibi me dialecticae studium regente, quanta invidia tabescere, quanto dolore aestuare coeperit magister noster non est facile exprimere; nec conceptae miseriae aestum diu sustinens, callide aggressus est me tunc etiam removere. Et quia in me quid aperte ageret non habebat, ei scholas auferre molitus est, pessimis obiectis criminibus, qui mihi suum concesserat magisterium, alio quodam aemulo meo ad officium eius substituto».

[28] Cfr. *ibid.*, 121A-122A, p. 6: «Ille quippe antea aliquos habebat qualescunque discipulos, maxime propter lectionem Prisciani in qua plurimum valere credebatur. Postquam autem magister advenit, omnes penitus amisit; et sic a regimine scolarum cessare compulsus est. Nec post multum tempus, quasi jam ulterius de mundana desperans gloria, ipse quoque ad monasticam comversus est vitam. Post reditum vero magistri nostri ad urbem, quos conflictus disputationum scholares nostri tam cum ipso quam cum discipulis ejus habuerint, et quos fortuna eventus in his bellis dederit nostris, immo mihi ipsi in eis, te quoque res ipsa dudum edocuit».

to assert his arguments on dialectic against those of William of Champeaux. It was certainly completed by the time he wrote the *Theologia 'Summi boni'* in around 1120[29].

3. *Goswin and Goscelin*

A different perspective on these rivalries is preserved in the *Vita Goswini*, a recording of the memories of Goswin (1086-1166) about his own education in Paris before he became a monk at Anchin in 1114[30]. Goswin came to Paris to study dialectic, and befriended William's disciple, Goscelin, but started to attract students after challenging Abelard in debate. He recalled that it was in the course of transcribing a certain controversial commentary on Priscian's *Institutiones grammaticae* that he started to question what relevance of studying Priscian to teaching he should live, that he decided to give up teaching and return to his native region of Douai, where he became a monk of Anchin by 1114[31].

If William of Champeaux only left Notre-Dame at Easter 1111, it is quite possible that he initially installed as his replacement, his leading disciple, Goscelin, whose opinions on dialectic are recorded at length alongside those of William and Abelard in Orléans, Bibl. mun. 266. Abelard's account of a teacher with a certain reputation in grammar, who subsequently became a monk fits in completely with Goswin, who taught for a short while at Douai 1112-1114, before becoming a monk at Anchin.

[29] Cfr. Id., *Theologia 'Summi boni'* III, 43, ed. E. M. Buytaert – C. J. Mews, Turnhout 1987 (CCCM, 13), p. 176.

[30] The *Vita prima* of Goswin (*Vita Goswini*) was printed from Douai, Bibl. mun. 825 by Richard Gibbon, Douai 1620; excerpts were reprinted in *Recueil des historiens des Gaules et de la France*, vol. 14, ed. L. Delisle, Paris 1877, pp. 442-448 (partially accessible online with useful notes by Werner Robl). Robl estimates his date of birth at 1082; Mirko Breitenstein gives it as 1086, in an excellent detailed summary of Goswin's life in *Biographisch-Bibliographisches Kirchenlexikon*, Band 25, Nordhausen 2006, coll. 484-488.

[31] Cfr. *Vita Goswini*, ed. Delisle cit., p. 444: «Quid proficit ad aeternitatem promerendam recte loquendi regulas scire, et recte vivendi regulam non tenere? Numquid qui perite loquitur et perdite vivit, haberi non debet pro perito, sed pro perituro. Si Priscianus clavem tenet scientiae saecularis, non ideo sequitur ut sit claviger paradisi; et sermone diserto non absolvet Domini desertores, nec a judice summo requiretur utrum legerimus Priscianum, sed si morem tenuerimus Christianum».

His decision to challenge Abelard to a debate at Sainte-Geneviève provoked a short lived period of fame that he abandoned when in Goswin's terms, he realized that Priscian did not offer a guide to living. As a monk, Goswin, who became prior of Saint-Medard, Soissons, before becoming abbot of Anchin, supervised collections of the complete works of his contemporaries, particularly Bernard of Clairvaux, Hugh of Saint-Victor, and quite possibly of Abelard himself. A good monastic library included many scholastic authors.

4. *Abelard's* Dialectica *and Thierry of Chartres*

4.1. William of Champeaux created one type of intellectual community at Saint-Victor through his teaching that philosophy could be studied through grammar, dialectic, and rhetoric, alongside theological questions inspired by Scripture. A different sort of emphasis was encouraged at the cathedral school of Chartres, where Plato's *Timaeus* and other Platonic texts were given a particular place of honour. According to a humorous anecdote, he tried to study the quadrivium under Thierry of Chartres, but found it more difficult than he imagined, a story that fits in with comments that Abelard makes in the *Dialectica* about his having studied, but not absorbed the principles of arithmetic[32]. Minio-Paluello observed that Abelard had passing familiarity with the text of the *Prior Analytics* known to Thierry of Chartres[33]. In particular, however, I would draw attention to Abelard's discussion in the fifth treatise of the *Dialectica* about the notion of a unified whole (*totus*) descending into parts, which he argues refers not a single nature, but to a multiplicity of individuals[34]. This leads Abelard to comment on the error of those who identify the Pla-

[32] See C. J. MEWS, *In Search of a Name and its Significance: A Twelfth-Century Anecdote about Thierry and Peter Abaelard*, in «Traditio», 44 (1988), pp. 175-200; and cfr. PETRUS ABAELARDUS, *Dialectica*, ed. de Rijk cit. (above, note 10), p. 59: «Etsi ab arithmeticis solutiones audierim, nullam tamen a me proferendam iudico, quem eius artis ignarum omnino recognosco».

[33] Cfr. L. MINIO-PALUELLO, *I Primi Analitici: la redazione carnutense usata da Abelardo e la 'Vulgata' con scolii tradotti dal greco*, in «Rivista di filosofia neo-scolastica», 46 (1954), pp. 211-223, reprinted in ID., *Opuscula. The Latin Aristotle*, Amsterdam 1972, pp. 229-241.

[34] Cfr. PETRUS ABAELARDUS, *ibid.*, pp. 546-563.

tonic world soul as proceeding from Nous in the same way as the Holy Spirit proceeds from the Son[35]. Abelard's hostility to this analogy is much less sophisticated here than it is in the *Theologia 'Summi boni'*, where he invokes the notion of *involucrum*, drawn from his reading of Chalcidius[36]. This criticism of attempts to Christianize Plato is certainly not a retraction of his earlier teaching (as Cousin speculated in the nineteenth century), but a valuable insight into the early gestation of ideas that would become more clearly articulated in the *Theologia 'Summi boni'*. Throughout the *Dialectica*, Abelard accords Aristotle a place of honour. Here we see Abelard having to respond to the ideas of another school, in which Plato is accorded central authority as offering insight fully compatible with Christian doctrine.

As Tullio Gregory so brilliantly demonstrated in his 1955 study, *Anima mundi*, the desire to relate the world soul to the Holy Spirit was a key feature of the thought of the young William of Conches[37]. As a former student of Richard Southern, I am fully aware of the debates that have surrounded the question of the significance of the school at Chartres, as well as of the authorship of texts surrounding the school, that I cannot enter into here[38]. I see no reason to doubt, however, that wherever Thierry and William of Conches taught, Bernard of Chartres inspired a community of learning in which Platonic texts, notably the *Timaeus*, Macrobius's Commentary on the *Somnium Scipionis* and the *Consolatio philosophiae* played a key role.

[35] Cfr. *ibid.*, p. 558.

[36] Cfr. Id., *Theologia 'Summi boni'*, III, 43, ed. Buytaert – Mews cit., p. 101.

[37] Cfr. T. Gregory, Anima mundi. *La filosofia di Guglielmo di Conches e la scuola di Chartres*, Firenze 1955.

[38] Much has been published since R. W. Southern published his critique of the importance of the school of Chartres, *Humanism and the School of Chartres*, in Id., *Medieval Humanism and Other Studies*, Oxford 1970, pp. 51-85; see the detailed summary of evidence in: P. Dronke, *New Approaches to the School of Chartres*, in «Annuario de Estudios Medievales», 6 (1969) [published 1971], pp. 117-140; R. Giacone, *Masters, Books and Library at Chartres According to the Cartularies of Notre-Dame and Saint-Père*, in «Vivarium», 12 (1974), pp. 30-51; N. Häring, *Chartres and Paris Revisited*, in *Essays in Honour of Anton Charles Pegis*, ed. R. O'Donnell, Toronto 1974, pp. 268-329, and the response of Southern in *The Schools of Paris and the School of Chartres*, in *Renaissance and Renewal in the Twelfth Century*, ed. R. L. Benson – G. Constable, Cambridge (Mass.) 1982, pp. 113-137.

4.2. The widely copied glosses on the *Timaeus* attributed to Bernard of Chartres by Paul Dutton (correctly in my view) steer away from explicit identification of the Holy Spirit with the *anima mundi*[39]. It is with Thierry of Chartres, in his commentary on the six days of creation that we do find the statement, put quite crudely, that what Plato called the *anima mundi,* Christians call the Holy Spirit[40]. Thierry goes much further than Bernard of Chartres in trying to show that what Plato's teaching in the *Timaeus* is fully consistent with the first chapters of Genesis. Thierry introduces the notion in passing that God is the efficient cause of creation, the Son as his wisdom the formal cause, and the Holy Spirit the final cause, God's benignity, while the elements were the material cause[41]. Thierry is not concerned with the Trinitarian subtleties that concerned Abelard, namely that the world soul is created, while the Holy Spirit is eternal, to my mind an argument that the *De sex dierum operibus* is an early work from before 1120. He does not repeat this identification of the world soul with the Holy Spirit in any of his commentaries on the *De Trinitate* of Boethius. I would also argue that Hugh of Saint-Victor, in his *De tribus diebus* was similarly responding to this early Chartrian school by developing the notion that the sensible world (*mundus sensilis*), an image from the *Timaeus*, was like a book in which one could discern the power, wisdom, and benignity of God[42].

[39] BERNARDUS CARNOTENSIS (attr.), *Glosae in Platonem*, ed. P. E. Dutton, Toronto 1991.

[40] Cfr. THEODORICUS CARNOTENSIS, *Tractatus de sex dierum operibus*, in *Commentaries on Boethius by Thierry of Chartres and his School*, ed. N. M. Häring, Toronto 1971, pp. 566-567: «Plato vero in *Timaeo* eundem spiritum mundi animam uocat (...). Christiani vero illud idem Spiritum sanctum appellant».

[41] Cfr. *ibid.*, p. 556: «Si quis igitur subtiliter consideret mundi fabricam, efficientem ipsius causam Deum esse cognoscet, formalem vero Dei sapientiam, finalem eiusdem benignitatem, materialem vero quatuor elementa quae et ipse creator in principio de nichilo creavit. (...) Nam Pater est efficiens causa, Filius vero formalis, Spiritus sanctus finalis, quatuor vero elementa materialis».

[42] HUGO DE SANCTO VICTORE, *De tribus diebus*, ed. D. Poirel, Turnhout 2002 (CCCM, 157). D. POIREL argues that Hugh inspired Abelard's use of the power-wisdom-benignity triad in *Livre de la Nature et débat trinitaire au XIIe siècle: Le «De Tribus Diebus» de Hugues de Saint-Victor*, Turnhout 2002 (Bibliotheca Victorina, 14). I argue that both Hugh was inspired by his reading of the *Timaeus* in C. J. MEWS, *The World As Text: The Bible and the Book of Nature in Twelfth-Century Theology*, in *Scripture and Pluralism. Reading the Bible in the Religiously Plural Worlds*

William of Conches identifies the world soul with the Holy Spirit in his early glosses on Boethius (in which he seems to reprise earlier glosses on the *Timaeus* found in an Uppsala manuscript, the authorship of which is debated), but moves away from this claim in his later writing, more concerned with the structure of the physical world than with the Trinitarian questions that preoccupied Abelard[43]. While we are uncertain about many questions about the dating of the writings of Thierry and William of Conches, I would suggest that when Abelard wrote those comments about Platonists at the end of the *Dialectica*, he was familiar with attempts of a rival educational community to put forward a vision of philosophy very different from his own, one which put Plato in centre stage. Abelard refers to Thierry as an already established master, present at the Council of Soissons in 1121, under the authority of the bishop of Chartres. When he composed the *Theologia 'Summi boni'* Abelard was already aware of rather crude attempts at Chartres to relate Platonic teaching to Christian doctrine. By developing the idea not yet articulated in the *Dialectica* that the world soul was an *involucrum* (a notion he could have absorbed from Bernard of Chartres), Abelard formulated a more sophisticated response to the desire of the young Thierry and William of Conches to relate Platonic teaching to Christian doctrine. By 1120, after those turbulent years during which he was officially engaged in tutoring Heloise in the study of philosophy, Abelard had enlarged the range of authors whom he saw as engaging in the study of wisdom. It was now no longer

of the Middle Ages and the Renaissance, ed. T. J. Heffernan – T. E. Burman, Leiden 2005, pp. 95-122; and that Abelard and Hugh were both inspired by Thierry in ID., *William of Champeaux, Abelard, and Hugh of Saint-Victor: Platonism, Theology, and Scripture in Early Twelfth-Century France*, in *Bibel und Exegese in Sankt Viktor zu Paris. Formen und Funktionen eines Grundtextes in europäischem Rahmen*, ed. R. Berndt, Münster 2009, pp. 118-152 (Corpus Victorinum. Instrumenta, 3).

[43] GUILLELMUS DE CONCHIS, *Glosae super Boetium*, III, m. 9, ed. L. Nauta, Turnhout 1999 (CCCM, 158), pp. 169, 520 - 170, 531: «Quare videndum est quid sit anima mundi et quid eius proprietates. Anima mundi est naturalis vigor quo quaedam res tantum habent moveri, quaedam crescere, quaedam sentire, quaedam discernere. Sed quid sit ille vigor naturalis quaeritur. Sed ut michi videtur, ille naturalis vigor est spiritus sanctus, id est divina et benigna concordia, quia divino amore et concordia habent omnia esse, moveri, vivere, crescere, sentire, discernere. Qui bene dicitur naturalis vigor, quia divina amore omnia nascuntur et vigent. Dicitur bene anima mundi, quia solo divino amore et caritate omnia quae in mundo vivunt habent vivere».

just Aristotle, but a much wider tradition of philosophy, Platonic and Peripatetic, that he wished to relate to the study of Scripture, as all engaged in reflection on the supreme good.

5. *Conclusion*

5.1. The ten years between 1110 and 1120 were marked by an astonishing rivalry between a number of competing communities of learning. William of Champeaux, who taught at Notre-Dame perhaps from the early 1090s until 1111, established a school in which the study of philosophy, based around the study of grammar, dialectic, and rhetoric as all part of *logica*, occupied a more important role than in the school of Anselm of Laon, where the major emphasis was on study of the Bible. In Easter 1111, William moved with a small group of disciples to the disused chapel of Saint-Victor to teach both human and divine learning. The young Abelard established a rival school at Sainte-Geneviève, based much more firmly around the authority of Aristotle. By 1113, Abelard had ousted two other rivals, Goscelin of Soissons, and young Goswin, who soon turned to an alternative community of learning, that of the abbey of Anchin. William of Champeaux, now bishop of Châlons-sur-Marne, soon turned his attention to another community, ordaining Bernard as abbot of Clairvaux in 1115. Here, William's attention seems to shift much more to Scripture, above all the Song of Songs (and perhaps also Gregory's *Moralia in Job*, of which he made an abbreviation). In that same year, a young German student, Hugh, came to St Victor, and helped shape the intellectual life of that community in a new direction, inheriting William's desire to combine the study of philosophy with that of Scripture, but with a subtly different focus. Hugh was not interested in the speculation about language provoked by the *Glosulae* on Priscian's *Institutiones grammaticae*, that did so much to stimulate reflection in both dialectic and theology in the early twelfth century.

5.2. Abelard's *Theologia 'Summi boni'* marks a new stage in the evolution not just of his thought but of the community of learning that he sought to encourage. No longer familiar just with the Aristotelian dialectic, as he had expounded it in the *Dialectica*, he wished to engage with a much wider range of philosophical writing, involving Plato, Macrobius, Cicero as much as Aristotle and Boethius. He took much further an intuition shared in different ways by William of Champeaux and Bernard of Chartres, that the study of philosophy was not incompatible with the teaching of Scripture. Abelard was responding not just to Roscelin of Compiègne and William of Champeaux, but also I would suggest to the community of learning at Chartres, where the study of Plato took centre stage. Abelard had also broadened his thinking during the years 1115-1117, through his engagement with the young Heloise, with whom he created another kind of community of learning. But that is another story.

CONCETTO MARTELLO

PROFEZIA E MITO

ESEGESI E SCRITTURA PROFANA NELLE SCUOLE DI CHARTRES

1. *I sensi della scrittura profana. I maestri*

Lungo il processo di secolarizzazione del sapere attuatosi nelle scuole della Francia settentrionale nella prima metà del secolo XII, i maestri di Chartres partecipano e danno rilievo a una riflessione sull'applicazione ai miti, assimilati ai testi letterari e profani, dei tradizionali modi di lettura dell'esegesi biblica e di concetti esegetici nuovi o rinnovati. Sulla loro scia, in ambienti esterni alle scuole chartriane ma da parte di soggetti in qualche modo collegati o concordi rispetto a esse, viene avvertita nella seconda metà del secolo l'esigenza di una teorizzazione degli aspetti generali, per così dire, dell'esegesi, intesa come approccio euristico ed ermeneutico sia al testo sacro sia alla scrittura profana. Tale riflessione è un indizio della crescita della biblioteca filosofica e dell'allargamento dell'orizzonte intellettuale e una tappa nella maturazione della consapevolezza critica nei confronti del testo in quanto tale, nel percorso che conduce fino alle formulazioni della scolastica matura. Ma l'attenzione alle regole di elaborazione e di fruizione della scrittura profana evidenzia anche la fecondità del rapporto intercorrente, sullo scorcio dell'età della riforma ecclesiastica, tra il pensiero cristiano, che ha nella teoria e nelle pratiche esegetiche i suoi strumenti di comprensione del reale più peculiari e incisivi, e la tradizione filosofico-letteraria risalente al mondo antico, recepita soprattutto nello studio delle arti liberali e negli oggetti delle loro applicazioni, che sono la ragione e la natura.

10.1484/M.NUTRIX-EB.1.101245

Teodorico di Chartres tocca la questione dell'interpretazione della scrittura profana non nel *Tractatus de sex dierum operibus* – esegesi letterale e fisico-cosmologica di *Genesi 1* nel cui *incipit* si richiama alla teoria dei sensi biblici ampiamente condivisa nell'ambito della sua generazione[1], tanto da essere sostanzialmente corrispondente a quella, più articolata e motivata, di Ugo di San Vittore[2] – ma nelle *Lectiones in Boethii librum De Trinitate*, nel corso del commento all'espressione boeziana secondo cui l'essere

[1] Cfr. THEODORICUS CARNOTENSIS, *Tractatus de sex dierum operibus*, 1, ed. N. M. Häring (*Commentaries on Boethius by Thierry of Chartres and his School*), Toronto 1971, p. 555,1-6: «De septem diebus et sex operum distintionibus primam geneseos partem secundum phisicam et ad litteram ego expositurus, inprimis de intentione auctoris et de libri utilitate pauca premittam. Postea vero ad sensum littere hystorialem exponendum veniam ut et allegoricam et moralem lectionem que a sanctis doctoribus aperte execute sunt ex toto pretermittam».

[2] Cfr. HUGO DE SANCTO VICTORE, *Didascalicon, De studio legendi*, V, 2, PL 176, 789B-790B, ed. C. H. Buttimer, Washington 1939, pp. 95,15 - 96,21: «Primo omnium sciendum est, quod divina scriptura triplicem habet modum intelligendi, id est, historiam, allegoriam, tropologiam. Sane non omnia quae in divino reperiuntur eloquio ad hanc intorquenda sunt interpretationem, ut singula historiam, allegoriam et tropologiam simul continere credantur. Quod etsi in multis congrue assignari possit, ubique tamen observare aut difficile est aut impossibile. Sicut enim in citharis et huiusmodi organis musicis non quidem omnia quae tanguntur canorum aliquid resonant, sed tantum chordae, cetera tamen in toto citharae corpore ideo facta sunt, ut esset ubi connecterentur, et quo tenderentur illa quae ad cantilenae suavitatem modulaturus est artifex, ita in divinis eloquiis quaedam posita sunt, quae tantum spiritualiter intelligi volunt, quaedam vero morum gravitati deserviunt, quaedam etiam secundum simplicem sensum historiae dicta sunt, nonnulla autem quae et historice, et allegorice, et tropologice convenienter exponi possunt. Unde modo mirabili omnis divina scriptura ita per Dei sapientiam convenienter suis partibus aptata est atque disposita, ut quidquid in ea continetur aut vice chordarum spiritualis intelligentiae suavitatem personet, aut per historiae seriem et litterae soliditatem mysteriorum dicta sparsim posita continens, et quasi in unum connectens, ad modum ligni concavi super extensas chordas simul copulet, earumque sonum recipiens in se, dulciorem auribus referat, quem non solum chorda edidit, sed et lignum modulo corporis sui formavit. sic et mel in favo gratius, et quidquid maiori exercitio quaeritur, maiori etiam desiderio invenitur. Oportet ergo sic tractare divinam scripturam, ut nec ubique historiam, nec ubique allegoriam, nec ubique quaeramus tropologiam, sed singula in suis locis, prout ratio postulat, competenter assignare. Saepe tamen in una eademque littera omnia simul reperiri possunt, sicut historiae veritas et mysticum aliquid per allegoriam insinuet, et quid agendum sit pariter per tropologiam demonstret». E cfr. ID., *De Scripturis et scriptoribus sacris praenotatiunculae*, 3, PL 175, 12B: «Dicitur allegoria quasi alieniloquium, quia aliud dicitura et aliud significatur, quae subdividitur in simplicem allegoriam et anagogen. Et est simplex allegoria, cum per visibile factum aliud invisibile factum significatur. Anagoge id est sursum ductio, cum per visibile invisibile factum declaratur».

deriva dalla forma[3]. Qui l'argomentazione si basa sulla definizione di Dio come *forma essendi*, intesa non nel senso di *imago*, termine con cui Boezio esprime la figura sensibile, ma nel senso di essere in sé, da cui è prodotto l'essere di tutte le cose[4]. Tale forma, unica[5] e intesa come mente divina, genera le idee, cioè le forme specifiche, le essenze degli esseri creati; queste ultime, che non rientrano a pieno titolo nell'essere in quanto intermedie tra le sostanze e la mente di Dio[6], e la materia primordiale, che non è essere in quanto intermedia tra le sostanze e il nulla[7], sono i principi dell'essere delle sostanze naturali, seppure le forme sono sovraordinate rispetto alla materia, come l'atto rispetto alla potenza e l'immobilità rispetto alla mobilità[8]. All'interno di tale argomentazione di carattere onto-teologico, Teodorico introduce il tema della somiglianza funzionale tra la mente divina e l'umana, una sorta di analogia secondo la quale, allo stesso modo in cui la prima forma genera le essenze delle cose naturali, la mente umana genera le forme degli enti artificiali e fantastici. L'uomo infatti pensa le cose che egli stesso costruisce prima che queste siano in atto e le sue immaginazioni, come la chimera o il centauro[9].

Dal punto di vista che qui ci interessa, appare di un certo rilievo la nozione di *figmentum*, che corrisponde all'invenzione

[3] Cfr. Anicius Manlius Severinus Boethius, *Opuscula theologica*, I. *De sancta Trinitate*, 3, PL 64, 1250B, ed. C. Moreschini (Boethius, *De consolatione Philosophiae. Opuscula theologica*), München – Leipzig 2000, p. 169,83: «Omne namque esse ex forma est».

[4] Cfr. Theodoricus Carnotensis, *Lectiones in Boethii librum De Trinitate*, 2, 39, ed. Häring cit. (alla nota 1), p. 167,38-42, e 43, p. 168,76-82: «Dicit enim auctor quod Deus est FORMA que non est IMAGO. Et QUE EST ESSE ET EX QUA EST ESSE omnium rerum. Et hec descriptio est vere forme et que est forma formarum: scilicet divinitas. (...) Dicitur autem prima forma que est divinitas forma formarum quia est generativa formarum. Mens etenim divina generat et concipit intra se formas i.e. naturas rerum que a philosophis vocantur ydee. (...) Concipit enim et tenet eas intra se et ab ipsa veniunt in possibilitatem sic quod habent esse ex ipsa prima forma et materia i.e. possibilitate i.e. habent per eas esse».

[5] Cfr. Id., *Glosa super Boethii librum De Trinitate*, 2, 19, ed. Häring cit., p. 272,21-25.

[6] Cfr. *ibid.*, 38, pp. 276,57 - 277,59.

[7] Cfr. *ibid.*, p. 276,56-57.

[8] Cfr. Id., *Lectiones in Boethii librum De Trinitate*, 2, 40, ed. Häring cit., p. 167,55-57: «(...) Sciendum quod sunt duo rerum principia licet unum sit causa alterius et possit esse sine alio: scilicet i.e. inmutabilitas sine possibilitate i.e. sine mutabilitate».

[9] Cfr. *ibid.*, 44, p. 169,86-90.

poetica ed è compresa nel significato letterale della *fabula*. Dei due prodotti della mente umana, *idola* e *figmenta*, i primi sono forme materiali, le immagini delle realtà artificiali, come a esempio la forma della casa, i secondi sono pure immagini, come la chimera e il centauro, non sensibili e non reali in quanto non dotate di materia, frutto della fantasia dei poeti[10]. Teodorico, attraverso questa pagina, riconosce alla scrittura di carattere letterario piena dignità di *ars* e il suo essere, in quanto tale, parte integrante del sapere filosofico. In ogni caso, l'uso del termine e della nozione di *figmentum* nel senso di invenzione o immagine letteraria non costituisce un caso isolato nell'ambito della produzione filosofico-teologica interna alle esperienze intellettuali e scolastiche di Chartres o a esse vicina. Mi riferisco innanzitutto, per l'affinità del contesto compositivo nel quale si situa tale termine rispetto a quello teodoriciano, a Gilberto di Poitiers, il quale, nel commento all'opuscolo boeziano contro Eutiche e Nestorio, afferma che l'autore, perché risultasse più evidente il suo accordo con i Padri e la sua distanza dal primo dei due eretici, ha proposto un'esposizione sia della verità dei cattolici sia delle invenzioni di Eutiche[11]. Qui di *figmentum* è sottolineato il significato di menzogna contrapposta a verità; è tuttavia rilevabile che per suo tramite Gilberto intende riferirsi a forme espressive diverse da quelle che hanno comunemente un contenuto veritativo, che non attengono quindi né alla scrittura sacra né al linguaggio teologico.

Ma nel sottolineare la diffusione di una sensibilità esegetica rivolta verso le opere dei poeti nell'ambiente chartriano della prima metà del secolo XII, intendo riferirmi principalmente ai commenti al *Timeo*, testo profano per eccellenza e ricco di immagini e figure retoriche, seppure percepito come 'parallelo', sul piano contenutistico, al capitolo iniziale del *Genesi*, allo stesso modo in cui, di conseguenza, la sua interpretazione è concepita come parallela rispetto all'esegesi biblica. In tali commenti sono infatti presenti i segni di una più ampia e articolata riflessione sui sensi della scrittura poetica, e in particolare, nelle *Glosae super Platonem*, appartenenti certamente all'ambiente chartriano e pubblicate nel

[10] Cfr. *ibid.*, 46, p. 169,9-16.

[11] Cfr. GILBERTUS PICTAVIENSIS, *Expositio in Boecii librum contra Euticen et Nestorium*, 6, 59, ed. N. M. Häring, Toronto 1966, p. 339,39.

1991 da Paul Edward Dutton, che le ha attribuite, forse azzardatamente, a Bernardo di Chartres, il termine *figmentum* viene accostato esplicitamente, seppure nell'unica occasione in cui è usato, alla scrittura dei poeti, cioè degli autori di opere letterarie[12]. Il brano in questione prende le mosse dalla considerazione di Platone secondo cui è impresa superiore alle capacità della mente umana conoscere le potenze divine e invisibili e bisogna quindi affidarsi alle credenze degli antichi[13], che sono incongrue quanto alla verità ma necessarie quanto all'autorità, cioè sono espresse attraverso narrazioni e immagini poetiche, che tuttavia possono essere intese anche attraverso l'attribuzione di significati compatibili con le verità filosofico-teologiche. Giove, Saturno e gli altri personaggi mitologici, a esempio, possono non essere intesi come corpi celesti o come sostanze antropomorfe, e piuttosto essere concepiti come qualcosa riguardante la divina potenza[14].

In definitiva si può dire che da un lato la difficoltà per l'uomo di dominare razionalmente i temi riguardanti il divino, dall'altro lato le conseguenze del diluvio di cui narra il *Genesi*, che avrebbe distrutto i materiali culturali delle più antiche civiltà, cioè i libri dei sapienti, e causato la morte di questi ultimi[15], hanno determinato la necessità dei racconti poetici e della loro decodificazione in termini concettualmente appropriati; e i poeti hanno raccolto tale oppotunità e hanno prodotto i loro racconti fantastici, sotto la spinta del fascino dei miti. Con *figmentum* sono quindi indicati la trama narrativa e il contenuto immaginifico della scrittura letteraria, compresi nel suo significato letterale, cioè il contenuto puramente rappresentativo, che non è desunto in modo diretto dalla realtà sensibile, né naturale né artificiale, delle invenzioni poetiche; con *fabula*, che ricorre due volte nell'opera[16], si intende il genere letterario del racconto fantastico, o meglio l'insieme dei generi letterari contenuti nel mito[17]. Ma nelle *Glosae* attribuite a

[12] Cfr. BERNARDUS CARNOTENSIS (attr.), *Glosae super Platonem*, (in seguito: *Glosae*) 6, ed. P. E. Dutton (*The* Glosae super Platonem *of Bernard of Chartres*), Toronto 1991, p. 194,134.

[13] Cfr. PLATO, *Timaeus*, 40d.

[14] Cfr. *Glosae*, *ibid.*, ed. Dutton, p. 194,135-136.

[15] Cfr. *ibid.*, p. 194,132.

[16] Oltre al luogo citato, cfr. anche *ibid.*, 3, p. 151,154.

[17] Cfr. P. DRONKE, *Fabula: Explorations into the Uses of Myth in Medieval Platonism*, Leiden – Köln 1974.

Bernardo tali termini fanno parte di una rete di nozioni esegetiche che comprende anche *involucrum* e *integumentum*[18]. E il primo, che ricorre complessivamente quattro volte, indica la forma espressiva della *fabula*[19], nella quale sono riconoscibili più strati semantici, come risulta dal suo uso sempre in riferimento al testo del *Timeo*, per introdurre l'interpretazione proposta dall'autore del commento e in una locuzione in base alla quale si mostra l'accesso ai significati del racconto attraverso la sua forma espressiva, cioè *per involucrum*[20]. Con il termine *integumentum*, usato tre volte in tutto, l'autore delle *Glosae* indica invece in modo del tutto evidente il significato secondo e pregnante del mito, contrapposto alla lettera di esso[21]. A proposito del racconto riguardante la composizione dell'anima del mondo da parte del Demiurgo[22], è precisato che esso non si deve intendere nel suo significato letterale, secondo cui l'anima è composta materialmente dai costituenti descritti[23], ma in quello nascosto, filosoficamente comprensibile e, per così dire, 'spirituale'[24], secondo cui Platone si riferisce alle diverse facoltà e funzioni dell'anima[25]. E poco più avanti, a proposito del brano del *Timeo* in cui Platone parla della divisione dell'anima in parti[26], il concetto è ripetuto[27].

Dei termini costituenti tale linguaggio esegetico, nelle *Glosae super Platonem* di Guglielmo di Conches sono presenti *figmentum*, usato una sola volta, e *integumentum*, in dieci occasioni. Col primo di essi è indicato lo sviluppo drammatico, l'invenzione letteraria, del *Timeo*, incentrato da Platone sulla giustizia naturale e ambientato il giorno dopo del dialogo de *La Repubblica*, che è dedicato alla giustizia positiva e il cui contenuto viene ricapitolato, in mo-

[18] Cfr. P. E. Dutton, *Introduction*, in Id., *The* Glosae super Platonem cit. (alla nota 12), p. 59.

[19] Cfr. M.-D. Chenu, *Involucrum. Le mythe selon les théologiens médiévaux*, in «Archives d'histoire doctrinale et littéraire du Moyen Âge», 22 (1955), pp. 75-79.

[20] Cfr. *Glosae*, 3, p. 145,1; p. 148,81-82; 5, p. 175,50; 5, p. 180,180.

[21] Cfr. *ibid.*, 3, p. 149,94-95.

[22] Cfr. Plato, *Timaeus*, 34c-35a.

[23] Cfr. *Glosae*, 5, p. 174,33-34.

[24] Cfr. *ibid.*, p. 174,34.

[25] Cfr. *ibid.*, p. 174,34-35.

[26] Plato, *Timaeus*, 35b.

[27] Cfr. *Glosae*, *ibid.*, p. 178,126-127.

do da costituire una trattazione unitaria[28]. Guglielmo afferma infatti che il filosofo greco, contestualmente alla ricapitolazione del contenuto de *La Repubblica*, introduce i personaggi che agiscono nello sviluppo, per così dire, "narrativo" del nuovo dialogo[29]. Il termine *integumentum*, il cui uso nelle *Glosae* di Guglielmo è già stato oggetto di un fondamentale e noto studio di Édouard Jeauneau[30], è riferito al mito di Erittonio, nato dalla Terra fecondata dal seme di Vulcano, cui Atena, con la quale il dio del fuoco voleva congiungersi, era sfuggita[31], al racconto di Timeo sulla composizione e la divisione dell'anima del mondo da parte del Demiurgo[32], alla descrizione del moto dei pianeti secondo la quale essi si muovono in quanto ricevono l'essere dall'anima o in quanto il loro moto è perpetuo[33], all'esposizione riguardante la generazione degli dei, ai quali l'artefice dell'universo ha annunciato la loro natura immortale e dato le necessarie direttive circa il modo in

[28] Cfr. GUILLELMUS DE CONCHIS, *Glosae super Platonem*, 12, ed. É. Jeauneau, Paris 1965, p. 71.

[29] *Ibidem*.

[30] Cfr. É. JEAUNEAU, *L'usage de la notion d'*integumentum *à travers les Gloses de Guillaume de Conches*, in «Archives d'Histoire Doctrinale et Littéraire du Moyen Âge», 24 (1957), pp. 35-100, ora in ID., *«Lectio philosophorum»: Recherches sur l'école de Chartres*, Amsterdam 1973, pp. 127-192; cfr. inoltre: R. W. SOUTHERN, *Platonism, Scholastic Method and the School of Chartres*, Reading 1979, p. 22; DUTTON, *Introduction* cit. (alla nota 18), p. 59.

[31] Cfr. GUILLELMUS DE CONCHIS, *ibid.*, 28, pp. 93-94: «Huius integumentis talis est veritas. Vulcanus aliquando dicitur ignis. (...) Aliquando dicitur vulcanus fervor ingenii. (...) Hic Palladi se commiscere desiderat quando ex fervore ingenii aliquis perfecte sapientie aspirat. Sed Pallas reluctatur quia nullus in hac vita perfectam potest habere sapientiam. Sed (...) semen tamen elicit quia, etsi pergectam non habeat sapientiam, aliquam tamen adquirit. (...) Inde nascitur Erictonius, in superiori parte homo, in inferiori draco quia ex sapientia predicta nascitur et cura celestium que rationalis est et cura temporalium que utilis est et astuta ut draco».

[32] Cfr. *ibid.*, 74, p. 150: «Deinde subiungit qualiter, more suo per integumenta loquens»; 76, p. 153: «Postquam ostendit ex quibus anima mundi excogitata sit, subiungit et qualiter, integumentum non deserens»; 79, p. 156: «Exposita igitur summa integumenti ad literam veniamus»; 80, p. 158: «Adhuc Plato integumento suo deservit dicens quod, divisa substantia anime in partes, in uno latere duplas, in altero triplas, quia nimis hiabant spacia illa et ampla erant, implevit unumquodque duobus mediis»; 87, p. 167: «Ostensa causa et modo excogitationis anime, subiungit qualiter coniuncta sit mundo et quid in digniori parte illius, id est in celestibus, operetur, more suo deserviens integumento».

[33] Cfr. *ibid.*, 98, p. 181: «Ostensa causa creationis planetarum, subiungit de qualitatibus corporum illorum et de motu (...) id est motibus per integumentum superius descriptis qui dicuntur vitales vel quia ab anima habent esse vel quia sunt perpetui».

cui essi avrebbero dovuto formare gli altri esseri viventi[34], e al racconto della formazione dell'anima umana dall'anima del mondo[35].

Ma l'occorrenza che, a proposito di quest'ultimo tema, conclude l'*expositio* della narrazione cosmologica del *Timeo* appare, tra tutte, la più significativa in ordine alla possibilità di ricavare elementi teorici di un'esegesi applicabile alla scrittura profana: secondo la pedissequa ricapitolazione di Gugliemo, Platone, dopo aver esposto la creazione dell'anima umana, afferma che Dio ha formato le anime in numero pari rispetto agli astri e ne ha assegnato una a ciascuno. Il filosofo chartriano aggiunge che coloro che commentano letteralmente affermano che qui Platone ha sostenuto una dottrina contraria alla fede cristiana, in quanto nei testi sacri è scritto che Dio crea ogni giorno nuove anime. Guglielmo non si meraviglia che un «accademico» commetta degli errori di carattere dottrinale, ma aggiunge che se non ci si ferma alle parole di Platone e si accede al senso autentico della sua opera, non soltanto non si trovano in essa opinioni contrarie alla fede ma anche si scopre una profondissima filosofia nascosta nelle figure delle parole[36].

Nel *Timeo* vanno quindi individuati, a giudizio dello Chartriano, uno strato semantico letterale e un significato più profondo e nascosto, espresso attraverso il termine e il concetto di *integumentum*, autentica metafora filosofica e addirittura metafisica, che, in quanto tale, esprime una verità razionalizzabile e non è in contraddizione rispetto alla fede cristiana. Ciò che non è accettabile se interpretato 'alla lettera', può risultare quindi conguo rispetto alla verità se assunto nella sua forma di «tropo» e nel suo 'significato secondo', che palesano una sorta di 'senso spirituale', per così dire, dei testi profani.

[34] Cfr. *ibid.*, 113, p. 203: «Finito tractatu de creatione celestis animalis tam visibilis quam invisibilis, transit ad creationem ceterorum animalium, more suo ad integumentum se transferens quod tale est quod, creatis stellis et spiritibus, convocavit eos Deus in uno conventu habitaque oratione iniunxit eis officium formandi corpora ceterorum animalium, et maxime hominis, coniungendique animam corpori et conservandi eam cum corpore, dandi cibi incrementa et dissolvendi».

[35] Cfr. *ibid.*, 118, p. 209: «Sed quia non est Creatoris promittere et non exequi, ostendit Plato qualiter executus sit promissum, id est creationem humane anime, more suo deserviens integumento».

[36] Cfr. *ibid.*, 119, pp. 210-211.

Che si tratti di una riflessione non occasionale e condivisa negli ambienti culturali più 'avanzati' è comprovato dall'uso che anche Pietro Abelardo fa del vocabolario dell'esegesi profana sopra evidenziato sin dalla *Theologia «Summi boni»*, risalente agli anni precedenti il concilio di Soissons del 1121, nel corso del quale viene condannata per la prima volta l'interpretazione abelardiana della Trinità. In tale opera il termine *involucrum*, inteso come 'significato letterale', per così dire, della narrazione dei filosofi, occorre sette volte, *integumentum* una sola volta ma nel significato inequivocabile di figura del mito, *figmentum*, che esprime la finzione narrativa tipica della scrittura profana, 3 volte, tutt'e tre nei paragrafi dal 37 al 51 del libro I, secondo l'edizione di Eligius M. Buytaert e Constant J. Mews, quindi sempre e solo a proposito dei *testimonia philosophorum*[37]. Nella successiva *Theologia christiana*, in cui è rivisto e ampliato il contenuto della precedente, *involucrum* occorre sette volte e solo l'ultima a proposito della sacra scrittura, due volte *integumentum*, peraltro nello stesso contesto in cui compare un'unica volta nella *«Summi boni»*, e *figmentum* 8 volte, delle quali le prime tre riproducono le corrispondenti occorrenze della *«Summi boni»* mentre le altre, tra i paragrafi 120 e 126 del II libro dell'edizione critica di Buytaert, sono inserite in un'ampia digressione dedicata al contributo fornito al perseguimento della verità da parte dei filosofi e dei poeti, contro coloro che criticano in modo eccessivo la dilettica e le arti liberali[38]. Infine nella *Theologia «Scholarium»*, che manifesta il culmine dell'impegno, da parte di Abelardo, di sistemazione e di sintesi delle precedenti 'edizioni' e la cui ultima redazione si colloca a ridosso della sua seconda e definitiva condanna, subita nel concilio di Sens del 1140, le occorrenze di *involucrum* sono sei, identiche a

[37] PETRUS ABAELARDUS, *Theologia «Summi boni»*, I 37, ed. E. M. Buytaert – C. J. Mews (*Opera theologica*, III), Turnhout 1987 (CCCM, 13), p. 99,364; 41, p. 100,390; 43, p. 101,429; 44, p. 103,468; 46, p. 103,483; 49, p. 104,506; 51, p. 105,522 (*involucrum*). *Ibid.*, I, 43, p. 101,433 (*integumentum*). *Ibid.*, I, 41, p. 100,392-393, 395 e 397 (*figmentum*).

[38] ID., *Theologia christiana*, I, 89, ed. E. M. Buytaert (*Opera theologica*, II), Turnhout 1969 (CCCM, 12), p. 109,1178; 97, p. 112,1275; 103, p. 114,1319; 106, p. 116,1364; 107, p. 117,1404; 109, p. 117,1421; II, 126, p. 191,1922 (*involucrum*). *Ibid.*, I, 105, p. 116,1359; 106, p. 116,1368 (*integumentum*). *Ibid.*, I, 103, p. 114,1322, 1324 e 1326; II, 120, p. 187,1833; 122, p. 187,1849; 123, p. 189,1886-1887; 124, p. 189,1889; 126, p. 191,1919 (*figmentum*).

quelle della *Theologia christiana* a eccezione dell'ultima, che si trova in un contesto non omogeneno rispetto alla trattazione riguardante le opere filosofico-letterarie, le due occorrenze di *integumentum* riproducono quelle della *Theologia christiana*, *figmentum* è usato sette volte, cinque delle quali in modo identico rispetto alla precedente versione della *Theologia*, le restanti due corrispondenti, ma non identiche, rispetto alla settima della *Theologia christiana*, come quest'ultima dedicate alla citazione delle *Sententiae* di Isidoro di Siviglia a proposito della differenza tra la *lectio sacra* e l'accostarsi alle finzioni dei poeti[39].

In Abelardo il tema agostiniano della rivelazione creaturale, visibile nel «libro della natura», accanto alla rivelazione scritta, da leggere e ascoltare[40], conduce alla valorizzazione, oltre che della ragione dialettica in quanto condizione esclusiva della conoscenza possibile, della filosofia, di cui la *ratio* è «organo» e che ha avuto nell'antichità e continua ad avere, accanto alle sue peculiari funzioni epistemiche in ordine alla struttura del mondo fisico e ai rapporti tra i suoi corpi, il compito di riconoscere nelle creature l'impronta di Dio[41]. Ma in quanto la *ratio* ha negli enti sensibili e nelle loro qualità accidentali gli oggetti che le sono propri, solo in senso traslato può riferirsi al divino, ricorrendo a metafore e miti, *involucra* che nascondono dietro la narrazione fittizia significati razionalizzabili e autenticamente verosimili, riguardanti alcuni tra i capisaldi della fede, l'esistenza di Dio, la sua unità e trinità, l'onnipotenza[42]. E in tal modo il Palatino, oltre a manifestare la

[39] ID., *Theologia «Scholarium»*, I, 147, ed. Buytaert – Mews (*Opera theologica*, III) cit., p. 379,1728; 157, p. 383,1836-1837; 163, p. 385,1879; 166, p. 386,1921; 167, p. 387,1960; 170, p. 388,1981 (*involucrum*). *Ibid.*, I, 165, p. 386,1916; 166, p. 386,1921 (*integumentum*). *Ibid.*, I, 163, p. 385,1881, 1884 e 1885; II, 22, p. 417,319-320; 24, p. 417,333; 25, p. 418,358 e 361 (*figmentum*). Per la citazione isidoriana, cfr. ISIDORUS HISPALENSIS, *Sententiae*, III, 13, PL 83, 685A-686A.

[40] Cfr. AURELIUS AUGUSTINUS, *Enarrationes in Psalmos*, 45, 7, PL 36, 518, ed. E. Dekkers – J. Fraipont, 3 voll., Turnhout 1956 (CCSL, 38-39-40), I, p. 522,4-7: «Liber tibi sit pagina divina, ut haec audias; liber tibi sit orbis terrarum, ut haec videas. In istis codicibus non ea legunt, nisi qui litteras noverunt: in toto mundo legat et idiota».

[41] Cfr. PETRUS ABAELARDUS, *Theologia «Summi boni»*, II, 64, p. 135,547-574 e p. 139,678; ID., *Theologia christiana*, III, 116, p. 236,1346, e 130, p. 244,1570; ID., *Theologia «Scholarium»*, II, 68, p. 441,1042, e 93, p. 453,1399.

[42] Cfr. ID., *Theologia christiana*, V, 17, p. 354,266-79. ID., *Theologia «Scholarium»*, III, 17, p. 507,249-261.

diffusione tra i *novatores* delle pratiche esegetiche applicate alla scrittura filosofico-letteraria e del loro vocabolario tecnico, e quindi a confermare l'esistenza di canali di comunicazione tra le diverse, ma spesso affini, esperienze scolastiche, fornisce una solida motivazione teorica all'esigenza di estendere ai testi 'poetici' il metodo esegetico della *lectio sacra*.

2. *I sensi della scrittura profana. Gli epigoni*

Il linguaggio e le idee riscontrati nelle opere dei maestri chartriani vissuti nel corso della prima metà del secolo XII sono anche rintracciabili nei testi di autori appartenenti alla generazione successiva e ad ambienti estranei a Chartres. Mi riferisco a Bernardo Silvestre, i cui rapporti con la scuola sono oscuri ma che dedica a Teodorico di Chartres la sua *Cosmographia*[43], e a Clarembaldo di Arras, allievo, probabilmente a Parigi, oltre che di Ugo di San Vittore, dello stesso Teodorico, i cui temi ripropone nelle sue opere, integrandoli con la più moderata prospettiva teorica di Ugo e amalgamandoli con le direttive spirituali di Bernardo di Clairvaux.

Nel *Tractatulus super librum Genesis* di quest'ultimo, è riscontrabile il termine *figmentum* nel significato di finzione letteraria afferente al mito, e addirittura di mito *tout court*, affine a quello che assume nell'opera di Teodorico e di Gilberto di Poitiers. Riferendosi infatti alla *fabula* contenuta nel *De nuptiis Philologiae et Mercurii* di Marziano Capella a proposito del giorno natale di Psiche, che ricevette dagli dei molti doni, tra i quali un diadema d'oro che Giove aveva sottratto alla più degna delle sue figlie, Eternità, Clarembaldo ritiene che debba intendersi come l'esposizione, in termini figurati, della creazione dell'anima[44]. È qui riproposto il

[43] BERNARDUS SILVESTRIS, *Cosmographia* (*De mundi universitate*), ed. P. Dronke, Leiden 1978, p. 96.

[44] Cfr. CLAREMBALDUS ATREBATENSIS, *Tractatulus super librum Genesis*, 18, ed. (con tr. it. e comm.) in C. MARTELLO, *Fisica della creazione. La cosmologia di Clarembaldo di Arras*, Catania 1998 (Symbolon, 18), [pp. 219-244], p. 243,8-13: «Subsignans namque causam cur suo illa digna coniugio videretur, dicit deos in natali die Psyches ad convivium corrogatos multa dona virgini contulisse, inter quos et Iovem diadema aureum capiti eius imposuisse quod ipse honoratiori filie sue Eternitati detraxerat. In quo nimirum figmento veram de creatione anime sententiam involvit philosophus. Psyche enim grece, anima dicitur latine».

linguaggio chartriano dell'esegesi profana, attraverso l'uso del termine *figmentum* nell'accezione di invenzione narrativa o immagine compresa nel significato letterale della scrittura dei miti, e ribadito che nella *fabula* la forma espressiva nasconde (*involvit*, che ha lo stesso radicale di *involucrum*, rinvenuto nelle *Glosae* attribuite a Bernardo di Chartres come parte integrante del lessico esegetico) un contenuto filosofico, in quanto espresso da un filosofo, come nel caso in questione la dottrina riguardante la creazione dell'anima, e vero, cioè compatibile con la fede cristiana.

Ma su tale linguaggio chartriano dell'esegesi del mito si sofferma in modo più articolato, tanto da fare legittimamente supporre che esso sia sorretto da una teorizzazione che 'attraversa' il secolo XII accomunando e caratterizzando le pur diverse personalità che appartengono o si richiamano alla scuola di Chartres e ne esprimono lo 'spirito', l'autore del breve ma denso commento al *De nuptiis Philologiae et Mercurii* in cui Édouard Jeauneau ha ritenuto di individuare Bernardo Silvestre, se è questi l'autore del commento all'*Eneide* che gli è stato tradizionalmente attribuito[45], in quanto a quest'ultimo il commento al *De nuptiis* rinvia a più riprese e spesso si uniforma[46]. E a giudizio dell'autore di tale commento a Marziano, la figura è un genere dell'insegnamento, nel senso che è una forma espressiva, chiamata comunemente involucro, la quale ha due aspetti: l'allegoria e l'integumento. L'allegoria, in forma di narrazione storica, cela una verità diversa da quella che la storia comunque esprime, come nel caso della lotta di Giacobbe di cui narra il Genesi; l'integumento cela la parte di verità che è comprensibile da parte della ragione umana ed è nascosta in una narrazione favolosa, come a proposito di Orfeo. L'allegoria, che è la figura della profezia intesa come visione e linguaggio della Verità, riguarda dunque la sacra scrittura, l'integumento la filosofia[47].

[45] Cfr. BERNARDUS SILVESTRIS, *Commentum super sex libros Eneidos Virgilii*, ed. G. Riedel, Greifswald 1924; quindi la successiva edizione: *Commentum quod dicitur Bernardi Silvestris super sex libros Eneidos Virgilii*, edd. J. & E. Jones, Lincoln (Nebr.) 1977 (cfr. infine la recente traduzione in lingua italiana: *Commento all'Eneide. Libri 1-6*, Roma 2008, a c. di B. Basile).

[46] Cfr. É. JEAUNEAU, *Note sur l'École de Chartres*, in «Studi Medievali», Ser. 3ª, 5 (1964), [pp. 821-865], pp. 844-846; I. RAMELLI, *Tutti i commenti a Marziano Capella*, Milano 2006, pp. 1744-1745.

[47] Cfr. BERNARDUS SILVESTRIS (attr.), *Commentum in Martianum*, ed. in JEAU-

Ci sono fin qui elementi sufficienti per cogliere nel testo un'organica dottrina esegetica, incentrata sui «tropi», cioè sulle figure di significazione, della scrittura. Il linguaggio figurato richiede un *involucrum*, cioè una forma espressiva che, attraverso la lettera, nasconde il suo significato più profondo e pregnante, e rimanda a quest'ultimo, cioè a un piano semantico veritativo, l'*allegoria*, cioè la figura che esprime la verità nascosta in una narrazione storicamente vera, come il racconto scritturale sacro, o l'*integumentum*, cioè la figura che esprime il significato razionale dei miti, in un certo senso l''allegoria dei poeti', secondo la successiva e problematica distinzione del *Convivio* dantesco tra la concezione profana e quella teologica del senso allegorico[48]. L'autore del *Commentario su Marziano Capella* inoltre afferma che il linguaggio figurato è spesso caratterizzato da un intento imitativo: come infatti in Virgilio Enea attraversa gl'inferi fino a raggiungere il padre Anchise, guidato dalla Sibilla, così nel *De nuptiis* Mercurio attraversa le diverse regioni del cosmo per raggiungere Giove, accompagnato dalla Virtù, e nella *Consolatio Philosophiae* Boezio si innalza fino al sommo bene, guidato dalla Filosofia. Dagli esempi addotti si ricava non solo che le tre diverse figure

NEAU, *Note sur l'École de Chartres* cit., Appendice (B), p. 856 (ora in ID., *Lectio philosophorum* cit., p. 40); cfr. anche l'edizione critica in H. J. WESTRA, *The Commentary on Martianus Capella's* De nuptiis Philologiae et Mercurii *Attributed to Bernardus Silvestris* (Pontifical Institute of Mediaeval Studies, Studies and texts, 80), Toronto 1986, p. 45, e l'edizione, che riproduce, con traduzione italiana a fronte l'ed. Westra, in RAMELLI, *Tutti i commenti a Marziano Capella* cit., p. 1764. Tale riflessione si basa sulle differenze storiche dell'allegoria cristiana rispetto alla sua concezione pagana, su cui cfr. i seguenti studi: R. HAHN, *Die Allegorie in der antiken Rhetorik*, Tübingen 1967; PH. ROLLISON, *Classical Theories of Allegory and Christian Culture*, Pittsburh – Brighton 1981; M. IRVINE, *Interpretation and the Semiotics of Allegory in Clement of Alexandria, Origen and Augustin*, in «Semiotica», 63 (1987), pp. 33-71; B. CLAUSI, *Elementi di ermeneutica monastica nel* De schematibus et tropis *di Beda*, in «Orpheus», N. S. 11 (1990), pp. 277-307; ID., *L'esegesi patristica*, in *La Bibbia libro di tutti?*, Atti del Convegno di Studi (Catania, 3-4 aprile 2003), Firenze – Milano 2004, pp. 151-176; C. MARTELLO, *Allegorismo e saperi profani nell'esegesi esamerale del XII secolo*, *ibid.*, pp. 177-197.

[48] DANTE ALIGHIERI, *Convivio*, II, 1, 4, ed. M. Simonelli, Bologna 1966, p. 31: «Veramente li Teologi questo senso prendono altrimenti che li poeti; ma però che mia intenzione è qui lo modo de li poeti seguitare, prendo lo senso allegorico secondo che per li poeti è usato». Su questo complesso tema mi limito a rimandare all'ampio studio di J. PÉPIN, *Dante et la tradition de l'allégorie*, in ID., *La tradition de l'allégorie. De Philon d'Alexandrie a Dante*, Paris 1987, pp. 251-326.

esprimono pressoché lo stesso concetto[49] ma anche che la scrittura del mito è affine a quella poetica, cioè alla scrittura letteraria e profana in generale, e che quindi non può essere che unica la loro esegesi.

3. Allegoria *e* integumentum*: esegesi biblica e interpretazione dei testi profani*

Le differenze tra *allegoria* e *integumentum* nel commento a Marziano attribuito a Bernardo Sivestre rappresentano quindi il rapporto intercorrente tra l'esegesi sacra e la profana in quanto evidenziano le tre caratteristiche fondamentali del linguaggio figurato dell'opera poetica, la natura meramente rappresentativa, l'inapplicabilità alla teologia e l'equivocità. Infatti in primo luogo è detto che solo nel caso del testo allegorico, e quindi sacro, il significato letterale è vero, in quanto, come s'è visto, esprime una fattualità storica, mentre nel caso dell'integumento, il testo denota pure immagini ed esprime un significato veritativo, in quanto razionale, solo figuratamente. In secondo luogo, i *Commentarii in Somnium Scipionis* di Macrobio sono citati per sottolineare che la forma espressiva figurata, fondamentale senso spirituale delle sacre scritture, non si addice sempre a una trattazione filosofica e profana[50], in quanto, quando si affrontano temi teologici, non è consentito usare rappresentazioni favolistiche, quando invece si prendono in esame temi riguardanti realtà più accessibili alle facoltà razionali e rappresentative, come l'anima o gli elementi fisici, è possibile ricorrere agli integumenti. Per questo motivo Virgilio per descrivere la vita dell'anima unita al corpo ricorre a un liguaggio figurato, Platone afferma *figuraliter* che il numero è la materia dell'anima e Marziano Capella, svelando la deificazione della natura umana, parla da sapiente che non dice nulla senza riferirsi a un mistero[51]. Infine, nel commento al *De nuptiis* attribuito a Bernardo, è affermato che nella scrittura profana una forma espressiva figurata può avere signifi-

[49] Cfr. BERNARDUS SILVESTRIS (attr.), *Commentum in Martianum*, ed. Jeauneau, p. 857 (p. 41) (ed. Westra, pp. 46-47; ed. Ramelli, pp. 1764-1766).

[50] Cfr. AMBROSIUS THEODOSIUS MACROBIUS, *Commentarii in Somnium Scipionis*, I, 2, 13-4, ed. I. Willis, Leipzig 1963, pp. 6,18 - 7,4.

[51] Cfr. BERNARDUS SILVESTRIS (attr.), *Commentum in Martianum*, ed. Jeauneau, pp. 856-857 (pp. 40-41) (ed. Westra, pp. 45-46; ed. Ramelli, p. 1764).

cati diversi, ed è quindi equivoca, così come figure diverse possono esprimere il medesimo significato. Infatti risulta equivoco in Virgilio il significato razionale del nome Giunone, riferito all'aria e alla vita pratica, il nome Mercurio è applicato alla stella, causa dell'eloquenza, e all'eloquenza stessa, mentre con Giove e Anchise è espressa la medesima realtà. Sarà opportuno dunque distinguere i diversi significati a cui si applicano equivocamente le figure[52].

Nel testo in questione, quel che più conta, dal punto di vista di chi intenda ricostruire la trama dei rapporti tra il pensiero religioso e i saperi profani, è comunque il confronto che l'autore opera tra la pagina divina e la scrittura filosofica e letteraria a proposito delle figure di significazione; attraverso tale comparazione, nella prima egli individua un piano semantico letterale vero, in quanto corrispondente ad avvenimenti realmente accaduti, e un significato allegorico di carattere squisitamente spirituale e profetico, nella seconda riconosce una lettera meramente immaginifica e un significato secondo di carattere filosofico e razionale.

Per quanto in particolare riguarda la riflessione sui sensi della sacra scrittura dei maestri di Chartres e dei loro allievi ed epigoni, vanno assunte come fondamentali esempi la teorizzazione di Teodorico di Chartres, contenuta nel già citato *incipit* del *Tractatus de sex dierum operibus*, quella del *Tractatulus super librum Genesis* di Clarembaldo di Arras, che si pone sulla scia della prima ma anche della più ampia riflessione contenta nel *Didascalicon* e nelle *Praenotatiuncolae de Scripturis et scriptoribus sacris* di Ugo di San Vittore, ed è quindi espressione di un punto di vista ampiamente condiviso. Clarembaldo sostiene che il testo biblico può essere interpretato in tre modi, cioè secondo le connotazioni allegoriche, le implicazioni morali e il contenuto storico che esprime[53].

[52] Cfr. *ibid.*, ed. Jeauneau, p. 857 (p. 41) (ed. Westra, pp. 46-47; ed. Ramelli, pp. 1764-1766).

[53] Cfr. CLAREMBALDUS ATREBATENSIS, *Tractatulus super librum Genesis*, 4, ed. Martello cit. (alla nota 44), p. 223,3-9: «Igitur ut sancti perhibent doctores tribus modis exponendus est id est historialiter, allegorice, moraliter. Historialiter hoc modo ut exponantur res geste iuxta littere sonum et significationem. Allegorice ita ut in rebus narratis aliud figuretur quod vel ad Christum respiciat, vel ad ecclesiam. Unde allegoria grece alieniloquium latine interpretatur. Moraliter vero sic, ut per ea que narrantur ad bonam vitam informemur». *Ibid.*, 17, p. 242,4-5: «Tres etenim lectiones, scilicet allegoria, moralis, historialis in hac sacra scriptura exequende et observande sunt». E cfr. HUGO DE SANCTO VICTORE, *Didascalicon*,

In altri termini, egli afferma che la lettera della sacra scrittura corrisponde alla verità storica dei fatti narrati e che tali fatti sono il fondamento di ogni ulteriore scoperta di senso e rimandano a un significato spirituale, che a sua volta comprende l'allegoria, assunta come *tropo* che, in linea con la tradizione cristiana, esprime figuratamente il significato profetico della rivelazione[54], e la sua valenza morale[55]. Insomma, la precisazione nel secolo XII, quanto meno a Chartres e negli ambienti culturali ispirati all'esperienza chartriana, della concezione dell'allegoria come significato spirituale e nel contempo come figura comporta l'individuazione, da parte dell'autore del *Commentario su Marziano Capella* attribuito a Bernardo Silvestre, di una corrispondenza tra essa e l'*integumentum*, in quanto entrambi veicolano il significato figurato del testo, sacro e vero nel primo caso, poetico e fittizio, ancorché pregnante, nel secondo.

La distinzione, capitale nell'esegesi medievale, tra *allegoria in factis* (o *facti*), secondo cui la narrazione di un evento storico rimanda a un significato spirituale e veritativo, e *allegoria in verbis* (o *dicti*), secondo cui il significato allegorico è evocato attraverso forme simboliche, non è assente nei testi fin qui citati, e particolarmente in quelli di Ugo e di Clarembaldo, seppure non è inserita nel modello teorico riguardante i sensi della scrittura sacra. Piuttosto emerge la tendenza a privilegiare, in quest'ultima, i *facta*, nei quali vengono compresi i *dicta*, e a individuare nei primi il senso allegorico primario della sacra scrittura, in linea con la tradizione più condivisa, ma tutto sommato anche con i processi di

De studio legendi, V, 2, 789C, ed. Buttimer cit. (alla nota 2), p. 95,15-17: «Primo omnium sciendum est, quod divina scriptura triplicem habet modum intelligendi, id est, historiam, allegoriam, tropologiam».

[54] Cfr. H. DE LUBAC, *Exégèse médiévale. Les quatre sens de l'Écriture*, 4 voll., Paris 1959, II, pp. 384-396 (tr. it., Milano 1988, II, pp. 15-28); A. STRUBEL, *«Allegoria in factis» et «allegoria in uerbis»*, in «Poétique», 23 (1975), pp. 342-357; J. CHYDENIUS, *La théorie du symbolisme médiéval*, in «Poétique», 23 (1975), pp. 322-341; PÉPIN, *Dante et la tradition de l'allégorie* cit. (alla nota 48), pp. 303-306.

[55] Cfr. HUGO DE SANCTO VICTORE, *ibid.*, VI, 3, 801C, p. 116,20-25: «Fundamentum autem et principium doctrinae sacrae historia est. (...) Aedificaturus ergo primum fundamentum historiae pone, deinde per significationem typicam in arcem fidei fabricam mentis erige. Ad extremum vero, per moralitatis gratiam quasi pulcherrimo superducto colore edificium pinge». *Ibid.*, VI, 4, 803A, p. 119,4-6: «Quod sub terra est fundamentum figurare diximus historiam, fabricam quae superaedificatur allegoriam insinuare».

razionalizzazione del sapere di cui tali autori sono, in diversa misura, partecipi. Infatti la preferenza per l'*allegoria in factis* non è un atteggiamento univoco all'interno della tradizione medievale dell'esegesi e attraverso l'enucleazione e la messa in evidenza dell'*allegoria in verbis* si manifesta talvolta la presenza di un punto di vista simbolico che affonda le radici nella spiritualità pagana ellenistica e tardoantica[56], che è elevata a dignità filosofica, anzi 'ultrafilosofica', dal neoplatonismo[57] e che penetra nel Medioevo soprattutto attraverso il *corpus dionysianum*[58]. E tuttavia gli 'scolastici' della prima metà del secolo XII sono in ogni caso estranei al simbolismo, inteso come veicolo di accesso alla teologia mistica, della tradizione dell'*allegoria in verbis*, che pure si ritrova, ma in posizione subordinata rispetto alle *res* e ai *facta*, sia nel *Didascalicon* e nel *De sacramentis christianae fidei* di Ugo di San Vittore, dove è assimilata al linguaggio delle sacre scritture, veicolo di significati spirituali ma come tale meno sicuro e diretto delle *res* che esprime[59], sia nel *Tractatulus* di Clarembaldo, in cui è avvertibile la sua

[56] Cfr. PÉPIN, *Dante et la tradition de l'allégorie* cit. (alla nota 48), pp. 295-303; M. NASTA, *Les êtres de Paroles. Herméneutique du langage figuré*, Bruxelles 2001.

[57] Cfr. J. PÉPIN, *La théorie de l'exégèse allégorique chez Philon d'Alexandrie*, in ID., *Dante et tradition de l'allégorie* cit. (alla nota 48), pp. 7-40; ID., *L'affrontement d'Homère et de Moïse aux premiers siècles chrétiens*, *ibid.*, pp. 41-56; ID., *Porphyre, exégète d'Homère*, *ibid.*, pp. 57-80.

[58] Cfr. ID., *La lecture du «De antro nimpharum» de Porphyre en Occident*, *ibid.*, pp. 81-90; *La théorie du symbolisme dans la tradition dionysienne*, *ibid.*, pp. 199-221; *La «Lettre IX» de Denys sur le symbolisme, et sa traduction par Jean Scot Érigène*, *ibid.*, pp. 223-233; *"Mystères" et "symboles" chez Jean Scot Érigène*, *ibid.*, pp. 235-250. E cfr. F. ZAMBON, Allegoria in verbis*: per una distinzione tra simboli e allegoria nell'ermeneutica medievale*, in *Simbolo, Metafora, Allegoria*, Atti del IV Convegno italo-tedesco (Bressanone 1976), a c. di D. Goldin, Padova 1980 (Quaderni del Circolo Filologico Linguistico Padovano, 11), pp. 73-106.

[59] Cfr. HUGO DE SANCTO VICTORE, *ibid.*, V, 2, 790CD, pp. 96,24 - 97,6: «Sciendum est etiam, quod in divino eloquio non tantum verba, sed etiam res significare habent, qui modus non adeo in aliis scripturis inveniri solet. philosophus solam vocum novit significationem, sed excellentior valde est rerum significatio quam vocum, quia hanc usus instituit, illam natura dictavit. haec hominum vox est, illa vox Dei ad homines. haec prolata perit, illa creata subsistit. vox tenuis est nota sensuum, res divinae rationis est simulacrum, quod ergo sonus oris, qui simul subsistere incipit et desinit, ad rationem mentis est, hoc omne spatium temporis ad aeternitatem. ratio mentis intrinsecum verbum est, quod sono vocis, id est, verbo extrinseco manifestatur. et divina sapientia, quam de corde suo Pater eructavit, in se invisibilis, per creaturas et in creaturis agnoscitur». ID., *De sacramentis christianae fidei*, I, Prol., 5, PL 176, 185AB: «Unde apparet quantum divina Scriptura caeteris omnibus scripturis non solum in materia sua, sed etiam in mo-

presenza come determinazione della profezia, che è intesa come rivelazione attraverso un'intuizione intellettuale e il cui significato occupa lo spazio del concetto tradizionale e onnicomprensivo di *allegoria*, che ne è la rappresentazione[60]. Il paradigma teorico di base è ampliato dall'Atrebatese, sempre sulla scia di Ugo di San Vittore, attraverso la specificazione che l'allegoria comprende anche il senso anagogico, cioè il piano semantico più squisitamente spirituale in quanto riguardante Dio e le sostanze celesti[61], e quindi distinguibile dalla semplice allegoria, che è in generale il veicolo con cui è espressa una verità invisibile ed edificante attraverso la descrizione di un fatto visibile.

Alla luce di quest'ultimo testo di Clarembaldo e delle sue autorevoli fonti, il confronto tra l'esegesi sacra e la profana si arricchisce di un ulteriore elemento: l'integumento, in quanto esprime figuratamente un significato razionalizzabile ed è quindi privo di un contenuto autenticamente spirituale e di valenze squisitamente teologiche, appare anche privo di dirette implicazioni e di pressanti ed esplicite incombenze di carattere morale. Tutti gli autori fin qui menzionati, in quanto si sono occupati dell'interpretazione della *fabula* e della scrittura letteraria, non mettono in risalto infatti un suo senso tropologico, quanto meno non sentono il bisogno di sottolinearne la visibilità e la centralità in ordine al rapporto intercorrente tra i diversi approcci semantici a tali forme di scrittura. Conseguenza di ciò è la consapevolezza che in uno degli ambienti culturali più avanzati della 'scolasti-

do tractandi, subtilitate et profunditate praecellat; cum in caeteris quidem scripturis solae voces significare inveniantur; in hac autem non solum voces, sed etiam res significativae sint. Sicut igitur in eo sensu qui inter voces et res versatur necessaria est cognitio vocum, sic in illo qui inter res et facta vel facienda mystica constat, necessaria est cognitio rerum».

60 Cfr. CLAREMBALDUS ATREBATENSIS, *Tractatulus super librum Genesis*, 3, ed. Martello cit. (alla nota 44), pp. 222,11 - 223,23: «Prophetia vero pluribus modis denuntiatur. (...) Aliquando per intelligentiam, sicut David regi aut Ysaie aut Paulo ad tercium celum rapto. Sed que per intelligentiam denuntiantur, aut factis denuntiantur aut dictis. Factis, ut archa Noe vel sacrificio Abrahe. Item que dictis, aut predicendo futura, ut 'Ecce virgo concipiet et pariet filium' (*Is* 7, 14). Aut ostendendo presentia, ut 'Hoc nunc os ex ossibus meis et caro de carne mea' (*Gn* 2, 23). Aut item res gestas narrando, ut 'In principio creavit Deus celum et terram' (*Gn* 1, 1)».

61 Cfr. *ibid.*, 17, p. 242,5-6: «Anagogica que est de vita celestium ad allegoriam pertinet». E cfr. HUGO DE SANCTO VICTORE, *De Scripturis et scriptoribus sacris praenotatiunculae*, 3, PL 175, 12B (testo cit. *supra*, alla nota 2).

ca' del secolo XII, elettivamente rappresentativo dell'esigenza di razionalizzazione insita nella civiltà urbana della 'porzione' centro-settentrionale del regno di Francia, mentre la teorizzazione dei sensi biblici va strutturandosi secondo il tradizionale modello quadripartito che l'esegesi, non solo sacra ma anche profana, assumerà nelle sue formulazioni scolastiche più mature, la riflessione sul linguaggio del mito e della forma espressiva figurata della scrittura poetica rimane ferma alla contrapposizione di base tra *figmentum* e *integumentum*, tra un significato letterale frutto dell'invenzione dei poeti e un contenuto più profondo e razionale. E tuttavia, tale riflessione è in ultima analisi riconducibile alla coeva definizione dei quattro sensi della scrittura sacra, sbocco di una tradizione di pensiero percepita come squisitamente cristiana ma che risale alla tarda antichità pagana[62]. L'esegesi quindi rappresenta ed esprime l'esito dei percorsi, non sempre lineari, attraverso cui il pensiero cristiano ha trovato nella cultura tardoantica pagana alcune importanti condizioni dottrinali e spirituali su cui edificare e consolidare la propria egemonia religiosa e civile, dimostrandosi in grado, su queste basi, di influenzare le scienze e le pratiche profane. In particolare la *sacra lectio*, in quanto ha recepito e inglobato aspetti rilevanti dei saperi risalenti alla filosofia antica, se non classica, dalle arti del 'trivio' intese come «organo» della *lectio historialis* della sacra scrittura alle teorie cosmogoniche e cosmologiche utilizzate come termine di confronto con la letteratura esamerale[63], oltre a sostenere la crescita di una «dottrina» dei teologi, vera e propria teologia razionale, suscita nuove esperienze filosofiche, come negli Chartriani e nei loro epigoni, ma anche in altri ambienti 'scolastici' come è provato dal *Didascalicon* e dal *Fons philosophiae* rispettivamente di Ugo e di Goffredo di San Vittore, l'esigenza di chiedersi, estendendo ai testi filosofici e letterari l'interesse dell'uomo di cultura fedele alla Chiesa universale, se e in quale misura sono applicabili a essi alcuni strumenti di comprensione e di interpretazione della scrittura rivelata.

[62] Cfr. C. SPICQ, *Esquisse d'une histoire de l'exégèse latine au moyen âge*, Paris 1944; J. DANIÉLOU, Sacramentum futuri. *Études sur les origines de la typologie biblique*, Paris 1950; J. PÉPIN, *Mythe et allégorie. Les origines grecques et les contestations judéochétiennes*, Paris 1976; ID., *La tradition de l'allégorie* cit. (alla nota 48), pp. 41-80.

[63] Cfr. A. TARABOCHIA CANAVERO, *Esegesi biblica e cosmologia. Note sull'interpretazione patristica e medievale di Genesi 1, 2*, Milano 1981.

PIERFRANCESCO DE FEO

I LIMITI DELL'UMANESIMO ANTICO E MODERNO NEL PENSIERO DI GUALTIERO DI SAN VITTORE

1. *La figura di Gualtiero nella scuola di San Vittore e il* Contra quatuor labyrinthos Franciae

Quando la scuola di San Vittore inizia la propria attività culturale all'inizio del secolo XII, la città di Parigi è l'indiscussa capitale di una fiorente rinascenza spirituale e culturale, animata da molteplici centri di irradiamento degli studi, tra i quali sono già rinomati la scuola capitolare di Notre-Dame, quella dei cosiddetti 'artisti' sul Parvus Pons e Santa Genoveffa. L'abbazia di San Vittore è all'inizio soltanto un oratorio, presso cui nel 1108 Guglielmo di Champeaux, professore di retorica e arcidiacono, si ritira, allo scopo di dedicarsi unicamente alla preghiera[1]. Buona parte dei suoi discepoli lo segue, per cui il modesto oratorio si trasforma in una comunità monastica che ben presto adotta la regola dei canonici agostiniani. Nel 1115 viene eletto il primo abate, nella persona di Gilduino, «qui était à la fois un savant et un organisateur»[2]. Questi redige, probabilmente intorno al 1130, il *Liber Ordinis Sancti Victoris Parisiensis*, una vera miniera di notizie sull'organizzazione dell'abbazia e sulla vita dei monaci[3]. La compo-

[1] Per il Bonnard, Guglielmo si ritira dall'insegnamento in conseguenza di una crisi personale, successiva alla sconfitta subita nel corso della celebre disputa con il suo allievo Abelardo, sul tema della natura degli universali. Cfr. F. BONNARD, *Histoire de l'abbaye royale et de l'ordre des chanoines réguliers de Saint-Victor de Paris*, 2 voll., Paris 1904, I, pp. 9-12.

[2] Cfr. J. BOUSSARD, *Nouvelle histoire de Paris*, 7 voll., Paris 1992, II, p. 210.

[3] GILDUINUS SANCTI VICTORIS, *Liber Ordinis Sancti Victoris Parisiensis*, edd. L. Jocqué – L. Milis, Turnhout 1984 (CCCM, 61).

10.1484/M.NUTRIX-EB.1.101246

sizione di sermoni diventa quasi un obbligo per gli uomini di cultura vittorini, vista l'importanza che assume, per il loro carisma, la predicazione. Ogni vittorino deve esercitarsi in essa, per cui consacra molto tempo alla lettura privata nel chiostro. Lo *scriptorium* svolge la sua attività a pieno regime già verso il 1140: il grande teologo Ugo ne è il primo noto animatore e coordinatore[4]. Ben presto San Vittore si dota di una scuola che fornisce agli aspiranti monaci gli strumenti filosofici e teologici necessari a un'adeguata evangelizzazione della cultura; l'abbazia parigina diventa uno dei più interessanti centri di mediazione tra la tradizione monastica e la nascente cultura universitaria cittadina, al punto che tra i suoi esponenti figurano sostenitori di posizioni profondamente alternative in relazione al rapporto tra ragione e fede.

Nel 1173, alla morte di Riccardo, viene eletto priore Gualtiero, uomo di intransigenti vedute conservatrici, in un periodo in cui occorre ristabilire un clima di austerità in una comunità danneggiata dalla deleteria opera dell'abate Ervisio, che ha compromesso la pace claustrale al punto da dover essere rimosso su diretto intervento del papa Alessandro III[5]. Non sono pervenute biografie dirette di Gualtiero. Egli nasce in territorio anglosassone verso il 1120; si trasferisce a Parigi ed entra a San Vittore a circa 20 anni, verso il 1140, sotto l'abate Gilduino; viene eletto vice-priore nel 1162 e priore nel 1173; muore fra il 10 settembre 1179 e il 20 agosto 1180[6]. Soltanto due opere sono state individuate come certamente appartenenti a Gualtiero: si tratta del *Contra quatuor labyrinthos Franciae* e di una raccolta di *Sermones*, in numero certo di 21[7].

Mentre i *Sermones* costituiscono l'opera di una vita, in quanto la loro composizione è cadenzata dall'avvicendarsi dei tempi li-

[4] Cfr. F. GASPARRI, Scriptorium *et bureau d'écriture de l'abbaye de Saint Victor*, in *L'abbaye parisienne de Saint-Victor au Moyen Âge*, a c. di J. Longère, Turnhout 1991 (Bibliotheca Victorina, 1), p. 132.

[5] Cfr. F. HUGONIN, *Notice sur Richard de Saint-Victor*, in PL 196, XIII-XVIII.

[6] Notizie indirette sulla vita di Gualtiero sono raccolte dal curatore dell'edizione critica dei suoi *Sermones*: cfr. J. CHÂTILLON, *Introduction*, in GALTERIUS DE SANCTO VICTORE, *Sermones*, ed. J. Châtillon, Turnhout 1975 (CCCM, 30), [pp. 3-185], pp. 3-10; e cfr. anche A. M. PIAZZONI, *I Vittorini*, in *Storia della teologia nel Medioevo*, 3 voll., dir. di G. d'Onofrio, Casale Monferrato 1996, II, [pp. 179-208], p. 198.

[7] Cfr. CHÂTILLON, *Introduction* cit., p. 8.

turgici nell'annuale iterazione del memoriale salvifico, il *Contra quatuor labyrinthos Franciae* si pone al termine della produzione dell'autore: è naturale, dunque, cogliere in quest'opera il frutto più maturo della sua riflessione. Il testimone più autorevole dell'opera è il manoscritto conservato nella Biblioteca Nazionale di Parigi sotto la collocazione Arsenal 379. Sono pervenuti altri due codici, entrambi incompleti: il primo, conservato anch'esso a Parigi, con la collocazione lat. 17187, ff. 198-259^{v}, è una copia dell'Arsenal 379 ad opera del Maurino Edmond Martène, che può aiutare in caso di lettura difficile; il secondo, del secolo XII, si trova alla Biblioteca Vaticana come ms. Reginense lat. 1283, ff. 570-600, e riproduce solo il primo libro, scritto e rubricato con molta cura. Una edizione critica integrale del testo sulla base di questi testimoni è stata curata da Palemon Glorieux nel 1952[8].

Gualtiero spiega nel prologo dell'opera il criterio di scelta del titolo:

> Quisquis hoc legerit non dubitabit quatuor labyrinthos Franciae (...) uno aristotelico spiritu afflatos dum ineffabilia sanctae Trinitatis et incarnationis scolastica levitate tractarent, multas hereses olim vomuisse et adhuc errores pullulare[9].

Il minotauro, nelle intenzioni dell'autore, è lo spirito aristotelico che accomuna i quattro labirinti di Francia: la filosofia di Aristotele offusca la ragione umana, confondendola nei meandri dei suoi sofismi. I quattro 'labirinti' nei quali questo pericoloso mostro si nasconde sono l'insigne logico Pietro Abelardo, il sottile e profondo metafisico Gilberto Porreta, il grande maestro di teologia Pietro Lombardo e il suo illustre discepolo Pietro di Poi-

[8] Cfr. P. GLORIEUX, *Le* Contra Quatuor labyrinthos Franciae *de Ghautier de Saint-Victor*, in «Archives d'histoire doctrinale et littéraire du moyen âge», 19 (1952), [pp. 187-335], ed. del testo pp. 195-334 (nelle note seguenti l'opera sarà citata, senza precisarlo, da questa edizione con indicazione delle pagine e delle righe). Il solo secondo libro è stato edito da B. GEYER, di seguito al testo delle *Sententiae divinitatis*, nel suo studio *Die Sententiae Divinitatis, ein Sentenzebuch der gilbertischen Schule*, in «Beiträge zur Geschichte der Philosophie des Mittelalters», 7.2-3 (1909), alle pp. 175*-198*. F. DELHAYE, nello studio *Le Microcosmus de Godefroy de Saint Victor*, 2 voll., Lille 1951, I, alle pp. 244-251 ha pubblicato i primi nove capitoli del quarto libro.

[9] GUALTERUS DE SANCTO VICTORE, *Contra quatuor labyrinthos Franciae*, Prol., p. 201,2-6. Nelle note seguenti l'opera sarà citata senza esplicitare il nome dell'autore.

tiers. Pietro Lombardo, pur essendo nato a Novara, si può considerare parigino in relazione al luogo della sua missione religiosa e della contemporanea azione culturale. In realtà, Gualtiero commette un grossolano errore di attribuzione, poiché nel secondo libro del *Contra quatuor labyrinthos Franciae* pone sotto accusa le *Sententiae divinitatis*, opera che ritiene essere stata scritta da Abelardo, ma che è un manuale anonimo della scuola porretana, molto vicino, dunque, al pensiero di Gilberto: soltanto tramite numerosi passi di Bernardo di Chiaravalle è imbastita, seppur in modo indiretto, una critica ad opere effettivamente composte dal Maestro Palatino.

Gualtiero reputa tali rilevanti personalità del panorama culturale coevo quattro cavillosi dialettici della peggior specie, caduti, per colpa dei loro errori metodologici, in eresie già ripetutamente condannate dai concili della Chiesa antica e che pure essi hanno cercato di mascherare, pretendendo di far apparire le loro dottrine conformi a quelle dei santi Padri e dei Dottori della Chiesa.

2. *Gli errori dei filosofi antichi nel quarto libro del* Contra quatuor labyrinthos Franciae

In quest'opera dal taglio fieramente apologetico in difesa dell'ortodossia dogmatica trinitaria e cristologica, i primi sette capitoli del quarto libro costituiscono in modo evidente una sezione a parte, in cui l'indagine sul tema del rapporto tra ragione e fede, analizzato nei restanti libri sul versante della teologia rivelata, mostra un Gualtiero capace di misurarsi anche con questioni riguardanti l'etica, la cosmologia e le discipline liberali. Le arti liberali con il loro retaggio classico, propedeutiche agli studi teologici per il giovane aspirante monaco, divengono ora oggetto di riflessione nella piena maturità. Lo strumento adoperato per affermare le proprie tesi rimane l'invettiva, in questo caso indirizzata non ai teologi contemporanei ma ai filosofi antichi. All'inizio del quarto libro Gualtiero, proprio con l'intenzione di istituire un'analogia tra i limiti dei filosofi antichi e gli errori metodologici dei moderni dottori ecclesiastici, richiama i labirinti di Francia:

> Igitur isti theatrales ut sint ecclesiastici doctores necesse est divinas artes sequantur non liberales, apostolos imitentur non

philosophos. (...) Audi quantum mali faciat nimia subtilitas et quam infesta sit veritati[10].

È evidente come per Gualtiero l'eccessiva fiducia nella pratica delle arti liberali, e in particolare l'abuso della *nimia subtilitas* della ragione dialettica, coincidano con l'esasperazione dello *spiritus aristotelicus* denunciato nel prologo[11]. Il trivio e il quadrivio riassumono in effetti nell'alto Medioevo l'ambito di indagine della filosofia autonomo dalla rivelazione divina: nel pensiero di Gualtiero rifluisce la tradizione agostiniana[12]. In quest'ottica la condanna dei dialettici contemporanei gli consente di estendere la sua polemica ai filosofi antichi, i quali si vengono a trovare non per opzione epistemologica ma per la loro peculiare posizione nell'economia del piano salvifico in un'analoga condizione; il settimo capitolo si chiude significativamente riecheggiando la critica di Girolamo al *princeps dialecticorum*, Aristotele[13]. Nell'ottavo e nel nono capitolo, inoltre, prima di ritornare nel decimo alla critica articolata delle opinioni di uno dei quattro autori bersaglio

[10] *Ibid.*, IV, 1, p. 270,3-11.

[11] Il titolo dell'ottavo capitolo del quarto libro conferma questa equiparazione; cfr. *ibid.*, 8, p. 197,32-33: «Quod novi immo omnes heretici a philosophis et dialecticis generantur».

[12] Cfr. AUGUSTINUS HIPPONENSIS, *De doctrina christiana*, II, 40, PL 34, 63, ed. I. Martin, Turnhout 1996 (CCSL, 32), [pp. 1-167], pp. 73,4 - 74,23: «Sicut enim Aegyptii non tantum idola habebant et onera gravia, quae populus Israhel detestaretur et fugeret, sed etiam vasa atque ornamenta de auro et argento et vestem, quae ille populus exiens de Aegypto sibi potius tamquam ad usum meliorem clanculo vindicavit, non auctoritate propria, sed praecepto Dei ipsis Aegyptiis nescienter commodantibus ea, quibus non bene utebantur, sic doctrinae omnes gentilium non solum simulata et superstitiosa figmenta gravesque sarcinas supervacanei laboris habent, quae unusquisque nostrum duce Christo de societate gentilium exiens debet abominari atque vitare, sed etiam liberales disciplinas usui veritatis aptiores et quaedam morum praecepta utilissima continent deque ipso uno Deo colendo nonnulla vera inveniuntur apud eos, quod eorum tamquam aurum et argentum, quod non ipsi instituerunt, sed de quibusdam quasi metallis divinae providentiae, quae ubique infusa est, eruerunt et, quo perverse atque iniuriose ad obsequia daemonum abutuntur, cum ab eorum misera societate sese animo separat, debet ab eis auferre christianus ad usum iustum praedicandi evangelii».

[13] Cfr. HIERONYMUS STRIDONIUS, *In epistolam ad Titum*, III, PL 26, 631C, ed. F. Bucchi, Turnhout 2003 (CCSL, 77C), pp. 66,240 - 67,243. Cfr. *Contra quatuor labyrinthos Franciae*, IV, 7, p. 274, 15-17: «Dialectici quorum Aristoteles princeps est, solent argumentationum retia tendere et vagam rethorice libertatem etiam [l'edizione Bucchi legge *in* anziché *etiam*] syllogismorum spineta concludere».

delle sue critiche (in questo caso Pietro di Poitiers), il vittorino ripropone circolarmente il tema delle *profanae vocum novitates* che aveva introdotto in chiusura del terzo libro:

> Non fallitur talibus optimus trapezeta, apostolica veritate devitans profanas vocum novitates et appositiones falsi nominis scientiae quam quidam promittentes circa fidem naufragaverunt, et inserverunt se doloribus multis, languentes circa quaestiones et pugna verborum. Ex his sunt sententiae Abailardi et Porete, Lumbardi et Pictavini (...). Sicut enim rerum omnium, ita propositionum infinita conversio est[14].

L'*infinita conversio propositionum* riflette la *conversio omnium rerum*. Le regole relative alla convertibilità delle proposizioni, esposte nel decimo capitolo del *Peri hermeneias* di Aristotele, consentono, in determinati casi, di scambiare la *pars subiectiva* di una proposizione, che esprime il soggetto, e quella *declarativa*, che dichiara ciò di cui si predica il soggetto, assicurando la produzione di un nuovo asserto veridico; anche nei casi in cui tale conversione non è direttamente realizzabile, è possibile tuttavia rinvenire una modalità indiretta per renderla lecita[15]. Ma un'applicazione integrale e totalizzante di questo principio renderebbe la convertibilità delle proposizioni virtualmente infinita. Ora, il realismo aristotelico, partendo dal presupposto che l'ordine delle proposizioni rispecchi l'ordine del reale, sarebbe costretto a riconoscere di conseguenza la convertibilità del reale. La ragione, privata di ogni possibilità di penetrare la verità delle cose, sarebbe condannata a smarrirsi nell'indefinito vagare di labirinti invalicabili. Il ragionamento di Gualtiero tende a dimostrare come lo spirito aristotelico sia la causa diretta delle eresie di cui sono diventati seguaci gli illustri professori di dialettica da lui bersagliati. Non la ragione umana in generale, dunque, ma un determinato tipo di dialettica risulta la vera imputata: Gualtiero, in realtà, combatte la dialettica con la dialettica, o meglio, la cervellotica e inconcludente dialettica aristotelica con la vera ragione dialettica che, se correttamente applicata, non può mai contraddire le asserzioni vere della fede. Non sussiste alcun dubbio sul fatto che il dato di fede vada anche te-

[14] *Contra quatuor labyrinthos Franciae*, IV, 8-9, pp. 274,33 - 275,15.

[15] Cfr. G. D'ONOFRIO, Fons scientiae. *La dialettica nell'Occidente tardo-antico*, Napoli 1986 (Nuovo Medioevo, 30), p. 215.

nuto presente come un elemento di certezza conoscitiva, a partire dal quale è sempre possibile *a posteriori* giudicare il grado di correttezza del procedimento seguito dall'argomentare dei filosofi; ma è significativo osservare che Gualtiero non si accontenta di fare proprio tale semplice atteggiamento censorio nei confronti delle arditezze speculative dell'*intelligere* svincolato dal *credere*, ma si preoccupa invece di denunciare sul piano stesso dei precetti della dialettica l'intrinseca scorrettezza del procedimento seguito da Aristotele e, sulla sua scia, dai pericolosi 'labirinti di Francia'. Per lui è infatti fondamentale ammettere che la *ratio* sia in grado di argomentare *probabiliter*, cioè che possa comprovare e confermare sulla base dei propri criteri la correttezza dei suoi procedimenti, anche se non si può recedere dal principio che tutte le argomentazioni vere inevitabilmente concordano o non contraddicono le affermazioni della Scrittura e della tradizione conciliare[16].

Per questo l'analisi dei sette capitoli dedicati alla cultura antica consente di evidenziare il tentativo, operato da Gualtiero, di mostrare non solo quanto sia difficile ricercare una proficua calibratura del rapporto tra fede e ragione, rinunciando alla chiarezza contenutistica e alla limpida univocità linguistica dei Padri in nome di una pretestuosa e dannosa applicazione di cavillose distinzioni dialettiche al dato rivelato, ma altresì di smascherare le contraddizioni insite nello stesso statuto epistemologico di un sapere fondato sulla dialettica aristotelica.

Il primo capitolo si apre con la già ricordata menzione dei *theatrales doctores*; nel definire con tale polemico epiteto i teologi amanti della dialettica, Gualtiero sembra utilizzare l'accezione che il termine, sostantivato, riveste nel *Didascalicon* di Ugo: «theatrica dicitur scientia ludorum a theatro ubi populus ad ludendum convenire solebat»[17]. Questa disciplina occupa l'ultimo posto nella gerarchia delle arti meccaniche, che sono subordinate alle arti

[16] Questa posizione viene esplicitata da Gualtiero che, rifacendosi ad Agostino, scrive in *Contra quatuor labyrinthos Franciae*, III, 15, pp. 268,27 - 269,37: «Cessent proinde novi doctores, immo novi ex veteribus heretici, non dialectici, has profanas vocum novitates emittere quas hactenus nec divina scriptura docuit nec catholica credidit. (...) Alios autem ita lego ut quantalibet sanctitate doctrinaque polleant, non ideo verum putem quia ipsi ita senserunt, sed quia michi vel per illos auctores canonicos vel probabili ratione quod a vero non abhorreat persuadere potuerunt; et ita et meos libros legi volo».

[17] HUGO DE SANCTO VICTORE, *Didascalicon*, II, 28, PL 176, 762D, ed. C. H.

liberali in quanto connesse non con la conoscenza dell'opera creatrice divina ma con quella degli esiti dell'agire umano: «opus humanum, quod natura non est sed imitatur naturam, mechanicum, id est adulterinum nominatur»[18]. Le arti liberali, predisponendo l'animo all'acquisizione della sapienza, consentono infatti all'uomo, secondo la divisione del sapere raccomandata dal *Didascalicon*, di rintracciare nella regolamentazione rigorosa delle verità intelligibili un riflesso dell'*ordo Dei* operante nella realtà delle creature visibili[19]; le arti meccaniche, invece, si limitano ad imitare la natura, donde la loro derivazione illegittima e quindi adulterina dall'*ordo rerum*. Se Gualtiero, nel riproporre con accezione polemica l'infimo valore della *theatrica,* eredita un insegnamento di Ugo, al contrario, nell'attribuire la teatralità agli *ecclesiastici doctores*, cultori delle arti liberali, implicitamente estende l'illegittimità delle discipline meccaniche al trivio e al quadrivio, lasciando intendere che la vera libertà risiede soltanto nella *sequela Christi*: non *imitatio* dell'*ordo Dei* tramite la scienza dell'*ordo verborum*, ma semplice e santa *imitatio apostolorum*. L'imitazione degli apostoli riveste un valore superiore rispetto allo studio delle arti liberali anche in considerazione del fatto che i moderni dottori della Chiesa non studiano *quod natura est*, la realtà delle cose, ma seguono dottrine pericolose e fuorvianti, imitando filosofi che si sono rivelati assolutamente incapaci di cogliere la verità. A conferma del fallimento della filosofia antica, Gualtiero invoca la testimonianza di Seneca, introducendo una lunga citazione («de quibus Seneca ait») dall'ottantottesima epistola *Ad Lucilium*:

> Philosophi quantum habent supervacui, quantum ab usu recedentis, ipsi quoque ad sillabarum distinctiones et coniunctionum ac propositionum proprietates descenderunt et invidere grammaticis, invidere geometricis. Quicquid in illorum artibus supervacuum erat transtulere in suam. Sic effectum est

Buttimer, Washington D. C. 1939 (The Catholic University of America Studies in Medieval and Renaissance Latin, 10), p. 44,4.

[18] *Ibid.*, I, 10, 747D, p. 16,14-15.

[19] Cfr. *ibid.*, III, 3, 768A, p. 53,5-7: «Sunt enim quasi optima quaedam instrumenta et rudimenta quibus via paratur animo ad plenam philosophicae veritatis notitiam. Hinc trivium et quadrivium nomen accepit, eo quod his, quasi quibusdam viis, vivax animus ad secreta sophiae introeat. Nemo tunc tempore nomine magistri dignus videbatur, qui non harum septem scientiam profiteri posset».

> ut diligentius loqui scirent quam vivere. Audi quantum mali faciat nimia subtilitas et quam infesta sit veritati. Pitagoras ait de omni re in utramque partem disputari posse ex aequo, et de hac ipsa an omnis res in utramque partem disputabilis sit. Nausiphanes ait ex his quae videntur esse nichil magis esse quam non esse. Parmenides ait ex his quae videntur, nichil esse universo. Zenon elates omnia negotia de negotio deiecit; ait nichil esse. Circa eadem fere pyrronei versantur, et Megarici, et cretici, et achademici qui novam induxerunt scientiam: nichil scire. Haec omnia in illum supervacuum studiorum liberalium gregem coire. Illi mihi non profuturam scientiam tradunt; hi spem omnis scientiae eripiunt. Satius est supervacua scire quam nichil. Illi non praeferunt lumen quod per acies dirigatur ad verum; hi oculos michi effodiunt. Si Pitagorae credo nihil in rerum natura est nisi dubium. Si Nausiphani hoc unum certum est: nichil esse certi. Si Parmenidi, nichil est praeter unum. Si Zenoni, nec unum quidem. Quid ergo nos scimus? Quid ista quae nos circumstant, alunt, sustinent? Tota rerum natura umbra est, aut inanis aut fallax. Non facile dixerim utrum magis irascar illis qui nos nichil scire voluerunt an illis qui ne hoc quidem nobis reliquerunt nichil scire[20].

Questo testo senechiano è un vero e proprio *topos* polemico contro la vana curiosità dei filosofi antichi, accusati di avere eletto ad oggetto del loro studio ciò che era superfluo nelle altre discipli-

[20] LUCIUS ANNAEUS SENECA, *Ad Lucilium epistulae morales*, 88, ed. L. D. Reynolds, 2 voll., Oxford 1965, I, pp. 322,43 - 323,50; cit. in *Contra quatuor labyrinthos Franciae*, IV, 1, p. 270,5-27. La citazione delle *Epistulae ad Lucilium* testimonia la presenza di Seneca nella biblioteca di San Vittore in questa seconda metà del secolo XII. Jacqueline Hamesse, analizzando i florilegi altomedievali, osserva che fino al secolo XII non sono contemplati florilegi filosofici. I passi dei pensatori non vengono infatti raccolti con l'esplicito intento di evidenziarne la portata speculativa, ma soltanto per il fascino che esercitano sui lettori contemporanei. In queste raccolte si segnalano le citazioni morali da Seneca. Cfr. J. HAMESSE, *Les florilèges à l'époque de saint Anselme*, in «Rivista di storia della filosofia», 48 (1993), [pp. 477-495], p. 488. Leighton Durham Reynolds evidenzia come, dopo gli studi compiuti da Martino di Braga nella Spagna visigotica, Seneca scompaia dalla cultura medievale fino al secolo XI, quando torna ad essere attestata la presenza di suoi scritti. Particolarmente nel sud-ovest della Germania e nel Nord della Francia, le opere che si ritrovano con maggiore frequenza sono il *De beneficiis*, il *De clementia* e le prime ottantotto lettere indirizzate a Lucilio. Il dato ha una particolare rilevanza, sia perché San Vittore, abbazia parigina, è situata al nord della Francia sia perché tutte le citazioni di Seneca effettuate da Gualtiero riguardano soltanto questa prima sezione della raccolta. Cfr. L. D. REYNOLDS, *The Medieval Tradition of Seneca's Letters*, Oxford 1965.

ne, con il risultato di sapere «diligentius loqui quam vivere». E la «nimia subtilitas» che li caratterizza non è soltanto inutile, ma anche «infesta», ossia nociva, alla verità. Essi, dunque, slittano inevitabilmente verso il relativismo e lo scetticismo. Già il sofista Protagora[21] sosteneva «de omni re in utramque partem disputari posse ex aequo, et de hac ipsa an omnis res in utramque partem disputabilis sit». Analogamente anche Nausifane, che si richiamava all'atomismo democriteo e fu maestro di Epicuro, viene presentato come uno scettico[22]. Parmenide e Zenone vengono tacciati di nichilismo ontologico, mentre *pyrronei*, *megarici*, *cretici* e *achademici* hanno professato, a detta di Seneca, un nichilismo gnoseologico: per tutti costoro «ista quae nos circumstant, alunt, sustinent (...), tota rerum natura umbra est, aut inanis aut fallax».

L'ironia di Seneca colpisce con eguale forza sia chi rifiuta la conoscibilità della realtà che ci circonda, sia il filone più rigorosamente scettico, che nega la stessa possibilità di affermare o negare tale conoscibilità. Ma fin dall'inizio del secondo capitolo, Gualtiero individua nello stesso Seneca un esponente ancora più pericoloso della cultura pagana, rivelando in tal modo la mera strumentalità dell'evocazione delle sue stesse parole: «et ipse Seneca peior ceteris convincitur»[23]. Il filosofo romano, nell'ottica cristiana, è infatti responsabile di molteplici errori dottrinali: ritiene che l'anima sia parte di Dio o uguale a Dio; seguendo l'insegnamento di Platone, Virgilio ed Epicuro, sostiene che il *mundus* sia un *animal* vivente ed eterno; ammette la trasmigrazione delle anime[24]. Ma al di sopra di tutti gli altri, il suo errore più imperdonabile, oggetto di una critica diretta e quanto mai feroce da parte del vittorino, riguarda l'ammissibilità del suicidio e la collocazione «in celesti-

[21] Nel testo della citazione di Gualtiero, è riportato il nome *Pitagoras* anziché *Protagoras*; cfr. *Contra quatuor labyrinthos Franciae*, IV, 1, p. 270,11-12.

[22] Nausifane, autore poco noto, viene classificato dai pochi che ne fanno menzione, tra i quali Clemente Alessandrino, come un Abderita maestro di Epicuro, seguace nel contempo dello scetticismo pirroniano e della fisica atomistica. In realtà, l'espressione a lui attribuita da Seneca è di Metrodoro di Chio; cfr. K. PRAECHTER, *Die Philosophie des Altertums*, Basel – Stuttgart 1958, p. 110.

[23] *Contra quatuor labyrinthos Franciae*, IV, 2, p. 270,30.

[24] Cfr. *ibid.*, pp. 270,30 - 271,1: «Animam quippe, sive rationem hominis, nunc Deum nunc partem Dei nunc aequalem Deo nunc etiam superiorem, an sit post mortem an in alia corpora etiam bestiarum recidat, Iovem Deum, hunc mundum animal aeternum Deum esse, sequens Platonem, Virgilium, Epicurum, varie dogmatizat».

bus», «diis similes», degli uomini che si uccidono in circostanze ritenute adeguate[25]. Per rimarcare la gravità di questa dottrina, Gualtiero introduce una serie di citazioni tratte ancora dalle *Epistulae ad Lucilium*, ma riportate senza alcun rispetto della sequenza argomentativa impostata dall'autore[26]. Per Seneca il sapiente è inferiore a Dio solo per l'ineluttabilità della propria condizione mortale, non per minore felicità, e acquista, con l'esercizio dell'impassibilità, una superiorità sul contingente che è frutto di una libera scelta anziché della predeterminata condizione di eccellenza connaturata alla *primitas* ontologica divina: «Deus non vincit sapientem felicitate etsi vincit aetate; sapiens tam aequo animo omnia apud alios videt contemnitque quam Iupiter, et hoc se magis suspicit quod Iupiter illis uti non potest, sapiens non vult»[27].

Nel *collage* di brani senechiani realizzato da Gualtiero risulta evidente l'intenzione di selezionare i passaggi dai quali più accentuato e sconcertante emerge un appassionato elogio del suicidio, corredato degli esempi illustri di Catone e Socrate e sostenuto da svariate argomentazioni:

> Nichil interest illa [*scil.* mors] ad nos veniat an ad illam nos. (...) Ego expectem vel morbi crudelitatem vel hominis, cum possim per media exire tormenta? Non est opus vasto vulnere dividi precordia; scalpello aperitur ad libertatem via. (...) Non deerit ad mortem ingenium cui non defuerit animus. (...) Invenies etiam professos sapientiam qui vim inferendam vitae suae negent et nefas iudicent ipsum intemptatorem sui fieri. Hoc qui dicit libertatis viam cludit[28].

È indifferente, secondo il filosofo romano, aspettare la morte o correrle volontariamente incontro; anzi, nel caso di una straziante sofferenza causata da una malattia, è giustificabile volersi libe-

[25] Cfr. *ibid.*, p. 271,3.

[26] Cfr. Lucius Annaeus Seneca, *Ad Lucilium epistulae morales*, 73, ed. Reynolds *cit.* (alla nota 20), pp. 223,23 - 224,1; 67, pp. 195,22 - 197,11; 69, p. 202,2-6; 70, pp. 204,9 - 209,4; questi passi sono riportati in *Contra quatuor labyrinthos Franciae*, *ibid.*, p. 271,3-33, rispettivamente alle ll. 3-6, 7-13, 13-16, 16-33.

[27] Lucius Annaeus Seneca, *ibid.*, 73, pp. 223,23 - 224,1, in *Contra quatuor labyrinthos Franciae*, *ibid.*, p. 271,3-6.

[28] Lucius Annaeus Seneca, *ibid.*, 69, p. 202,3-4 e 70, pp. 206,1 - 209,4, in *Contra quatuor labyrinthos Franciae*, *ibid.*, p. 271,14-33 (è stato necessario correggere parzialmente la punteggiatura dell'edizione Glorieux).

rare del male togliendosi la vita. Suicidarsi è anche un atto di coraggio e chi è contrario al suicidio vuol privare l'uomo di un suo diritto. Gualtiero, che respinge in blocco tali argomentazioni, aggiunge che sarebbero innumerevoli le ulteriori testimonianze che potrebbero essere portate per evidenziare la fallacia della dottrina di Seneca, ma questi, come abile usignolo, è in grado di affascinare i suoi uditori con efficacia proporzionale alla soavità del suo stile, ottenendo purtroppo il risultato di renderli «creduliores» e «scelerastiores», cioè di allontanarli dalla verità e dal bene[29]. L'errore di Seneca viene quindi ulteriormente denunciato da Gualtiero, nelle righe seguenti, appoggiandosi all'*auctoritas* di Agostino:

> Augustinus ait: «homicidae flammis se donent, aquis praefocent, laqueo suspendant, praecipitio collidant et pereant; quod Christus non docuit: immo diabolo praecipitium suadenti, 'redi', inquit, 'retro Sathana' (*Mt* 4, 10)»[30].

Cristo non ha mai insegnato il suicidio e ha respinto, tra le tentazioni di Satana, anche quella che lo invitava a gettarsi da un dirupo. Inoltre lo stesso Seneca non diede prova di coraggio e virilità quando dovette affrontare la morte: «omni femina mollior», pose fine alla vita ricoprendosi di morbide piume, fra tiepidi lavacri, aprendosi le vene e morendo nel sonno. In breve, «ipsam mortem mortisque dolorem vertit sibi in magnam voluptatem»[31]. Né a lui né a Nerone né a Socrate né a Catone è stata destinata la beatitudine ultraterrena[32]. Gualtiero ritiene anzi applicabili a Seneca le parole con le quali Cristo sembra decretare un giudizio di condanna nei confronti del traditore suicida Giuda Iscariota: «Crede mihi; melius illi erat si natus non fuisset ho-

[29] *Contra quatuor labyrinthos Franciae*, *ibid.*, p. 271,33-34: «Hucusque pauca de innumeris. Ecce qualibus doctrinis dulcisonis luscinia haec, eo fortius quo suavius, allicit auditores, quo fiant creduliores et scelerastiores».

[30] *Ibid.*, pp. 271,35 - 272,1; la citazione è da AUGUSTINUS HIPPONENSIS, *In Iohannis evangelium tractatus*, LI, PL 35, 1767, ed. R. Willems, Turnhout 1990 (CCSL, 36), p. 443,20-23.

[31] *Contra quatuor labyrinthos Franciae*, *ibid.*, p. 272,12-13.

[32] Cfr. *ibid.*, p. 272,13-15: «Iste igitur non quidem fratricida sed peior suicida; stoicus professione, epicurus morte; putasne cum Nerone et Socrate et Catone receptus sit in coelo?».

mo» (*Mt* 26, 24)[33]. Il vittorino non ignora che Girolamo include il filosofo romano nel suo «catalogus sanctorum», ossia nel *De viris inlustribus*[34]. Tale menzione non risulta tuttavia determinante per riscattarne l'operato, secondo Gualtiero. Il vittorino sa bene che Girolamo inserisce spesso nel suo catalogo anche autori non ortodossi, come Origene o il vescovo ariano Eusebio, pronto a lodarne i pregi e a smascherarne le mancanze sul piano umano o dottrinale[35].

Dopo aver analizzato e condannato il pensiero e la figura di Seneca, nel terzo capitolo Gualtiero porta la sua attenzione su Socrate, presentandolo come maestro di Seneca e di tutti gli altri filosofi menzionati. Attingendo ancora a Girolamo, il vittorino riporta un aneddoto al fine di ridicolizzare il filosofo ateniese. Si narra che una concubina di Socrate, adirata con lui, gli abbia versato addosso urina, e che egli, senza scomporsi minimamente, si sia asciugato la barba e abbia esclamato: «sapevo bene che dopo il tuono sarebbe venuta la pioggia»[36]. Il commento di Gualtiero all'episodio è aspro, secondo il suo stile, e nell'occasione anche ironico:

> Merito Seneca hunc prophetam tali unda candidatum et proprio veneno extinctum e carcere levat in coelum. Ecce habent scolastici quo clarius audiant praeceptorem suum[37].

Gualtiero accenna soltanto alla figura di Socrate, connotandola negativamente. Ma questo suo intento denigratorio appare quasi in esplicito contrasto con l'importanza riconosciuta al maestro di

[33] *Ibid.*, p. 272,15-16.

[34] Cfr. HIERONYMUS STRIDONIUS, *De viris illustribus*, 12, PL 23, 629A, ed. A. Ceresa-Gastaldo, Firenze 1988 (Biblioteca patristica, 12), p. 100: «Lucius Annaeus Seneca Cordubensis, Sotionis stoici discipulus et patruus Lucani poetae, continentissimae vitae fuit, quem non ponerem in catalogo sanctorum nisi me illae Epistulae provocarent, quae leguntur a plurimis Pauli ad Senecam et Senecae ad Paulum».

[35] Cfr. *Contra quatuor labyrinthos Franciae*, *ibid.*, p. 272,17-18: «Nec deterreat quod Ieronymus illum quasi continentissimum in cathalogo sanctorum posuit; sic enim et Eusebium episcopum, fontem ut ipse scribit Arrii, et alios multos quos ipse damnat hereticos; ex quibus Origenem prae ceteris, et vituperans et laudans continentissimum usque adeo ut se castraret, quod nequaquam fecit Seneca qui vel uno ut scribit abutatur».

[36] Cfr. *ibid*, IV, 3, pp. 272,33 - 273,1; cfr. HIERONYMUS STRIDONIUS, *Adversus Jovinianum*, I, 48, PL 23, 279A.

[37] *Contra quatuor labyrinthos Franciae*, *ibid.*, p. 273,1-4.

Platone da Ugo di San Vittore, che ne segnala il merito principale, cioè la fondazione della filosofia morale[38].

Nel quarto e nel quinto capitolo, molto brevi, Gualtiero ribadisce l'inconciliabilità tra la fede cristiana e la cultura antica. Nel quarto capitolo, ancora seguendo Girolamo, il vittorino indirizza

[38] Cfr. V. CILENTO, *Il metodo e la dottrina del* Microcosmus *di Goffredo di S. Vittore*, Napoli s.d., p. 67. E cfr. HUGO DE SANCTO VICTORE, *Didascalicon*, III, 2, 766B, ed. Buttimer cit. (alla nota 17), p. 50,3: «Ethicae inventor Socrates fuit, de qua viginti quattuor libros secundum positivam iustitiam scripsit». Questa affermazione di Ugo pone il problema di quale possa essere la fonte da cui egli ricava la notizia che Socrate sia stato fondatore dell'etica e soprattutto che fu autore di un trattato di ventiquattro libri sulla giustizia positiva. Convergono in questa posizione due filoni della tradizione socratica medievale. La convinzione che Socrate sia stato il primo filosofo a riflettere sulla questione etica è presente in Agostino e, successivamente, in Isidoro di Siviglia. Agostino ne parla, ad esempio, nel *De Civitate Dei*, VIII, 3, PL 41, 226, edd. B. Dombart – A. Kalb, 2 voll., Turnhout 1955 (CCSL, 47-48), I, p. 218,1-4: «Socrates ergo, primus universam philosophiam ad corrigendos componendosque mores flexisse memoratur, cum ante illum omnes magis physicis, id est naturalibus, rebus perscrutandis operam maximam inpenderent». Isidoro di Siviglia si esprime in termini più precisi; cfr. ISIDORUS HISPALENSIS, *Etymologiarum sive Originum libri XX*, II, 24, 5, PL 82, 141C, ed. A. Valastro-Canale, 2 voll., Torino 2004, I, p. 232: «Ethicam Socrates primus ad corrigendos conponendosque mores instituit, atque omne studium eius ad bene vivendi disputationem perduxit, dividens eam in quattuor virtutibus animae, id est prudentiam, iustitiam, fortitudinem, temperantiam». Il passo di Isidoro è con ogni probabilità presente all'orizzonte di Gerardo di Cszanád; cfr. GERARDUS MORESENUS SEU CSANADENSIS, *Deliberatio supra hymnum trium puerorum*, IV, ed. G. Silagi, Turnhout 1978 (CCCM, 49), pp. 40,69 - 41,79: «Tuusque Socrates ad corrigendos mores componendos primus instituens et ad omne studium eius bene uiuendi disputacionem perducens eamque in quattuor virtutibus animae dividens, nimirum: Prudentia, iusticia, fortitudine, temperantia, subiungens loicam, quae rationalis vocatur, per quam discursis rerum morumque causis vim earum rationabiliter perscrutatus, dividens eam in supra praedictas geminas disciplinas, dialecticam utique et rethoricam, in quibus tribus generibus philosophiae etiam divina eloquia tota a peritis constare videntur». Se è agevole constatare la consapevolezza che Ugo ha acquisito, tramite autori noti e presenti al suo orizzonte culturale, a proposito dell'importanza del ruolo rivestito da Socrate nella storia dell'etica, è più problematico rintracciare la fonte da cui il vittorino ha attinto la notizia di un'opera scritta da Socrate sulla giustizia. A tal proposito, di considerevole importanza è un passo del commento di Guglielmo di Conches al *Timeo* di Platone; cfr. GUILLELMUS DE CONCHIS, *Glosae super Platonem*, super Prooem. Calcidii, ed. É. Jeauneau, Turnhout 2006 (CCCM, 203), p. 7,11-17: «Cuius [*scil.* iustitiae] diffinitione in scolis Socratis relata, ait: '(...) iustitia est quae plurimum prodest illi qui mininum potest. Qui enim plurimum potest se et sua sine omni iustitia conservaret, sed qui minimum minime'. Et quia tam perfectam de ea dederat diffinitionem, rogaverunt eum sui discipuli ut de illa tractatum componeret. Quorum satisfaciens voluntati, de parte ipsius iustitiae, id est de positiva iustitia, tractavit». Una conferma del fatto che il commento di Guglielmo circolasse nell'ambiente vittorino nel corso del secolo XII può venire proprio dal *pamphlet* di Gualtiero, che lo cita in *Contra quatuor labyrinthos Franciae*, IV, 6, p. 273,28.

i suoi strali polemici agli esponenti di maggior rilievo del movimento letterario latino:

> 'Quae pars fidelis cum infideli? quae communicatio lucis ad tenebras? qui consensus Christi ad Belial?' (*2Cor* 6, 14-15) quid faciet cum psalterio Horatius, cum Evangeliis Maro, cum Apostolis Cicero? Non scandalizatur frater si te viderit in idolio recumbentem? Et licet omnia sint 'munda mundis' (*Tt* 1, 15) et 'nichil reiiciendum quod cum gratiarum actione percipitur' (*1Tm* 4, 4), tamen simul bibere non debemus calicem Christi et calicem daemoniorum[39].

Il quinto capitolo, invece, riporta un noto passo del *De doctrina christiana* in cui Agostino fa ammenda della sua entusiastica adesione alla filosofia accademica, foriera, in alcuni casi, di gravi errori, dai quali è necessario preservare l'integrità dell'ortodossia[40]. Il sesto capitolo, dopo un accenno polemico agli errori di Gugliemo di Conches su cui torneremo, si chiude con un'ulteriore citazione da Girolamo, che condanna il costume, in voga anche presso alcuni sacerdoti cristiani, di leggere e declamare i classici antichi[41]. Nel settimo capitolo Gualtiero approfondisce quindi con osservazioni di carattere speculativo la sua critica alla dialettica aristotelica, denunciando la labilità dell'ontologia dello Stagirita. Aristotele non ha saputo definire la *natura*, la prima categoria

[39] HIERONYMUS STRIDONIUS, *Epistulae*, 22, *ad Eustochium*, 29, PL 22, 416, ed. I. Hilberg, Wien – Leipzig 1910 (CSEL, 54, *Epistulae* 1-70), pp. 188,17 - 189,8. Cfr. *Contra quatuor labyrinthos Franciae*, IV, 4, p. 273,12-17.

[40] In *Contra quatuor labyrinthos Franciae*, *ibid.*, 5, p. 273,19-23; cfr. AUGUSTINUS HIPPONENSIS, *Retractationum libri duo*, I, 1, 4, PL 32, 587, ed. A. Mutzenbecher, Turnhout 1984 (CCSL, 57), p. 10,99-102: «Laus qua Platonem vel platonicos seu achademicos philosophos tam extuli, quantum impios homines non oportuit, non immerito mihi displicet praesertim contra quorum errores magnos defendenda est christiana doctrina».

[41] Cfr. HIERONYMUS STRIDONIUS, *Epistulae*, 21, *ad Damasum*, 13, 385-386, ed. Hilberg cit. (alla nota 39), p. 122,5-8 e pp. 123,19 - 124,2: «Daemonum, ait, cibus et carmina poetarum, saecularis sapientia, rethoricorum pompa verborum; haec sua omnes suavitate delectant et dum aures versibus dulci modulatione cupentibus capiunt, animam quoque penetrant et pectoris interna devinciunt. (...) At nunc etiam sacerdotes Dei omissis evangeliis et prophetis videmus comoedias legere, amatoria bucolicorum versuum verba cantare, tenere Virgilium; et id quod in pueris necessitatis est, crimen in se facere voluntatis». In *Contra quatuor labyrinthos Franciae*, *ibid.*, p. 274,1-12. Nel testo di Gualtiero al posto di *currentibus* compare il termine *cupentibus*.

che sostiene le altre nove, mentre tutte le sue dimostrazioni vertono *de naturalibus*:

> Quod si Aristoteles (...) primam cathegoriarum quae ceteras novem sustinet, id est naturam, diffinire nequit, quas diffinitiones de naturalibus, id est secundis substantiis et reliquis, veraciter dare potuit qui de prima nullam aliam dedit (...) nescio. Prorsus qui aurum nescit nec aurea discernit. Sed ne hebes, immo ceteris ut appareret subtilior, solus quintum elementum asseruit. Ita per quasdam novas regulas partim veras, et conexiones verborum, etiam et sillabarum distinctiones auricalcum pro auro posteris vendidit, id est pro veritate et veris verisimilia sinibus stultorum reposuit[42].

I *naturalia* sono identificati con le sostanze seconde «et reliqua». Ma le sostanze seconde si basano sulle prime, perché i generi e le specie sussistono solo negli individui. Dunque, siccome i *naturalia* si basano sulla *natura*, quest'ultima viene a identificarsi con le sostanze individuali. Ma dell'individuo non si può avere scienza[43]. In questo modo Aristotele impedisce ogni esito fruttuoso alla ricerca della verità, pervenendo soltanto a conclusioni verosimili, dal momento che il fondamento della logica e dell'ontologia risulta privo di definizione; la sua onto-gnoseologia si chiude in un circolo vizioso, individuando le condizioni di possibilità di conoscenza della sostanza prima nella conoscenza di sostanze da essa derivate. Sulla base di questa critica Gualtiero, per l'ennesima volta sulla scia di Girolamo, raffigura la dialettica come una vana arte del contendere, contraria ai precetti evangelici:

> Si igitur illi [*scil.* dialectici] haec faciunt quorum proprie ars contentio est, quid debet facere christianus nisi omnino fugere contentionem. 'Si quis videtur esse contentiosus', ait Apostolus, 'nos talem consuetudinem non habemus neque Ecclesia Dei' (*1Cor* 11, 16)[44].

[42] *Contra quatuor labyrinthos Franciae*, *ibid.*, 7, p. 274, 23-31.

[43] Cfr. D'ONOFRIO, Fons scientiae cit. (alla nota 15), p. 174: «Solo le sostanze seconde sono (...) capaci di indicare la sostanza prima, cioè di rivelare con il nome (e quindi permettere di conoscere) l'individuo, proprio in base all'univocità di predicazione che sussiste tra l'individuo e l'universale corrispondente. È dunque evidente ancora una volta che la scienza dell'individuo è direttamente subordinata alla scienza dell'universale».

[44] HIERONYMUS STRIDONIUS, *In epistulam ad Titum*, III, 631D, ed. Bucchi cit.

L'analisi di questa sezione dedicata ai filosofi antichi consente di focalizzare tre nuclei tematici: il rapporto tra fede e dialettica, la condanna del suicidio, il confronto tra la cosmologia di Seneca e quella di Guglielmo di Conches.

3. *Rapporto tra fede e dialettica e analisi etica del suicidio*

Una ragione profonda delle ripetute citazioni da Girolamo va ricercata nell'intento di mutuarne programmaticamente la congrua modalità di accostamento agli autori pagani o non ortodossi. Prendendo le mosse dalla valutazione espressa da Girolamo a proposito di Origene, descritto come valido filosofo ma cattivo dogmatico, Gualtiero delinea infatti quello che è a suo parere il metodo corretto per un proficuo approccio al pensiero di Seneca e degli antichi[45]:

> Proinde huius Senecae et similium libros et doctrinas soli legant quorum est separare pretiosum a vili, omnia probare et quod bonum est tenere, non qui blandis sermonibus illaquerentur ad mortem[46].

L'*omnia probare* (ossia il 'sottoporre tutto a vaglio critico') descrive un'opera di mediazione analitica da parte dell'interprete, che, separando il «pretiosum» dal «vile», consente di «tenere quod bonum est», di salvare come patrimonio prezioso gli elementi positivi di una dottrina che, come nel caso del pensiero dei filosofi menzionati, presenti in misura preponderante aspetti negativi. L'espressione «calix daemoniorum», anch'essa ripresa da Girolamo, non può dunque essere intesa nel senso che la cultura antica sia di per se stessa e nella sua interezza opera del demonio, altrimenti non sarebbe possibile alcun discernimento tra il «pretiosum» e il «vile». Ma alcuni contenuti di tale cultura possono ave-

(alla nota 13), p. 67,247-249. Cfr. *Contra quatuor labyrinthos Franciae*, IV, 7, p. 274,19-23.

[45] Cfr. HIERONYMUS STRIDONIUS, *Epistulae*, 84, *ad Pammachium et Oceanum*, 2, 744, ed. I. Hilberg, Wien – Leipzig 1912 (CSEL, 55, *Epistulae* 71-120), p. 122,5-6: «Laudavi interpretem, non dogmatisten, ingenium, non fidem, philosophum, non apostolum».

[46] *Contra quatuor labyrinthos Franciae*, *ibid.*, p. 274,25-28.

re effetti letali per coloro che vi si accostano senza la necessaria prudenza, invischiati nella pania del «blandus sermo» dei suoi banditori[47]. E tuttavia alla luce del principio paolino secondo cui «tutto concorre al bene di coloro che amano Dio» (*Rm* 8, 28), è giusto concludere che l'uomo «mundus», docile all'azione della grazia, è in grado di progredire nella santità traendo alimento anche dalle dottrine più perniciose.

Anche sul versante etico, la ragione pratica priva della grazia non solo non può, per Gualtiero, guidare l'uomo a un autentico rispetto della legge di Dio, ma è inevitabile altresì che contraddica se stessa. È quanto egli tenta di evidenziare, polemizzando nei confronti della giustificazione del suicidio operata da Seneca. La posizione del filosofo romano risulta comprensibile alla luce della morale stoica, il cui fine è οἰκεῖοσις, adeguamento e adesione della propria condotta alla razionalità del Λόγος, principio immanente di tutta la realtà. Solo tramite tale adesione l'essere umano può orientarsi verso i veri beni e conseguire la propria perfezione[48]. In Girolamo l'οἰκεῖοσις diventa *synderesis*, scintilla della coscienza cui è strettamente connesso il senso del peccato[49]. Ora, ciò che non è né secondo il Λόγος né contrario ad esso, è, secondo la dottrina stoica, un indifferente. La morte rientra tra le realtà indifferenti, eppure in Seneca sembra essere un bene, anche se 'tragico', in quanto fine di tutti i mali[50]. Il suicidio può costituire un atto positivo di coraggio e, se dunque non è ammissibile qualora consegua a una debolezza causata dalla pavida incapacità di affrontare un dolore transeunte, lo diventa di fronte alla necessità di affermare la propria dignità e li-

[47] Cfr. *ibid.*, 2, p. 272,27-28. E cfr. *supra*, il passaggio citato in corrispondenza della nota 39.

[48] Cfr. LUCIUS ANNAEUS SENECA, *Naturales quaestiones,* II, 36 e 45, ed. T. H. Corcoran, 2 voll., Cambridge 1971-1972, I, pp. 158 e 172.

[49] Cfr. HIERONYMUS STRIDONIUS, *Commentaria in Hiezechielem*, I, 1, PL 25, 22AB, ed. F. Glorie, Turnhout 1964 (CCSL, 75), pp. 11,209 - 12,222: «Plerique, iuxta Platonem, rationale animae, et irascitivum, et concupiscitivum (...) ad hominem, et leonem ac vitulum referunt. (...) Quartamque ponunt quae super haec et extra haec tria est, quam Graeci vocant συντήρησιν, quae scintilla conscientiae in Cain quoque pectore, postquam eiectus est de paradiso, non exstinguitur, et qua victi voluptatibus (...) ipsaque interdum rationis decepti similitudine, nos peccare sentimus».

[50] Cfr. J.C. GARCÍA-BORRÓN, *Seneca y los estoicos*, Barcelona 1956, p. 199.

bertà contro le avversità procurate dalla sorte o dalla malvagità umana[51]: «ego expectem vel morbi crudelitatem vel hominis, cum possim per media exire tormenta et adversa discutere?»[52]. Il suicidio, soltanto in tal caso, è finalizzato alla difesa della dignità della persona umana, che attraverso di esso realizza l'unico riscatto morale possibile e la liberazione da vincoli altrimenti insolubili, verso la libertà del cielo[53].

L'apologia del suicidio come atto di liberazione dalle sofferenze della vita avvicina lo stoico Seneca alla classica dottrina epicurea[54]. Nei passi ricordati delle *Epistulae ad Lucilium* le sue due fondamentali argomentazioni a favore del suicidio ruotano intorno all'esaltazione del coraggio del suicida e alla conquista della libertà che egli realizza. La fallacia di queste argomentazioni per Gualtiero è smentita in modo evidente dai fatti: descrivendo gli ultimi istanti della vita di Seneca, egli mostra che il suicidio del filosofo romano, lungi dall'essere un atto di nobile virilità, è stato espressione di un animo corrotto, lussurioso e flaccido; contro il preannuncio di liberazione e di gloria ultraterrena, il vittorino nega qualsiasi possibilità di salvezza per i suicidi, ridicolizzando il magistero socratico cui Seneca si è ispirato. Esistono chiaramente motivazioni più profonde per cui Gualtiero si oppone al suicidio. Esso costituisce un atto innaturale di violenza nei confronti di se stessi direttamente contrario all'amore divino nei confronti della creatura: «furiosi qui seipsos occidant»[55]. Ancora più significativamente, Seneca è ritenuto un omicida; già Agostino ha insegnato che il suicidio non è un peccato di minor rilievo dell'omicidio, ma, anzi, è a esso assimilabile[56].

[51] Cfr. *ibid.*, pp. 217-218.

[52] Cit. *supra*, in corrispondenza della nota 28.

[53] Vedi ancora il passaggio senechiano citato *supra*, *ibid.*; e cfr. GARCÍA-BORRÓN, *ibid.*, pp. 219-220.

[54] Cfr. A. MARTIN, s.v. *Suicide*, in *Dictionnaire de théologie catholique*, XIV/2, Paris 1941, [coll. 2739-2748], col. 2740.

[55] *Contra quatuor labyrinthos Franciae*, IV, 4, p. 273,7.

[56] Cfr. AUGUSTINUS HIPPONENSIS, *De Civitate Dei*, I, 20, 35, edd. Dombart – Kalb cit. (alla nota 38), I, p. 23,40-41: «Restat ut de homine intelligamus, quod dictum est: 'Non occides' (*Ex* 20, 13), nec alterum ergo, nec te. Neque enim qui se occidit aliud quam hominem occidit». Questa visione del suicidio come modalità differente ma sostanzialmente equivalente all'omicidio influenza tutto il Medioevo; cfr. MARTIN, *Suicide* cit., col. 2742.

La vita appartiene soltanto a Dio; essa quindi è investita di un valore assoluto e oggettivo, nei confronti del quale non può essere invocata la soggettività del libero arbitrio, come ritiene Seneca. Ma queste argomentazioni non vengono esplicitate, né s'invocano versetti biblici o autorità patristiche. Gualtiero non sviluppa le argomentazioni classiche della teologia cristiana relative alla tematica del suicidio, alla cui condanna pur concorreva il consenso comune del popolo cristiano e dei teologi, non soltanto di impostazione tradizionalista. Questo tentativo di sconfiggere il proprio avversario utilizzando le sue stesse armi, finalizzato a un più deciso smascheramento della pericolosità della sua dottrina, contribuisce a rendere originale la posizione del vittorino nei suoi confronti. Tra i Padri della Chiesa, come Agostino e Girolamo, prevale in effetti una visione complessivamente positiva della figura di Seneca, esaltato a motivo di un presunto carteggio con san Paolo e in virtù del riconoscimento di aspetti della sua dottrina morale non lontani dallo spirito evangelico[57]. Il vittorino ribalta i termini della questione: Seneca è colpevole proprio perché non ha saputo riconoscere nella fede di Paolo la verità di Cristo a cui convertirsi; il modo in cui è morto, non ostentando coraggio ma rifugiandosi vilmente in un atto edonistico, ne costituisce infine una prova inoppugnabile, e l'immoralità del suo atto chiude la via al cielo anziché aprirla, perché è impossibile che Dio ricompensi l'immoralità:

> Potuit autem iste fortis, ut falso putatur, contemptor mundi fieri facillime non tantum christianus sed martyr toto biennio quo Paulus Romae mansit, si non magis elegisset suum balneum quam Christi baptismum vel Pauli magisterium[58].

[57] Cfr. AUGUSTINUS HIPPONENSIS, *Epistulae*, 153, ad Macedonium, 5, 14, PL 33, 659, ed. A. Goldbacher, 5 voll., Praha – Wien – Leipzig 1895-1923 (CSEL, 34/1-2, 44, 57, 58), II, p. 412,1-3: «Merito ait Seneca, qui temporibus apostolorum fuit, cuius etiam quaedam ad Paulum apostolum leguntur epistulae: omnes odit, qui malos odit».

[58] *Contra quatuor labyrinthos Franciae*, IV, 2, p. 272,28-31.

4. *Il confronto tra Seneca e Guglielmo di Conches a proposito dell'origine del cosmo*

Come abbiamo accennato sopra, il sesto capitolo del quarto libro dell'opera di Gualtiero si apre con un interessante riferimento polemico alle glosse di Guglielmo di Conches al *Timeo* di Platone. La critica alla cosmologia chartriana – seppur soltanto accennata e suggerita dal presupposto che sussistano elementi di affinità tra la dottrina dell'*anima mundi*, principio vivificante il mondo secondo il commento di Guglielmo al testo platonico, e quella del *mundus animal* qui attribuita dal vittorino a Seneca – testimonia, se non la partecipazione, almeno la conoscenza, da parte di Gualtiero, di un vivace dibattito in atto tra i suoi contemporanei, paradigmatico della rinnovata complessità dei rapporti tra fede e cultura nel ricco panorama speculativo del secolo XII:

> Quapropter idem est pene Tymeum Platonis et philosophiam magistri Willelmi de Conchis legere, stellas, animasia, etiam deos credere[59].

Una delle tematiche più delicate e ambigue con cui si confrontano i commentatori del *Timeo* platonico riguarda l'origine del mondo nel suo rapporto con Dio[60]. Gugliemo di Conches tenta di risolverla operando una sintesi tra la dottrina agostiniana e quella boeziana del tempo e della sua origine. Per Agostino, il tempo è cominciato con il mondo: non ha senso, dunque, chiedersi quando Dio abbia creato il mondo[61]. Per Boezio, invece, una derivazione eterna di qualcosa da Dio non risulta filosoficamente contraddittoria, in quanto l'assoluta distanza ontologica tra la causa divina e i suoi effetti è spiegazione sufficiente della loro diversità da essa e non comporta aprioristicamente una diversifica-

[59] *Ibid.*, 6, p. 273,28-29.

[60] Cfr. T. GREGORY, *Il platonismo medievale*, Roma 1958, p. 79: «L'assoluta diversità dell'essere di Dio e del mondo esclude ogni possibilità di porli sul piano di una identica eternità: ma proprio questo i polemisti cristiani non vogliono riconoscere, obbiettando che una creazione *ab aeterno* implicherebbe una coeternità e una identità di valore dei due termini».

[61] Cfr. AUGUSTINUS HIPPONENSIS, *Confessiones*, XI, 13, 15, PL 32, 815, ed. L. Verheijen 1981 (CCSL, 27), p. 202,12-14: «Si autem ante caelum et terram nullum erat tempus, cur quaeritur, [*scil.* Domine,] quid tunc faciebas? Non enim erat tunc, ubi non erat tempus».

zione di ordine temporale di tutto ciò che è da lui derivato[62]. Guglielmo ritiene che il mondo abbia la stessa estensione del tempo e, attraverso la distinzione tra *aeternus* (che non ha inizio né fine), *sempiternus* (che ha inizio non nel tempo ma con il tempo e che non ha fine se non con la fine del tempo) e *perpetuus* (che ha inizio nel tempo e non ha fine), lo diversifica tanto da Dio quanto dall'anima umana[63]. Ora, Dio, dalla sua eternità, non può dare direttamente origine a cose transeunti, ma solo a cose sempiterne: ne deriva che la sua opera di creazione concerne in modo diretto le cause seconde, sempiterne, dalle quali derivano tutti gli effetti temporali. Il *Timeo* insegna tale mediazione nella creazione con il *figmentum* del demiurgo, che affida agli astri il completamento della sua opera plasmatrice[64]. Su questa base, Guglielmo introduce la dottrina delle cause seconde all'interno del cosmo cristiano:

> Finito tractatu de creatione caelestis animalis, tam visibilis quam invisibilis, transit ad creationem ceterorum animalium, more suo ad integumentum se transferens quod tale est quod, creatis stellis ac spiritibus, convocavit eos Deus in uno conventu habitaque oratione iniunxit eis officium formandi corpora ceterorum animalium et maxime hominis, coniungendique animam corpori et servandi eam cum corpore, dandi cibi incrementa et dissolvendi. Huius rei est veritas quod stellae et spiritus a Deo vocantur cum ab ipso ad aliquid agendum aptantur; ad ipsos loquitur cum providet quae per ipsos fiant; iniungit praedicta officia quia per effectum stellarum et ministerium spirituum illa implentur[65].

Tale interpretazione platonizzante della dottrina delle cause seconde, per cui gli astri svolgono la funzione di ministri ausiliari

[62] Cfr. ANICIUS MANLIUS SEVERINUS BOETHIUS, *Consolatio philosophiae*, V, pr. 6, 11, PL 63, 859B, ed. C. Moreschini, München – Leipzig 2000, p. 424,38-40: «Neque Deus conditis rebus antiquior videri debet temporis quantitate, sed simplici potius proprietate naturae».

[63] Cfr. GUILLELMUS DE CONCHIS, *Glosae super Platonem*, I, ed. Jeauneau cit. (alla nota 38), p. 78,19-23: «Est *aeternum* quod caret principio et fine ut Creator; *sempiternum* quod, carens fine, habet principium non in tempore sed cum tempore ut mundus; *perpetuum* est quod incipit in tempore et caret fine ut anima hominis». I corsivi sono miei.

[64] Cfr. GREGORY, *Il platonismo* cit. (alla nota 60), pp. 93-94.

[65] GUILLELMUS DE CONCHIS, *ibid.*, II, p. 204,1-12.

dell'opera creatrice di Dio, deve essere apparsa agli occhi di Gualtiero sensibilmente contraria all'ortodossia. Se, infatti, è sicuramente l'effetto di un suo eccesso verbale l'attribuire al maestro di Chartres l'idea che le stelle siano non solo esseri viventi, ma addirittura «dei», è tuttavia evidente, secondo la posizione dottrinale di Guglielmo, quale emerge da questo passaggio del suo commento, che gli astri, nel passo sovracitato, rivestono il ruolo di sostanze concreatrici, partecipi di una prerogativa che dovrebbe essere riconosciuta solo al Dio creatore[66]. Ma il punto più complesso della teoria delle mediazioni cosmiche introdotta da Guglielmo di Conches è nella sua ipotesi di identificazione tra l'*anima mundi* del *Timeo*, e lo Spirito Santo della rivelazione cristiana:

> Anima mundi est naturalis vigor quo quaedam res tantum habent moveri, quaedam crescere, quaedam sentire, quaedam discernere. Sed quid sit ille vigor naturalis quaeritur. Sed ut michi videtur ille vigor naturalis est spiritus sanctus, id est divina et benigna concordia, quia divino amore et concordia habent omnia esse, moveri, vivere, crescere, sentire, discernere[67].

La critica di Gualtiero, a difesa della purezza del dogma religioso, è a questo proposito inevitabile e impietosa. Nell'ambito della cosmologia platonica, l'*anima mundi* è ontologicamente subordinata al demiurgo: non può dunque essere lecito spingere l'analogia tra la triade platonica, costituita dal demiurgo, dal νοῦς e dall'*anima mundi*, e la Trinità cristiana fino all'identificazione dello Spirito santo con la terza ipostasi del *Timeo*. Non mancano dunque possibili elementi di confronto, a parere di Gualtiero, tra la cosmologia di Seneca e quella di Guglielmo di Conches, che ricadono parallelamente, quantunque non proprio esplicitamente,

[66] Poco sopra, nel terzo capitolo, Gualtiero anticipa la propria avversione per ogni sorta di mediazione intra-cosmica con un accenno polemico al «quintum elementum Aristotelis», l'etere incorruttibile nel quale sarebbe individuabile, secondo Seneca, la collocazione meritata dopo la morte dai suicidi; cfr. *Contra quatuor labyrinthos Franciae*, IV, 3, p. 273,4-6: «Nec iam liceat christianos rapi ad tertium coelum eo quod Aristotelis quintum elementum, incompellabile, scilicet coelum, ex auctoritate Senecae obtineant pessimi homicidae».

[67] GUILLELMUS DE CONCHIS, *Glosae super Boetium*, In Consolationem, III, m. 9, ed. L. Nauta, Turnhout 1999 (CCCM, 158), p. 169,522-528.

sotto gli strali della sua polemica. A dire il vero Guglielmo di Conches ha mutato le proprie posizioni dottrinali con maggiore attenzione all'ortodossia in opere posteriori, come il *Dragmaticon*[68]. La cronologia delle sue opere più tarde non va oltre il 1150, data nettamente anteriore alla composizione del *Contra quatuor labyrinthos Franciae*[69]. Dunque Gualtiero ha forse intenzionalmente ignorato, o non ha considerato significativo questo cambiamento di prospettiva. In effetti, la retrovisione operata da Guglielmo non rinnega il naturalismo platonico e la dottrina delle cause seconde, ma rende soltanto tali dottrine più accettabili all'ortodossia. L'unica modalità di cui i platonici del secolo XII dispongono per adoperare il concetto di *anima mundi* senza cadere nell'eresia, rimane la sua identificazione *tout court* con la «natura», che, secondo le cosmologie di Chartres, si definisce come complesso delle cause seconde, unificate da un principio vitale che le regge tutte, spesso identico all'«ignis artificiosus» della cosmologia stoica[70].

Per comprendere correttamente il senso di questo accostamento è allora utile richiamare un passo delle *Naturales Quaestiones* senechiane:

> Eundem quem nos Iovem intellegunt, rectorem custodemque universi, animum ac spiritum mundi, operis huius dominum et artificem, cui nomen omne convenit. Vis illum fatum vocare, non errabis; hic est ex quo suspensa sunt omnia, causa causarum. Vis illum providentiam dicere, recte dices; est enim cuius consilio huic mundo providetur. (...) Vis illum naturam vocare, non peccabis; hic est ex quo nata sunt omnia, cuius spiritu vivimus. Vis illum vocare mundum, non falleris; ipse enim est hoc quod vides totum, partibus suis inditus et se sustinens et sua[71].

Seneca definisce inoltre Dio come «mens universi»[72]; e afferma: «nostri melior pars animus est, in illo nulla pars extra animum

[68] Cfr. GREGORY, *Il platonismo* cit. (alla nota 60), p. 134.

[69] Sulla cronologia delle opere di Guglielmo di Conches, cfr. J.H. NEWELL Jr., s.v. *William of Conches*, in *Dictionary of Literary Biography*, CXV, *Medieval Philosophers*, New York 1992, p. 353.

[70] Cfr. GREGORY, *ibid.*, pp. 135-136.

[71] LUCIUS ANNAEUS SENECA, *Naturales Quaestiones*, II, 45, ed. Corcoran cit. (alla nota 48), p. 172.

[72] *Ibid.*, I, praef., 13, p. 10.

est»; per concludere: «totus est ratio»[73]. Si evince nel pensiero teologico del filosofo stoico un'ambiguità che Gualtiero coglie in modo generico: Dio è «causa causarum» ma anche «hoc quod vides totum». Probabilmente tale posizione è dettata dall'esigenza di conservare, all'interno di una concezione monista, un elemento di trascendenza della *ratio* rispetto alla pura materialità[74]. Gualtiero osserva in proposito che se Dio fosse l'unica anima del mondo, sarebbe assurdo ammettere il suo dividersi tra tutti gli esseri viventi, persino tra le bestie. L'accostamento tra Seneca e Guglielmo di Conches è dunque, in definitiva, affascinante, e forse non del tutto privo di fondamento. Per entrambi Dio trascende la materia, in una modalità che è evidente nel secondo Guglielmo, molto più nebulosa e aporetica in Seneca; per entrambi il *mundus* è *animal*. Se però, per Seneca, la *causa causarum* si manifesta in modo immanente nella *ratio universalis*, che è *spiritus*, *natura*, ciò non è ammissibile per Guglielmo, se non identificando, come accade nel primo periodo della sua produzione, l'*anima mundi* con lo Spirito Santo[75].

Un pensiero che si fonda in ambito cosmologico su una rivalutazione del ruolo delle cause seconde nell'economia della creazione, che si concretizza in campo teoretico in una adesione entusiastica alla cultura pagana, che conduce nella sfera etica a una esaltazione delle virtù naturali guidate dalla sola ragione, non può trovare accoglienza nella visione teologica della verità propria di Gualtiero: in ultima analisi è la stessa idea che possa essere autonomamente e intrinsecamente potente, sapiente e buono anche ciò che, quantunque subordinato a Dio, è altro da Lui, che minaccia alla base, nella sua percezione, la solidità della fede cristiana[76].

[73] *Ibid.*,14, pp. 10-12.

[74] Cfr. GARCÍA BORRÓN, *Seneca* cit. (alla nota 50), p. 51.

[75] Afferma al proposito MICHEL SPANNEUT nel suo studio *Permanence du Stoïcisme. De Zénon a Malraux*, Gembloux 1973, pp. 183-184: «Si la théologie de Guillame et ses hésitations mêmes nous empêchent de lui attribuer un animisme qui aurait l'Esprit Saint pour élément vital, il n'est pas moins vrai qu'il en subi la tentation. Guillame de Saint-Thierry n'a pas manqué de révéleur l'erreur chez lui, et chez Abélard d'ailleurs, en termes qui évoquent le stoïcisme». Anche Italo Ronca individua in Seneca una delle fonti principali di Guglielmo: cfr. GUILLELMUS DE CONCHIS, *A Dialogue on Natural Philosophy* (Dragmaticon Philosophiae), Transl. (...) with a Short Introduction and Explanatory Notes, a c. di I. Ronca, Notre Dame (IN) 1997 (Notre Dame Texts in Medieval Culture, 2).

[76] La triplice critica di Gualtiero può effettivamente richiamare la tradiziona-

5. *Il quinto labirinto di Francia*

Ma una simile impostazione risulta invece del tutto in sintonia con il pensiero di un confratello di Gualtiero, Goffredo, che, nato intorno al 1125, diventa monaco a San Vittore e vi muore dopo il 1194[77]. Goffredo studia le discipline liberali dal 1140 al 1145, a Parigi, e matura la propria vocazione di monaco vittorino tra il 1155 e il 1160[78]. Le due opere di maggior spessore di Goffredo sono il *Fons philosophiae*, del 1178, che si può definire una propedeutica in versi agli studi liberali e teologici, largamente debitrice del *Didascalicon* di Ugo, e il *Microcosmus*, del 1185, che è una esegesi allegorica in prospettiva antropologica del racconto della creazione[79]. La costante tendenza a rivalutare la natura e l'uomo, il rifiuto del *contemptus mundi* e l'ammirazione per Seneca, tratti peculiari o quantomeno presenti nei due studi, sono i capi d'accusa che hanno reso Goffredo una vittima diretta delle persecuzioni di Gualtiero, che attorno al 1180, in qualità di priore, lo ha costretto ad allontanarsi dalla scuola, assegnandogli un priorato rurale, ma di fatto emarginandolo dalla comunità. Goffredo ha fatto ritorno a Parigi, infatti, solo negli ultimi anni della sua vita[80].

Il *Fons philosophiae* è dedicato a Stefano, abate dell'abbazia parigina di Santa Genoveffa. Si può supporre che Goffredo abbia conosciuto Stefano e ne abbia invocato la protezione proprio nel periodo in cui Gualtiero era priore a San Vittore[81]. L'opera, affa-

le determinazione trinitaria degli attributi divini: l'ordine del creato, il conoscere e l'agire hanno come proprio modello archetipale la potenza, la sapienza e la bontà di Dio.

77 Cfr. PIAZZONI, *I Vittorini* cit. (alla nota 6), pp. 198-199.

78 Cfr. CILENTO, *Il metodo* cit. (alla nota 38), p. 67; PIAZZONI, *ibid.*, p. 199.

79 Cfr. GODEFRIDUS DE SANCTO VICTORE, *Fons philosophiae*, ed. P. Michaud-Quantin, Namur 1956 (Analecta Mediaevalia Namurcensia, 8); ID., *Microcosmus*, ed. P. Delhaye, in ID., *Le Microcosmus de Godefroy de Saint-Victor*, Lille – Gembloux 1951 (Mèmoires et travaux publiès par les professeurs des facultès catholiques de Lille, 56).

80 Cfr. PIAZZONI, *ibid.*, p. 198; CILENTO, *ibid.*, pp. 63-67; P. MASTRANDREA, *Lettori cristiani di Seneca filosofo*, Brescia 1988, pp. 79-83.

81 Cfr. GODEFRIDUS DE SANCTO VICTORE, *Fons philosophiae*, prol. (*Epistula ad abbatem sancti Genovefae de monte*), ed. Michaud-Quantin cit. (alla nota 79), pp. 33-34. Cfr. P. DELHAYE, *Le Microcosmus de Godefroy de Saint-Victor. Étude théologique*, Lille – Gembloux, 1951 (Mèmoires et travaux publiès par les professeurs des facultès catholiques de Lille, 57), pp. 29-30 e pp. 187-198. Il Delhaye, inter-

scinante trasfigurazione poetico-allegorica del confronto-incontro tra la sacra dottrina e la scienza umana, rivela in Goffredo un marcato interesse per le arti liberali, ma accompagnato dalla consapevolezza di quanto trivio e quadrivio non costituiscano un *bonum in se*, poiché necessitano di un approccio che sappia valorizzarli in modo adeguato:

> Septem tamen transiens rivos computavi (...).
> Emanabat vertice montis fons illimis
> quem natura fecerat a diebus primis (...).
> Ille gustu suavior et saporus quidem,
> attamen non omnibus sapiebat idem (...),
> nunc acetum visus est, nunc nectar eidem[82].

Dai versi di Goffredo traspare anche in modo evidente l'ammirazione per la morale naturale degli antichi, e in particolar modo di Seneca:

> Seneca Lucilio commendavit quaedam
> quae vix Evangelio postponenda credam[83].

Nel *Microcosmus* Goffredo sviluppa poi un ottimismo antropologico che riconosce alla natura umana una bontà sostanziale, non compromessa dal peccato originale: l'uomo, pur non essendo in grado di aspirare alla vita eterna senza la grazia divina, possiede virtù naturali al cui rinvenimento si perviene tramite l'indagine razionale[84]. Su di esse si fonda la morale naturale pagana, meritevole dunque di essere lodata e seguita. Non soltanto come *opus gratiae*, ma anche come *opus naturae*, l'uomo risulta dotato di un valore intrinseco:

> Mortale non costitutivum hominis sed peccatoris est (...) peccator est animal rationale mortale; homo vero secundum primum statum sic: homo est animal rationale vitale;

rogandosi su quali possano essere le motivazioni che hanno portato Goffredo a dedicare la sua opera a Stefano, prospetta l'ipotesi di anni di studentato trascorsi in comune a Bologna, anche se non si pronuncia in modo decisivo.

82 Godefridus de Sancto Victore, *ibid.*, p. 36.

83 *Ibid.*, p. 49.

84 Cfr. Id., *Microcosmus*, I, 19, ed. Delhaye cit. (alla nota 79), p. 46,3-4: «Quia igitur naturalia priora sunt gratuitis, quid philosophus inspexerit in naturalibus spiritus humani primum videamus».

> secundum ultimum sic: homo est animal rationale immortale[85].

Anche il tema classico dell'uomo-microcosmo si concilia in Goffredo con un'istanza teologica, ossia con l'analogia fra la raffigurazione dell'uomo come *minor mundus*, a un tempo parte e immagine perfetta del mondo universale, e il principio del corpo mistico, che rende l'uomo simile a Cristo in quanto membro vivo del suo corpo spirituale[86]. Questa coerenza tra lettura cosmologica e teologica dell'antropologia consente di progettare l'esistenza umana come attuazione nel singolo individuo della medesima perfezione che Dio ha realizzato fin da principio con la creazione dell'universo:

> Hunc huius mundi ornatum tribus diebus iuxta Moysi narrationem in megacosmo factum, et nos in microcosmo prosequimur usque ad consummationem tam ipsius mundi quam nostri[87].

Il testo del *Microcosmus* aspira a dare concretezza e articolato sviluppo a questo progetto: l'esaltazione dell'opera di Dio e dell'intima connessione fra l'uomo e l'universo diventa la modalità più efficace per mostrare l'intrinseca bontà di alcune caratteristiche dell'essere umano, naturalmente insite in lui fin dalla creazione[88].

Entusiasmo nei confronti delle arti liberali, esaltazione di Seneca, naturalismo cosmologico: il pensiero di Goffredo propone,

[85] *Ibid.*, I, 2, p. 36,3-8.

[86] Cfr. *ibid.*, I, 18, p. 45,19-31: «Sciendum igitur quod neque philosophus neque theologus hominem forinsecus inspexerunt dum eum vel mundi vel microcosmi nomine appellaverunt, mentis potius oculos ad spiritum qui intus erat defixerunt et eum, qualis esset, diligenti indagine considerantes invenerunt. (...) Nam cum alia sint humani spiritus naturalia a deo creatore sibi data, alia gratuita a deo recreatore sibi superaddita, philosophus naturalia, theologus gratuita inspexit dum hominem vel microcosmum vel mundum appellavit». E *ibid.*, III, 239, p. 261,20-24: «Si ea caritate qua divinitati suae univit naturam tuam, humanitati quoque suae uniat personam tuam, hic est incorporet te suae humanitati tanquam membrum capiti, ut sitis invicem tu membrum capitis et ipse caput membri».

[87] *Ibid.*, II, 80, p. 92,23-26. Cfr. V. CILENTO, *Medioevo monastico e scolastico*, Milano – Napoli 1961, pp. 232-233: «In tal modo, la natura non è già disordine e confusione e nebulosa inconsistenza, ma una terra, un cielo, un giardino in cui crescono frutti, simboli delle azioni buone e sagge e delle discipline scientifiche dell'uomo secondo la natura».

[88] Cfr. DELHAYE, *Le Microcosmus de Godefroy de Saint-Victor. Étude théologique* cit. (alla nota 81), p. 171.

in modo simmetricamente opposto, le tematiche su cui Gualtiero intesse la propria polemica. Considerando che Gualtiero privilegia quale strumento apologetico l'invettiva personale, prende allora corpo l'ipotesi che la sezione dedicata alla filosofia antica all'inizio del quarto libro del *Contra quatuor labyrinthos Franciae* abbia direttamente come sottofondo polemico l'opera di Goffredo[89]: puntuali corrispondenze testuali tra le parole di Gualtiero e i versi del *Fons philosophiae* consentono illuminanti riscontri in questo senso. Soprattutto nel quarto e nel settimo capitolo, il priore vittorino tradisce la precisa intenzione di ribattere, colpo su colpo, al complesso di argomentazioni che il confratello elabora a favore di un incontro fra la cultura cristiana e i frutti più fecondi di quella antica. Per esempio, nell'epistola proemiale al *Fons philosophiae*, che contiene la dedica a Stefano, Goffredo, riecheggiando la salmodia biblica, parla di un calice ricolmo di acqua e vino, allegoria del connubio tra arti liberali e teologia[90]. Prontamente Gualtiero risponde, nel quarto capitolo, contrapponendo, secondo una figura ispirata da Girolamo, il «calix Christi» al «calix daemoniorum»[91]. Insistendo sulla medesima immagine, Goffredo introduce quindi un'ulteriore distinzione, relativa a due differenti modalità di presentazione della *theologia*, considerata prima in connubio con le *artes*, poi nel vertice della sua trascendenza epistemologica[92]. Egli sottopone all'esame critico del destinatario la plausibilità dell'accostamento fra le due discipline, ostentando come una posizione di maggiore apertura nei confronti della cultura classica non sia incompatibile con l'assoluta preminenza che deve essere accordata al superiore sapere teologico:

[89] Cfr. *ibid.*, pp. 244-251.

[90] Cfr. GODEFRIDUS DE SANCTO VICTORE, *Fons philosophiae*, prol., ed. Michaud-Quantin cit. (alla nota 79), p. 33: «Calicem plenum mixto vestrae destinavi, Pater, eruditionis examinandum iudicio, quatinus utrumque sit in manibus vestris, eius videlicet vel status vel eversio. Continet autem mixtum dupliciter, vel materiae scilicet, vel artificii varietate». Cfr CILENTO, *Il metodo* cit. (alla nota 38), p. 65.

[91] Cfr. nel testo citato *supra*, in corrispondenza alla nota 39: «Quid faciet cum psalterio Horatius, cum Evangeliis Maro, cum Apostolis Cicero? (...) Simul bibere non debemus calicem Christi et calicem demoniorum».

[92] Cfr. GODEFRIDUS DE SANCTO VICTORE, *ibid.*, p. 33: «Prima namque pars eius aquam simul et vinum guttatim fluit, secunda vero pars sanguinem uvae meracissimum pari modo fluens, delicatissimae simul carnis edulium ministrat».

Tunc ad summam denique me philosophiam
verti, theologicam scilicet sophiam,
cuius ut dulcedinem prelibavi divam
dixi: nullam poculis his impono briam[93].

Goffredo arriva a identificare la sapienza teologica con il genere più alto di filosofia. Ma, dal momento che la filosofia si basa sulle arti liberali, tale architettura del sapere conferisce al trivio e al quadrivio uno statuto di profonda dignità, in evidente contrasto con la posizione di Gualtiero. Anche la polemica presente nel settimo capitolo del quarto libro del *Contra quatuor labyrinthos Franciae* contro la bellicosità dei dialettici è allora facilmente inquadrabile nell'ottica di una replica polemica all'atteggiamento conciliante del *Fons philosophiae* di Goffredo, che rappresenta allegoricamente la dialettica come una bevanda eccitante che provoca aggressività. L'esercizio di questa disciplina viene da lui efficacemente raffigurato nelle forme di un combattimento armato[94]:

Instruit ingenium validi tironis
et ad exercitum preparat agonis;
illis donat gladios oppositionis,
his e contra clipeum dat responsionis.
Dat loricas ferreas, firmat rationes,
sillogismos triplices per contextiones
texit, nectens simplices propositiones,
nectens ypotheticas compositiones
addit eius copia telorum
de periermeneias luco succisorum,
de rudi materia analecticorum,
de silvosis etiam locis topicorum (...).
Preparat Porphirius ad fluenta vias,
iuvat Aristotiles per cathegorias,
ubi, nisi cautius ambulare scias,
timeo ne citius errabundus fias[95].

E sempre riferendosi alla dialettica, Goffredo applica, ma in un contesto ben diverso, una distinzione analoga al «separare pretiosum a vili» raccomandato da Gualtiero.

[93] *Ibid.*, p. 51.
[94] Cfr. CILENTO, *Il metodo* cit. (alla nota 38), p. 77.
[95] GODEFRIDUS DE SANCTO VICTORE, *ibid.*, p. 40.

Hic est enim gladius in se pretiosus.
Quem si gerit sapiens, erit fructuosus,
quod si forte strinxerit illum furiosus,
tam sibi quam ceteris erit perniciosus[96].

Sono parole dalle quali si evince comunque anche una certa prudenza nei confronti dell'eccessiva fiducia nel potere delle arti liberali, che sembra avvicinare il suo pensiero alla cautela raccomandata dal polemico confratello: l'elogio «iuvat Aristotiles per cathegorias» è infatti corretto da un avvertimento sul rischio di cadere in gravi errori con l'avere troppa confidenza negli strumenti razionali, e l'aggettivo «furiosus» denota ogni abuso di distinzioni dialettiche come innaturale esito di un razionalismo pernicioso. Al «furiosus» Goffredo contrappone tuttavia l'autentico «sapiens», colui che sa utilizzare la cultura profana come un bene, rispetto alla quale la sapienza teologica rappresenta l'ottimo da conseguire proprio per il suo tramite. Per Gualtiero, invece, la vera sapienza divina non è soltanto il bene assoluto contrapposto a un bene relativo, ma l'unico principio catartico di quanto di male si nasconde ancora nella sapienza antica. Questo è il significato più profondo della sua contrapposizione tra «calix Christi» e «calix demoniorum». La vera sapienza non rende gli uomini semplicemente «sapientes», integrando le imperfezioni di una sapienza terrena naturalmente limitata: semmai li purifica, eliminando ogni grave impedimento al prezioso conseguimento della verità e del bene. Riferendosi ai Padri della Chiesa, e in generale ai sostenitori dell'ortodossia cattolica, Gualtiero parla di «divina philosophia», una filosofia che è resa divina dall'efficacia della grazia che redime dal male[97].

L'evidente intento polemico nei confronti dell'opera di Goffredo consente anche di capire il motivo per cui, nel criticare i modelli etici pagani, Gualtiero abbia puntato i propri strali soprattutto contro la figura di Seneca. Proprio una esaltazione dei meriti del filosofo romano nei versi del *Fons philosophiae*, culminante in un ardito accostamento delle *Epistulae ad Lucilium* al Vangelo, ha suscitato in Gualtiero un veemente rifiuto interiore.

[96] *Ibidem*.
[97] *Contra quatuor labyrinthos Franciae*, II, 5, p. 237,18.

Goffredo sottolinea in questo passaggio l'importante contributo offerto da Seneca al perfezionamento di un'etica delle virtù naturali: il pensatore stoico è stato, nonostante il suo paganesimo, un «sapiens», che ha comunque partecipato, seppur in modo imperfetto, della vera sapienza. Proprio reagendo a questa pretesa di celebrare in Seneca il fondatore di una morale naturale in parte conciliabile con il Cristianesimo, Gualtiero ha dato corpo alla condanna delle idee del confratello, incentrando la propria analisi sulla gravissima erroneità dell'apologia senechiana del suicidio.

La polemica contro Goffredo vale probabilmente anche quale sottofondo giustificativo delle critiche di Gualtiero a Guglielmo di Conches, il cui pensiero cosmologico gli appare erroneamente coerente con il percorso speculativo del *Microcosmus*. La scuola di San Vittore si rivela in effetti, anche relativamente a questo aspetto, fucina di idee caratterizzate dalla polivocità; a una diversa visione della creazione del mondo vi corrisponde una evidente differenziazione di posizioni sul versante antropologico. Goffredo attinge a Ugo l'idea della creazione di tutte le cose in due tempi. Per Ugo, però, Dio crea in un primo momento un universo senza forma e un uomo naturale privo dei doni eminenti della grazia, mentre in seguito rende l'universo un cosmo e dona la grazia all'uomo:

> Ipsa rationalis creatura quodam suo modo prius informis facta est, postmodum per conversionem ad Creatorem suum formanda; et idcirco foris prius ei demonstrata est informis materia, postea formata, ut quanta fortis inter esse et pulchrum esse distantia discerneret[98].

Goffredo, invece, come si esprime il Delhaye, «instaura un parallelo di natura allegorica tra i primi tre giorni della creazione e i doni naturali dell'uomo»; per lui «la natura non è più (cosmologicamente) confusione prima dell'ordine e (moralmente) resistenza alla grazia»[99]. Un motivo ulteriore, per Gualtiero, per stigmatizzare questa visione che, riconoscendo un valore intrinseco

[98] HUGO DE SANCTO VICTORE, *De Sacramentis christianae fidei*, I, pars I, 3, PL 176, 189A.

[99] DELHAYE, *Le microcosmus de Godefroy de Saint-Victor. Étude théologique* cit. (alla nota 81), p. 172.

seppur causato al mondo *naturaliter* inteso, presenta analogie preoccupanti con la dottrina delle cause seconde tipica del naturalismo platonico.

La sezione dedicata ai filosofi antichi permette di comprendere che è lecito individuare nell'opuscolo polemico di Gualtiero un sottaciuto, ma non meno insidioso, 'quinto labirinto di Francia': Goffredo di San Vittore, il quale anziché apprendere la Sapienza alla «schola Christi», è ricaduto negli errori degli antichi filosofi, analogamente a quanto è accaduto ai «novi doctores», improvvidamente assimilatisi per la loro presunzione di sapere agli antichi eresiarchi. Testimonianza, al di là della rozza superficie, di un'interessante critica di filoni antichi e coevi dell'umanesimo filosofico e del razionalismo teologico, il *Contra quatuor labyrinthos Franciae*, frutto più maturo e consapevole della produzione di Gualtiero, messo a confronto con il *Fons philosophiae* e il *Microcosmus*, prodotti della vivace e ottimistica vena speculativa del confratello Goffredo, costituisce la nota estrema, profondo basso di una polifonia di pensiero che rimane caratteristica peculiare e affascinante della scuola di San Vittore.

MARC GEOFFROY

RAISON ET FOI OU RAISON ET LOI

LE PHILOSOPHE ET LA CITÉ SELON AVERROÈS, D'APRÈS AL-FĀRĀBĪ ET IBN BĀĞĞA (AVEMPACE)

L'autorité ou la figure d'Averroès furent souvent invoquées dans les discussions latines médiévales concernant le rapport entre raison et foi[1]. Cependant, les œuvres originales dans lesquelles le philosophe cordouan avait traité de ces questions[2] n'ont pas été connues des Latins[3]. Cette absence n'est pas seulement liée aux

[1] On pense bien sûr aux nombreuses querelles sur l'unité de l'intellect et la «double vérité», prolongées jusqu'au cœur de l'époque moderne, qui ne sont pas l'objet de la présente discussion. Pour l'ensemble de cette question, on renvoie à A. DE LIBERA, *Raison et foi. Archéologie d'une crise d'Albert le Grand à Jean-Paul II*, Paris 2003.

[2] A savoir le *Faṣl al-maqāl*, traduit de nombreuses fois en langues européennes; notamment AVERROÈ, *Il trattato decisivo sull'accordo della religione con la filosofia*, introd. et tr. M. Campanini, Milano 1994 (I Classici della BUR); AVERROES, *Decisive Treatise and Epistle Dedicatory: Determining the Connection Between the Law and Wisdom*, tr. angl. Ch. E. Butterworth, Chicago 2002; AVERROÈS, *Discours décisif*, introd. A. de Libera, tr. fr. et notes par M. Geoffroy, Paris 1996 (GF 871); on référera dans la suite à cette dernière traduction, qui donne une édition du texte en vis-à-vis; et le K. *al-Kašf 'an manāhiğ al-adilla* (*Dévoilement des procédés de la démonstration*), dont on ne mentionnera que les éditions récentes: IBN RUŠD, *Manāhiğ al-adilla fī 'aqā'id al-milla*, éd. M. Qāsim, al-Qāhira 1959; IBN RUŠD, *al-Kašf 'an manāhiğ al-adilla fī 'aqā'id al-milla*, cur. M. 'Ā. al-Ğābirī, Bayrūt 1998; tr. all. M. MÜLLER, *Philosophie und Theologie von Averroes. Aus dem Arabischen übersetzt*, München 1875, pp. 26-122; tr. esp. M. ALONSO, *Teologia de Averroes*, Madrid – Granada 1947, pp. 149-365; tr. fr. partielle dans AVERROÈS, *L'Islam et la raison. Anthologie de textes juridiques, théologiques et polémiques*, introd. A. de Libera, tr. et notes M. Geoffroy, Paris 2000 (GF 1132), pp. 95-160; tr. angl. [peu fiable] I. NAJJAR, *Faith and Reason in Islam. Averroes' Exposition of Religious Arguments*, Oxford 2001.

[3] Il y a cependant des exceptions, indirectes et tardives. Il faut signaler notamment l'adaptation dialoguée du *Faṣl al-Maqāl* par le philosophe juif espagnol du XIIIe siècle Shem Tov ibn Falaqera sour le titre *Igeret ha-vikuaḥ* («Epître du dia-

10.1484/M.NUTRIX-EB.1.101247

aléas de la transmission. Le propos et les buts des écrits théologiques d'Averroès, inscrits dans un contexte propre à la dogmatique musulmane et à des conditions politiques spécifiques, n'auraient aucunement été accessibles aux lecteurs latins, et sans doute pour cette raison, n'ont pas suscité l'intérêt des traducteurs. Certes, les différentes formes de rationalité religieuse en Chrétienté, en Islam ou dans le judaïsme au Moyen Age ont toutes postulé la non exclusion réciproque des savoirs rationnel et révélé, mais sous ce dénominateur commun se présentent des réalités très différentes. L'objet de la présente contribution est de montrer, à partir de quelques exemples, l'ancrage de la doctrine d'Averroès sur le rapport entre religion et philosophie dans un ensemble de conceptions spécifiquement islamiques de la foi (*īmān*), de la raison-intellect (*'aql*) et de la Loi (*šarī'a*), ainsi que dans un contexte socio-culturel déterminé. Il faudra pour cela considérer quelques antécédents lointains d'Averroès, son rapport à al-Fārābī, mais surtout à son compatriote et prédécesseur immédiat Ibn Bāǧǧa, Avempace. On pourra ainsi examiner l'écart qui sépare, à une génération de distance, le point de vue d'Avempace de celui d'Averroès, conduisant d'une conception 'isolationniste' du philosophe, *faylasūf*, dans la société musulmane, à la possibilité de concevoir une cité musulmane intégrant la philosophie aristotélicienne.

Partons d'une comparaison: la conception scolastique du rapport entre raison et foi implique une différence qualitative (réalité divine et surnaturelle; connaissance accessible à l'esprit humain) en fonction de laquelle les choses connaissables se distribuent en ce qui est l'objet d'une adhésion de la foi, et ce qui

logue»). Celle-ci a été traduite en latin en Italie à la fin du XVe siècle. Le texte latin est édité par G. DAHAN, Epistola Dialogi. *Une traduction latine de l'*Igeret ha-vikuaḥ *de Shem Tov ibn Falaqera. Etude et traduction*, in «Sefarad», 39 (1979), pp. 1-112. Encore plus tardivement (début du XVIe siècle), on a connu une traduction latine du K. *al-Kašf 'an manāhiǧ al-adilla* par Abraham de Balmes. Celle-ci a été signalée pour la première fois par G. TAMANI, *Una traduzione ebraico-latina delle questioni sulla fisica di Averroè*, in «Italia», 13-15 [In Memory of Giuseppe Sermoneta], Jérusalem 2001, pp. 91-101, spéc. p. 92, dans les mss. Città del Vaticano, Biblioteca Apostolica Vaticana, Ottob. lat. 2060 et Milano, Biblioteca Ambrosiana, G.290.inf. Le texte de cette version a été étudié en particulier par S. DI DONATO, *Il* Kitab al-Kašf 'an Manāhiǧ al-adilla fi 'aqā'id al-milla *di Averroè nella traduzione ebraico-latina di Abraham De Balmes*, in «Annali di Cà Foscari», 41 (2002), vol. 3 (serie orientale, 33), pp. 5-36.

est l'objet d'une connaissance rationnelle. La foi découle d'une révélation de la vérité surnaturelle, qui par son caractère même d'être inaccessible à la raison, demande la soumission de l'intelligence. De ce fait même, elle ne peut être qu'une vertu surnaturelle, effet de la grâce, par laquelle le croyant prend pour vraies les choses que Dieu a révélées, non pas à cause de leur vérité intrinsèque, mais en raison de l'autorité de Dieu qui révèle. C'est le contenu même de la Révélation, inaccessible à la raison, qui détermine une certaine modalité d'adhésion à une vérité révélée qui excède les possibilités de la raison naturelle. La raison créée étant subordonnée à la Vérité incréée, elle doit se soumettre à cette dernière lorsqu'elle se révèle. Les vérités de foi étant surnaturelles, l'homme ne peut les atteindre et y croire uniquement par sa puissance naturelle, bien que la raison ait à collaborer avec la grâce pour accomplir l'acte de foi. La raison est seulement ce qui corrobore la foi, lui offre des «motifs de crédibilité» ou conçoit les «préambules de la foi», vérités philosophiques qui sont logiquement antérieures à celle-ci: l'existence de Dieu, l'existence de l'âme humaine spirituelle et immortelle, la capacité pour l'homme d'atteindre des certitudes par l'usage de sa raison, l'existence de la liberté, etc.

Il faut souligner la différence fondamentale que présente à cet égard la conception du rapport entre raison et foi dans un contexte marqué par la théologie musulmane du *kalām*, avec celle de la scolastique[4], de deux points de vue. 1) La distinction entre connaissance «naturelle» et «surnaturelle» n'y a pas la même pertinence; la croyance religieuse et la connaissance rationnelle ne portent pas sur des objets différents. Ce qui est objet de foi et/ou de connaissance rationnelle dépend des sujets connaissants. La foi musulmane finit par se résoudre, *pour le philosophe*, dans la connaissance démonstrative, et par s'identifier avec elle. L'Islam du philosophe aristotélicien musulman est une religion dépourvue de mystère, une religion naturelle, dont tout le contenu, aussi bien point de vue des prescriptions rituelles, légales, que des

[4] Parallèlement, ce qui est une autre question, il faut considérer la différence de nature entre la conception chrétienne de la théologie et la science musulmane (et juive) du *kalām*. On peut renvoyer pour cela à G. DAHAN, *Foi, raison, politique. Averroès, Maïmonide, Thomas d'Aquin*, in «Le Trimestre psychanalytique», 1 (1995), pp. 137-147.

dogmes, peut être expliqué de manière rationnelle par celui qui détient l'instrument de la philosophie. 2) Dans la dogmatique de l'Islam, c'est en référence à la Loi (*šarī'a*), et non au contenu de la foi, que sont déterminés 2.1) la légitimité ou non de l'usage de la raison, et 2.2) la primauté *a*) de la raison sur la foi, ou *b*) à l'inverse, de la foi sur la raison, l'une et l'autre étant supposées dans l'un et l'autre cas se confirmer mutuellement.

Malgré le niveau singulièrement élevé des études, de la connaissance philosophique, et l'ampleur des corpus disponibles, la situation concrète du philosophe dans l'Occident musulman au XIIe siècle est intellectuellement, sinon socialement, marginale. Son enseignement est dispensé dans des cercles rares et restreints. Il ne partage pas, objectivement, les croyances religieuses de ses coreligionnaires, et il est à la merci des docteurs de la Loi musulmane qui peuvent condamner non seulement ses enseignements mais sa personne au nom de la *šarī'a*. C'est ce qui a entraîné une tendance à prôner un certain retrait de la société, comme le propose ce passage d'Avempace (m. 533 h. / 1139):

> Quant aux hommes heureux, pour autant qu'ils puissent exister dans ces cités, ils n'accéderont à la béatitude que par l'isolement, et par conséquent, le seul régime valable sera celui de l'homme solitaire, que celui-ci soit seul ou qu'il en existe plusieurs, dans la mesure où aucune communauté, ou cité, ne s'accorde avec leur doctrine[5].

Avempace justifie ainsi le titre de son grand traité de philosophie, le *Régime du solitaire*. Le parcours de l'homme Avempace[6], musi-

[5] IBN BĀĞĞA (AVEMPACE), *Tadbīr al-Mutawaḥḥid* (*Le régime du Solitaire*), in *Rasā'il* IBN BĀĞĞA *al-ilāhiyya (Opera metaphysica)*, éd. M. Faḫrī, Bayrūt 1968, pp. 37-96 (pour ceci, p. 43; nous traduisons). Il existe une traduction espagnole récente, IBN BĀĞĞA (Avempace), *El régimen del solitario* [*Tadbīr al-mutawaḥid*], introd., tr. et notes J. Lomba, Madrid 1997; et une traduction italienne, AVEMPACE, *Il regime del solitario*, introd. et tr. M. Campanini – A. Illuminati, Milano 2002 (BUR Classici, 1381).

[6] Sur la biographie du personnage, cfr. M. ASÍN PALACIOS, *El filósofo zaragozano Avempace*, in «Revista Aragón», 7 (1900), pp. 193-197; 234-238; 278-281; 300-302; 338-340; 8 (1900), pp. 241-246; 301-302; 348-350; D. M. DUNLOP, art. «Ibn Bāǧǧa», in *Encyclopédie de l'Islam*, 2e éd., Leiden 1960-2006, III, pp. 750b-752a; ID., *Remarks on the Life and Works of Ibn Bājjah*, in *Proceedings of the XXIInd Congress of Orientalists*, II, Leiden 1957, pp. 188-196; A. GONZÁLEZ PALENCIA, *Historia de la literatura arábigo-española*, Madrid 1945², pp. 207 seqq.

cien et poète, homme de cour et ministre et médecin de plusieurs dignitaires almoravides, représente pourtant une dénégation du modèle de vie proposé par le philosophe Avempace. L'auteur du *Régime du solitaire* ne fut en effet pas un solitaire. Tout au plus une sorte d'original dans l'élite intellectuelle de son temps, un esprit d'exception et sans doute parfois tenté par la provocation, qui se maintint, à une époque, relativement à l'écart de la politique, mais jamais de la société. Pour expliquer les raisons de cette duplicité, de ce divorce à peu près total entre la vie concrète et l'idéal philosophique, il est un facteur qu'il est d'usage d'invoquer depuis Leo Strauss: la persécution.

Celle-ci a existé mais elle est demeurée assez limitée. Les cas où des accusations d'impiété, de *zandaqa* (terme qui recouvre en principe l'impiété caractérisée, manifeste ou dissimulée, mais qui peut aussi, en manière de procès d'intention, désigner toute forme de pensée ou de pratique de savoir jugée hétérodoxe par le courant religieux dominant, en Espagne musulmane, le juridisme malikite – par exemple le *šī'isme*, le *mu'tazilisme*, ou le simple intérêt pour les sciences rationnelles) aboutirent à de vraies condamnations demeurèrent exceptionnels. Si la persécution du *zindīq* est occasionnelle, elle est cependant récurrente. Les antécédents occupent sans doute d'autant plus le souvenir des *falāsifa* qu'ils sont assez peu nombreux. Pour ne citer que des cas de persécution qui eurent lieu dans des périodes assez proches de celle d'Avempace, pendant la période du Califat omeyyade, sous le règne du jeune calife Hišām II et la régence du Chambellan al-Manṣūr, trois savants et poètes, Ibn al-Iflīlī, (m. 441 h. / 1050), Sa'īd b. Fatḥūn al-Saraqusṭī, ainsi qu'un jeune prince omeyyade, échappèrent de peu à la mort en raison d'une accusation de *zandaqa* pour l'intérêt qu'ils portaient au *kalām*, à la philosophie et à la logique[7]. Des trois, le premier fut emprisonné et le second dut s'exiler d'al-Andalus. Quant au jeune prince, il n'échappa que de peu à la peine capitale. En l'occurrence, l'affaire était sans doute politique. Le 'Régent' al-Manṣūr, soucieux de s'assurer les bonnes grâces des Docteurs malikites, a pu vouloir leur offrir à peu de frais ce gage d'orthodoxie. Il se peut aussi qu'il ait vu dans les réu-

[7] Cfr. M. I. Fierro, *Heresy in al-Andalus*, in *The Legacy of Muslim Spain*, éd. S. K. Jayyusi, 2 voll., Leiden 1994, II, [pp. 895-908], pp. 900-901.

nions savantes des trois personnages le prétexte à la préparation d'un complot qu'il fallait étouffer dans l'oeuf[8]. Le philosophe, même courtisan, est toujours à la merci d'un mouvement d'humeur du prince, ou de considérations de basse politique dont il peut à tout moment faire les frais.

Avempace lui-même, en son temps, n'échappa pas à de semblables griefs. Dans le milieu courtisan sous les Almoravides, ce genre d'accusations, motivées par les rancoeurs personnelles, allaient bon train. Il fut qualifié de *zindīq* par le grand médecin Ibn Zuhr (Avenzoar), qui lui vouait une haine féroce, et fut peut-être même à l'origine de son assassinat à Fès en 1139. Les témoignages historiques dont nous disposons attestent que les adeptes de la philosophie, comme le ministre Mālik ibn Wuhayb (m. 1130), logicien et astronome réputé en son temps et protecteur d'Avempace auprès des Almoravides[9], ayant à concilier les intérêts de leur vie publique avec leur intérêt privé pour la science, ne se départirent jamais d'une extrême prudence dans l'exercice de celle-ci. Ibn Wuhayb est réputé avoir à un moment de sa vie renoncé à l'étude de la philosophie, ou du moins à aborder ces questions publiquement, pour ne s'adonner plus qu'aux sciences licites, c'est-à-dire traditionnelles.

Dans ce contexte, le position du philosophe est paradoxale: la fréquentation du prince et du milieu courtisan est une nécessité. En effet, il n'existe aucune institution proprement dédiée à l'enseignement des sciences autres que religieuses (la tradition, le Droit musulman). Le *faylasūf* ne fait pas profession de penser, et son activité ne lui confère pas de statut social particulier. L'élite courtisane est à la fois pour le philosophe le seul lieu où exister socialement, et le lieu où il risque en principe le plus d'être persécuté, car la publicité qu'il y acquiert l'expose à des jalousies rapidement transformables en procès d'hérésie. C'est de cette précarité que naît probablement la conception du philosophe solitaire, qui légitime tout à la fois son existence dans la société réelle et son retrait d'ordre purement intellectuel, qui lui permet *a*) de se préserver de la nuisance que lui peut occasionner la vie

[8] Cfr. *ibidem*.

[9] Cfr. D. M. Dunlop, *Philosophical Predecessors and Contemporaries of Ibn Bājjah*, in «Islamic Quarterly», 2 (1955), [pp. 100-116], pp. 101-104.

sociale et *b*) d'utiliser cette dernière comme un instrument de sa promotion.

Considérons de plus près la position d'Avempace:

> Il est donc évident que le solitaire ne doit pas fréquenter les hommes qui aspirent aux choses corporelles, ni ceux dont la fin est spirituelle, mais mêlée à de la matérialité. Ce sont seulement les hommes de science qu'il doit fréquenter. Mais des hommes de science, il en existe peu dans certaines sociétés mais beaucoup dans d'autres, au point que dans certaines, il n'en existe même pas du tout. C'est pourquoi, dans certaines sociétés, il est du devoir du solitaire de s'isoler des hommes en général autant que possible, et de ne se trouver en relation avec eux que pour les choses nécessaires, ou dans la mesure du nécessaire. Ou encore d'émigrer vers des sociétés où existent les sciences, s'il s'en trouve[10].

Le jugement du philosophe sur la réalité de son temps transparaît de façon assez claire: si la société arabo-hispanique ne peut sans doute pas être comptée parmi les sociétés «où n'existent pas du tout» les «hommes de science», au moins faut-il reconnaître que ceux-ci y sont peu nombreux. Ce ne serait pas le cas de la cité vertueuse, gouvernée selon les principes de la raison, et vers laquelle le philosophe devrait «émigrer» si elle existait. Mais cela n'étant pas le cas, il lui faut s'appliquer à lui-même une sorte de prophylaxie sociale, en se retranchant du monde «autant que possible», et en ne se mêlant à la communauté que «dans la mesure du nécessaire».

C'est tout de même déjà beaucoup, car il y va des conditions matérielles de son existence. Du monde des hommes, il peut et doit tout ignorer, sinon la nécessité d'en tirer sa subsistance. Ainsi on s'explique que ce type de philosophe puisse être ce que fut Avempace: un courtisan avisé et un contempteur du monde. La suite immédiate du texte n'est donc paradoxale qu'en apparence, et c'est l'auteur lui-même qui se charge de lever le paradoxe:

> Et il n'y a là aucune contradiction avec ce qui est dit dans la science politique, ni ce qui ressort de la science physique. En effet, il y apparaît que l'homme est social par nature[11]. Et dans

[10] Ibn Bāǧǧa (Avempace), *Tadbīr al-Mutawaḥḥid*, éd. M. Faḫrī cit. (à la note 5), p. 90.

[11] Avempace ne connaît pas directement cette thèse par la *Politique* d'Aristote,

> la politique, il apparaît que l'isolation est entièrement mauvaise. Mais ceci n'est le cas que par essence, tandis que par accident, ce peut être un bien, comme c'est le cas de beaucoup de choses d'ordre naturel. Ainsi le pain et la viande sont-ils, par leurs natures, des aliments, et [par conséquent] bénéfiques; et l'opium ou la coloquinte, des poisons mortels. Cependant, il se peut qu'il arrive au corps des états hors nature, dans lesquels ces deux produits lui seront bénéfiques, et devront lui être administrés, tandis que les aliments naturels lui seraient nocifs, et devront être évités. Mais ces états, ce sont nécessairement des maladies, qui sont hors nature. [Ces produits] sont donc bénéfiques en moindre part, et par accident, tandis que les aliments sont bénéfiques en majeure part, et essentiellement[12].

La société idéale est comparable au corps sain, la société réelle au corps malade. Il importe peu à la pertinence de cette comparaison que dans la réalité des faits, la proportion des corps sains sur les corps malades soit infiniment plus élevée que celle des sociétés idéales sur les sociétés «malades», imparfaites. La santé consiste dans un état d'équilibre unique, singulier, entre les quatre humeurs, qui assure le fonctionnement «sain» des parties du corps, de même que le modèle de la société idéale est *un*, car il n'existe qu'une seule loi conforme au modèle de la raison, qui offre une quantité indénombrable, pléthorique, de possibilités d'écart, de déviance par rapport à la norme. À partir de quoi, sans doute, on peut admettre que la plupart, voire la quasi totalité des sociétés soient *de facto* imparfaites, vicieuses et «hors nature», tandis que la

qui n'a pas été traduite en arabe, mais sans doute par un texte aujourd'hui perdu, censé être la traduction arabe de la *République* de Platon (qui est probablement une paraphrase tardo-antique de ce texte). Le contenu n'en est connu aujourd'hui qu'à travers le commentaire qu'en a laissé Averroès, lui-même conservé seulement en hébreu. Cfr. AVERROES' *Commentary on Plato's Republic*, éd. et tr. E. I. J. Rosenthal, Cambridge 1956; et AVERROES *on Plato's Republic*, tr. R. Lerner, Ithaca (NY) 2005[2]. On dispose d'une excellente rétroversion arabe, IBN RUŠD, *al-Ḍarūrī fī al-siyāsa. Muḫtaṣar kitāb al-Siyāsa li-Aflāṭūn*, tr. A. Šaḥlān, Bayrūt 1998, qui nous paraît plus fidèle que les deux traductions anglaises précitées. Pour autant que l'on puisse en juger par la reformulation d'Averroès, le thème de la naturalité de la condition sociale était bien présent dans cette «*République* de Platon». Cfr. par ex. p. 74 (Šaḥlān): «L'homme a besoin, pour réaliser sa vertu, d'un autre que lui. C'est pourquoi il a été dit avec raison que l'homme est social par nature».

[12] IBN BĀĞĞA (AVEMPACE), *Tadbīr al-Mutawaḥḥid*, éd. M. Faḫrī, pp. 90-91.

société bonne et seule conforme à la norme naturelle peut, en un temps donné, n'être réalisée dans aucun lieu du monde.

C'est à ce prix qu'est résolu le dilemme entre vivre conformément à la raison en solitaire et vivre dans le monde, mais en dépit de la raison. L'état de solitaire, antinaturel par soi, est le remède de l'âme contre le désordre du corps social. Si la société était saine et «conforme à l'ordre naturel», elle serait un moyen approprié pour l'individu philosophe d'assurer sa propre santé. Mais ce n'est pas le cas. Si la santé de la société n'importe que comme moyen d'assurer la perfection intellectuelle de l'individu, et que par ailleurs celui-ci est susceptible d'atteindre la perfection «en solitaire», pour l'individu qui a assuré son salut en rompant intellectuellement avec les normes communes de la société, la société n'a simplement plus de valeur du tout, ni intrinsèque, pour l'ignorant (que l'on ne pourrait soigner que dans une société bonne), ni extrinsèque, relative à la réalisation personnelle du philosophe. Il est vain de «soigner» une société malade. Là s'arrête l'analogie avec la médecine. Ayant conscience d'être «meilleur» que la société, le «solitaire» s'interdit d'en assumer les valeurs, par souci de soi. Mais il n'y aucune nécessité pour lui d'entrer avec elles en confrontation ouverte, de risquer ainsi d'y perdre sa subsistance ou d'attirer sur sa tête les foudres des persécuteurs, puisque l'engagement social n'aurait de sens, et d'intérêt philosophique que dans une société «bonne». Encore n'y aurait-il pas, même ce cas, beaucoup à faire, puisque cette société serait bonne, et qu'il n'y a aurait donc pas besoin de la réformer. Quant à la société réelle, celle qui, précisément, nécessiterait une réforme, le philosophe ne s'y engagera pas, du moment qu'il peut philosopher convenablement au dehors d'elle tout en y demeurant.

On peut discuter de savoir si l'orientation foncièrement individualiste de la philosophie d'Avempace constitue ou non un geste de rupture avec une tendance générale dans la philosophie arabe[13]: si oui, c'est la religion du philosophe qui est en question,

[13] C'est ce que soutient E. I. J. ROSENTHAL dans deux écrits, *The Place of Politics in the Philosophy of Ibn Bājja*, in «Islamic Culture», 25.1 (1959), pp. 187-211; et *Politic Thought of Medieval Islam* [chap. VIII, «Ibn Bājja: individualist deviation»], Cambridge 1962, pp. 158-174. L'individualisme d'Avempace est contesté par O. LEAMAN, *Ibn Bājja on Society and Philosophy*, in «Der Islam», 57.1 (1980), pp. 109-119. Notre compréhension de l'attitude politique d'Avempace se rapproche

car la part nécessairement faite aux normes communes, chez les philosophes arabes, prend naturellement la forme d'une reconnaissance de la Loi révélée, la *šarī'a*. La référence la plus immédiate dont pouvait disposer Avempace à cet égard est sans doute la pensée d'al-Fārābī (m. 950). Celui-ci admet naturellement la supériorité de la félicité «intellectuelle» du philosophe sur le bonheur des masses, garanti par l'observance des Lois de la communauté, mais ceci n'implique pas le déni de toute valeur à l'ordre social, lui-même fondé sur l'adhésion à la Révélation[14]. Faire la part de celle-ci, adhérer malgré tout au Coran et à la Loi revient, dans ce contexte, à conserver une socialité indispensable même à l'homme ayant atteint le bonheur «théorétique», comme le veut Aristote lorsqu'il affirme qu'un humain ne peut être pleinement humain s'il ne vit dans une communauté[15]. Dans l'héritage philosophique de ses prédécesseurs arabes, Avempace trouve en tous cas une «religion» créditée de la fonction positive d'étendre le domaine de la vérité au monde politique. La religion, expression rhétorique que le Prophète donne à une vérité également connue de manière démonstrative par le philosophe, est nécessaire à la fondation de la société[16]. Sa reconnaissance est inséparable du

de celle de Rosenthal: il nous semble qu'Avempace ne conçoit pas la notion d'un devoir du philosophe à l'égard d'autrui, contrairement à ce que pense LEAMAN, *ibid.*, notamment p. 114.

[14] Il n'importe pas pour le propos qui suit que cette religion nécessaire à la société ait été, pour al-Fārābī, l'Islam, comme le comprennent la plupart des interprètes, ou plutôt une religion philosophique sans existence réelle, qu'al-Fārābī lui-même aurait voulu voir fondée de son temps. Comme l'indiquent d'importants et récents travaux de Philippe Vallat, encore inédits pour la plupart, tout porte en effet à croire qu'al-Fārābī considérait de toutes les façons l'Islam comme une «mauvaise» religion, d'emblée incapable de remplir les fonctions qu'il assignait à la religion dans son système philosophique, en raison de sa faiblesse argumentative et de ses insuffisances morales. Cfr. par exemple PH. VALLAT, *Vrai philosophe et faux prophète selon al-Fārābī. Aspects historiques et théoriques de l'art des symboles*, in *Miroir et Savoir. La transmission d'un thème platonicien, des Alexandrins à la philosophie arabo-musulmane*. Actes du colloque international tenu à Leuven et Louvain-la-Neuve, les 17 et 18 nov. 2005, éd. par D. De Smet – M. Sebti – G. de Callataÿ (Ancient and Medieval Philosophy. De Wulf-Mansion Centre. Ser. 1, 38), Louvain 2008, p. 117-143.

[15] Cfr. ARISTOTELES, *Ethica Nicomachea*, X, 1177b^{26}-1178a^{2}; 1078b$^{5-7}$. Aristote observe cependant un certain clivage entre les deux finalités, le bonheur théorétique et le bonheur social, en affirmant que plus le divin est développé dans la nature humaine, moins l'homme est dépendant de ses relations sociales.

[16] Pour al-Fārābī, l'apparition de la philosophie est antérieure à celle de la reli-

souci politique. Le modèle de hiérarchie de la société juste et vertueuse étant tiré de la hiérarchie de l'univers, il est nécessaire que l'organisation sociale reproduise le modèle de celle de l'univers, connue par le philosophe. C'est cette société qui est la cité idéale et «vertueuse» d'al-Fārābī. Dans cette version arabisée du philosophe-roi, le législateur de la cité idéale serait donc un prophète, ou le représentant d'un prophète lorsqu'il n'en existe pas actuellement, car c'est le prophète, c'est-à-dire l'homme qui tout à la fois connaît la vérité (et en ce sens, il est philosophe) et sait l'exprimer au grand nombre sous la forme de la religion, qui est capable d'inscrire politiquement la vérité dans le corps social. C'est pourquoi les écrits politiques d'al-Fārābī, comme en particulier les *Opinions des habitants de la cité vertueuse* et la *Politique civile*[17] «commencent par une cosmologie, avec la structure de l'univers, le caractère de chacune de ses principales parties et la manière dont elles fonctionnent ensemble, le tout exposé au lecteur dans le style d'un prédicateur qui dit à son audience: c'est ainsi que ça se passe! Il présente ensuite la structure de l'âme et du corps humains, leurs parties et leur fonctionnement. Il passe enfin à la présentation de la structure de la cité, de ses parties, de la façon dont elles doivent être organisées, des différentes manières dont les cités et nations actuelles sont réellement organisées et de la description des opinions et des actions de chacune de ces cités»[18].

Dans cette perspective classique, l'élitisme intellectuel qui accompagne l'exercice de la philosophie n'exclut pas la recherche d'un modèle politique conforme à l'exigence de vérité, prolongement philosophiquement nécessaire de l'avènement de la vérité dont le philosophe, au plan individuel, est l'auteur principal.

gion. L'ère des prophètes fait suite à celle des philosophes, et elle la complète en assurant la diffusion dans l'humanité des hautes vérités découvertes par l'usage de l'art syllogistique des philosophes. Cfr. l'explication de l'apparition des sciences par AL-FĀRĀBĪ, *Kitāb al-ḥurūf*, éd. M. Mahdī, Bayrūt 1970, pp. 131-157. La religion est la rhétorisation de la philosophie, en ce sens elle lui est subordonnée, mais elle marque aussi le progrès de l'humanité parce qu'elle généralise l'accès à la vérité.

[17] AL-FĀRĀBĪ (ALFARABI), *Arā' ahl al-madīnat al-fāḍila* («Les opinions des habitants de la cité vertueuse») et *al-Siyāsa al-madaniyya* («La politique civile»), également intitulé *Mabādi' al-wuǧūd* («les Principes de l'être»). Sur ces textes, cfr. l'ouvrage de Muhsin Mahdi, cité note suivante.

[18] M. MAHDI, *La Cité vertueuse d'Alfarabi*, tr. F. Zabbal, Paris 2000, pp. 85-86. Cet ouvrage rassemble les articles, remaniés et traduits en français, que le grand historien irakien de la philosophie a consacrés à politique d'al-Fārābī.

Un problème demeure cependant: quel est au juste la réalité de cette cité idéale dont la conception est l'accomplissement de la philosophie? Certes, comme le relève Muhsin Mahdi, «Alfarabi était conscient de la tension majeure entre la poursuite du salut privé et celle du salut public. Mais il est quasi le seul philosophe musulman à avoir choisi d'explorer cette tension; ce faisant, il a mis en évidence l'esprit philanthropique de la philosophie et la noble dévotion du philosophe au bien-être de la communauté»[19].

Cette sollicitude, cette 'sensibilité' pourraient-elle ne consister que dans le fait de *penser* la nécessité de cette cité, ou commandent-t-elles sa mise en œuvre? La réponse ne va pas de soi. Il se pourrait fort bien que le type de philosophie politique représenté par al-Fārābī puisse trouver sa fin dans l'acte même d'avoir élaboré le modèle abstrait de la «société vertueuse», tout à fait indépendamment de sa survenue effective. Cette conception de la cité idéale ne serait-elle pas finalement une métaphore de la perfection individuelle, du «gouvernement», du «régime» (*tadbīr*) personnel qu'Avempace lui aussi invite le philosophe à établir sur soi-même à défaut de pouvoir l'établir sur la terre? La cité idéale serait ce lieu où le philosophe peut dire, et faire «comme si»; sa signification première serait celle de norme éthique produite dans l'esprit, permettant au philosophe de réfléchir sa propre perfection en la projetant mentalement dans un espace politique lui-même produit par sa pensée, où il pourra perfectionner et mettre à l'épreuve «sa philanthropie», sa «dévotion au bien-être de la communauté», etc. A la remarque de Glaucon observant, dans la *République* de Platon, que la cité dont on vient de tracer les règles n'existait nulle part sur la terre, Socrate répondait qu' «il n'importe nullement que cette cité existe ou doive exister un jour. C'est aux lois de celle-là seule que le sage conformera sa conduite»[20].

Il n'est pas certain qu'al-Fārābī eût répondu différemment. Le lecteur moderne qu'est Muhsin Mahdi ne tombe-t-il pas ici dans l'erreur de croire que tout discours ayant pour objet la cité doive être un discours adressé à la cité? Dans une certaine mesure, il faut donner raison à Leaman affirmant que l'attitude d'Avempace

[19] *Ibid.*, p. 89.
[20] PLATO, *Respublica*, IX, 592b.

ne diffère pas fondamentalement de celle d'al-Fārābī ni de ses prédécesseurs musulmans. «Philantropie» ou «misanthropie» ne seraient pas des positions philosophiques, mais des traits de caractère. Al-Fārābī, plus «philanthrope» qu'Ibn Bāǧǧa, a pu concevoir la cité idéale avec philanthropie, comme objet de désir pour l'âme noble, sans que sa problématique politique n'ait davantage que celle d'Avempace intégré la question de la possibilité de la réalisation. L'impossibilité tient peut-être à la nature même de la démarche empruntée, et à la finalité assignée à la philosophie dans la culture que partagent al-Fārābī et Avempace. Celles-ci sont résumées par Leaman, à propos du second: «Ibn Bājja's problem is how the philosopher in the imperfect state should relate to society. This problem arises within the context of Neoplatonic philosophy. The philosopher is regarded as a seeker of contact (*ittiṣāl*) with the spiritual forms (...). The philosopher seeks to rise above the masses and their dependence upon the world of appearances, to rise to the level of reality which is is attainable only by the use of reason»[21].

En effet, le programme du philosophe arabe est fondamentalement d'ordre personnel. Son but est l'union avec l'intellect agent, la structure intelligible de l'univers, à laquelle on atteint par le perfectionnement de la pensée. A terme, l'intellect du philosophe s'identifie avec l'intelligence séparée. Pensant toutes les choses de l'univers, il est censé *devenir* le monde sur le mode le plus éminent, le mode intelligible. L'ambition est de reproduire en soi-même l'intelligibilité du monde. L'univers, comme objet de connaissance, ne vaut que rapporté à la personne du philosophe, qui se sert de cette connaissance pour accéder à un état d'être universel. Le philosophe parfait *devient* le monde qu'il intellige. La difficulté de penser l'engagement dans le monde selon cette perspective apparaît alors clairement: la destination du philosophe étant de 's'élever' au-dessus du monde pour le comprendre, le monde se voit réalisé sur le mode le plus noble, le plus vrai, dans l'intellect du philosophe. Dès lors, le monde concret, doué d'un mode d'existence inférieur au «monde» pensé par le philosophe, cesse presque forcément d'avoir de l'importance. C'est la réalisation intellectuelle qui est la fin de l'activité philo-

[21] LEAMAN, *Ibn Bājja on Society and Philosophy* cit. (à la note 13), p. 110.

sophique. Or cette réalisation est achevée par l'individu, et en lui. Quant au monde extérieur, il n'est que le *substrat* de l'intelligible, que le philosophe dépasse dès lors qu'il en a extrait l'intelligibilité.

D'autre part, toujours d'après Leaman: «The difficulty which this passed on to the *falāsifa* is that they as muslims believed that the *Qur'ān* is given to all believers as a perfect guide to salvation and happiness (...).Yet to be a Muslim, to follow *Sharī'a*, does not seem necessarily to involve being a philosopher»[22]. *Mutatis mutandis*, c'est le problème posé à Aristote qui constatait que certains hommes sont incapables de philosopher mais capables d'agir vertueusement et conformément au bien, et devait pour cela formuler une distinction entre le bonheur supérieur, «théorétique» du philosophe, et le bonheur pratique consistant dans une action conforme au devoir. «This distinction was taken up with alacrity by the *falāsifa*, since they could then argue that the *Sharī'a* was provided for the use of the masses in order to show them how to attein knowledge and happiness appropriate to them as non-intellectual beings»[23].

La société idéale, où tous les membres d'une nation pourraient atteindre le maximum de la perfection dont ils sont capables, aurait donc à organiser harmonieusement les relations de deux classes d'hommes: une «élite» de savants vivant selon la philosophie, et une «masse» de croyants ordinaires ayant pour loi la *šarī'a*. Mais en un sens, dira-t-on, c'est déjà le cas, puisque de fait, il existe des philosophes dans la société, et que celle-ci est gouvernée, en principe, par la Loi révélée. Qu'est-ce qui manque donc au philosophe musulman pour que la société où il vit lui apparaisse idéale? Le gouvernement des autres ne peut faire partie de ses aspirations. Il ne peut songer à devenir le philosophe-roi de Platon, cette notion ne pouvant pas avoir d'actualité dans son contexte, puisque ce qu'attend Platon du philosophe est d'établir des lois sages qui feront le bonheur de la communauté[24], alors que dans la communauté régie par la Loi religieuse, ces lois sages sont censées exister déjà en l'espèce de la *šarī'a*. Il n'est pas

[22] *Ibidem*.
[23] *Ibid.*, p. 111.
[24] Cfr. PLATO, *Respublica*, VI, 502ac, 503b seqq.

question de devenir un philosophe-roi législateur puisque la Loi est déjà donnée, et que le philosophe-roi ne saurait être que le Prophète-philosophe fondateur d'une Loi déjà existante, la figure emblématique décrite par al-Fārābī. Que veulent donc les philosophes, et par conséquent, quel sens donner aux récriminations d'Avempace contre la société de son temps? La seule réponse possible est que les philosophes veulent qu'on les laisse tranquilles. Leur problème n'est pas de gouverner mais de philosopher en paix. La société musulmane, pour peu qu'elle leur permette d'exister, est déjà, pour eux, en bonne partie, la société idéale. Le thème de la «cité vertueuse» leur sert vraisemblablement de modèle à exhiber face à une société réelle où leur statut est insuffisamment garanti. Ce serait un emblème plutôt qu'un programme politique.

La situation d'Averroès n'est pas différente. Lui aussi se représente la société idéale sous les traits d'une cité musulmane à l'intérieur de laquelle le philosophe aurait droit de cité. Il juge d'ailleurs explicitement, au moins à une certaine époque, que la situation politique de son temps représente un état proche de l'avènement de celle-ci[25]. Il se différencie cependant de ses prédécesseurs d'une manière décisive en ne recevant pas seulement la *šarī'a* telle qu'elle est, mais en prenant au contraire une part active à son interprétation, afin de servir l'objectif du philosophe, qui est d'assurer son droit de cité dans la communauté musulmane. A cette fin, Averroès mobilise les ressources de la dogmatique musulmane pour tenter de mettre définitivement le philosophe à l'abri du soupçon de *duplicité* qui le compromet toujours. Dans cette défense, les notions de foi (*īmān*) d'assentiment (*taṣdīq*), ainsi que de Loi (*šarī'a*) ont fait l'objet d'une élaboration particulière, dans laquelle Averroès s'est attaché à montrer comment le pluralisme des voies d'accès à la connaissance pouvait être entièrement fondé dans la dogmatique musulmane elle-même.

[25] Affirmant par exemple dans le commentaire sur la *République*, *al-Ḍarūrī fī al-siyāsa*, tr. Šaḥlān cit. (à la note 11), p. 129, qu'il est possible que la cité vertueuse existe pourvu que règnent pendant suffisamment de temps des souverains éduqués par des philosophes, en une époque où la philosophie serait parvenue à son achèvement, «comme c'est le cas de notre temps et au sein de notre communauté».

On a dit que pour nos philosophes, les rôles respectifs de la religion et de la philosophie ne tenaient pas aux objets connus (réalités naturelles ou surnaturelles), mais à l'existence d'une communauté sociale et politique au sein de laquelle les relations entre les deux sortes de connaissance doivent être déterminées et aménagées en fonction d'un objectif politique: le bien commun. On notera, comme l'a fait récemment Cecilia Martini dans sa traduction italienne de *L'Harmonie entre les opinions de Platon et d'Aristote* d'al-Fārābī[26], qu'Averroès s'appuie sur l'antécédent offert par al-Fārābī pour soutenir par exemple que les croyances «bonnes» sont celles qui sont appropriées aux capacités mentales de différentes sortes d'hommes. La religion propose à tous les humains (pour Averroès, y compris les philosophes) une collection cohérente de connaissances et de préceptes appropriée à leurs esprits, qui doivent être reçues, interprétées de manière différenciée, et il est juste que ceux qui n'ont pas la capacité d'appréhender la réalité au travers des concepts philosophiques (comme par ex. celui de substance immatérielle) qui seuls donnent à connaître la réalité de manière absolument vraie, la conçoivent au moyen de formules dogmatiques qui, prises à la lettre, peuvent être objectivement éloignées des vérités philosophiques, voire en apparence contraires à ces dernières. Cette croyance, qui peut être supplantée par une interprétation allégorique du texte religieux, mettant en conformité sa signification avec la vérité philosophique, est cependant vraie relativement à ceux qui la tiennent. Al-Fārābī dit ainsi, dans l'*Harmonie*, à propos de la conception de l'être divin:

> Celui qui se représente que le premier Créateur est un corps, qu'il agit par un mouvement et dans le temps, mais qui est incapable de former avec son esprit une vérité plus subtile et plus appropriée, et dans l'imagination duquel aucune signification représentée ne s'impose fermement chaque fois qu'il imagine qu'il n'est pas un corps et qu'il agit sans mouvement, à tel point que, si on le contraint [à se représenter ainsi le Créateur], il persévèrera dans l'erreur et l'égarement avec plus de force, celui-là est excusable et il a raison pour ce qu'il se représente et ce qu'il croit. Puis celui dont l'esprit est ca-

[26] AL-FĀRĀBĪ, *L'Armonia delle opinioni dei due sapienti: il divino Platone e Aristotele*, introd., tr. e comm. di C. Martini, Pisa 2008.

pable de reconnaître qu'il n'est pas un corps, que son action n'est pas un mouvement, encore qu'il soit incapable de se représenter qu'il n'est pas dans un lieu – veut-on l'y contraindre, l'y obliger, que cela le conduit à pire et à plus néfaste encore –, lui aussi a raison pour ce qu'il croit comme il est excusable pour ce qu'il connaît[27].

Ce passage, comme l'a noté Cecilia Martini, inspire directement Averroès lorsque celui-ci écrit dans le *Faṣl al-maqāl*:

> À cette classe d'humains dont l'assentiment ne se produit que du fait de l'imagination – c'est-à-dire qui n'assentent à l'existence d'une chose qu'en tant qu'ils l'imaginent – il est fort difficile d'assentir à l'existence d'un être qui n'entretient aucun rapport à quelque chose d'imaginable. Ceci vaut également pour ceux qui comprennent seulement par cette relation le fait d'être dans un lieu, et qui se haussent dans la réflexion quelque peu au-dessus de la classe précédente en rejetant la croyance en la corporéité divine[28].

Pour Averroès comme pour al-Fārābī, l'assentiment donné au sens littéral des textes religieux, avec leurs images, leurs approximations et leurs ambiguïtés, est *réellement* la vérité pour les non philosophes, tandis qu'elle n'est pour le philosophe que le substitut rhétorique de la vérité vraie. Pour Averroès, l'adhésion aux arguments formulés dans la révélation, pour lesquels on n'a pas de démonstration (mais seulement les arguments persuasifs formulés par le Coran), est qualifié explicitement d'acte de foi (*īmān*)[29], tandis que la «foi», pour le philosophe, n'est autre que la certitude (*yaqīn*) procurée par la démonstration philosophique. Cette certitude démonstrative est nécessairement aussi doublée, chez Averroès, de la conviction que le révélation musulmane donne l'ex-

[27] Abū Naṣr al-Fārābī, *L'Harmonie entre les opinions de Platon et d'Aristote*, éd. et tr. F. M. Najjar et D. Mallet, Dimašq 1999, p. 138; cfr. la tr. de C. Martini cit. (à la note préc.), pp. 67-68; et ses commentaires pp. 208-210.

[28] Ibn Rušd (Averroes Cordubensis), *Faṣl al-maqāl fī mā bayna al-ḥikma wa-l-šarī'a min al-ittiṣāl* (*Le livre du discours décisif sur l'accord de la religion et de la philosophie*), tr. Geoffroy cit. (à la note 2) (par la suite: *Discours décisif*), p. 143.

[29] L'adhésion au sens littéral du texte révélé relève de l'obligation légale (*farḍ*) impérée par le texte lui-même, qui relève de la charge (*taklīf*) imposée par Dieu aux hommes. Cfr. par ex. *ibid.*, p. 147: «L'interprétation (*ta'wīl*) pratiquée par des gens auxquels il est fait obligation de *croire* (*farḍu-hu al-īmān*) en le sens obvie est infidélité» (nous soulignons).

pression rhétorique *la plus appropriée qui soit* de la vérité philosophique:

> Les arguments révélés exposés dans le Livre précieux [*scil.* le Coran] à l'intention de tous possèdent trois propriétés, qui prouvent l'insupérabilité du Livre. Premièrement, il n'y a pas d'arguments plus propres qu'eux à produire la persuasion et l'assentiment (*taṣdīq*) de tous. Deuxièmement, de par leur nature, ils se soutiennent si éminemment que seuls peuvent en découvrir l'interprétation (...) les hommes de démonstration. Troisièmement, ils comportent, à l'intention des hommes habilités à connaître la vérité des indices signalant l'interprétation vraie[30].

Il semble que le philosophe ne «croie» pas, à proprement parler, à ce que dit la révélation coranique; qu'il croie seulement que les non philosophes doivent y croire, pour des raisons politiques, et que la vérification de l'authenticité de la révélation se trouve dans la qualité de la persuasion qu'elle exerce sur les non philosophes:

> Comme (...) l'existence des hommes de la classe élitaire, et la réalisation de leur félicité, ne seront jamais achevés qu'avec le concours des hommes de la classe commune, l'enseignement adressé au commun est indispensable à l'existence des hommes de la classe élitaire, et à leur vie. Et puis, dans la période de l'enfance et de l'adolescence, il n'y a personne qui doute de ces enseignements. Plus tard, lorsque celui qui devient philosophe passe à des connaissances qui lui sont propres, il faut absolument, dans l'intérêt de sa vertu, qu'il ne dédaigne point les enseignements dans lesquels il a été éduqué, mais qu'il les interprète de la meilleure manière[31].

La parole révélée convient à la foule, à la masse (*al-ǧumhūr*), tandis que la connaissance philosophique, d'un accès difficile en raison de ce qu'elle exige de dispositions naturelles et d'apprentissage[32], est réservée à un petit nombre, elle est celle de l'élite intellectuelle (*al-ḫawāṣṣ*):

[30] *Ibid.*, p. 169.

[31] Id., *Tahafot at-tahafot* (*Incohérence de l'incohérence*), éd. M. Bouyges, Beyrouth 1992³ (Bibliotheca Arabica Scholasticorum, 3), p. 582; tr. in Averroès, *L'Islam et la raison*, cit. (à la note 2), p. 199.

[32] La cause pour laquelle certains hommes (en fait, la plupart d'entre eux) ne

> Dans la mesure où les enseignements révélés ont pour fin la diffusion de la sagesse par les méthodes communes, les philosophes les considèrent assurément comme indispensables, car la philosophie, quant à elle, n'a d'autre finalité que de faire connaître une félicité intellectuelle à certains individus, ceux qui sont en mesure de faire l'apprentissage de la sagesse (*ḥikma*), alors que les révélations, elles, visent l'enseignement de la foule en général, bien que nous ne trouvions aucune d'entre les lois révélées qui ne signale aussi les choses qui concernent en propre les sages[33].

Cet ensemble d'affirmations pourrait être jugé simplement opportuniste s'il n'était appuyé, pour Averroès, sur une véritable théorie, dont le maître mot est la notion d'assentiment (*taṣdīq*). Dans le lexique philosophique arabe, ce terme a acquis l'acception particulière d'«assentiment» à un complexe prédicatif, à un contenu propositionnel, faisant suite à la représentation, *taṣawwur*, la saisie conceptuelle d'une nature simple ou d'une quiddité. L'assentiment est ainsi, dans la plupart des cas, un jugement de vérité portant sur l'attribution d'une notion à une autre (par exemple, l'assentiment (*taṣdīq*) à la proposition «le monde est créé», faisant suite à la représentation, *taṣawwur*, de «monde» et de «créé»). Les différents arts logiques, la démonstration, la dialectique, la rhétorique, usant chacun de leurs moyens d'argumentation propre, ont en commun la production de l'assentiment[34]. Cette no-

peuvent pas accéder à la démonstration est double, tenant à la fois de l'inné et de l'acquis: le manque de dispositions naturelles, et les défauts de la formation intellectuelle dans un environnement donné, par exemple une nation où les arts philosophiques sont insuffisamment cultivés; cfr. par ex. *Discours décisif*, p. 115. Lorsque Averroès cherche, dans le Grand Commentaire au *De anima*, les raisons pour lesquelles l'homme quoique voué en principe à la perfection intellectuelle (perfection dernière de l'homme en tant qu'homme), n'y parvient pas en fait, cette même alternative reparaît; cfr. IBN RUŠD (AVERROES CORDUBENSIS), *Commentarium Magnum in Aristotelis De anima Libros*, éd. F. S. Crawford, Cambridge (Mass.) 1953 (Corpus Commentariorum Averrois in Aristotelem, 6/1), pp. 494-495: «Intelligere hoc acquiritur per exercitium et usum in rebus naturalibus, sed nondum habemus de exercitio et usu tantum per quod possumus acquirere hanc intellectionem, aut erit hoc propter diminutionem nostre nature naturaliter».

33 ID., *Tahafot at-tahafot*, éd. Bouyges, p. 585; *L'Islam et la raison* cit. (à la note 2), p. 198.

34 Cfr. H. A. WOLFSON, *The Terms* Taṣawwur *and* Taṣdīq *in Arabic Philosophy and their Greek, Latin and Hebrew Equivalents*, in «The Moslem World», 33 (1943), pp. 114-123; J. VAN ESS, *Die Erkenntnisslehre des ʿAḍudaddīn al-Īcī. Übersetzung und*

tion permettant d'organiser et de hiérarchiser les disciplines logiques allait être reprise chez les scolastiques, où le *taṣdīq* se trouverait significativement rendu par *credulitas* ou *fides*. L'adoption du *taṣdīq* comme critère d'une typologie des discours logiques a pour arrière-plan l'histoire complexe des traductions arabes d'Aristote, dont les terminologies ont varié suivant les temps et les lieux. Un lien privilégié le relie cependant au terme aristotélicien de πίστις, utilisée par le Stagirite dans des acceptions diverses[35]. Le lien notionnel avec le *taṣdīq* des logiciens arabes est cependant assuré au travers d'emplois, chez Aristote, de πίστις au sens de «conscience du caractère certain de la connaissance que nous avons d'une chose, par le sens, l'opinion ou la science», comme en *De anima*, II (428a[19]), dont la version arabo-latine, dans le Grand Commentaire d'Averroès, qui donne *fides*, indique que l'arabe traduisait par *taṣdīq*. Le *taṣdīq* renvoie moins à un contenu de connaissance objectif qu'à un acte de l'esprit par lequel celui-ci juge comme vrai ce qu'il connaît. C'est l'acte unique du sujet connaissant acquiesçant à sa connaissance, quelque en soit la provenance. Il est analogue dans tous les cas. Les objets de la πίστις peuvent au demeurant, chez Aristote, être indifféremment l'induction, la raison, les premiers principes indémontrables, la déduction syllogistique, etc.[36] De ce point de vue, on peut comprendre pourquoi Averroès juge que l'acte de connaissance du croyant persuadé par la rhétorique coranique revient au même que celui du philosophe. C'est ainsi qu'il faut comprendre l'affirmation suivante dans le *Faṣl al-maqāl*:

> Il existe une hiérarchie des natures humaines pour ce qui est de l'assentiment (*taṣdīq*): certains hommes assentent par l'effet de la démonstration, d'autres assentent par l'effet des arguments dialectiques du [même] assentiment que celui par lequel l'homme de démonstration assent par (*taṣdīq*[a] *ṣāḥib*

Kommentar des ersten Buches seiner Mawāqif, Wiesbaden 1966, pp. 95-113; et la récente étude de J. LAMEER sur l'origine de ces notions, *Conception and Belief in Sadr al-Dīn Shirāzī (ca. 1571-1635). Al-risāla fī l-taṣawwur wa-l-taṣdīq*, introd. et tr. angl. J. Lameer, Tihrān 2006, pp. 19-35.

[35] Elles sont étudiées par H. A. WOLFSON, *The Double Faith Theory in Clement, Saadia, Averroes and St. Thomas, and its Origins in Aristotle and the Stoics*, in «The Jewish Quarterly Review», N. S., 33.2 (1942), pp. 213-264, spéc. pp. 215-223.

[36] Cfr. WOLFSON, *ibid.*

> *al-burhān bi-l-burhān*), car leurs natures ne les disposent pas à davantage; d'autres enfin assentent par l'effet des arguments rhétoriques comme l'homme de démonstration (*ka-taṣdīq ṣāḥib al-burhān*) assent aux arguments démonstratifs[37].

D'un point de vue subjectif, indépendamment du contenu de connaissance et des moyens employés pour la faire acquérir, c'est effectivement «la même chose» que le croyant croit et que le philosophe sait. Ce dernier est cependant le seul à bénéficier de la «certitude» (*yaqīn*), telle qu'elle a été déterminée pour les logiciens arabes par al-Fārābī[38], définie comme la connaissance obtenue par la seule force contraignante du syllogisme, reposant sur les prémisses naturelles et premières. Cette certitude constitue l'acte d'assentiment (*taṣdīq*) parfait, tel que nous croyons qu'une chose à propos de laquelle nous formons un jugement ne peut être dans la réalité extérieure autrement qu'elle n'est; et telle que même si nous concevons à propos de notre assentiment l'idée que cet assentiment n'est pas vrai, il soit impossible d'assentir à ce que nous concevons (ce qui distingue la certitude démonstrative de la certitude dialectique). L'assentiment d'ordre simplement rhétorique est le plus éloigné de la certitude, la vérité de ce qui est alors conçu n'ayant presque rien d'intrinsèque, mais il assure le même «repos de l'âme» (*sukūn al-nafs*) que toute connaissance objet d'assentiment[39].

Il en est ainsi parce que l'opinion, susceptible en elle-même d'être vraie ou fausse, est étayée par les procédés rhétoriques, ce que recouvre également le terme πίστις dans la *Rhétorique* d'Aristote (rendu en arabe par *taṣdīq*) qui compensent le déficit de certitude absolue dans l'exacte mesure de ce qui est nécessaire pour établir une équivalence de fait entre la certitude (*yaqīn*) du philosophe et la croyance de l'homme ordinaire. Parmi les procédés de la persuasion, certains étant propre à l'art rhétorique lui-même, les enthymèmes; d'autres, extérieurs et adjuvants (les lois, les témoignages, et en particulier, la moralité de l'orateur)[40], l'excel-

[37] *Discours décisif*, p. 117 (tr. modifiée).

[38] Cfr. D. Black, *Knowledge* ('ilm) *and Certitude* (yaqīn) *in al-Fārābī's Epistemology*, in «Arabic Sciences and Philosophy», 16.1 (2006), pp. 11-45.

[39] Cfr. *ibid.*, p. 36.

[40] Cfr. Aristoteles, *Rhetorica*, I, 1354a[11] seqq.

lence rhétorique du Coran est établie à la fois par la qualité insupérable des arguments dont il fait état, par l'utilité des règles qu'il énonce; et enfin, garantie par l'éminente qualité morale du Prophète législateur qui le profère. La connaissance imparfaite que le croyant obtiendra par la révélation sera *pour lui* aussi parfaite que celle, parfaitement adéquate au réel vrai, que le philosophe tire de la démonstration.

La démonstration et la rhétorique du Coran ont la même extension: tout ce que fait connaître la philosophie, la religion l'exprime aussi. Comme l'art philosophique, la rhétorique religieuse est susceptible de couvrir tout le champ des connaissances humaines, pratiques et théoriques. C'est en effet en considérant les deux fonctions de la rhétorique nommées par Aristote au début de la *Rhétorique*[41] qu'Averroès rend compte de l'exhaustivité de la connaissance religieuse: le discours rhétorique de la révélation coranique sert à la fois à persuader les hommes des actions bonnes et justes, enseignement qui équivaut à la philosophie pratique; et à leur communiquer des notions d'ordre métaphysique, connues scientifiquement par la pratique de la philosophie théorique[42]:

> Il ne faut pas, avec toutes les sortes d'hommes, utiliser la démonstration des choses théoriques qu'on voudrait qu'ils croient; et cela ou bien parce que l'homme a crû sous l'influence d'opinions notoires s'écartant du vrai, de sorte que, lorsqu'on le conduit aux choses selon lesquelles il a crû, il est facile de le persuader ou bien parce que sa complexion n'est pas du tout apte à admettre la démonstration ou bien parce qu'il n'est pas possible de mettre en évidence, pour lui, la démonstration dans ce peu de temps où l'on voudrait obtenir de lui une conviction. C'est pourquoi nous sommes parfois contraints d'induire la conviction au moyen des prémisses qui sont communes à nous et à celui à qui on s'adresse, je veux dire au moyen des prémisses louées[43].

La rhétorique sert aussi bien à pousser les hommes, contre leur nature, à agir droitement, qu'à leur enseigner des connaissances

[41] Cfr. *ibid.*, 1355a^{20} seqq.

[42] Cfr. Ibn Rušd (Averroes Cordubensis), *Commentaire moyen à la* Rhétorique *d'Aristote*, éd. M. Aouad, 3 voll., Paris 2003 (Textes et traditions, 5), II, pp. 8-9.

[43] *Ibid.*, p. 9.

théoriques (sur Dieu, l'origine du monde, l'immortalité de l'âme, la vie future, etc.) sans lesquelles leur félicité ne peut être accomplie. C'est cette tâche qu'assume la parole révélée, dans laquelle les hommes de la foule sont obligés de croire parce que la Loi le leur ordonne.

En approfondissant la signification de l'«assentiment» au Coran dans les termes de la logique, Averroès explicite en termes philosophiques la foi religieuse. La primauté de la Loi, de la *šarī'a*, dans la conscience religieuse de l'Islam n'implique évidemment aucune minoration de l'acte de «foi», assentiment inconditionnel et immédiat de l'esprit au contenu de la révélation. Dès la première théologie musulmane apparaîtront ainsi des recueils intitulés *kitāb al-īmān*, qui s'attachent à caractériser l'acte de foi, et des débats autour de la question de savoir si la foi comporte les actes ou se définit seulement par l'adhésion du cœur, indépendamment des actes[44]. Comme on l'a noté plus haut, cet assentiment immédiat s'exprime en arabe par le terme *īmān*, dérivant de la racine *'amn*, qui connote l'idée de «se confier à», «s'en remettre à», donnant des termes comme *amana* (sincérité, bonne foi) ou *amāna*, fidélité, loyauté, et donc l'idée de protection, sauvegarde accordée, «sauf-conduit» (*amān*). L'*īmān* est entendu comme conviction de la vérité d'une chose, assurée par la fiabilité de sa source, qui s'accompagne d'un sentiment d'assurance, précisément procuré par la «bonne foi» de Celui qui révèle le contenu de la foi. C'est la raison, notamment, pour laquelle la possession de l'*īmān* s'attribue, de la façon la plus éminente, dans l'Islam, à Dieu lui-même. *Al-Mu'min* (le «Croyant», celui qui a l'*īmān*) est l'un des «quatre-vingt dix neufs noms» divins utilisés dans le Coran dans la mesure où Dieu est l'être qui, en raison de sa nature parfaite, est le plus à même d'énoncer sa propre véridicité[45], les autres *mu'minūn* (croyants) ne l'étant que par Lui.

[44] Cfr. par ex. sur le sujet, W. MADELUNG, *Early Sunnī Doctrine Concerning Faith as Reflected in the* Kitāb al-Īmān *of Abū 'Ubayd al-Qāsim b. Sallām (d. 224/839)*, in «Studia Islamica», 32 (1970), pp. 233-254.

[45] Cfr. par ex. AL-ĪǦĪ, *Šarḥ al-mawāqif* (*Commentaire sur les* Positions), cité dans L. GARDET, *Les noms et les statuts. Le problème de la foi et des oeuvres en Islām*, in «Studia Islamica», 5 (1956), [pp. 61-123], p. 66: «dire que Dieu est *mu'min* signifie qu'il témoigne de sa propre véridicité, qu'il prononce le témoignage de foi en Lui-même («Je suis Dieu; point de divinité – si ce n'est Moi [*Cor*, 20, 14]), comme le croyant, son serviteur, prononce le témoignage de foi en Dieu; et

La perception musulmane de l'*īmān*, analysée en détail par Louis Gardet dans plusieurs travaux[46], est ainsi expliquée par lui: «L'acte de foi est fonction de l'attitude de celui en qui l'on croit, et lui répond l'état de sécurité qui en résulte»[47]. Il en résulte que «pour la pensée musulmane, *īmān* connote moins 'adhésion (surnaturelle) à une vérité inévidente' que témoignage rendu à un suprême Garant»[48]. En conséquence, la différence entre raison et foi ne recoupe pas une distinction entre nature et «surnature», qui seule serait le domaine propre de l'acte de foi. Il n'y a pas de différence qualitative, on l'a vu, entre la connaissance objet de conception rationnelle et celle qui est objet de foi (*īmān*). Ainsi, les démonstrations rationnelles enseignées par les théologiens musulmans, les *mutakallimūn*, portant sur les preuves de l'existence de Dieu, la nature de ses attributs, etc. ne le sont pas au titre de «préambules de la foi», connaissance naturelle indiquant seulement la possibilité de ce qu'il y a à croire. La connaissance qui en est issue n'est pas différente dans son essence de celle issue de l'adhésion de foi donnée au texte coranique. L'une et l'autre, par des voies plus ou moins directes, «sont garanties par l'obligation légale qui les impèrent. Leur source et leur mode de procéder diffèrent, mais non leur objet»[49]. Elles confluent vers le même objet, selon plusieurs voies d'accès à la vérité. Ce qui est connu par la foi est la même chose que ce qui peut être connu par la raison.

qu'Il témoigne de la véridicité de son Envoyé. Secondairement, on dira Dieu *mu'min* en ce sens qu'il crée les miracles qui feront croyants les hommes; en ce sens enfin qu'il opèrera en ses serviteurs cet état de sécurité (*aman*), de tranquillité de l'âme (*ṭuma'nīna*) qui est l'Etat même du croyant». À la limite, on pourrait rapprocher ce problème du nom divin *al-mu'min* de la discussion, bien connue, sur la valeur objective ou subjective du génitif dans l'expression πίστις Χριστοῦ utilisée dans les épîtres pauliniennes. Cfr. par ex. P. HOWARD, *Notes and Observations on the 'Faith of Christ'*, in «Harvard Theological Review», 60 (1967), pp. 459-465; ID., *Romans 3:21-31 and the Inclusion of the Gentiles*, in «Harvard Theological Review», 63 (1970), pp. 223-233. Dans la mesure où la notion de 'foi du Christ' correspondrait à la résolution dont témoigne le Christ dans son sacrifice, il s'agit tout de même d'une manière bien moins radicale d'attribuer une «foi» à Dieu que ce qui est affirmé dans le dogme musulman.

[46] Cfr. GARDET, *Les noms et les statuts* cit.; L. GARDET – G. ANAWATI, *Introduction à la théologie musulmane. Essai de Théologie comparée*, Paris 1981[3] (Etudes de philosophie médiévale, 37).

[47] GARDET, *Les noms et les statuts*, p. 67.

[48] *Ibidem*.

[49] GARDET – ANAWATI, *Introduction* cit., p. 351.

C'est donc à la Loi qu'il revient de déterminer ce qui peut être connu par la foi et par la raison. C'est en effet la *šarī'a* qui règle l'usage de la connaissance humaine, en légitime et en hiérarchise les sources. C'est de ce point de vue qu'Averroès pose la question, au début du *Faṣl al-maqāl* du statut légal (*ḥukm*) de «l'étude de la philosophie et de la logique»:

> [Il s'agit de] rechercher dans la perspective de l'examen (*naẓar*) juridique si l'étude (*naẓar*) de la philosophie et des sciences de la logique est permise (*mubāḥ*) par la loi révélée, ou bien condamnée par elle, ou bien encore prescrite, soit en tant que recommandation, soit en tant qu'obligation (*wuğūb*)[50].

Le point de vue adopté par Averroès reflète une situation propre à l'Islam, qui se prolonge en un sens jusque dans le présent: des interprétations divergentes de la Loi donnent lieu, dans la tradition musulmane, à différents types d'attitudes vis-à-vis du *naẓar*, de l'utilisation de l'intelligence, de la raison (*'aql*). Tant l'«examen rationnel» (*naẓar*) et l'usage du *'aql*, que la foi (*īmān*) sont reçus comme des obligations légales (*wuğūb*) prescrites explicitement par le Texte sacré. Cependant, si la compréhension de l'attitude d'esprit impliquée dans l'*īmān* est moins discutée (en raison de son caractère immédiat et inconditionnel), la question a été en revanche de savoir quel contenu donner à l'injonction de *naẓar* et de *'aql* contenue dans le Texte sacré.

On trouve dans le Coran un grand nombre d'injonctions, sur le mode impératif, qui permettent de considérer l'acte de foi (*īmān*) comme légalement obligatoire, ouvrant un problème dans lequel s'engagerait la réflexion des théologiens du *kalām*: d'une part, cela paraît impliquer que l'*islām*, comme simple adhésion extérieure au message et aux commandements de la prédication coranique, est en quelque sorte à distinguer de l'*īmān*, adhésion du cœur[51]: s'il a été prescrit au musulman, comme obligation légale, d'avoir la foi, au même titre que d'accomplir les prières rituelles, d'observer des interdits alimentaires, etc., c'est bien que l'on peut concevoir, au moins en théorie, qu'un homme qui professe l'*islām*

[50] *Discours décisif*, p. 103.

[51] Sur la distinction entre *islām* et *īmān*, cfr. GARDET, *Les noms et les statuts* cit., pp. 84-87.

n'ait pas la foi. Son *islām* ne serait alors pas valide (l'*īmān* est une condition nécessaire de l'*islām*), mais il en est distinct par le fait qu'il est impossible d'établir catégoriquement qu'un musulman a la foi, tandis que l'*islām* se juge par un acte extérieur (la récitation de la profession de foi, la *šahāda*). D'autre part, la «foi» qui est requise par le texte révélé ne peut, semble-t-il, être accordée que par celui qui, précisément, accorde déjà «foi» à ce même texte, ce qui indiquerait que l'*īmān* ne peut se fonder exclusivement sur lui-même. Aussi les théologiens mu'tazilites seront-ils amenés à soutenir que ce sont la «raison» (*'aql*) et l'«examen rationnel» (*naẓar*), lesquels apparaissent également comme une obligation (*wuǧūb*) dans le Coran[52], qui constituent le fondement premier de l'adhésion à la révélation, de l'*islām:* c'est l'usage de la raison humaine qui permet de vérifier la véridicité du message révélé, dans lequel, en conséquence, on pourra *croire*. L'école aš'arite s'accorderait avec sa rivale mu'tazilite pour reconnaître l'examen rationnel comme obligation légale. La divergence porte seulement sur le source de cette obligation: savons-nous que le raisonnement est obligatoire *ex auditu* (par la tradition des textes religieux qui l'affirment), auquel cas la foi prime sur le raisonnement; ou par la raison, comme l'affirment au contraire les mu'tazilites, alors que selon la doctrine aš'arite, l'usage de la raison est purement et premièrement une obligation légale: si la Loi ne lui en avait prescrit l'obligation, la raison n'aurait pu s'élever à la connaissance de Dieu[53]. Ces divergences sont néanmoins secondaires. Dans l'univers du *kalām*, les connaissances rationnelle et révélée, différant

[52] Le terme *'aql*, qui allait signifier «intellect», rendant le νοῦς grec, ne se trouve pas dans le Coran, qui utilise seulement le verbe correspondant, *'aqala*, *ya'qilu*, dans des énoncés incitant à «réfléchir justement», ou «discerner des liens» (ce qui est la signification étymologique du terme) entre les signes donnés par Dieu ou les prophètes et la nécessité de croire dans la révélation; cfr. par ex. *Cor* 2, 21-22; 14, 10, et *passim*. L'expression revient souvent dans le texte coranique pour exprimer une sorte d'étonnement devant l'incrédulité de ceux qui, ayant reçu des signes, persévèrent à ne pas croire: «Que ne 'réfléchissent'-ils?», «*a-fa-lā ya'qilūna*». Il en va de même pour le terme qui se verrait donner dans la tradition théologique la signification d'«examen», ou «recherche rationnelle», *al-naẓar*. Le Coran adresse au croyant des injonctions à «considérer» les merveilles de la création pour reconnaître l'existence de Dieu (cfr. par ex. *Cor* 7, 85; 69, 2; 88, 17-18 et *passim*).

[53] C'est la thèse *aš'arite* telle qu'elle est formulée par al-Ġazālī dans son traité de *kalām*, *al-Iqtiṣād fī al-i'tiqād* (*La Thésaurisation de la dogmatique*); cfr. GARDET – ANAWATI, *Introduction* cit. (à la note 46), p. 350.

par leur source, présentent une identité d'objet qui explique qu'elles sont à l'œuvre conjointement dans les actes de connaissance, en dépit du débat sur la primauté de l'une ou de l'autre.

Les adversaires des *mutakallimūn* jugent au contraire que la *šarī'a* interdit le principe même d'un usage autonome de la raison. C'est eux que cherche principalement à convaincre le *Faṣl al-maqāl*. La «science» (*'ilm*) se réduit pour eux à un assentiment immédiat au contenu de la révélation. La foi est alors le seul instrument de connaissance, non parce que le *'aql* serait par définition incapable de connaître les réalités de la foi, mais parce que la *šarī'a* interdit qu'il soit utilisé à autre chose qu'à assimiler le contenu de la révélation. Le seul usage légitime du *'aql* (fait de comprendre justement, de «lier» entre elles les choses conçues) est alors le fait, pour l'homme, de laisser configurer son entendement par les énoncés de la révélation, du Coran et de la Tradition prophétique, qui suffiraient à rendre compte de tout ce qui est utile et indispensable à l'homme de savoir et de faire. L'«examen» rationnel, *naẓar*, est révoqué aussi bien comme méthode pour déduire de la révélation les statuts légaux (*aḥkām*) des actes non expressément qualifiés dans le Coran ou la Tradition (au lieu de cela, on considère que tout cas de figure nouveau peut être rapporté immédiatement à un cas d'espèce déjà qualifié dans le corpus de la Tradition); que pour l'interprétation allégorique (*ta'wīl*) des textes du Coran et de la Tradition, au plan théologique. Cette attitude que l'on qualifie de «littéraliste», «traditionaliste», s'incarne historiquement dans un courant qui recouvre, en Orient, l'école juridique et théologique appelée hanbalite, d'après son fondateur le grand traditionniste Ibn Ḥanbal (m. 241 h. / 855)[54]. Ces traditionalistes on été souvent désignés du terme péjoratif de *ḥašwiyya*[55] par leurs adversaires théologiens du *kalām*, un terme que reprendra Averroès pour désigner ses contemporains les docteurs de le Loi traditionalistes malikites d'al-Andalus, qui dans une certaine tradition doxographique attestée notamment chez le Cadi Abū Bakr ibn al-'Arabī (m. 543 h. / 1148), juriste sévillan

[54] Pour cette école, cfr. l'étude classique de H. LAOUST, *Le Hanbalisme sous le califat de Bagdad*, Paris 1959.

[55] Il désigne de manière générale les savants de bas étage, ceux qui remplissent ou «farcissent» (*ḥašw*) les marges des livres de paraphrases inutiles; cfr. *Encyclopédie de l'Islam*, 2e éd., Leiden 1960-2006, III, p. 277, s.v. «Ḥašwiyya».

disciple d'al-Ġazālī, ont été explicitement assimilés aux disciples d'Ibn Ḥanbal[56]. Les docteurs malikites, adversaires désignés, peut-être en partie fictifs[57], d'Averroès dans sa défense de la philosophie, s'inscrivent très exactement dans cette lignée.

Pour la tradition du *kalām*, le rejet des instruments du *naẓar* par les traditionalistes s'oppose à l'autorité même des textes révélés. Le fait que ceux-ci instaurent l'«examen rationnel» comme obligation légale apparaît comme une évidence pour toute une tradition ancrée dans la pratique du *kalām*, comme le rappelle Averroès:

> La majorité des savants de notre religion reconnaissent la validité du syllogisme rationnel (*qiyās 'aqlī*), excepté un petit nombre de littéralistes bornés (*ḥašwiyya*), que l'on peut réfuter pas des énoncés révélés de sens univoque[58].

L'obligation de l'examen rationnel imposée par la Loi répond pour les théologiens à une nécessité de raison qui compénètre la Loi elle-même. Selon les théologiens du *kalām*, le recours au *naẓar* comme source de connaissance est requis dans ce monde parce que la connaissance de Dieu n'y est qu'acquise et possible (*mumkin*), non première et nécessaire (*ḍarūrī*) comme elle le serait dans la vision béatifique assurée dans l'Au-delà. Cette distinction théologique (dans le bas monde, la connaissance n'est pas donnée, mais contingente, et dépend d'une investigation humaine) jouera un rôle fondamental pour accréditer l'idée que la connaissance religieuse peut trouver un prolongement naturel dans une recherche de la science. On invoquera ainsi la conception kala-

[56] Dans le K. *al-'Awāṣīm mina-l-qawāṣīm* (*Les Morceaux bien gardés sur les récits des vicissitudes*) d'Abū Bakr ibn al-'Arabī; cfr. D. SERRANO, *¿Por qué llamaron los Almohades antropomorfistas a los almorávides?*, in *Los Almohades: problemas y perspectivas*, éds. P. Cressier – M. Fierro – L. Molina, 2 voll., Madrid 2005 (Estudios árabes e islámicos: monografías, 11), II, pp. 815-852.

[57] SERRANO, *ibid.*, p. 816, note qu'une opposition explicite de la part des docteurs de la Loi andalous à la théorie du droit (*uṣūl al-fiqh*) et à la théologie n'est pas véritablement attestée à la première moitié du XIIe siècle en al-Andalus. Au contraire, les sciences du *naẓar* (*kalām*, science de fondement du droit, *uṣūl al-fiqh*) n'y auraient plus fait l'objet d'un rejet de la part des clercs contemporains. Cependant, pour des raisons polémiques, les Almohades auraient amplifié la figure du docteur de la Loi littéraliste borné, qui se refuse à interpréter allégoriquement les versets coraniques où Dieu est dépeint avec des traits corporels (la main, le pied, la face, etc.).

[58] *Discours décisif*, p. 109.

mique de la science acquise dans des domaines extérieurs aux thématiques proprement dites du *kalām*, notamment pour intégrer au cursus musulman l'étude de la logique, présentée comme l'instrument du *naẓar*, bien que la science logique en tant que telle ne soit pas partie intégrante du *kalām*, et que les auteurs ne soient jamais (du moins jusqu'à l'époque d'Averroès) allés jusqu'à incorporer des traités de logique en bonne et due forme dans leurs sommes de théologie. Al-Ġazālī explique ainsi dans l'une de ses œuvres de logique, intitulée *Mi'yār al-'aql* («Le calibre de l'intellect»), que le premier but de cette œuvre est de «faire entendre les méthodes de la pensée et du raisonnement (*naẓar*) (...) parce que les sciences théoriques, n'étant pas données ni conférées par la nature innée (*al-fiṭra wa-l-ǧarīza*), sont nécessairement objets d'acquisition et de recherche»[59]. C'est aussi en se référant à cette exigence du *kalām* qu'Avicenne, par exemple, introduisant sa définition de la logique comme connaissance des méthodes par lesquelles l'esprit procède «du connu à l'inconnu» explique que

> Étant donné que la plupart de ce qu'on détient [de la connaissance du vrai] ne se produit que par l'acquisition (*kasb*), et que cette acquisition est acquisition de l'inconnu, tandis que ce qui fait acquérir (*muksib*) l'inconnu est le connu, il faut que l'homme commence par savoir de quelle manière il pourra acquérir l'inconnu à partir du connu, et quel est, en lui-même, l'état et l'ordonnancement des choses connues, en fonction desquelles celles-ci produisent la connaissance de l'inconnu, c'est-à-dire en tant qu'une fois qu'elles sont agencées dans l'esprit de la façon qui convient, l'esprit se transporte d'elles vers l'inconnu qui est recherché, en sorte qu'il le connaisse[60].

C'est du fait de cette limitation inhérente à la connaissance humaine (elle doit être acquise), limitation dont la reconnaissance rend précisément compte de l'injonction coranique à «examiner»

[59] Abū Ḥāmid al-Ġazālī (Algazzali, Algazel), *Mi'yār al-'ilm fī al-Manṭiq* (*Le Calibre de la science*), éd. A. Šams al-Dīn, Bayrūt 1410 h. / 1990, p. 26.

[60] Ibn Sīnā (Avicenna), *al-Šifā'. al-Manṭiq*. 1 – *al-Madḫal* (*L'Introduction*), éd. Ǧ. Qanawātī *et alii*, al-Qāhira 1371 h. / 1952; réimpr. Ibn Sīnā, *al-Šifā'. al-Manṭiq*, 1, Qum 1405 h. / 1984, p. 17, 1-6; cfr. aussi Abū Ḥāmid al-Ġazālī (Algazzali, Algazel), *Maqaṣid al-falāsifa* (*Les Intentions des philosophes*), éd. A. F. al-Mazīdī, Bayrūt 1424 h. / 2003, p. 13: «Il est donc évident que toute science qui est recherchée (*maṭlūb*) n'est acquise que par une science qui précède».

ou «considérer» les êtres créés pour connaître Dieu, que le *naẓar*, obligation religieuse, s'identifie tout simplement, pour Averroès, avec la logique:

> Puisque donc il est bien établi que la Révélation déclare obligatoire l'examen des étants au moyen de la raison et la réflexion sur ceux-ci, et que par ailleurs réfléchir n'est rien d'autre qu'inférer, extraire l'inconnu du connu – ce en quoi consiste en fait le syllogisme, ou qui s'opère au moyen de lui –, alors nous avons l'obligation de recourir au syllogisme rationnel pour l'examen des étants. Il est évident en outre que ce procédé d'examen auquel appelle la Révélation; et qu'elle encourage, est nécessairement celui qui est le plus parfait et qui recourt à l'espèce de syllogisme le plus parfait, que l'on appelle 'démonstration'[61].

Ce qui vaut pour la connaissance religieuse (elle doit être fondée sur l'investigation rationnelle parce qu'elle n'est pas donnée) vaut de la même façon pour la connaissance philosophique, et le *naẓar* (examen rationnel) est donc l'instrument aussi bien de la connaissance religieuse (celle du théologien) que philosophique. La transition entre l'un et l'autre registre va de soi, puisqu'il n'y a pratiquement pas de différence de nature entre l'objet de la connaissance religieuse et l'objet de la connaissance philosophique. La limitation inhérente à la nature humaine vaut dans les deux cas. L'homme n'ayant pas d'emblée de connaissance parfaite, sa science doit être le résultat d'une actualisation graduelle, ce qui est le cas lorsque le musulman acquiert sa connaissance des dogmes en faisant usage du *'aql*, et de même lorsque, philosophe, il s'approprie la connaissance de la structure intelligible de l'univers par l'usage du syllogisme. La θεωρία aristotélicienne se recoupe avec l'impératif coranique du *naẓar* qui enjoint de considérer les êtres pour connaître Dieu, qui chez les théologiens caractérise le mode humain et imparfait d'accès à la connaissance religieuse, lequel fait pendant à la vision béatifique. Dans un parallélisme exact avec la conception du théologien (l'acquisition de la science religieuse par l'examen rationnel dispose à la vision béatifique), le philosophe considère de même que la finalité ultime de la connaissance naturelle de l'univers est une forme de

[61] *Discours décisif*, pp. 105-107.

perfection surnaturelle de l'intellect, qualifiée de conjonction (*ittiṣāl*) avec l'intellect agent, correspondant à l'état du philosophe parfait, et caractérisée comme une *béatitude* philosophique[62]. On connaît en outre l'importance de ce thème pour Averroès[63].

C'est également le principe fondamental du *kalām* (l'autorité de la révélation doit être étayée par le raisonnement) qu'Averroès oppose aux *ḥašwiyya* dans le K. *al-Kašf ʿan manāhiǧ al-adilla* («Dévoilement des procédés de la démonstration»):

> Quant à la secte nommée *ḥašwiyya*, ses adeptes considèrent l'autorité (*samʿ*) comme la [seule] voie pour connaître l'existence de Dieu Très Haut, en excluant la raison (*ʿaql*). C'est-à-dire que [selon eux] il suffit, pour arriver à la foi dans Son existence, à laquelle les hommes sont légalement obligés d'assentir (*taṣdīq*), de la recevoir de la part de l'auteur de la Révélation. La foi (*īmān*) se produit ainsi, de la même façon que l'on reçoit de sa part [les dogmes concernant] les conditions de la vie future (*šurūṭ al-maʿād*) et les autres dogmes auxquels il n'y a aucun moyen d'accéder (*lā madḫal*) par la raison. Il est évident que cette secte égarée est incapable [de comprendre] l'intention mise par la Révélation dans la méthode qu'elle a instaurée au profit de l'ensemble des hommes pour [les] conduire à connaître l'existence de Dieu[64].

Dans ce dernier passage, Averroès prend en compte une distinction, elle-même reprise aux traités de *kalām*, entre question «rationnelles» (*ʿaqliyyāt*), qui sont celles relatives à la divinité (*ilāhiyyāt*), et «traditionnelles» (*samʿiyyāt*)[65]. Les premières sont connues par la raison et confirmées par la révélation, et elles pourraient être connues de la même manière y compris en l'absence de la révélation; les secondes, relatives à la prophétologie, à

[62] Sur ce thème, cfr. en particulier H. A. DAVIDSON, *Alfarabi, Avicenna & Averroes, on Intellect. Their Cosmologies, Theories of the Active Intellect, and Theories of Human Intellect*, New York 1992, pp. 34 seqq.

[63] Cfr. M. GEOFFROY, *Averroès sur l'intellect comme cause agente et cause formelle, et la question de la «jonction»*, in *Averroès et les averroïsmes juifs et latins*, Actes du colloque international, Paris (16-18 juin 2005), éd. J. B. Brenet, Turnhout 2007 (Textes et études du Moyen Âge, 40), pp. 77-110.

[64] IBN RUŠD (AVERROES CORDUBENSIS), *al-Kašf ʿan manāhiǧ al-adilla fī ʿaqāʾid al-milla*, éd. al-Ǧābirī cit. (à la note 2), pp. 101-102 (notre traduction).

[65] Sur l'organisation des traités de *kalām*, cfr. GARDET – ANAWATI, *Introduction* cit. (à la note 46), pp. 136-186.

l'eschatologie et à l'imamat, sont déterminées par l'autorité de la révélation, elles ne seraient pas connues des hommes si Dieu ne les avaient révélées, et la raison a la charge d'en confirmer la vérité, la question des «conditions de la vie future», de la survie de l'âme et de la rétribution ou du châtiment dans l'Au-delà étant d'une importance primordiale pour Averroès[66]. L'affirmation, de la part d'Averroès, que la connaissance de la vie future, autrement dit l'eschatologie, n'est pas entièrement accessible à la raison peut sembler mettre à mal l'idée que toute connaissance religieuse serait aussi objet de connaissance rationnelle. Toutes les réalités connaissables ne seraient pas sur le même plan, mais certaines auraient besoin, pour être vraiment connues, de l'autorité de la révélation. Elles ne pourraient être atteintes de manière parfaitement adéquate par le simple «apprentissage» (*ta'līm*), c'est-à-dire la raison discursive. La contribution du prophète est alors indispensable, et la transmission de ces connaissances est considéré comme un «miracle», une opération excédant les possibilités habituelles de la nature (*ḫāriq li-l-'āda*) et prouvant au demeurant la véridicité du prophète:

> [On sait que les prophètes instaurent des lois sous inspiration divine] à cause des actes qu'ils prescrivent, et des sciences auxquelles ils éveillent l'esprit, lesquels ne ressemblent pas aux sciences et aux actes pouvant être atteints par l'apprentissage. En effet, si la chose qui sort de l'habituel (*ḫāriq li-l-mu'tād*) est de l'ordre de la connaissance, [ce qui est le cas] de l'instauration des lois, elle signifie que leur instauration n'est pas le fait de l'apprentissage[67].

Il ne faut certainement pas entendre par là que les réalité de la vie future sont inaccessibles *au philosophe* en raison des faibles lumières de la raison humaine, mais seulement à celui qui n'est pas

[66] La croyance dans la vie future (*ma'ād*), ou le jour du jugement, est comptée par Averroès, qui suit en cela al-Ġazālī (*Fayṣal al-tafriqa bayna l-islām wa-l-zandaqa* [«l'Arrêt qui départage la croyance et la mécréance»], éd. S. Dunyā, le Caire, Dār iḥyā' al-kutub al-'arabiyya, 1381 h. / 1961, p. 195-196) auquel Averroès se réfère, comme l'un des trois «fondements de la révélation» (*uṣūl al-šarā'i'*), ensemble avec «la croyance en Dieu» et «la croyance dans le prophète». Cfr. *Discours décisif*, p. 139.

[67] Ibn Rušd (Averroes Cordubensis), *ibid.*, éd. al-Ǧābirī cit., pp. 180-181 (notre traduction).

philosophe. L'investigation philosophique est capable de rendre compte de manière démonstrative du devenir de l'âme humaine *post mortem*. Comme l'a parfaitement montré Richard Taylor[68], il ne fait aucun doute qu'Averroès philosophe, comme une conséquence nécessaire de la théorie de l'unité de l'intellect, nie l'immortalité personnelle de l'âme humaine. L'ensemble des facultés de l'âme étant inhérentes aux corps, excepté l'intellect, ce qui peut survivre de la personne humaine est quelque chose qui s'est rapporté à lui de façon accidentelle, par la médiation des formes individuelles de l'imagination dont l'individu se servait pour penser, l'intellect en acte séparé, dont l'actualité et l'éternité transcende l'existence des individus pensants. C'est seulement dans la mesure de la participation à la pensée séparée qu'a acquise la personne au cours de son existence qu'elle peut être dite éternelle. Cette participation peut être pleine et entière, dans le cas du philosophe parfait, ayant atteint le stade de la «jonction» avec l'Intellect agent, mais aussi extrêmement faible, intermittente, ce qui est le cas de l'homme intellectuellement inférieur. Celui-ci ne peut être dit éternel que dans un sens très relatif, dans la mesure où l'intellect éternel lui a parfois été prêté pour donner le contenu de sa pensée (l'intellect spéculatif). La destination eschatologique de l'humanité est néanmoins que chaque individu parvienne au maximum de la perfection dont il est susceptible. Or c'est précisément de cela qu'ont parlé aussi, à leur manière, les Lois révélées, comme l'affirme expressément un passage du Grand Commentaire au *De anima* d'Aristote:

> Et universaliter ista intentio apparuit a remotis, scilicet anima esse immortalem, scilicet intellectum speculativum. Unde Plato dixit quod universalia sunt neque generabilia neque corruptibilia, et quod sunt existentia extra mentem. Et est sermo verus ex hoc modo (...). Et universaliter ista intentio anime est pars vera in propositionibus probabilibus que dant animam esse utrunque, scilicet mortalem et non mortalem (...). Et hoc apologizaverunt Antiqui, et in representatione illius conveniunt omnes leges[69].

[68] R. Taylor, *Personnal Immortality in Averroes' Mature Philosophical Psychology*, in «Documenti e studi sulla tradizione filosofica medievale», 9 (1998), pp. 87-110.

[69] Ibn Rušd (Averroes Cordubensis), *Commentarium Magnum in Aristotelis De anima Libros*, éd. Crawford cit. (à la note 31), p. 409.

On comprend ainsi en quoi la connaissance religieuse est déclarée supérieure à la connaissance rationnelle dans ces domaines. Ce n'est pas que l'inspiration du prophète puisse faire connaître de manière plus précise, plus conforme, la réalité de l'Au-delà qui ne serait accessible à la raison que de manière diffuse, imparfaite; mais elle peut *représenter*, mettre en images (rhétoriques) cette réalité d'une manière conforme à ce que sera, pour l'homme non intellectuel, l'éternité à laquelle ce dernier peut prétendre, et la lui faire désirer avec non moins d'ardeur que le philosophe, pour sa part, désire réaliser sa propre finalité, qui est de s'assimiler à l'Intellect agent. Mais, par définition, la félicité du non philosophe ne peut être proposée par la philosophie, puisque celle-ci ne parle qu'au philosophe. C'est en quelque sorte l'extension eschatologique de la distinction trouvée chez Aristote entre le bonheur théorétique, résultant de la perfection de la vertu rationnelle, et un bonheur inférieur, accessible à tous les humains qui agissent conformément à leur devoir moral[70]. La félicité éternelle de l'homme non intellectuel, inférieure, ne peut être représentée que par des exemples d'un ordre d'existence objectivement inférieur mais qui, précisément, n'apparaît pas comme tel aux hommes inférieurs, par la jouissance de délices corporels dans l'Au-delà. La religion, en particulier l'Islam, ne fait ici que prendre acte de l'existence nécessaire d'une telle hiérarchie entre les humains. C'est, pour Averroès, une indication de la supériorité de l'Islam sur les autres religions que de donner des réalités auxquelles les hommes ordinaires n'ont pas accès la représentation la mieux adaptée à leurs facultés. Le Prophète de l'Islam peut ainsi se prévaloir d'avoir estimé cela:

> La représentation par des choses sensibles serait plus à même de faire comprendre ces réalités à la foule, et que de la sorte, la foule serait mue davantage à rechercher ces délices ou à fuir ces tourments. C'est donc pourquoi ils [certains Prophètes, dont Muḥammad] apportèrent la nouvelle que Dieu allait opérer le retour des âmes bienheureuses dans des corps où elles jouiraient pour l'éternité de ce qu'il y a de plus délectable dans l'ordre sensible, exemplifié par le Paradis; et

[70] Cfr. ARISTOTELES, *Ethica Nicomachea*, X, $1177b^{26}$-$1178a^{2}$ (cfr. *supra*, à la note 15).

> opérer le retour des âmes damnées dans des corps où elles éprouveraient pour l'éternité les plus cruels des supplices dans l'ordre sensible, exemplifiés par le Feu. C'est ainsi que notre Révélation, l'Islam, représente cet état. Et il se trouve, chez nous, des arguments propres à assurer l'assentiment commun de tout le monde[71].

Le rôle de la religion est essentiellement de combler le décalage entre la vérité philosophique et la connaissance accessible à la foule. Plus celui-ci est important, plus se vérifie la supériorité de la connaissance religieuse sur la science démonstrative accessible au petit nombre.

L'intervention d'Averroès dans le domaine théologique musulman est une initiative originale dont aucun des ses prédécesseurs n'eut l'initiative. Elle constitue une tentative de résoudre la tension entre l'orientation fondamentalement individualiste du philosophe et la dimension nécessairement sociale de son existence. Le philosophe connaît les meilleures conditions de sa réalisation personnelle dans la société. La perfection philosophique est le stade suprême, intellectuel, de la condition humaine, mais ce stade n'est que le point d'arrivée d'une multitude de perfections individuelles, relatives et inférieures à la perfection théorétique du *faylasūf*, la diversité des activités des hommes de la cité reflétant la diversité de degrés de la perfection humaine. La fin ultime de l'existence de la société est de «donner lieu» à l'existence du philosophe. La communauté humaine, comme tout ce qui est, tend nécessairement, en vertu de la loi naturelle, à produire le meilleur. Toute forme conçue par la nature est destinée à parvenir à sa perfection ultime, la nature, selon l'adage aristotélicien, ne faisant rien en vain. Le meilleur de l'humanité est la perfection de la faculté rationnelle, forme dernière de l'homme en tant qu'homme. Les autres fonctions assurées par le corps social ne sont qu'adjuvantes et subordonnées à cette fin, celle du philosophe, et les perfections de tous les hommes ne sont que relatives à la perfection du philosophe. Elles ne valent qu'en fonction de leur habilité à remplir la fonction de contribuer à la perfection du

[71] Ibn Rušd (Averroes Cordubensis), *al-Kašf 'an manāhiǧ al-adilla fī 'aqā'id al-milla*, éd. al-Ǧābirī cit. (à la note 2), pp. 201-202 (notre traduction).

philosophe. Le philosophe se trouve de ce fait appelé à agir sur le corps social dans le sens qui convient à sa propre perfection, qui dépend de la perfection des hommes inférieurs. Il doit donc avoir l'usage, en tant que philosophe, de plusieurs niveaux de discours, employables pour parler aux non philosophes, et les conduire, de manière politique, vers leur perfection relative. C'est à ce titre que le philosophe se fait interprète de la Loi religieuse, fondement de l'ordre social et politique[72].

[72] Ce volume étant déjà sous épreuves, il n'a pas été possible de prendre en compte, pour la traduction et la discussion des passages d'Avempace, le travail suivant, paru trop récemment: IBN BĀĞĞA, *La conduite de l'isolé et deux autre épîtres*, introduction, édition critique et commentaire par Charles Genequand (Textes et traditions, 19), Paris 2010. Il importe cependant de renvoyer à cette traduction et aux analyses de l'«Introduction» de Genequand, en particulier, pour ce qui nous intéresse, dans la section, pp. 36-52, intitulée «La politique d'Ibn Bāğğa», auxquelles nous souscrivons. On notera que la traduction du titre *Tadbīr al-Mutawaḥḥid* par *La conduite de l'isolé*, selon Genequand, plutôt que *Le régime du solitaire*, la formule reçue, est de loin préférable.

INES PETA

IL DIBATTITO TRA AL-ĠAZĀLĪ E IBN RUŠD

FILOSOFIA E LEGGE RIVELATA A CONFRONTO

La storia dei controversi rapporti tra filosofia e ortodossia religiosa nel mondo islamico medievale ebbe una delle sue rappresentazioni più significative nella critica contro il grande teologo, giurista e mistico orientale, Abū Ḥāmid al-Ġazālī (m. 505 h. / 1111)[1], sferrata dal noto filosofo andaluso Ibn Rušd (m. 594 h. / 1198)[2].

[1] Giurista, teologo e mistico, Abū Ḥāmid al-Ġazālī è il massimo rappresentante dell'ortodossia religiosa all'epoca del sultanato selgiuchide. Nato nel 449 h. / 1057 a Ṭūs, nel Khorasan, vissuto tra Baghdad e Damasco e morto nella stessa Ṭūs, fu scrittore prolifico in tutti gli ambiti del sapere religioso. Tra le sue opere principali si ricordano il *Tahāfut al-falāsifa* (*L'incoerenza dei filosofi*) – attacco alla filosofia di stampo neoplatonico – l'*Iqtiṣād fī-l-i'tiqād* (*Il giusto mezzo nel credo*) – compendio di teologia dogmatica aš'arita – l'*Iḥyā' 'ulūm ad-dīn* (*Il ravvivamento delle scienze religiose*) – *corpus* delle sue dottrine – e il *Munqiḏ min aḍ-ḍalāl* (*La salvezza dalla perdizione*) – autobiografia nella quale il racconto della crisi spirituale vissuta dall'autore, in seguito alla quale egli aderì al sufismo, diventa un vero e proprio percorso di rifondazione della conoscenza. Gli studi su questo autore sono ovviamente moltissimi. Per una visione d'insieme si rimanda a C. BAFFIONI, *Storia della filosofia islamica*, Milano 1991, pp. 265-287 e alla relativa bibliografia.

[2] Nato nel 520 h. / 1126 a Cordoba, Ibn Rušd (il latino Averroè) fu celebre, oltre che come filosofo, anche come giurista e come medico. Dal califfo almohade Abū Ya'qūb venne nominato *qāḍī* ('giudice') di Siviglia e fu incaricato di commentare le opere di Aristotele, per le quali è rimasto grandemente noto nel Medioevo latino. La sua vita pubblica ebbe però alterne fortune e dopo una decina d'anni dalla morte di Abū Ya'qūb fu soggetto alle persecuzioni almohadi, che lo costrinsero all'esilio. Oltre ai famosi commenti ad Aristotele, egli è noto per il *Tahāfut at-tahāfut* (*L'incoerenza dell'incoerenza*), contenente la confutazione delle critiche di al-Ġazālī alla filosofia, e per altri due trattati scritti al fine di conciliare la filosofia con l'Islām, dal punto di vista giuridico nel *Faṣl al-maqāl fī mā bayna-l-ḥikma wa-š-šarī'a min al-ittiṣāl* (*Il trattato decisivo sull'accordo della Legge rivelata con la filosofia*), da quello teologico nel *Kašf 'an manāhiğ al-adilla* (*Lo svelamen-*

10.1484/M.NUTRIX-EB.1.101248

Il primo, nel suo celebre *Tahāfut al-falāsifa* (*L'incoerenza dei filosofi*)[3], enumera 16 proposizioni di metafisica e 4 di fisica aventi rilevanza religiosa e le confuta una a una. Tale confutazione avviene con metodi strettamente filosofici. Al-Ġazālī, cioè, combatte la filosofia con la filosofia, avvalendosi della sua stessa metodologia per dimostrare l'intrinseca debolezza e incoerenza delle dottrine in questione. Tre di queste meritano, secondo l'autore, l'accusa di miscredenza (*takfīr*): l'eternità del mondo, la limitazione della conoscenza di Dio agli universali e la negazione della resurrezione dei corpi. Qualche anno dopo, egli scrive il *Fayṣal at-tafriqa bayna-l-Islām wa-z-zandaqa* (*Il criterio decisivo di distinzione tra l'Islām e la miscredenza*)[4], opera in cui si occupa propriamente del *takfīr*, esponendo con chiarezza in base a quali criteri giuridici scatti l'accusa di miscredenza e dunque su quali basi legali si fondi la sua condanna della filosofia. Il fatto è che la questione va precisamente ricondotta all'ambito legale, all'ambito della *šarī'a*, la Legge religiosa. Si tratta infatti di stabilire ciò che fa sì che l'uomo sia validamente costituito agli occhi di Dio nel suo statuto legale di credente o di miscredente. Come precisa al-Ġazālī stesso nel *Fayṣal*:

> La miscredenza è una disposizione giuridica, come ad esempio la schiavitù e la libertà, dal momento che implica la legittimazione della pena di morte e la condanna al Fuoco eterno[5].

to dei procedimenti della dimostrazione). Per un inquadramento della figura e del pensiero di Ibn Rušd si rimanda a *Storia della filosofia nell'Islam medievale*, a c. di C. D'Ancona, 2 voll., Torino 2005, II, pp. 723-782 (con bibliografia inclusa).

[3] Completato all'incirca nel 487 h. / 1094, il *Tahāfut* fu redatto a Baghdad dopo il *Maqāṣid al-falāsifa* (*Gli scopi dei filosofi*), testo che ne costituisce la premessa, in quanto riporta le idee dei filosofi musulmani che vengono poi contestate nel *Tahāfut*. Cfr. M. Bouyges, *Essai de chronologie des œuvres de al-Ghazali (Algazel)*, a c. di M. Allard, Beirut 1959, pp. 23-24.

[4] La collocazione cronologica esatta del *Fayṣal* non è conosciuta. Maurice Bouyges pone due punti di riferimento: un *terminus a quo*, rappresentato dal *Qisṭās al-mustaqīm* (*La giusta bilancia*), un opuscolo anti-bāṭinita scritto nel periodo dell'insegnamento a Baghdad, e dunque tra il 484 h. / 1091 e il 488 h. / 1095, e un *terminus ad quem*, l'*al-Munqiḏ min aḍ-ḍalāl*, composto sicuramente dopo il 499 h. / 1106, nel quale esso viene citato. Cfr. Bouyges, *Essai de cronologie* cit., p. 58.

[5] al-Ġazālī (Algazzali, Algazel), *Fayṣal at-tafriqa bayna-l-Islām wa-z-zandaqa*, ed. a c. di Hogga Mustapha, Parigi 1983, p. 8 (in seguito: al-Ġazālī, *Fayṣal at-tafriqa*). Tutti i brani riportati da quest'opera sono di mia traduzione.

Ed è proprio su questo terreno che Ibn Rušd affronta la questione del rapporto tra filosofia e religione, in particolare nel *Faṣl al-maqāl fī mā bayna-l-ḥikma wa-š-šarī'a min al-ittiṣāl* (*Il trattato decisivo sull'accordo della Legge rivelata con la filosofia*)[6] dove, in polemica con al-Ġazālī, tenta di dimostrare la validità giuridica della filosofia, difendendola dalla taccia di miscredenza di cui quest'ultimo l'aveva investita. Così egli apre il suo trattato:

> Il fine di questo scritto è indagare, dal punto di vista dello studio della Legge religiosa, se la speculazione filosofica e le scienze logiche siano lecite secondo il *šar'* o proibite o obbligatorie, sia perché commendevoli sia perché necessarie[7].

Come si vede, entrambi gli autori sottolineano il valore prettamente legale degli argomenti trattati nelle loro opere. Nel presente contributo, tenterò di mettere in evidenza proprio come le loro diverse opinioni dipendano dalla loro diversa concezione di questioni essenzialmente giuridiche, quali il tipo di conoscenza che la Rivelazione prescrive all'uomo di perseguire, i casi di applicazione del *ta'wīl* o interpretazione allegorica ai dati scritturali, la questione di chi abbia il diritto di praticarlo, la validità dell'*iğmā'* o consenso della comunità musulmana[8]. Le loro rispettive teorie su queste questioni servono infatti a mettere in luce in quali casi, secondo i due autori, scatti il *takfīr* e dunque in base a quali argomenti al-Ġazālī condanni ed Ibn Rušd difenda la filo-

[6] L'opera, redatta da Ibn Rušd nel 575/1179, venne da lui composta proprio allo scopo di rendere legittima la filosofia agli occhi dei giudici religiosi del suo tempo, che le erano in maggioranza ostili.

[7] IBN RUŠD (AVERROÈS CORDUBENSIS), *Faṣl al-maqāl fī mā bayna-l-ḥikma wa-š-šarī'a min al-ittiṣāl*, tr. it. di M. Campanini (AVERROÈ, *Il trattato decisivo sull'accordo della religione con la filosofia*), Milano 1999², p. 45 (testo arabo a fronte) (in seguito: AVERROÈ, *Il trattato decisivo*). Tutte queste qualificazioni ('lecito', obbligatorio', 'proibito' ecc.) corrispondono a categorie di atti precisamente definite nella teoria giuridica. Secondo il diritto islamico, infatti, tutti gli atti rientrano in cinque categorie normative: l'atto 'obbligatorio' (*wāğib*), che ognuno deve compiere e la cui omissione può pertanto essere punita; l'atto 'raccomandabile' o 'desiderabile' (*mandūb*), quello cioè considerato meritorio; l'atto 'lecito' (*mubāḥ*), ovvero quello che il credente è libero di compiere o meno, senza che ciò comporti merito o colpa; l'atto 'riprovevole' (*makrūh*), quello dal quale è cioè fortemente consigliato di astenersi; l'atto 'illecito' (*ḥarām*) e dunque punibile dalla legge.

[8] Nel trattare tali questioni ho tratto ampi spunti dall'interessante monografia di I. A. BELLO, *The medieval islamic controversy between philosophy and orthodoxy*, Leiden 1989, in cui se ne trova una approfondita analisi.

sofia. In tal modo, sarà possibile evidenziare la loro diversa idea del ruolo della ragione in generale e della filosofia in particolare nello studio delle cose religiose. Per far questo, mi baserò principalmente sul *Fayṣal* e sul *Faṣl*, ma farò riferimento – laddove sia necessario per integrare o approfondire alcuni concetti – anche ad altre opere.

Il primo problema che Ibn Rušd si trova ad affrontare nel suo trattato è quello di dimostrare che il tipo di conoscenza che il Corano incita a perseguire è dello stesso tipo della conoscenza filosofica. Il suo scopo è cioè quello di provare che la Legge religiosa rende obbligatorio (*wāǧib*) o quanto meno raccomandabile (*mandūb*) l'esercizio della filosofia. A tal fine egli cita alcuni versetti del Libro Sacro che esortano l'uomo ad osservare l'universo e a riflettere sulla creazione:

> Riflettete, o voi che avete occhi a guardare! (*Cor* 59, 2).
>
> Non han forse studiato il regno dei cieli e della terra e le cose tutte che Dio ha creato? (*Cor* 7, 185).
>
> E così mostrammo ad Abramo il regno dei cieli e della terra perché fosse di quei che solidamente sono convinti (*Cor* 6, 75).
>
> Ma non guardano dunque gli uomini al cammello, come fu creato, e al cielo, come fu innalzato? (*Cor* 471, 17-18).
>
> Ed essi meditano sulla creazione dei cieli e della terra (*Cor* 3, 191).

Secondo Ibn Rušd, il primo versetto mostra chiaramente «l'obbligatorietà dell'uso del ragionamento intellettuale, o del ragionamento intellettuale e di quello legale insieme»[9]; gli altri esortano «a speculare sugli esseri esistenti nella loro totalità»[10]. Dall'esame del Corano – la fonte prima della legislazione musulmana – Ibn Rušd fa derivare dunque l'obbligatorietà della speculazione razionale. E poiché la speculazione razionale consiste nella deduzione dell'ignoto dal già noto e il sillogismo è proprio quel processo che permette tale deduzione, egli ne ricava che l'uso del sillogismo è obbligatorio in forza della *šarī'a*:

[9] Averroè, *Il trattato decisivo*, p. 47.
[10] *Ibidem*.

> Siccome si è stabilito che la Legge religiosa rende obbligatoria la speculazione e l'indagine razionale sugli esseri esistenti (*an-naẓar bi-l-'aql fī-l-mawǧudāt*), e poiché essa consiste nella deduzione e nella derivazione dell'ignoto dal già noto – e questo è ciò che si chiama sillogismo (*al-qiyās*), ovvero ciò che si ottiene per mezzo del sillogismo – è pure obbligatorio che ci rivolgiamo allo studio della realtà esistente per mezzo del ragionamento razionale (*bi-l-qiyās al-'aqlī*). È inoltre evidente che questo tipo di analisi cui la Legge religiosa chiama e incita è la specie più perfetta di studio collegata alla specie più perfetta di ragionamento, cioè a quella che si chiama 'dimostrazione apodittica' (*burhān*)[11].

Se dunque lo studio della filosofia – ovvero lo studio di Dio e degli esseri esistenti mediante la dimostrazione – è precisamente lo stesso tipo di studio ordinato dalla Legge religiosa, ne consegue che chi vuole conoscere Dio e tutti gli esseri dimostrativamente è tenuto ad acquisire la conoscenza della filosofia.

Ora, anche al-Ġazālī affronta il problema della conoscenza in termini di categorie legali islamiche. Una dettagliata classificazione delle scienze da questa prospettiva si trova nel primo libro del primo tomo dell'*Iḥyā' 'ulūm ad-dīn* (*Il ravvivamento delle scienze religiose*), ovvero il *Kitāb al-'ilm* (*Il libro della conoscenza*)[12]. Qui, dopo aver citato numerosi testi coranici e tradizioni che fanno della scienza un obbligo per il credente, al-Ġazālī si preoccupa di precisare anzitutto di quale scienza si tratti e in secondo luogo di quale obbligo: o personale (*farḍ 'ayn*) o comunitario (*farḍ kifāyā*)[13].

[11] *Ibid.*, pp. 47-49.

[12] Composta nel periodo in cui abbandonò l'insegnamento a Baghdad per dedicarsi alla pratica di un austero sufismo (488 h. / 1095 – 499 h. / 1106), l'*Iḥyā' 'ulūm ad-dīn* si compone di quattro tomi, ciascuno suddiviso in dieci libri: *Gli atti del culto* (*al-'ibādāt*); *I costumi* (*al-ādāt*); *Le cause di perdizione* (*al-muhlikāt*); *I mezzi di salvezza* (*al-munǧiyāt*). Nel primo al-Ġazālī illustra il comportamento che l'uomo deve avere nella sua devozione a Dio, nel secondo quello che deve adottare nella società, nel terzo presenta i vizi umani ed i modi per combatterli, nel quarto descrive le virtù da coltivare per avanzare verso Dio. Il *Kitāb al-'ilm* è il primo libro del primo tomo di questa imponente opera religiosa.

[13] La categoria giuridica dell'obbligo (*farḍ*) comprende ciò che ogni singolo fedele ha il dovere di compiere – e che si definisce appunto 'obbligo personale' (*farḍ 'ayn*) – e ciò che invece ricade sulla collettività nel suo insieme, ed è pertanto 'obbligo comunitario' (*farḍ kifāyā*).

Egli comincia con il domandarsi quale scienza vada designata come obbligo personale: «Le persone differiscono sulla questione di quale conoscenza sia obbligatoria per ogni musulmano adulto e in relazione a ciò esse si dividono in più di venti gruppi»[14]. Senza entrare nei dettagli, egli mostra come ogni gruppo tenti di far prevalere la materia di cui è esperto: i teologi il *kalām*[15], i giuristi il *fiqh*[16], gli esegeti il *tafsīr*[17], e via dicendo. In realtà, dice al-Ġazālī, la scienza che il Corano e le tradizioni classificano come obbligo personale è quella che si definisce 'scienza pratica' (*'ilm al-mu'āmala*)[18], ovvero la scienza che regola le relazioni con Dio e con il prossimo, e che consta di tre parti: ciò cui bisogna credere (*i'tiqād*); ciò che bisogna compiere (*fi'l*); ciò che bisogna evitare (*tark*).

Quanto alla categoria dell'obbligo comunitario, questa comprende due diversi tipi di scienze: quelle religiose (*al-'ulūm aš-šar'iyya*) e quelle non religiose (*ġayr šar'iyya*). Le scienze non reli-

[14] AL-ĠAZĀLĪ, *Iḥyā' 'ulūm ad-dīn*, ed. T. Badawī, 4 voll., Il Cairo 1957, I, p. 14.

[15] L'*'ilm al-kalām*, letteralmente 'scienza della Parola (di Dio)', è la teologia, che in arabo è così chiamata perché in origine si occupava dell'attributo divino della Parola, espressa nel Corano, e solo in seguito passò ad indicare una riflessione razionale sui contenuti della Rivelazione. Essa è anche definita *'ilm at-tawḥīd*, ovvero 'scienza dell'Unicità (di Dio)'.

[16] Il termine *fiqh* significa propriamente 'riflessione', 'indagine speculativa'. Esso viene utilizzato per designare il diritto islamico, ovvero la scienza della Legge religiosa, in quanto è proprio l'esercizio della ragione che permette al giurista di risolvere i problemi legali non direttamente regolamentati dal Corano e dalla Sunna.

[17] La scienza dell'esegesi o *tafsīr* fu una delle prime scienze fiorite attorno al Libro Sacro, al fine di stabilirne una corretta lettura, soprattutto nell'interpretazione di quei versetti coranici cosiddetti 'ambigui' (*mutaš...bih...t*).

[18] Come al-Ġazālī spiega chiaramente all'inizio del libro, le scienze ultraterrene si dividono in: *'ilm al-mu'āmala* o 'scienza del comportamento' o 'della relazione' tra Dio e l'uomo e '*ilm al-mukāšafa* o 'scienza dello svelamento'. La prima si divide a sua volta in: 'scienza esteriore' (*'ilm ẓāhir*), quella che riguarda appunto i comportamenti esteriori, e che comprende le pratiche cultuali (*al-'ibādāt*) e i costumi (*al-ādāt*), e 'scienza interiore' (*'ilm bāṭin*), che comprende la scienza dei vizi da estirpare (*al-muhlikāt*) e delle virtù da coltivare (*al-munǧiyāt*). Come si vede, queste quattro divisioni corrispondono ai quattro tomi dell'*Iḥyā'*. La 'scienza dello svelamento' è invece la scienza che ha propriamente per oggetto Dio, i Suoi attributi e le Sue opere, che al-Ġazālī definisce come «la luce che appare in un cuore dopo che si è purificato dalle qualità riprovevoli». In questo senso, l'*'ilm al-mu'āmala* costituisce lo stadio preparatorio al più alto grado dell''*ilm al-mukāšafa*, poiché è solo dopo essersi purificato che il cuore può riceverla. Cfr. AL-ĠAZĀLĪ, *ibid.*, I, pp. 2-5.

giose sono o raccomandabili (*mandūb*) o biasimevoli (*makrūh*) o semplicemente permesse (*mubāḥ*). Sono raccomandabili quelle scienze legate al beneficio del mondo presente, come la scienza della medicina e l'aritmetica; sono biasimevoli la magia, la scienza dei talismani, la prestidigitazione; sono semplicemente permesse, infine, la poesia e la storia. Le scienze religiose, invece, sono tutte raccomandabili. Esse sono di quattro tipi: la scienza dei principi fondamentali (*al-usūl*), che comprende il Corano, la Sunna, il consenso comunitario (*iǧmāʿ*) e le tradizioni dei Compagni (*āṯār aṣ-ṣaḥāba*); la scienza dei principi derivati (*al-furūʿ*), che è di due tipi: la scienza che conduce al bene nel mondo presente, ovvero il *fiqh*, e quella che conduce al bene nel mondo futuro, ovvero la conoscenza degli stati del cuore, delle sue virtù e dei suoi vizi; le scienze propedeutiche (*al-muqaddimāt*), che fungono da strumenti (*ālāt*), e non sono religiose se non per il loro utilizzo, come la scienza del linguaggio, della grammatica e della scrittura; infine le scienze complementari (*al-mutammimāt*), che hanno per oggetto il Corano e le tradizioni del Profeta e dei Compagni. La scienza del Corano si divide in: quella legata alle parole, ovvero la scienza delle letture (*ʿilm al-qirāʾāt*); quella che si occupa del senso, ovvero la scienza dell'esegesi (*ʿilm at-tafsīr*); e quella che studia il Libro Sacro in quanto fonte di qualificazioni legali, ovvero la scienza delle fonti del diritto (*usūl al-fiqh*). Quanto alle scienze legate alle tradizioni del Profeta e dei Compagni, esse si occupano di studiarne l'affidabilità.

Per ciò che concerne il *kalām*, al-Ġazālī lo definisce un obbligo comunitario soltanto nella misura in cui esso permette di salvaguardare e proteggere l'ortodossia dalle tendenze eretiche che la minacciano, come ribadisce anche nel *Fayṣal*[19].

[19] Secondo al-Ġazālī immergersi nel *kalām* è addirittura dannoso per certe persone, ovvero: per coloro che credono fermamente in Dio e nei Suoi Profeti, la cui fede verrebbe soltanto turbata se venissero a conoscenza delle tesi del *kalām*, e per quegli infedeli ed eretici che, cresciuti nell'errore e nella menzogna e attaccati ostinatamente alle loro idee, non potrebbero essere riportati sulla retta via che con la spada, dato che la discussione non farebbe che accrescere la loro ostinazione. Nel *Fayṣal* egli spiega che lo studio della teologia è adatto solo per due categorie di uomini: coloro ai quali sopravvengono dei dubbi che il *kalām* può servire a dissolvere e coloro che, avendo una solida fede ed una perfetta intelligenza, vogliono acquisire questa abilità per curare con essa ogni fedele cui sopravviene un'incertezza e ridurre al silenzio ogni innovatore che tenti di diffondere false dottrine. Cfr. AL-ĠAZĀLĪ, *Fayṣal at-tafriqa*, pp. 35-36.

Ma veniamo alla filosofia. Scrive al-Ġazālī in proposito:

> Quanto alla filosofia, essa non è una scienza unica, ma si compone di quattro parti. Una di queste è la geometria e l'aritmetica, scienze entrambe permesse (...). La seconda parte è la logica, che esamina il modo e le regole della dimostrazione e il modo e le regole della definizione, le quali rientrano entrambe nel campo del *kalām*. La terza è (la scienza delle) cose divine (*al-ilāhiyyāt*)[20], che si occupa dell'essenza e degli attributi di Dio, e che è anch'essa inclusa nel *kalām*. In queste materie i filosofi non hanno un unico tipo di conoscenza, ma essi hanno le loro dottrine proprie, alcune delle quali sono miscredenza (*kufr*), altre innovazione (*bid'a*)[21]. E come la dottrina della Mu'tazila[22] non è una scienza a parte, ma i suoi partigiani rientrano nel gruppo dei *mutakallimūn*, così anche i filosofi. La quarta è (la scienza delle) cose naturali (*aṭ-ṭabī'iyyāt*), parte della quale è contraria alla Legge religiosa e alla vera religione: essa non è allora che ignoranza e non merita di essere menzionata in una classificazione delle scienze. Un'altra parte studia le qualità e le proprietà dei corpi e il loro modo di cambiare e trasformarsi. Ciò somiglia alla diagnosi dei medici, salvo che essi considerano in particolare nel corpo dell'uomo ciò che concerne la malattia e la salute, mentre gli altri osservano tutti i corpi dal punto di vista del cambiamento e dell'azione. Ma la medicina è superiore, in

[20] Si tratta della metafisica, chiamata dai filosofi musulmani 'scienza delle cose divine' in seguito alla loro interpretazione del titolo della *Metafisica* aristotelica (*metà tà physikà*) come 'ciò che è aldilà della fisica', il mondo divino, appunto. Cfr. C. Baffioni, *Filosofia e religione in Islām*, Roma 1997, pp. 89-90.

[21] Una *bid'a* o 'innovazione' è una tesi nuova rispetto a quanto stabilito dai grandi maestri del passato sulla base del Corano e della Sunna. Essendo ogni creazione originale recepita come sostanziale minaccia allo spirito dell'Islām, saldamente ancorato al Libro sacro e all'esempio del Profeta, il concetto stesso di 'innovazione', nella cultura islamica, è quasi sinonimo di 'eresia'.

[22] La Mu'tazila è considerata la prima scuola vera e propria di *kalām* del mondo islamico. Essa infatti fu la prima ad elaborare un sistema teologico ben definito impiegando il ragionamento per la dimostrazione teorica dei propri principi. Il termine deriva probabilmente da *i'tizāl*, 'separazione', e viene solitamente spiegato con il fatto che il presunto fondatore della scuola, Wāṣil ibn 'Aṭā' (m. 130 h. / 748 circa), avrebbe assunto una posizione diversa da quella del suo maestro, al-Ḥasan al-Baṣrī (m. 102 h. / 720), sulla questione di come si debba giudicare chi commette un peccato grave. Mentre secondo quest'ultimo bisognava giudicarlo come un ipocrita (*munāfiq*), Wāṣil ibn 'Aṭā' lo poneva in una categoria intermedia tra il miscredente ed il credente (*manzila bayna-l-manzilatayn*), quella dell'empio (*fāsiq*).

> quanto c'è bisogno di essa. Quanto alle loro scienze naturali, noi non ne abbiamo bisogno[23].

Come si vede, al-Ġazālī non rigetta interamente la filosofia: la matematica e la logica non rappresentano alcun pericolo per la religione, e non c'è motivo di rigettarle[24]. Ma quel che è interessante sottolineare qui è che egli fa rientrare sia la logica che la metafisica nel campo della teologia. Per quanto riguarda la logica, come egli sottolinea anche nel *Munqiḏ min aḍ-ḍalāl* (*La salvezza dalla perdizione*)[25], essa non è monopolio della filosofia, giacché il metodo dimostrativo è usato anche dai teologi. Questo è molto importante evidenziarlo in quanto serve a sottolineare una grande differenza tra al-Ġazālī ed Ibn Rušd. Quest'ultimo, infatti, dopo aver definito la filosofia all'inizio del *Faṣl*, continua ad illustrarla, elaborarla e trarne esempi dal sillogismo, che rientra nell'ambito della logica. Per Ibn Rušd, la logica è infatti parte integrante della filosofia, ma al-Ġazālī non la considera affatto tale. Perciò, dal suo punto di vista, una difesa della logica non è una difesa della filosofia, dato che logica e filosofia sono due cose ben diverse. Quanto alla metafisica, è chiaro che il metodo e la natura stessa di tale scienza non possono farne una parte della teologia, ma ciò che intende dire al-Ġazālī è che questo tipo di questioni trattate dalla filosofia e dal *kalām* rientrano nello stesso ambito, ambito che dovrebbe essere di esclusiva pertinenza della teologia, dato che i filosofi sono giunti con le loro teorie a interpretazioni radicalmente diverse da quelle dei teologi e in contrasto con le verità rivelate, come nel caso delle tre questioni sopra citate, che egli accusa di miscredenza.

Il parere di Ibn Rušd su questa questione è ovviamente antitetico a quello di al-Ġazālī. Nel *Faṣl* egli intende dimostrare non solo che sono proprio i filosofi gli unici ad avere il diritto di occuparsi di tali questioni, ma anche che le conclusioni cui essi

[23] AL-ĠAZĀLĪ, *Iḥyā' 'ulūm ad-dīn*, ed. Badawī cit. (alla nota 14), I, p. 23.

[24] Nel *Munqiḏ min aḍ-ḍalāl* al-Ġazālī divide la filosofia in sei branche, anziché quattro: matematica, logica, fisica, metafisica, politica ed etica. Oltre alla matematica e alla logica, egli spiega qui che anche la politica e l'etica sono in una certa misura innocue dal punto di vista religioso. Cfr. AL-ĠAZĀLĪ, *La salvezza della predizione*, in ID., *Scritti scelti*, a c. di L. Veccia Vaglieri – R. Rubinacci, Torino 1970, pp. 97-102.

[25] Cfr. *ibid.*, pp. 94-95.

giungono mediante la speculazione dimostrativa non possono essere diverse da quelle rivelate dalla Legge religiosa, «poiché il Vero non può contrastare col Vero, ma anzi gli si armonizza e gli porta testimonianza»[26]. È per provare questa asserzione che Ibn Rušd affronta la questione del *ta'wīl* o interpretazione allegorica dei testi scritturali. Egli ritiene infatti che quando una conclusione cui si perviene attraverso la dimostrazione si presenta in contrasto con il senso apparente delle Scritture, è necessario che questo senso apparente vada interpretato allegoricamente:

> Se la speculazione dimostrativa conduce alla conoscenza di qualche essere reale, non si sfugge al presupposto che tale essere reale o è menzionato o è sottaciuto dalle Scritture. Se è sottaciuto, non si presenta alcuna contraddizione (tra Legge religiosa e filosofia) (...). Se invece i testi religiosi ne parlano, delle due l'una: o il senso apparente della conclusione filosofica si accorda o contrasta con quei testi. Se si accorda, nessun problema. Ma se contrasta, si presenta la necessità di un'interpretazione allegorica delle Scritture[27].

Egli anzi arriva a dire:

> Di tutte le espressioni delle Scritture, il cui senso letterale contrasta con le conclusioni dimostrative, se si ha la pazienza di esaminare il Testo Sacro e di indagarlo attentamente in tutte le sue parti, si troveranno altre affermazioni parallele che porteranno testimonianza, proprio col loro senso letterale, alla (correttezza) dell'interpretazione allegorica, o almeno ci si avvicineranno moltissimo[28].

In conclusione, secondo Ibn Rušd, ogni contraddizione tra la parola rivelata e il risultato dell'indagine razionale non è che apparente e può essere ricomposta. Così, se un versetto coranico preso in senso letterale (*ẓāhir*) contraddice una conclusione filosofica, bisogna attribuirgli un senso allegorico (*bāṭin*) per renderlo conforme ad essa, e si troverà la conferma di questa interpretazione in un altro versetto.

[26] AVERROÈ, *Il trattato decisivo*, p. 61.

[27] *Ibidem*.

[28] *Ibid.*, p. 63.

Ora, anche al-Ġazālī condivide la necessità dell'interpretazione allegorica dei testi rivelati, e anzi afferma che essa è un dovere di tutte le scuole, soprattutto se non si vuole correre il rischio di cadere in un ingenuo antromorfismo, ad esempio interpretando alla lettera quei versetti coranici e tradizioni che attribuiscono a Dio organi corporei. È per questo «che ogni setta, per quanto si sforzi di attenersi al senso letterale, è costretta ad usare l'interpretazione allegorica, a meno che non voglia oltrepassare i limiti della stupidità e dell'ignoranza»[29]. Tuttavia, secondo al-Ġazālī, è possibile interpretare allegoricamente un testo solo quando sussiste la prova evidente (*burhān*) dell'impossibilità di accettare il suo senso letterale. Ed è proprio sulla prova evidente che i due autori sono in disaccordo. Vediamo in che senso.

Entrambi dividono i testi delle Scritture in tre categorie simili, ovvero: testi il cui significato apparente è comprensibile a tutti e che pertanto non vanno interpretati allegoricamente; testi che all'opposto necessitano di un'interpretazione allegorica; testi infine che, per la loro ambiguità, possono essere classificati come intermedi rispetto alle due precedenti categorie, nel senso che gli studiosi sono in disaccordo sulla necessità o meno della loro interpretazione[30]. Entrambi sono inoltre d'accordo sul fatto che interpretare allegoricamente i testi appartenenti alla prima categoria è una colpa, la gravità della quale dipende dalla natura del testo rivelato: se esso concerne uno dei fondamenti dell'Islām, si tratta di miscredenza (*kufr*); se invece concerne uno dei principi derivati, si tratta di innovazione (*bid'a*)[31]. Essi però non sono d'accordo sulla classificazione dei testi all'interno di queste categorie. al-Ġazālī infatti, a differenza di Ibn Rušd, colloca quei testi scritturali che riguardano la resurrezione corporale, la conoscenza da parte di Dio dei particolari e la creazione del mondo tra quelli non allegorizzabili. In relazione alle prime due questioni, egli scrive nel *Fayṣal*:

[29] AL-ĠAZĀLĪ, *Fayṣal at-tafriqa*, p. 18.

[30] Cfr. AVERROÈ, *Il trattato decisivo*, pp. 85-87; AL-ĠAZĀLĪ, *al-Mustaṣfā min 'ilm al-uṣūl*, 2 voll., Il Cairo 1904, I, pp. 336-337 e 384-386. Il *Mustaṣfā min 'ilm al-uṣūl* (*La chiarificazione della scienza delle fonti*) è un altro importante testo giuridico composto da al-Ġazālī nel 503 h. / 1109. Cfr. M. BOUYGES, *Essai de cronologie* cit. (alla nota 3), pp. 73-75.

[31] Cfr. AVERROÈ, *Il trattato decisivo*, p. 85; AL-ĠAZĀLĪ, *Fayṣal at-tafriqa*, p. 26.

Quando questo genere d'interpretazione si riferisce ad importanti e basilari principi della fede l'accusa di miscredenza spetta a chi altera il senso letterale senza una prova decisiva (*burhān qāṭiʿ*). È questo il caso di chi nega la resurrezione dei corpi umani ed i castighi sensibili nell'aldilà basandosi su supposizioni, fantasticherie e considerazioni inverosimili senza una prova decisiva. Accusarlo di miscredenza è categoricamente necessario, dato che non c'è una prova evidente dell'impossibilità di reintegrare gli spiriti nei loro corpi[32]. Affermare una cosa del genere comporta un grave danno per la religione, perciò bisogna accusare di miscredenza tutti coloro che appoggiano questa teoria, che è la dottrina della maggior parte dei filosofi. Allo stesso modo, l'accusa di miscredenza spetta a chi tra essi afferma che Dio Altissimo conosce solo Se stesso o che conosce solo gli universali, ignorando gli aspetti particolari relativi agli individui, perché queste affermazioni equivalgono a smentire nettamente il Profeta – su di lui il saluto e la benedizione di Dio – e non rientrano in nessuna classe dei gradi d'interpretazione allegorica che abbiamo menzionato[33], dato che le testimonianze del Corano e della

[32] Molti filosofi sostenevano che la resurrezione non potesse implicare il ricongiungimento dell'anima con il suo proprio corpo, giacché dopo la morte questo era divenuto polvere, e negavano anche che essa potesse entrare in un nuovo corpo, creato da Dio dal nulla, perché ritenevano inaccettabile l'idea che l'anima potesse tornare ad un corpo materiale. La materia, infatti, pertiene solo al mondo sublunare, ed è finita, mentre le anime sono infinite. Secondo al-Ġazālī, invece, l'onnipotenza di Dio consente di creare sia dal nulla sia dalla polvere nuovi corpi e di farli ricongiungere con l'anima.

[33] Secondo al-Ġazālī ci sono cinque gradi di esistenza, cui corrispondono cinque gradi di interpretazione testuale: l'esistenza essenziale (*al-wuǧūd aḏ-ḏātī*) è quella reale e certa che esiste concretamente al di fuori dei sensi e dell'intelletto; l'esistenza sensibile (*al-wuǧūd al-ḥissī*) è quella che viene percepita dai sensi ma che non ha esistenza al di fuori di essi; l'esistenza immaginativa (*al-wuǧūd al-ḫayyālī*) è la rappresentazione degli oggetti sensibili quando essi non sono più presenti ai sensi; l'esistenza mentale (*al-wuǧūd al-ʿaqlī*) è quella di un'entità da cui l'intelletto umano riesce a ricavare il significato astratto senza che la sua immagine sussista nella sua mente; l'esistenza analogica (*al-wuǧūd aš-šabahī*), infine, è quella di qualcosa che non esiste né nei sensi, né nell'intelletto, né nell'immaginazione, ma che ha delle caratteristiche simili ad un'entità realmente esistente. Secondo al-Ġazālī, chi riconosce come vera l'esistenza di ciò che ha riferito Muḥammad, in uno qualsiasi di questi cinque gradi, non può essere accusato di smentire il Profeta, giacché tale accusa spetta soltanto a chi li nega tutti e cinque, pretendendo che le parole dell'Inviato di Dio siano delle pure menzogne. Cfr. AL-ĠAZĀLĪ, *Fayṣal at-tafriqa*, pp. 8-15. Per un'approfondita analisi della teoria della corrispondenza tra gradi d'esistenza e gradi d'interpretazione testuale, si riman-

> Tradizione che rendono nota la resurrezione dei corpi e chiariscono che Dio Altissimo conosce precisamente tutto ciò che accade agli individui oltrepassano un limite che non ammette interpretazione allegorica[34].

Quanto alla creazione del mondo, al-Ġazālī non ne fa menzione nel *Fayṣal*, ma aveva trattato la questione nel *Tahāfut*, dove si era occupato di confutare filosoficamente i principali argomenti addotti dai filosofi a sostegno dell'eternità del mondo. Ora, non intendo soffermarmi qui sulla confutazione da parte di al-Ġazālī di questa come delle due precedenti dottrine, né sulla difesa che, sempre dal punto di vista filosofico, ne fa Ibn Rušd, perché il mio scopo è quello di trattare questo tema dal punto di vista strettamente legale. Quel che importa sottolineare, in questa prospettiva, è il fatto che, anche nel caso di quest'ultima questione – l'eternità del mondo, appunto – il *takfīr* si giustifica perché tale dottrina smentisce la Rivelazione laddove essa afferma la creazione dal nulla, negando così uno dei principi fondamentali dell'Islām: quello di un Dio Uno, Creatore e Legislatore e, perciò stesso, finendo per condurre ad una teologia dualista.

In pratica, quel che al-Ġazālī contesta alle suddette dottrine, è il fatto che esse si basino su un'interpretazione dei testi scritturali e non sul loro senso apparente. Ma tali testi non sono a suo avviso suscettibili della suddetta interpretazione, perché questa implica la negazione di alcuni attributi divini fondamentali, ovvero volontà, onnipotenza ed onniscienza, i quali sono palesemente e inequivocabilmente asseriti nel Corano. Negarli, significa pertanto contraddire l'autorità del Corano, cosa che implica l'imputazione di menzogna (*takḏīb*) al Profeta, e dunque la miscredenza, dal momento che «la miscredenza (*al-kufr*) è l'atto di giudicare menzognero (*takḏīb*) il Profeta – su di lui il saluto e la benedizione di Dio – in una delle cose che egli ha detto, mentre la fede (*al-īmān*) è l'atto di giudicarlo veritiero (*taṣdīq*) in tutto ciò che ha detto»[35].

Quanto a Ibn Rušd, egli tenta nel *Faṣl* di difendere queste dottrine e conciliarle con la Rivelazione. Egli affronta per prima

da a I. PETA, *Il concetto di miscredenza (kufr) tra rigore e tolleranza nell'analisi di Abū Ḥāmid al-Ġazālī*, in «Schede medievali», 44 (2006), pp. 113-126.

[34] AL-ĠAZĀLĪ, *Fayṣal at-tafriqa*, pp. 23-24.

[35] *Ibid.*, p. 7.

la questione della conoscenza di Dio dei particolari, sostenendo che al-Ġazālī abbia male interpretato la dottrina dei filosofi, giacché essi non hanno affatto sostenuto che Dio non conosce i particolari, ma semplicemente che Egli conosce in modo diverso da quello degli uomini, poiché «la scienza umana è un effetto dell'oggetto conosciuto e si produce quando (l'oggetto conosciuto) viene in esistenza, mentre cambia quando (l'oggetto conosciuto) si modifica; al contrario, la scienza che Dio ha degli esseri esistenti è la causa di questi stessi oggetti conosciuti che esistono»[36]. Ciò significa che i filosofi non hanno in questa questione contraddetto quanto affermato nel Corano e che pertanto l'accusa di miscredenza è in questo caso infondata.

Per quanto riguarda la questione del mondo, se esso è eterno o creato, Ibn Rušd considera la divergenza di opinione tra i teologi aš'ariti[37] ed i filosofi come apparente. Entrambi sono d'accordo – egli dichiara – sul fatto che il mondo appartiene a quella categoria di esseri – intermedia tra la l'essere creato e l'essere eterno[38] – che non sono preceduti da nulla né hanno come antecedente il tempo, ma che devono la loro esistenza a un agente: Dio. L'unica controversia qui riguarda la sua esistenza passata e il suo tempo passato, che i teologi ritengono finiti, mentre gli aristotelici li considerano infiniti. Nell'opinione di Ibn Rušd ciò che spiega questa polemica è la somiglianza che il mondo ha sia con l'essere generato sia con l'essere eterno:

36 AVERROÈ, *Il trattato decisivo*, p. 71.

37 La scuola teologica aš'arita, cui si richiamava al-Ġazālī, fu fondata da Abū-l-Ḥasan al-Aš'arī. Nato a Bassora nel 260 h. / 874, egli fu per molti anni allievo del mu'tazilita al-Ǧubbā'ī, ma finì col rompere con il maestro. Trasferitosi a Baghdad, egli si dedicò alla composizione di numerosi scritti, tra cui la sua opera maggiore, il *Kitāb al-ibāna* (*Il libro della dimostrazione*), in cui espone gli argomenti del suo credo cercando di armonizzare le tesi dei partigiani della speculazione con le posizioni dei tradizionisti, i quali all'indagine razionale opponevano un netto rifiuto. Morì a Baghdad nel 323 h. / 935, ma la sua opera gli sopravvisse e la scuola aš'arita, iniziatasi a formare già durante la vita del maestro, divenne ben presto la scuola teologica prevalente nell'Islam ortodosso.

38 Secondo Ibn Rušd l''essere creato' (*ḥādiṯ*) è quell'essere che deve la sua esistenza a un altro essere e a qualcosa di preesistente, cioè a una causa agente e ad una materia prima, e la cui esistenza è preceduta dal tempo. Rientrano pertanto in questa categoria i corpi la cui generazione è percepita per mezzo dei sensi, cioè l'acqua, l'aria, la terra, gli animali, le piante e simili. L''essere eterno' (*qadīm*) è invece quell'essere che non è prodotto da nulla e non è preceduto da qualcos'altro e che non ha come antecedente il tempo. Quest'essere è ovviamente Dio. Cfr. AVERROÈ, *Il trattato decisivo*, pp. 73-75.

> Dunque, il mondo sembra godere di una duplice rassomiglianza: con i singoli esistenti e con l'Eterno. Per cui, chi insiste sulla rassomiglianza del mondo con Dio piuttosto che con i contingenti, lo definisce 'eterno' (*qadīm*); mentre chi preferisce insistere sulla somiglianza coi contingenti, lo definisce 'prodotto' (*muḥdaṯ*). Ma in realtà il mondo non è propriamente né creato né eterno, poiché il creato è di necessità corruttibile, mentre l'eterno non ha alcuna causa che lo determini[39].

Perciò, secondo Ibn Rušd, le opinioni sul mondo non sono poi così divergenti l'una dall'altra da essere tacciate di miscredenza, né nell'uno né nell'altro caso. Ma quel che è soprattutto interessante sottolineare, nella prospettiva del presente articolo, è che, a suo avviso, l'opinione dei filosofi aristotelici è molto più in linea con il senso apparente delle Scritture rispetto a quella dei teologi. Per supportare questa affermazione, egli cita alcuni versetti del Corano:

> È Lui che ha creato i cieli e la terra in sei giorni, mentre il suo Trono si librava sull'acque (*Cor* 11, 7).
>
> Il giorno in cui la terra sarà cambiata in un'altra terra, e in altri cieli i cieli (*Cor* 14, 48).
>
> Poi s'accinse alla costruzione del cielo, che era tutto fumo (*Cor* 41, 11).

Ibn Rušd sostiene che il primo versetto, se preso alla lettera, indica che «una (certa forma di) essere, cioè il Trono e le acque, esisteva prima di questo essere e che esisteva un tempo prima di questo tempo, un tempo connesso alla tipologia dell'esistenza, e cioè il numero dei movimenti della sfera celeste»[40]; allo stesso modo, il secondo versetto, se inteso letteralmente, «indica che esisterà un altro essere dopo questo essere»[41], cioè dopo questo mondo; ancora, l'ultimo versetto, sempre se preso alla lettera, «indica che i cieli sono stati creati da qualcosa di preesistente»[42], ovvero il fumo.

[39] *Ibid.*, p. 75.
[40] *Ibid.*, p. 77.
[41] *Ibidem.*
[42] *Ibidem.*

Quel che intende dimostrare Ibn Rušd è che nemmeno i teologi, quando trattano del mondo, si mantengono fedeli alla lettera della Legge religiosa, ma anzi la interpretano allegoricamente, dato che dai passi delle Scritture analizzati non si ricava affatto la conclusione che Dio esisteva nell'assoluta privazione di ogni altro tipo di essere, ma anzi tali testi, se presi alla lettera, suggeriscono il contrario. Perciò egli si domanda:

> Come allora è concepibile che le allegorie dei teologi riscuotano un consenso universale, quando il significato letterale delle Scritture sull'esistenza del mondo è più rispettato dalle scuole dei filosofi?[43]

In realtà, come sottolinea Bello[44], i testi coranici riportati da Ibn Rušd vengono citati fuori dal loro contesto, e soprattutto egli non fa riferimento ai numerosi versetti del Libro sacro che affermano chiaramente che Dio è il Creatore (*ḫāliq*) di tutte le cose. E va sottolineato, in proposito, che in arabo la radice *ḫlq*, da cui deriva l'aggettivo *ḫāliq* (creatore), implica una precedenza temporale del creatore su ciò che crea, dunque, in questo caso, la precedenza di Dio sul mondo.

Quanto al tema della vita futura, nel *Faṣl* Ibn Rušd si limita a dire che si tratta di una questione controversa, giacché vi sono alcuni studiosi, come gli aš'ariti, secondo i quali i testi rivelati riguardanti tale materia vanno intesi alla lettera, perché non esiste alcuna prova evidente che induca a doverne rifiutare il senso apparente, e altri che invece ritengono indispensabile avanzarne un'interpretazione allegorica. Pertanto, egli ritiene che non possa essere accusato di miscredenza chi allegorizza i versetti in questione, giacché va incolpato di miscredenza solo chi nega l'esistenza reale nell'aldilà, e non certo chi interpreta allegoricamente il modo di esistere nella vita futura. In ogni caso, secondo Ibn Rušd, «coloro i quali nutrono opinioni differenti su questioni tanto astruse saranno premiati da Dio se hanno avuto ragione, ma ne saranno perdonati se avranno avuto torto», a patto però che a formularle siano coloro che ne hanno facoltà, perché invece «gli

[43] *Ibid.*, p. 78.

[44] Cfr. BELLO, *The medieval islamic controversy* cit. (alla nota 8), p. 149.

errori nella scienza che non sono commessi da questo genere di persone costituiscono una grave colpa»[45].

E qui bisogna sottolineare un'altra grande differenza tra al-Ġazālī ed Ibn Rušd, riguardante appunto chi abbia diritto di interpretare i testi rivelati. Secondo quest'ultimo ogni musulmano è obbligato a portare assenso (*taṣdīq*) alle verità rivelate, ma gli uomini «si diversificano qualitativamente riguardo a questo assenso, essendovi chi lo presta alla dimostrazione razionale (*bi-l-burhān*), chi alle dispute dialettiche (*bi-l-aqāwīl al-ǧadaliyya*) (...), e chi lo presta ai discorsi retorici (*bi-l-aqāwīl al-ḫaṭābiyya*)»[46]. Si tratta rispettivamente dei filosofi, dei teologi e delle masse. Ora, secondo Ibn Rušd, il dovere delle masse è quello di attenersi ai significati letterali delle Scritture, senza interpretarle allegoricamente; il dovere dei teologi è quello di applicare l'interpretazione dialettica a quei testi «in cui l'allegoria dia nel complesso indicazioni più complete e persuasive del senso letterale»[47]; il dovere dei filosofi, infine, è quello di applicare l'interpretazione dimostrativa a quei testi scritturali che necessitano di tale dimostrazione. L'interpretazione avanzata da quest'ultimo gruppo non deve però essere comunicata né alle genti della dialettica né a quelle della retorica, perché costoro non sarebbero in grado di comprenderla:

> Se si fa partecipe di queste interpretazioni allegoriche qualcuno che non è in grado di comprenderle, soprattutto se si tratta di conclusioni dimostrative remote dal senso comune, si induce alla miscredenza tanto l'interprete quanto chi riceve l'interpretazione. La causa di ciò sta nel fatto che il fine (dell'interprete) è il rifiuto del senso letterale e l'imposizione dell'allegoria: per cui, se si distrugge il senso letterale nella mente di chi è capace di comprendere solo quello, senza che egli sia contemporaneamente in grado di accogliere l'allegoria, si induce costui alla miscredenza soprattutto se si dibattono i principi della religione[48].

Ora, anche al-Ġazālī fa una differenziazione tra gli uomini in relazione alla loro comprensione delle Scritture. Egli però nel

[45] AVERROÈ, *Il trattato decisivo*, p. 79.
[46] *Ibid.*, p. 59.
[47] *Ibid.*, p. 99.
[48] *Ibid.*, p. 101.

Fayṣal li classifica in due categorie, contro le tre di Ibn Rušd: la prima è quella delle masse (*'awām al-ḫalq*), che hanno il dovere di «seguire i significati letterali astenendosi completamente dal cambiarli, guardarsi dall'inventare che un'interpretazione non autorizzata dai Compagni sia lecita, chiudere prontamente la porta ai quesiti, trattenersi dall'addentrarsi in discussioni e ricerche, e seguire anche ciò che è ambiguo nel Libro e nella Sunna»[49]; la seconda è quella degli uomini della speculazione (*an-nuẓẓār*), ovvero i teologi, ai quali «conviene sviluppare la loro ricerca nella misura imposta dalla necessità e tralasciare il senso letterale nella misura imposta dalla prova decisiva»[50].

Come si vede, queste due categorie corrispondono precisamente alle prime due citate da Ibn Rušd. Ad esse, però, quest'ultimo aggiunge le genti della dimostrazione (*ahl al-burhān*), ovvero i filosofi. Il fatto che questi ultimi non vengano citati da al-Ġazālī mostra chiaramente che per lui essi non hanno il diritto di interpretare le Scritture, compito che spetta esclusivamente ai teologi e ai giuristi. Per Ibn Rušd, invece, i filosofi sono i veri sapienti (*'ārifūn*), gli unici in grado di cogliere la verità nella sua pienezza, giacché essi vi pervengono tramite la dimostrazione, e la dimostrazione «non può non accompagnarsi all'interpretazione allegorica»[51], dato che è quest'ultima che permette di cogliere il vero significato dei testi rivelati. Anche al-Ġazālī, comunque, condivide con Ibn Rušd la necessità di non diffondere le interpretazioni allegoriche presso il popolo, poiché non sarebbe in grado di comprenderle. Eppure Ibn Rušd lo accusa di miscredenza, incolpandolo di aver rivelato le interpretazioni allegoriche alle masse, inserendole in testi legali, retorici e dialettici. A suo avviso, infatti, «è necessario che solo i libri scritti in stile dimostrativo contengano interpretazioni allegoriche, poiché tali libri sono letti solo da coloro che sono esperti nella dimostrazione»[52], e dunque non c'è il rischio che cadano in mani sbagliate.

In tal modo, Ibn Rušd ritorce contro al-Ġazālī l'accusa di miscredenza che questi aveva lanciato contro i filosofi. Egli infatti,

[49] AL-ĠAZĀLĪ, *Fayṣal at-tafriqa*, p. 20.

[50] *Ibidem*.

[51] AVERROÈ, *Il trattato decisivo*, p. 69.

[52] *Ibid.*, p. 89.

riferendosi a quest'ultimo, e in generale a coloro che propalano le interpretazioni allegoriche presso la gente impreparata a riceverle, aggiunge:

> Noi abbiamo verificato che costoro si illudono di essere tali e quali ai filosofi e che, con la loro singolare sapienza, pervengono a conclusioni affatto discordanti con la Legge religiosa in tutte le questioni, in specie quelle che non ammettono interpretazione allegorica. Costoro (sostengono) che sia necessario propalare tali conclusioni presso le masse. Convinti di ciò, divengono propagatori presso il volgo di credenze che inducono al pervertimento e sono causa di perdizione per le masse e per se stessi, in questo mondo e nell'altro[53].

In questo passo, non solo Ibn Rušd sottolinea la superiore capacità interpretativa dei filosofi, sostenendo implicitamente che solo questi ultimi sono in grado di cogliere la vera interpretazione delle Scritture, ma contesta la rivendicazione di al-Ġazālī e di altri come lui di giungere, con le loro pretese interpretazioni letterali, a conclusioni non discordi dalla Legge religiosa e che, invece, a suo avviso, si presentano come apertamente in conflitto con le Scritture. Egli si riferisce presumibilmente qui alle stesse tre questioni su cui al-Ġazālī accusa di miscredenza i filosofi, ovvero la resurrezione corporale, la conoscenza di Dio dei particolari e l'eternità del mondo, e in special modo a quest'ultima, verso la quale, come è stato detto, egli ritiene siano molto più aderenti alla lettera del Corano i filosofi che i teologi.

Il fatto che, secondo Ibn Rušd, i filosofi siano gli unici in grado di cogliere il vero significato delle Scritture, ha delle ripercussioni interessanti anche sulla sua concezione dell'*iǧmā'*, il consenso comunitario, il quale costituisce, dopo il Corano e la Sunna, la terza fonte del diritto musulmano, seguita dal *qiyās* o procedimento analogico-deduttivo[54]. Com'è noto, l'*iǧmā'* si definisce co-

[53] *Ibid.*, p. 103.

[54] Le quattro fonti del diritto islamico sono, in quest'ordine: il Corano, la Sunna, il *qiyās* o 'procedimento analogico-deduttivo', che consiste nell'utilizzare il ragionamento al fine di applicare su un piano differente, o per un nuovo caso, una norma già sanzionata, e infine l'*iǧmā'* o 'consenso' della comunità musulmana, ovvero il parere concorde della comunità dei credenti, o meglio dei dotti della comunità dei credenti, su una determinata questione religiosa. Esso è considerato infallibile sulla base di alcuni detti del Profeta, in particolare quello se-

me il consenso della comunità musulmana – e in particolare dei dotti della comunità musulmana, i *muǧtahidūn*[55]– su una determinata questione religiosa.

Ora, sia al-Ġazālī che Ibn Rušd si chiedono, nei loro rispettivi trattati, se qualcuno la cui opinione su un certo argomento contraddice un *iǧmāʿ* possa o meno essere accusato di miscredenza. Entrambi mostrano una grande tolleranza rispetto a questa questione. Al-Ġazālī, ad esempio, sottolinea nel *Fayṣal* che, pur essendo in teoria possibile incolpare di miscredenza chi contraddice un *iǧmāʿ*, in pratica è molto difficile verificare che un *iǧmāʿ* sia realmente tale, verificare cioè che tutte le condizioni giuridiche per la sua validità siano state adempiute[56], così come è molto difficile venire a sapere su quali questioni sia pervenuto il consenso comunitario. Perciò, conclude al-Ġazālī, chi formula un'interpretazione

condo cui «Dio non permetterà mai alla Sua comunità di trovarsi d'accordo su un errore».

[55] Il termine deriva dalla parola *iǧtihād*, letteralmente 'sforzo', 'applicazione', usata per designare l'impegno di elaborazione dottrinale che si opera a partire dalle fonti scritturali. I *muǧtahidūn* sono pertanto i dotti preposti ad accedere a tali fonti al fine di esprimere un parere qualificato che, se concorde con quello di altri *muǧtahidūn*, darà luogo all'*iǧmāʿ*.

[56] L'*iǧmāʿ* presuppone l'adempimento di una serie di condizioni, affinché possa essere considerato valido. Così le sintetizza AL-ĠAZĀLĪ, *Fayṣal at-tafriqa*, pp. 30-31: «Per quanto riguarda ciò che si basa sul consenso comunitario, stabilirlo è uno dei problemi più astrusi, dato che il consenso presuppone che coloro che sono investiti d'autorità si riuniscano in uno stesso luogo, si accordino su una stessa questione avvalendosi di parole chiare, poi si mantengano fermi su di essa per un certo tempo secondo alcuni e fino alla fine dei tempi secondo altri. O ancora esso presuppone che un *imām* li consulti per iscritto nelle varie zone della terra e riceva le loro sentenze contemporaneamente, in modo che esse coincidano chiaramente, così da essere impossibile in seguito ritrattarle o contestarle. Bisogna poi considerare se chi in seguito ha contraddetto il consenso comunitario possa essere incolpato di miscredenza, perché c'è chi dice che se è stato possibile essere in disaccordo nel tempo in cui fu formulato, allora dev'essere lecito accordarsi contro di esso, e non si può pertanto impedire ad uno di loro di ritornare in seguito sui propri passi. Ed anche questo punto è oscuro. In terzo luogo bisogna capire se secondo il sostenitore di tale opinione il fatto si basa su una trasmissione ininterrotta o se ad esso è pervenuto il consenso comunitario, dato che quando uno viene al mondo non sa quali sono le cose basate su una trasmissione ininterrotta e non distingue quelle soggette al consenso da quelle soggette al disaccordo, ma ne diventa consapevole a poco a poco e le impara a conoscere grazie alla lettura dei libri che trattano del disaccordo e del consenso degli antenati». Va sottolineato, in ogni caso, che per al-Ġazālī quando l'*iǧmāʿ* è certo, essendo considerato infallibile, non può assolutamente essere contraddetto e chi lo fa, se ne è a conoscenza, va accusato di miscredenza.

di una questione su cui è stato stabilito un *iǧmāʻ*, se non ne è a conoscenza, o se crede che esso non sia stato accertato, anche se ha torto, non può essere considerato uno che accusa di menzogna il Profeta e non è pertanto possibile tacciarlo di miscredenza[57].

Allo stesso modo Ibn Rušd, domandandosi se sia lecito che la dimostrazione porti a interpretare allegoricamente ciò che il consenso comunitario ha stabilito doversi mantenere secondo il senso letterale, o viceversa a dare un'interpretazione letterale di ciò che il consenso comunitario ha stabilito di sottoporre ad allegoria, scrive: «ciò non è giusto se il consenso comunitario è ottenuto con metodi certi; ma se è ottenuto grazie all'opinione soggettiva, allora è giusto»[58]. A differenza di al-Ġazālī, però, egli divide l'*iǧmāʻ* in due categorie: *iǧmāʻ* concernente le questioni teoretiche (*an-naẓariyyāt*) ed *iǧmāʻ* concernente le questioni pratiche (*al-ʻamaliyyāt*). Egli ritiene che l'*iǧmāʻ* del primo tipo non possa mai essere certo. Esso sarebbe tale, spiega Ibn Rušd, solo se adempisse alle seguenti condizioni, ovvero: se la totalità dei sapienti vissuti all'epoca in cui tale *iǧmāʻ* fu formulato ci fosse ben nota; se ci fosse pervenuta, grazie ad una rigorosa catena di trasmissione, l'opinione di ciascuno di essi; se infine i sapienti di quell'epoca fossero d'accordo sul fatto che non esiste nella Legge religiosa un senso esoterico che bisogna mantenere celato ai più. Ma questo non è possibile, dice il filosofo:

> È stato tramandato che molti dei primi musulmani erano convinti che la Legge possiede un senso apparente ed uno nascosto e che il senso esoterico non dev'essere conosciuto da chi non è dotato di scienza e non è in grado di comprenderlo (...). Com'è possibile allora immaginare che un consenso generalizzato sia pervenuto fino a noi riguardo a uno qualsiasi dei massimi problemi speculativi?[59]

Per quanto riguarda le questioni pratiche, invece, Ibn Rušd ritiene che, essendo tutti d'accordo sulla necessità di una loro ampia diffusione presso tutti gli uomini, è sufficiente, per pervenire ad un consenso su di esse, che un problema sia sviscerato da ogni

[57] Cfr. *ibid.*, pp. 78-79.

[58] AVERROÈ, *Il trattato decisivo*, p. 65.

[59] *Ibid.*, p. 67.

punto di vista e che non venga tramandata al riguardo alcuna particolare differenza di opinione tra i sapienti.

Detto questo, Ibn Rušd dichiara che, dal momento che «non si deve accusare di miscredenza chi infrange il consenso comunitario con l'interpretazione allegorica, poiché, in casi del genere, non può esistere un assenso generalizzato»[60], l'accusa di miscredenza rivolta da al-Ġazālī ai filosofi in relazione, ancora una volta, alle tre citate questioni dell'eternità del mondo, la non conoscenza dei particolari da parte di Dio e l'interpretazione allegorica della resurrezione dei corpi, non ha validità. Egli cioè fa qui intendere che al-Ġazālī abbia tacciato di miscredenza le suddette questioni perché queste costituirebbero una violazione dell'*iǧmā'* formulato su di esse. Infatti poco dopo scrive: «Sembra comunque che l'accusa di miscredenza (di al-Ġazālī) non debba essere intesa in modo assoluto, poiché nel *Libro della distinzione* (*Kitāb at-tafriqa*)[61] egli stesso spiega come la taccia di miscredenza per la violazione del consenso comunitario sia solo ipotizzabile»[62]. In realtà, come ho già evidenziato, il motivo per cui al-Ġazālī accusa di miscredenza tali questioni non è per la loro violazione del consenso comunitario, ma per la loro contraddizione del senso apparente dei testi scritturali che le concernono e che, secondo lui, non sono suscettibili di interpretazione allegorica.

In ogni caso, Ibn Rušd continua la sua argomentazione affermando che è inconcepibile che un valido *iǧmā'* possa essere formulato su questioni teoretiche di questo tipo quando gli unici ad essere esperti di questo genere di questioni sono i filosofi. Così, ancora una volta, egli ribadisce la «superiore capacità di assentire»[63] propria di questi ultimi, la cui fede è fondata sulla dimostrazione e, proprio in quanto fondata sulla dimostrazione, non può non accompagnarsi all'interpretazione allegorica. Perciò il filosofo conclude:

> Stando così le cose, non è verosimile che, relativamente alle interpretazioni allegoriche che Dio ha riservato come peculiari ai sapienti, si ottenga un consenso davvero generalizzato[64].

[60] *Ibidem.*

[61] Si tratta appunto del *Fayṣal at-tafriqa.*

[62] AVERROÈ, *Il trattato decisivo*, p. 69.

[63] *Ibidem.*

[64] *Ibid.*, p. 71.

Da quanto detto, appare evidente che per Ibn Rušd la ragione dimostrativa è l'unica in grado di riprodurre la struttura effettiva della realtà, avendo per oggetto gli enti nella loro essenza. In quanto tale, essa è anche l'unica in grado di cogliere il senso autentico del messaggio rivelato interpretandolo in modo conseguente alle conclusioni cui essa perviene. Ed è qui la fondamentale differenza tra al-Ġazālī ed Ibn Rušd. In sintesi, si può dire infatti che per quest'ultimo la ragione dimostrativa sia il criterio supremo di valutazione della Rivelazione, sia per così dire la priorità, cui la Rivelazione è subordinata. Per al-Ġazālī, invece, la dimostrazione non può mai essere certa, perché la ragione umana trova il suo limite nell'onnipotenza divina. Pertanto, sebbene anch'egli ritenga, come il filosofo, che quando Rivelazione e ragione sono in conflitto l'una con l'altra la prima vada interpretata allegoricamente, va specificato però che a suo avviso ci sono molti casi in cui la ragione da sola non basta a giustificare l'interpretazione allegorica del testo scritturale, perché alcune questioni – come quelle sopra trattate – sono al di fuori della portata delle cognizioni umane e per esse è necessario attenersi strettamente alle Scritture. Dunque per al-Ġazālī resta la Rivelazione la priorità cui subordinare la ragione dimostrativa.